C000016130

R. Shepherd. 1994

Nutrient Regulation of Insulin Secretion

PORTLAND PRESS RESEARCH MONOGRAPH I

Nutrient Regulation of Insulin Secretion

Edited by
Peter R. Flatt

Portland Press
London and Chapel Hill

Published by Portland Press Ltd, 59 Portland Place, London WIN 3AJ, U.K.
In North America orders should be sent to Portland Press Inc.,
P.O. Box 2191, Chapel Hill, NC 27515–2191, U.S.A.

ISBN 1 855 78 004 6   ISSN 0964–5845

British Library Cataloguing in Publication Data
A catalogue record for this book is available from the British Library

Although, at the time of going to press, the information contained in this
publication is believed to be correct, neither the authors nor the editors nor
the publisher assume any responsibility for any errors or omissions herein
contained. Opinions expressed in this book are those of the authors and are
not necessarily held by the editors or the publishers.

Printed in Great Britain by the University Press, Cambridge

Preface

Nutrient regulation of insulin secretion has fascinated scientists and clinicians ever since the discovery of insulin and recognition of its crucial involvement in metabolic regulation and in diseases including diabetes mellitus and obesity. Recent advances in knowledge of the role of the entero-insular axis, neural pathways and islet peptides in insulin secretion have been quite remarkable. Similarly major steps have been taken concerning elucidation of the stimulus–secretion coupling pathways in the pancreatic B-cell, and the mechanisms through which glucose, other nutrients and food-generated neuro-hormonal stimuli trigger secretion. These aspects are comprehensively reviewed herein together with the actions of antidiabetic sulphonylurea drugs and the mechanisms of defective insulin secretion and pancreatic B-cell destruction.

I wish to pay tribute to the authors of the Chapters. Their timely and well prepared contributions made this book possible. I am especially grateful to Sara and our family for creation of a happy and productive environment. Thanks are also due to Rhonda Oliver and Alan Beedle at Portland Press for friendly encouragement and assistance. It is our wish that this book will provide a valuable account of current understanding of the various mechanisms through which nutrients regulate insulin secretion. We hope to have done justice to the sterling experimental work already performed, and we apologize for those contributions that have been overlooked. Most of all, we would like to inspire new thoughts and motivation in young scientists and clinicians who may follow the fine example of Langerhans who as a medical student first identified the pancreatic islets.

Peter R. Flatt

University of Ulster, Coleraine, U.K. 1991

Contents

Abbreviations

ACBP	Acyl-CoA-binding protein
Ach	Acetylcholine
A channel	Transient outward K^+ channel
Ach channel	Acetylcholine-activated channel
ANP	Atrial natriuretic peptide
BB	BioBreeding
BCECF	2',7'-Biscarboxyethyl-5',(6')-carboxyfluorescein
BCH	2-Aminobicyclo[2,2,1]heptane-2-carboxylic acid
^{14}C-DMO	5,5-Dimethyl [2-^{14}C]oxazolidine- 2,4-dione
$[Ca^{2+}]_i$	Cytoplasmic calcium ion concentration
CCK	Cholecystokinin
CGA	Chromogranin A
CGRP	Calcitonin-gene-related peptide
C-peptide	Proinsulin connecting peptide
CRE	Cyclic-AMP-responsive element
CREB	Cyclic-AMP-responsive-element binding protein
CRF	Corticotropin-releasing factor
DBI	Diazepam-binding inhibitor
DiC_{10}	Didecanoylglycerol
DIDS	4,4'-Diisothiocyano-2,2'-stilbene disulphonic acid
ED_{50}	Half-maximal concentration for insulin secretion
E_k	K^+ equilibrium potential
G-protein	GTP-binding protein
GDIP	Glucose-dependent insulinotropic polypeptide
G_i-protein	Inhibitory G-protein
GIP	Gastric-inhibitory polypeptide
GLP	Glucagon-like peptide
GRP	Gastrin-releasing peptide
HETE	Hydroxyeicosatetraenoic acid
HIT	Hamster insulin-secreting tumour

HPETE	Hydroperoxyeicosatetraenoic acid
IAPP	Islet amyloid polypeptide
IBMX	Isobutylmethylxanthine
IDDM	Insulin-dependent diabetes mellitus
IGT	Impaired glucose tolerance
IL-I	Interleukin-1
$Ins(1,3,4,5)P_4$	Inositol 1,3,4,5-tetrakisphosphate
$Ins(1,4,5)P_3$	Inositol 1,4,5-trisphosphate
K^+–ATP channel	ATP-sensitive K^+ channel
K^+–Ca^{2+} channel	Ca^{2+}-activated K^+ channel
K^+–DR channel	Delayed rectifying K^+ channel
K^+–I channel	Inhibitor activated K^+ channel
K^+–V channel	Voltage-dependent K^+ channel
K^+–VCa channel	Voltage- and Ca^{2+}-dependent K^+ channel
NDGA	Nordihydroguaiaretic acid
NEDH	New England Deaconess Hospital
NIDDM	Non-insulin-dependent diabetes mellitus
NOD	Non-obese diabetic
NPY	Neuropeptide Y
NS channel	Non-selective cation channel
NZO	New Zealand obese
PG	Prostaglandin
PGI_2	Prostacyclin
pHi	Intracellular pH
PHI	Peptide histidine-isoleucinamide
PHM	Peptide histidine methionine
P_k	K^+ permeability
PKC	Protein kinase C
PLC	Phospholipase C
PLI	Pancreastatin-like immunoreactivity
PMA	Phorbol-12-myristate, 13-acetate
PMSF	Phenylmethanesulphonylfluoride
PSP	Pancreatic stone protein
PtdEtn	Phosphatidylethanolamine
PtdCho	Phosphatidylcholine
PtdIns	Phosphatidylinositol
PtdIns $4P$	Phosphatidylinositol 4-phosphate
$PtdIns(4,5)P_2$	Phosphatidylinositol 4,5-bisphosphate
PTP	Pancreatic thread protein
PYY	Peptide YY
reg	Regenerating gene
RER	Rough endoplasmic reticulum
RFLP	Restriction fragment length polymorphism
rig	Rat insulinoma gene

RIN	Radiation-induced transplantable insulinoma
SITS	4-Acetamide-4′-isothiocyanato-2,2′-stilbene disulphonic acid
SRP	Signal recognition particle
SSR	Signal sequence receptor
TEA$^+$	Tetraethylammonium ion
TGN	*Trans* Golgi network
TNF-α	Tumour necrosis factor
TRH	Thyrotropin-releasing hormone
VIP	Vasoactive intestinal polypeptide

Insulin secretion and the entero-insular axis

Linda M. Morgan

Department of Biochemistry, University of Surrey,
Guildford, GU2 5XH, U.K.

Introduction

The concept of an entero-insular axis has it origins in the 19th Century, following the observation that greater amounts of glucose could be given orally, rather than intravenously, without causing glycosurea. However, it was assumed that the major, if not only, stimulus to insulin secretion was the arterial blood glucose concentration. In the mid-1960s convincing evidence was first produced that the gut is able to modify the insulin response to an oral glucose load. Two groups of investigators independently showed that oral glucose is much more effective in raising circulating insulin levels than intravenous glucose, when given in amounts sufficient to produce similar degrees of arterial hyperglycaemia (McIntyre et al., 1964; Elrick et al., 1964). McIntyre and co-workers postulated that nutrients taken by mouth stimulated the secretion of one or more gastrointestinal hormones, which in turn stimulated insulin.

This potentiation of insulin secretion by gut factors is not confined to glucose-stimulated secretion. Dupré and co-workers (Dupré et al., 1969) demonstrated that an amino acid mixture taken orally was more effective at stimulating insulin secretion than was an intravenous infusion. The term 'entero-insular axis' was coined by Unger & Eisentraut in 1969 to embrace all those gut factors which contribute to enhanced insulin secretion after ingestion of a meal. Gastrointestinal hormones, collectively termed 'incretins' were originally regarded as the main, or possibly only, transmitters of messages from the gut to the pancreatic islets, apart from the absorbed substrates themselves. However, it is apparent that the entero-insular axis possesses a neural, as well as an endocrine, component, both of which appear to work by modulating pancreatic insulin secretion against the 'set' determined by the circulating blood glucose concentration. The role of neurotransmitters in insulin secretion is reviewed by Holst in Chapter 2 of this book.

Investigators in the 1960s had assumed that higher circulating levels of insulin were synonymous with increased insulin secretion. This assumption has more recently been questioned as a result of comparing peripheral venous plasma insulin and C-peptide responses to oral and intravenous glucose. Insulin and C-peptide are secreted in equimolar amounts. Insulin, however, unlike C-peptide, is extracted from the portal blood by the liver (Horwitz et al., 1975) and its metabolic clearance rate is constant and unaffected by meal ingestion (Licinio-Paixio et al., 1986). Consequently peripheral C-peptide measurement is a more reliable indication of insulin secretion than peripheral insulin concentrations, which reflect a balance between secretion and hepatic extraction. Observations (Gibby & Hales, 1983) that the increased plasma insulin response to hyperglycaemia, resulting from oral versus intravenous glucose, was not accompanied by a comparable increase in C-peptide, led to the conclusion that the higher plasma insulin levels seen after oral glucose were due to decreased fractional hepatic extraction of insulin rather than increased insulin secretion. Further work, based on matching the degree of hyperglycaemia in arterialized rather than venous blood, which is more representative of the stimulus to insulin secretion at the B-cell level, has demonstrated changes in C-peptide levels which indicate that the incretin effect is mediated by both increased secretion and decreased hepatic extraction in normal human subjects (Hampton et al., 1986; Shuster et al., 1988a). The relative importance of increased insulin secretion in contributing to the incretin effect also increases with the size of the carbohydrate load consumed (Hampton et al., 1986). The importance of measuring both circulating C-peptide and insulin levels is further illustrated in a recent study on obese subjects (Gama & Marks, 1989). It has been suggested (Faber et al., 1981) that obese subjects are hyperinsulinaemic owing to a decrease in the fractional hepatic extraction of insulin, in addition to pancreatic insulin overproduction. A group of obese subjects with elevated circulating C-peptide and insulin levels followed an energy-restricted diet, with only moderate weight loss. Their fasting and glucose-stimulated insulin concentrations fell, but C-peptide remained unchanged, indicating that in the early stages of energy restriction and weight loss, changes in the hepatic extraction of insulin is of primary importance in determining peripheral plasma insulin levels, thus re-emphasizing the need to measure both insulin and C-peptide levels when assessing insulin secretion.

Attempts have been made to quantify the relative contributions of the neural and endocrine components of the entero-insular axis. One study in rodents estimated that neurally mediated secretion accounts for approximately 20%, and hormone-mediated secretion 30%, of the insulin response to a liquid test meal (Berthoud, 1984). Pancreatic transplantation studies in animals have produced conflicting results, with some studies indicating that the entero-insular axis is almost entirely preserved despite pancreatic denervation (Lindkaer Jensen et al., 1976; Nauck et al., 1985) and others that it is abolished (Jakob et al., 1970). Differences in the sites of transplantation and venous drainage of the pancreas may account for the discrepancies. In man, a recent study on diabetic patients, who had received a paratopic pancreas transplant with physiological venous drainage, showed that the incretin effect in response to oral glucose was not only preserved, but quantitatively similar to that in normal subjects (Clark et al., 1989). In man, hormonal rather than neural factors may therefore be more important in mediating increased insulin secretion after oral carbohydrate.

Both the exocrine and endocrine pancreas are nevertheless subject to cholinergic, adrenergic and peptidergic innervation. Cholinergic mechanisms are responsible for enhancing the early insulin response to a meal in the so-called 'cephalic phase', which is independent of nutrient absorption, and also involved in enhancing insulin secretion in obesity (Ahren et al., 1986). The pancreas is also innervated by peptidergic neurones, many of which contain gut peptides which function as neurotransmitters. Cholecystokinin (CCK), vasoactive intestinal peptide (VIP) and gastrin releasing peptide (GRP)-containing neurones have all been implicated in the peptidergic stimulation of insulin release, and galanin in its suppression (Dockray, 1987). However, their precise physiological role remains uncertain. There is evidence that single neurones can contain more than one neurotransmitter and it is quite likely that their function is to modulate the action of the classical adrenergic and cholinergic transmitters.

The endocrine arm of the entero-insular axis is more amenable to experimental manipulation and is consequently better characterized, although far from completely understood. The following discussion will focus on this endocrine arm, its role in the regulation of insulin secretion and the possible pathophysiological significance of its modification by dietary changes.

Gastrointestinal endocrine hormones and insulin secretion

Many peptides have been isolated from intestinal and nervous tissue which have the ability to stimulate insulin secretion. Notably, gastrointestinal peptides bearing a structural relationship to secretin all have the ability, to a greater or lesser extent, to release insulin, a property also shared by CCK and gastrin (Dockray, 1987). However, for them to qualify for a physiological role as endocrine mediators of insulin release, the peptides must not only stimulate insulin release at concentrations that circulate *in vivo*, but must also be released in response to the ingestion of nutrients, especially glucose. Of the old-established, well-characterized gut hormones, secretin and gastrin are only very weak stimulators of insulin secretion. CCK is stimulated by protein, rather than carbohydrate ingestion. CCK was originally isolated from porcine intestine as a 33 amino acid peptide and this form of the hormone is a relatively weak stimulus to insulin secretion. Several smaller molecular forms have, however, been isolated from gut mucosa as well as from the brain, where they may fulfil a satiety function, and both the C-terminal octopeptide (CCK-8) and tetrapeptide (CCK-4) have been found to be potent insulin stimulators *in vitro* (Okabayashi *et al.*, 1983; Hermansen, 1984). CCK has been implicated as a neurotransmitter in stimulating insulin release as discussed above. It has also been shown that intravenous infusions leading to physiological concentrations of CCK-8 enhance the insulin response to intravenous arginine and mixed amino acids, but not to glucose infusions, suggesting that CCK might have a physiological role in the entero-insular axis after the ingestion of protein (Rushakoff *et al.*, 1987). However, other studies have failed to confirm an effect of CCK in man in augmenting insulin secretion stimulated by intravenous phenylalanine (Reimers *et al.*, 1988) or amino acid infusion mixtures of different compositions, although some of the data support a physiological role of CCK in the regulation of pancreatic polypeptide secretion (Schmid *et al.*, 1989).

The gastrointestinal hormone gastric inhibitory polypeptide or glucose-dependent insulinotropic polypeptide, better known by its acronym GIP, is generally recognized as being a major component of the entero-insular axis and, until recently, has been thought to be the peptide with the most potent insulin-stimulating activity secreted in response to glucose. Originally characterized in terms of its gastric acid inhibitory properties, GIP isolated from porcine intestine, predominantly from the jejunum, was subsequently shown to have a powerful insulinotropic effect, stimulating insulin secretion under physiological conditions in both dogs and man (Brown *et al.*, 1975; Jones *et al.*, 1987). More recently, human GIP, which differs from porcine GIP in two amino acid positions, has been sequenced and synthesized (Moody *et al.*, 1984). It has subsequently been shown to potentiate insulin secretion in physiological concentrations in man (Füessl *et al.*, 1988). Studies involving immunoneutralization of endogenous GIP in rodents accounts for about 50 % of the augmentation of insulin release seen after the administration of intraduodenal compared with intravenous glucose (Ebert & Creutzfeldt, 1982; Ebert *et al.*, 1983). Infusion of GIP antiserum appears more effective in abolishing the incretin effect when the animals were unrestrained and unanaesthetized (Lauritsen *et al.*, 1981), possibly reflecting a difference in the contribution of the neural component of the entero-insular axis.

Immunoreactive GIP, as identified by radioimmunoassay using

antisera raised against porcine GIP, circulates in man in several molecular forms, separable by gel filtration. The major form, 5 kDa GIP, corresponds to the biologically active hormone and is stimulated by nutrient ingestion. A high-molecular-mass component, unaffected by nutrient ingestion, has been identified, which may represent large-molecular-mass proteins interfering in the assay. In addition, an 8 kDa form, which increases only slightly after a meal, is not insulinotropic and appears not to contain the complete GIP sequence, has also been found (Krarup, 1988). Subsequent discussion refers to the 5 kDa form.

GIP secretion is stimulated by actively absorbed carbohydrates (Sykes *et al.*, 1980), amino acids (Penman *et al.*, 1981) and long-chain fatty acids (Kwasowski *et al.*, .1985). In man, fat is a more potent stimulant to GIP secretion on an equicaloric basis than is carbohydrate (Penman *et al.*, 1981), but in other animals, for example rats and pigs, which customarily consume a diet with a very much lower fat content than Western man, the situation is reversed, and carbohydrate provides the greater stimulus to GIP secretion (Ponter *et al.*, 1990). Protein ingestion is a poor stimulus to GIP secretion as relatively little is hydrolysed to its constituent amino acids before absorption. GIP secretion is dependent upon the active absorption of nutrients rather than their mere presence in the gut lumen. The addition of phloridzin to an oral glucose load, for example, inhibits both the absorption of glucose and the release of GIP (Sykes *et al.*, 1980). In addition, human subjects with lactose intolerance, who are unable to absorb a lactose load owing to low levels of mucosal disaccharidase activity, do not secrete GIP in response to oral lactose (Morgan *et al.*, 1980). Post-prandial circulating GIP levels after oral glucose in man are positively correlated with the size of the glucose load ingested when the volume of the test meal is kept constant (Hampton *et al.*, 1986). Recent measurement of rates of GIP secretion in pigs in which post-prandial glucose absorption rates have also been quantified (Roberts *et al.*, 1991) have also shown a close correlation between the rates of glucose absorption and GIP secretion (L. M. Morgan, A. B. Roberts, P. R. Ellis & A. G. Low, unpublished work). A nearly linear relationship between solid meal size of mixed composition and post-prandial GIP response in man has been demonstrated from 200–1200 kcal meals (Service *et al.*, 1983). However, the GIP responses to liquid mixed meals of similar energy density were not related to their size, but were influenced by their volume (Ebert & Creutzfeldt, 1989). Different rates of gastric emptying may explain these observations, as the physical form of the meal influences gastric emptying in addition to both its volume and calorie density (Hunt *et al.*, 1985; Low, 1991).

GIP stimulates insulin secretion only in the presence of mild-to-moderate hyperglycaemia (Andersen *et al.*, 1978). GIP secreted in response to fat ingestion alone therefore does not stimulate insulin secretion, serving as a safeguard against inappropriate insulin secretion and hypoglycaemia. This inability of GIP to stimulate insulin secretion under normoglycaemic conditions has led some workers to question its physiological role as an incretin in man when a mixed meal is ingested (Collier *et al.*, 1984; Fried *et al.*, 1989). Circulating glucose levels are generally lower after the ingestion of a mixed meal than after carbohydrate alone and it has been suggested that they are sufficiently raised to allow GIP to exert its insulinotropic effect for only a very limited time period. However, circulating glucose determinations in these studies were performed on venous blood which, as noted earlier, is not necessarily representative of the stimulus to insulin secretion at the pancreatic B-cell. This is especially relevant when circulating insulin levels are raised, causing arteriovenous glucose differences to increase (Hampton *et al.*, 1986). Provided arterial glucose levels are sufficiently raised, the GIP secreted in response to both the carbohydrate and fat components of the meal can act as a stimulus to insulin release.

In addition to the direct stimulation of insulin secretion, GIP also exhibits a range of biological activities which parallel the actions of insulin. It has been shown to augment insulin-dependent inhibition of hepatic glycogenolysis in both rodents (Hartmann *et al.*, 1986) and man (Elahi *et al.*, 1986). GIP also activates adipose tissue lipoprotein lipase (Eckel *et al.*, 1978) and has been shown recently to stimulate fatty acid synthesis *de novo* in rat adipose tissue (Oben *et al.*, 1991), actions shared with insulin which promote lipogenesis and fat deposition. The incretin effect of GIP *in vivo* may therefore contribute to a more effective uptake of glucose and triacylglycerols by virtue of increased insulin secretion and lipoprotein lipase activation. In addition, the direct action of GIP on adipose tissue may enhance the effect of insulin on the synthesis of fatty acids from glucose as precursor. Fat-stimulated GIP secretion may well be of primary importance in the physiological role of GIP on adipose tissue lipid metabolism.

GIP has been the most extensively investigated of the incretins. It is, however, clear that GIP is not the sole mediator of the endocrine arm of the entero-insular axis. Several other of the more recently isolated gastrointestinal peptides are secreted in response to oral, but not intravenous glucose, including peptide histidine methionine (PHM) and peptide YY, which qualifies them as potential mediators of the incretin effect (Shuster *et al.*, 1988*b*). In addition, a number of glucagon-like peptides are now recognized which have the ability to stimulate insulin secretion, and which are secreted from the gut in response to oral glucose. They were initially characterized through their ability to cross-react with antisera raised against pancreatic glucagon and were originally designated glucagon-like immunoreactants or GLIs. The mammalian glucagon precursor proglucagon is a 160 residue peptide (Bell *et al.*, 1983). It is processed differently in the pancreas and the small intestine (Mojsov *et al.*, 1986). In the pancreas, proglucagon gives rise to glucagon, glicentin-related pancreatic peptide (Moody *et al.*, 1981) and proglucagon 72–160 comprising two glucagon-like sequences, glucagon-like peptide-1 (GLP-1) of 37 amino acid residues, and GLP-2, of 35 residues separated by a 13 residue spacer peptide (Ørskov *et al.*, 1986; Mojsov *et al.*, 1986). In the gut, the main products are glicentin (Thim & Moody, 1981), oxyntomodulin (Bataille *et al.*, 1982) and the two glucagon-like sequences GLP-1 and GLP-2 as separate peptides (Ørskov *et al.*, 1986). GLP-1 is further cleaved and the major natural form found in porcine intestine is GLP-1$_{(7-36)}$ amide from which the N-terminal hexapeptide of the larger form has been deleted (Holst *et al.*, 1987). It is this truncated form of GLP-1 which is the major circulating form following a meal in man (Ørskov *et al.*, 1987).

While many of the glucagon-like peptides are weak stimulators of insulin secretion, GLP-1$_{(7-36)}$ amide has been found to be a potent stimulator of insulin secretion *in vitro* (Holst *et al.*, 1987; Mojsov *et al.*, 1987). GLP-1$_{(7-36)}$ has been found to have a potency equivalent to (Holst *et al.*, 1987) or greater than (Shima *et al.*, 1988) GIP in stimulating insulin secretion on a molar basis from the isolated perfused pancreas. Further studies in rat isolated perfused pancreas suggest a synergistic stimulatory effect of GLP-1$_{(7-36)}$ amide and GIP on insulin secretion, supporting the concept of several incretin factors in the entero-insular axis with functional interactions at the pancreatic B-cell level (Fehmann *et al.*, 1989).

Recent infusion studies suggest that the insulin secretory potency of GLP-1$_{(7-36)}$ amide is more powerful than GIP in molar terms in human volunteers, although its circulating level does not rise as high as GIP in response to an oral glucose load or test meal (Kreymann *et al.*, 1987; Takahashi *et al.*, 1990). Even though the experimental data on GLP-1$_{(7-36)}$ amide are still very scanty, present evidence suggests that it is likely to play an important role in the entero-insular axis, as a major incretin of the lower gut, where it is found in the highest concentrations (Kreymann *et al.*, 1988). GLP-1$_{(7-36)}$ amide shares with GIP the ability to stimulate fatty acid synthesis *de novo* in adipose tissue (Oben *et al.*, 1989). Its physiological function in lipid metabolism is at present not known, but may prove to be of equal importance with its incretin role.

Inhibition of insulin secretion via the entero-insular axis is less well documented. The neuropeptide galanin shares with neurotensin and somatostatin the ability to suppress insulin release under certain conditions (Bauer *et al.*, 1986). As with the insulin-stimulating gut hormones, there is some evidence for interaction between the insulin-inhibiting gastro-intestinal hormones in that the effects of galanin may be mediated in part via somatostatin (Tajiri *et al.*, 1990). Pancreatic somatostatin is accepted as a paracrine regulator of insulin secretion (see Chapter 3 by Marks *et al.* in this book). The endocrine role of somatostatin secreted by the antrum and small intestine in response to the ingestion of food is, however, less certain (Walsh, 1987). Fat is the major stimulus to somatostatin-28 secretion in humans (Ensinck et al., 1990). Arginine- and secretin-induced insulin secretion is attenuated by fat absorption, and insulin secretion is inhibited by infusions of somatostatin-28 that achieve steady-state post-prandial levels, which may indicate a physiological role for somatostatin as a regulator of insulin secretion in man (D'Alessio et al., 1989).

Actions of entero-insular hormones at pancreatic B-cell level

In general, entero-insular hormones amplify the insulin response of the B-cells to nutrient stimulation. Their effectiveness is critically dependent upon the prevailing arterial blood glucose level. Consequently the insulin secretory response is minimal at sub-threshold glucose concentrations, but is increasingly amplified by hyperglycaemia, such as that encountered after consumption of a carbohydrate-containing meal (Gerich et al., 1976).

Interpretation of the findings concerning the various brain–gut peptides in the control of insulin secretion is complicated by a variety of factors, including species differences, peptide impurity and instability, and the loss of functional receptors on collagenase-isolated islet cells. Supra-physiological hormone concentrations have also been used in many in vitro studies. The precise mode of action has thus been established only for a small number of entero-insular hormones. However, it appears that whereas glucose and other nutrients stimulate insulin secretion primarily by increasing cytoplasmic Ca^{2+}, neural and hormonal components of the entero-insular axis amplify secretion through activation of adenylate cyclase or phospholipase C (Morgan et al., 1988a). The mechanism of action of entero-insular hormones and neurotransmitters at the pancreatic B-cell level is considered in detail in Chapter 14 by Berggren et al.

Action of nutrients on the entero-insular axis

The literature concerning the effect of dietary composition on insulin secretion in animals and man is extensive and often contradictory. The mechanisms by which diet influences insulin secretion remain speculative, but could include an alteration in the contribution of the entero-insular axis to insulin secretion. Attention has focused on the dietary manipulation of GIP secretion. There is, at the present time, little information available on nutrient interactions with other potentially important incretins such as GLP-1$_{(7-36)}$ amide or CCK, and our understanding of the physiology of the entero-insular axis is correspondingly incomplete.

Changes in the carbohydrate content of the diet, more specifically, increasing sucrose intake in man, result in an exaggerated GIP response to an oral sucrose load (Reiser *et al.*, 1980) and also to a mixed meal (Mazzaferri *et al.*, 1984). Diets high in sucrose have been shown to increase basal insulin levels and glucose-stimulated insulin release in experimental animals (Hallfrisch *et al.*, 1979; Kergoat *et al.*, 1987). A direct relationship may, therefore, exist between the exaggerated GIP response and increased plasma insulin levels observed in experimental subjects on high-sucrose diets, possibly owing to enzyme induction leading to more rapid hydrolysis of sucrose into its constituent monosaccharides.

Changes in the fat content of the diet result in more pronounced changes in GIP secretion in some animal studies than do changes in the carbohydrate content. Rats, fed on either a cafeteria-style high-fat diet or a glucose-supplemented diet, for example, exhibit exaggerated acute plasma GIP and insulin responses to oral glucose when compared with animals fed on standard laboratory chow, but the effect is most marked in the cafeteria-fed group (Tan *et al.*, 1987). Rats are seemingly very sensitive to changes in the fat content of their diet. A high-fat diet, fed for only 4 days, causes both an increase in GIP and insulin secretion in response to food and some degree of insulin resistance (Hampton *et al.*, 1983). A similar, though less pronounced effect is seen in growing pigs when fed a high-fat diet for 11 weeks. In addition, the GIP content of the small intestine taken at the end of the experiment, was greater in pigs fed on a high-fat, high-energy diet compared with a group fed on a high-carbohydrate diet (Ponter *et al.*, 1991).

A normal laboratory rodent diet usually provides less than 10 % energy as fat. Pig-rearing diets are similarly low in fat. This compares with the approximately 40 % provision of energy by fat in a typical Western diet. Caution must therefore be exercised when extrapolating the results of animal studies to the human situation. The short-term (11 days) feeding of a high-fat diet to human volunteers caused no change in the GIP secretory response to a fat stimulus (Morgan *et al.*, 1983), although a longer period (35 days) of high-fat feeding resulted in a small, but significantly increased GIP response to oral glucose (Morgan *et al.*, 1988*b*). This was not accompanied by any change in insulin secretion, and the high-fat diet did not change the 'incretin' effect (that portion of insulin or C-peptide secretion expressed as the difference between insulin or C-peptide secretion after oral compared with intravenous glucose). However, it is possible that changes in gastrointestinal hormone secretion form the first link in a chain of events that are initiated by changes in diet and which would eventually lead to systemic metabolic changes in longer-term studies.

An increase in the fat content of the diet in general leads to an increase in GIP secretion in response to nutritional stimuli, which in animal studies can lead to hyperinsulinaemia and insulin resistance.

Hyperinsulinaemia is implicated as a risk factor in cardiovascular disease (Lichtenstein *et al.*, 1987). If an overactive entero-insular axis can contribute to this hyperglycaemia, is it possible to downregulate this contribution by reducing the fat content of the diet? Current epidemiological evidence on diet and the incidence of cardiovascular disease have led to recommendations to reduce dietary fat intakes (Committee on Medical Aspects of Food Policy, 1984), and the possible effects of low fat diets on the entero-insular axis and insulin secretion may form part of this benefit. Evidence to support this possibility comes from the observation of a marked attenuation of the GIP response to an oral fat load in healthy human volunteers after they had consumed a low-fat diet for 35 days (Morgan *et al.*, 1988*c*). However, in a subsequent study, a low-fat diet given for a similar period of time was without effect on the GIP and insulin response to a mixed meal, although glucose tolerance was improved (Morgan *et al.*, 1991). Clearly the nutritional stimulus for GIP secretion is of importance and the situation is complex because of the ability of both fat and carbohydrate to stimulate GIP secretion. Lowering the fat content of the diet of necessity leads to concomitant increases in carbohydrate consumption to maintain energy intake, and, as has been noted, this can lead to an increase in nutrient-stimulated GIP secretion owing to a potentiation of carbohydrate-stimulated GIP (Reiser *et al.*, 1980). Moreover, the type of carbohydrate substituted into the diet, particularly the sucrose content, may well be of importance in determining the GIP response to nutritional stimuli.

Certain types of dietary fibre (non-starch polysaccharides) particularly soluble fibre, improve glucose tolerance and attenuate postprandial insulin secretion when added to the diet (Jenkins *et al.*, 1978). One such, guar gum, a galactomannan has been successfully used as an adjunct therapy in the treatment of non-insulin-dependent diabetes mellitus (NIDDM). Addition of guar gum to a carbohydrate meal slows down the rate of absorption of glucose across the small intestine (Blackburn *et al.*, 1984) and reduces the blood glucose, insulin and GIP responses to both mixed and predominantly carbohydrate meals (Morgan *et al.*, 1978, 1985). The close correlation observed between post-prandial GIP and insulin levels in guar-supplemented meals suggests that changes in the entero-insular axis are in part responsible for the effects of guar on insulin secretion. Moreover, addition of guar to a 30 g oral fat load also attenuates fat-stimulated GIP secretion in man (L. M. Morgan, C. D. Travis & J. A. Tredger, unpublished work). Addition of guar gum or similar non-starch polysaccharide to the diet may therefore represent a way of lowering the contribution of the entero-insular axis to insulin secretion which circumvents some of the complexities associated with changing the fat or carbohydrate content of the diet. Not all dietary fibre has the ability to lower post-prandial GIP or insulin secretion (Morgan *et al.*, 1990). The varying effects of different dietary fibres on gastric emptying, rate and site of glucose absorption will all affect gastrointestinal hormone secretion. A shift in the rate of glucose absorption caused by the addition of fibre to a meal may be of importance in determining the post-prandial GLP-1$_{(7-36)}$ amide response, which has hitherto not been investigated, and which, as a putative major incretin of the lower small intestine, could significantly affect the overall incretin effect.

Developmentally, the entero-insular axis appears to begin to function within the first few weeks of birth (Lucas *et al.*, 1980). Suckling in puppies causes a release of gastrin and CCK, and a decrease in somatostatin (Uvnäs-Moberg, 1989), which could increase insulin secretion by their combined incretin action and thus promote the storage of ingested nutrients. There is evidence that diet can affect gastrointestinal hormones and insulin secretion from the earliest stages of development. Pre-term infants receiving milk feeds as a continuous infusion, as opposed to intermittent amounts, for example, were found to have higher circulating GIP, gastrin and insulin levels by 13 days of age (Aynsley-Green *et al.*, 1982). Thus, early changes in the entero-insular axis induced by diet may play a role in the development of an individual's capacity to secrete insulin, possibly for the rest of their life.

These examples suggest that insulin secretion is linked to the secretion of at least one of the major incretins and, although the situation is a complex one, it suggests a mechanism whereby long-term changes in the diet might influence the acute insulin response to nutritional stimuli. However, care needs to be exercised in the extrapolation of data between species, and both the nature of the prevailing diets and the test meal need to be taken into account in the interpretation of human studies.

The role of the entero-insular axis in disease

The possibility that the contribution of the entero-insular axis to insulin secretion may be modified by the diet raises the question of the association of gastrointestinal hormones and their role in the pathogenesis of diseases associated with insulin deficiency and excess. This is particularly relevant in diseases in which dietary factors have been shown to play an important part and two such, obesity and diabetes, will be considered in some detail below.

Animal studies
There is considerable evidence to link the entero-insular axis and diet with the disordered insulin secretion observed in various obesity–diabetes syndromes in rodents (Flatt *et al.*, 1984; Bailey & Flatt, 1988). Animals

with these syndromes, in common with NIDDM in man, exhibit hyperinsulinaemia, insulin resistance and glucose intolerance with or without fasting hyperglycaemia (see Bailey & Flatt, 1986 and Chapter 16 by Flatt *et al.* in this book).

The most striking evidence implicating a disordered entero-insular axis in the aetiology of obesity–diabetes has come from the study of the genetically obese hyperglycaemic (*ob/ob*) mouse. Animals homozygous for the *ob* gene exhibit hyperphagia and obesity as well as hyperinsulinaemia and insulin resistance. Short-term fasting and re-feeding experiments have shown that carbohydrate is a powerful insulin secretagogue when given orally (Flatt & Bailey, 1982), but that intraperitoneal glucose has very little insulinotropic effect (Flatt & Bailey, 1981). This dependence of insulin secretion on the route of administration of glucose suggests that either neural or hormonal pathways triggered by the ingestion of oral nutrients could be, in part, responsible for the observed hyperinsulinaemia. The mutant (*ob/ob*) mice exhibit a generalized endocrine cell hyperplasia of the small intestine (Polak *et al.*, 1975; Best *et al.*, 1977). Moreover, obese animals appear to be particularly sensitive to the insulinotropic effect of gastrointestinal hormones, as exaggerated insulin responses have been observed following the administration of many of these hormones, including GIP, GLP-1, CCK, neurotensin and growth hormone releasing factor (GHRF) (Flatt & Bailey, 1987; Flatt *et al.*, 1984; Bailey & Flatt, 1984, 1987). Hyperplasia of intestinal GIP-secreting K-cells is particularly marked in *ob/ob* mice and both intestinal GIP concentrations and circulating levels of the hormone are raised (Flatt *et al.*, 1983, 1985). GIP and dietary factors are further implicated in the insulin secretory response by the demonstration of exaggerated GIP responses to oral glucose, amino acids and fatty acids (Flatt *et al.*, 1984; Kwasowski *et al.*, 1985); the depressant effect of short-term food withdrawal on both GIP and insulin secretion (Flatt & Bailey, 1984), and the observation that age-related changes in plasma insulin that occur in these obese mice are paralleled by similar changes in GIP levels (Flatt *et al.*, 1984). GIP secretion is particularly responsive to increasing the fat content of the diet in these animals, and young *ob/ob* mice fed on high-fat diets exhibit increased K-cell numbers, intestinal GIP content and circulating GIP concentrations (Bailey *et al.*, 1986*b*).

Hyperplasia of gastrointestinal endocrine cells has been observed for other animal models of obesity–diabetes. The *db/db* mouse, for example, exhibits a more specific endocrine cell hyperplasia, where intestinal GIP and neurotensin concentrations are raised, but those of VIP, GRP, substance P and neurokinin A are unchanged (Flatt *et al.*, 1983; Sheppard *et al.*, 1985; Bailey *et al.*, 1986*a*). Not all genetically obese rodents exhibit high circulating GIP levels. Zucker fatty (*fa/fa*) rats, whose degree of hyperinsulinaemia is mild compared with *ob/ob* mice, have normal responses to nutritional stimuli (Morgan, 1979; Chan *et al.*, 1984). However, they do show an increased sensitivity to the insulin-releasing action of GIP (Chan *et al.*, 1984) and also its action on fatty acid incorporation into adipose tissue (Beck & Max, 1986).

Thus, circumstantial evidence strongly implicates the involvement of various gastrointestinal hormones of the entero-insular axis in the pathology of these obesity–diabetes syndromes, both by increased secretion of gastrointestinal hormones (perhaps as a result of hyperphagia on the part of the animals) or, as is the case for GIP, an increased sensitivity to its biological actions, both in secreting insulin and by increasing fat deposition.

Clinical studies

Despite the similarities between animal models of obesity–diabetes and human NIDDM, the role of the entero-insular axis in conditions of insulin deficiency or excess in man is much less well-defined. Investigators have concentrated on the role of GIP and few measurements of other gastrointestinal hormones have been made; consequently the picture is far from complete.

Insulin-dependent diabetes mellitus (IDDM) patients generally have a B-cell function of approximately 20 % of normal at the onset of disease. After starting insulin treatment this normally improves transiently, reaching a maximum 2–6 months later, but thereafter declines steadily. No correlation has been found between these changes in B-cell function and the GIP responses to a standard meal (Krarup *et al.*, 1983, 1985). Several studies of patients with IDDM have not revealed any abnormality of GIP release (Krarup *et al.*, 1985), although some conflicting results have been obtained demonstrating both diminished (Reynolds *et al.*, 1979) and increased (Creutzfeldt & Ebert, 1977) GIP secretion. Gel-filtration profiles of immunoreactive GIP are similar in normal and diabetic subjects (Krarup *et al.*, 1987); thus, the secretion of an abnormal GIP form or differences in the cross-reactivity of the antisera with the different molecular forms of GIP cannot explain these discrepancies. The pancreatic B-cells in IDDM retain their responsiveness to intravenous GIP infusions in the post-prandial physiological range, thus GIP may play a part in meal-induced insulin release in diabetic patients. However, other factors, such as a reduced B-cell mass, seem more important in determining the magnitude of the B-cell response to a meal.

NIDDM more closely resembles the animal models described previously. It is frequently accompanied by obesity, and insulin resistance is a constant feature, although the insulin response to different stimuli can be exaggerated, normal or impaired (de Fronzo *et al.*, 1983). Published reports have shown a great variability in both basal and stimulated GIP levels in NIDDM, with responses to glucose and other stimuli reported as increased (Brown *et al.*, 1975; Mazzaferri *et al.*, 1985; Elahi *et al.*, 1984), normal (Service *et al.*, 1984; Levitt *et al.*, 1980) or diminished (Alam & Buchanan, 1980; Service *et al.*, 1984; Groop, 1989). The reasons for this great variability are not known, but could include the heterogeneity of the diabetic population [a bimodal distribution of GIP responses was found in one study (Ebert & Creutzfeldt, 1980) involving large numbers of patients with NIDDM], the degree of obesity and the molecular heterogeneity of GIP. Studies have variously noted an association between exaggerated GIP release and the hyperinsulinaemia of early NIDDM (Mazzaferri *et al.*, 1985) and between a decreased GIP response to a test meal and a reduced insulin response in NIDDM. A causal relationship between GIP secretion and B-cell function has been postulated. In contrast, other studies have failed to demonstrate such a relationship (Groop, 1989; Creutzfeldt *et al.*, 1983). A reduced incretin effect has been reported in NIDDM which could contribute to the delayed and impaired insulin secretion found in this condition (Tronier *et al.*, 1985; Nauck *et al.*, 1986). However, the sensitivity of the B-cell to GIP has been reported as normal (Elahi *et al.*, 1984). While there is, therefore, some evidence for a disordered entero-insular axis in NIDDM, the role of GIP in any disturbance of insulin secretion is uncertain.

Hyperinsulinaemia is one of the most characteristic biochemical disorders of human obesity and in most situations reflects hypersecretion of insulin in addition to a decreased fractional hepatic extraction. It has long been speculated that the hyperinsulinaemia of obesity may be related to an overactive entero-insular axis, but the question remains controversial. As with NIDDM, studies of GIP secretion in obesity demonstrate great variability. Some studies have demonstrated elevated fasting GIP levels in obesity (Elahi *et al.*, 1984; Mazzaferri *et al.*, 1985; Salera *et al.*, 1982), and exaggerated GIP responses to oral glucose (Creutzfeldt *et al.*, 1978; Elahi *et al.*, 1984; Mazzaferri *et al.*, 1985) or a liquid mixed test meal (Creutzfeldt *et al.*, 1978; Ebert *et al.*, 1979). These have been contradicted by others who failed to find any augmentation of post-nutrient GIP levels in obesity (Lauritsen *et al.*, 1980; Jorde *et al.*, 1983; Amland *et al.*, 1984) or blunted nutrient-stimulated GIP responses (Service *et al.*, 1984; Groop, 1989).

In addition to the factors described previously, differences in meal size and composition are undoubtedly a factor in the variability of the GIP responses obtained. Some of the exaggerated GIP responses in obese individuals observed in early studies in response to large liquid mixed test meals have subsequently been shown to be secondary to an accelerated rate of gastric emptying (Ebert & Creutzfeldt, 1989); intraduodenal infusion of the same test meal or reduction in its size normalize the GIP responses. Preceding diet also has an influence on post-prandial GIP release (Mazzaferri *et al.*, 1984; Morgan *et al.*, 1988*b,c*). This has been largely ignored in previous studies comparing obese and normal individuals in spite of the known differences between the nutritional intakes of normal-weight and obese subjects and the demonstration that food restriction for 5 days reduces the GIP response to a test meal in obese subjects (Willms *et al.*, 1978).

Post-prandial GIP secretion is not always related to C-peptide responses in obese subjects (Service *et al.*, 1984; Ebert & Creutzfeldt, 1989), although some striking associations between GIP and insulin hyper-secretion have been observed among obese American Indians, in whom hereditary factors play a part in their increased incidence of obesity and NIDDM, as compared with the American Caucasian population. B-cell sensitivity to GIP appears normal in human obesity as evaluated by insulin responses to infusions of porcine GIP during a hyperglycaemic clamp in obese and lean subjects (Amland *et al.*, 1985) in contrast with animal studies on Zucker fatty rats.

In conclusion, GIP hypersecretion has been demonstrated in obese subjects in response to certain nutritional stimuli, although this has not always been related to increased insulin secretion. GIP hypersecretion appears to be especially marked in obese individuals in whom hereditary factors play a part in their obesity, in keeping with observations of disordered GIP secretion in genetically obese diabetic rodents. GIP may thus contribute in some part to the hyperinsulinaemia of obesity, but clearly cannot be involved in all situations. However, a direct metabolic role of GIP in the pathogenesis of obesity cannot be excluded in view of the effects of the hormone on the promotion of fat deposition in adipose tissue, activating lipoprotein lipase (Eckel *et al.*, 1978) and stimulating fatty acid synthesis *de novo* (Oben *et al.*, 1991). The role of other gastrointestinal hormones of the entero-insular axis has not been investigated and any contribution they might make to the hyperinsulinaemia of obesity must remain speculative.

Conclusions

The entero-insular axis makes a considerable contribution to total insulin secretion and the demonstration that gastrointestinal hormone secretion can be modified by dietary manipulation has implications in our understanding of the pathology of diseases such as atherosclerosis, obesity and NIDDM, in which insulin secretion is disordered and which have a strong dietary component in their aetiology and treatment. This is illustrated by the studies on the role of GIP in obesity, and its contribution both to the entero-insular axis and to adipose tissue metabolism. These studies do, however, also illustrate the complexity of the system in terms of the multiplicity of factors influencing the observed hormonal responses to different nutritional stimuli and the caution which must be exercised in extrapolating data from animal to human studies.

GIP-induced insulin secretion forms just one part of the entero-insular axis. Other gastrointestinal hormones such as GLP-1$_{(7-36)}$ amide and CCK are also implicated and other, as yet unidentified, gut peptides may also contribute. These new areas are just beginning to be explored. Our knowledge of the precise mechanism of action of the various insulin-stimulating gut hormones and peptides at pancreatic B-cell level is also far from complete. The entero-insular axis is fundamental to the inter-relationship between diet and insulin secretion and its investigation remains essential to our understanding of insulin secretion.

References

Ahren, B., Taborsky, G. J. & Porte, D. (1986) Neuropeptidergic versus cholinergic and adrenergic regulation of islet hormone secretion. Diabetologia **29**, 827–836

Alam, M. J. & Buchanan, K. D. (1980) Gastric inhibitory polypeptide (GIP) responses in diabetes using three different antibodies. Regul. Pept. **1**, S2

Amland, P. F., Jorde, R., Burhol, P. G. & Giercksky, K.-E. (1984) Similar plasma GIP responses in obese and lean subjects after an oral test meal and after intraduodenal stimulation with fat and glucose. Int. J. Obesity **8**, 649–653

Amland, P. F., Jorde, R., Burhol, P. G. & Giercksky, K.-E. (1985) Effect of intravenously infused porcine GIP on serum insulin in obese and lean subjects studied with the hypoglycaemic clamp technique. Scand. J. Gastroenterol. **20**, 309–314

Andersen, D. K., Elahi, D., Brown, J. C., Tobin, J. D. & Andres, R. (1978) Oral glucose augmentation of insulin secretion. Interactions of gastric inhibitory polypeptide with ambient glucose and insulin levels. J. Clin. Invest. **62**, 152–161

Aynsley-Green, A., Adrian, T. E. & Bloom, S. R. (1982) Feeding and the development of enteroinsular hormone secretion in the preterm infant: effects of continuous gastric infusions of human milk compared with intermittent boluses. Acta Paediatr. Scand. **71**, 379–383

Bailey, C. J. & Flatt, P. R. (1984) Neurotensin modulation of the plasma insulin response to glucose in obese hyperglycaemic (*ob/ob*) mice. Biochem. Soc. Trans. **12**, 1092–1093

Bailey, C. J. & Flatt, P. R. (1986) Animal models of diabetes. In Recent Advances in Diabetes (Nattrass, M., ed.), vol. 2, pp. 71–89, Churchill Livingstone, Edinburgh

Bailey, C. J. & Flatt, P. R. (1987) Glucagon-like peptide-1 and the entero-insular axis in obese hyperglycaemic (*ob/ob*) mice. Life Sci. **40**, 521–525

Bailey, C. J. & Flatt, P. R. (1988) The entero-insular axis in models of hyperinsulinaemic and hypoinsulinaemic diabetes. In Frontiers in Diabetes Research: Lessons from Animal Diabetes (Shafrir, E. & Renold, A. E., eds.), vol. 2, pp. 217–224, John Libbey & Co., London

Bailey, C. J., Flatt, P. R., Deacon, C. F., Shaw, C. & Conlon, J. M. (1986*a*) Substance P, neurokinin A, vasoactive intestinal polypeptide and gastrin releasing peptide in the intestine and pancreas of spontaneously obese-diabetic mice. Regul. Pept. **16**, 339–348

Bailey, C. J., Flatt, P. R., Kwasowski, P., Powell, C. J. & Marks, V. (1986*b*) Immunoreactive gastric inhibitory polypeptide and K cell hyperplasia in obese hyperglycaemic (*ob/ob*) mice fed high fat and high carbohydrate cafeteria diets. Acta Endocrinol. (Copenhagen) **112**, 224–229

Bataille, D., Coudray, A., Carlqvist, M., Rosselin, G. & Mutt, V. (1982) Isolation of glucagon-37 (bioactive enteroglucagon/oxyntomodulin) from porcine jejuno-ileum. FEBS Lett. **146**, 73–78

Bauer, F.-C., Ginsberg, L., Venetikou, M., Mackay, D. J., Burris, J.-M. & Bloom, S. R. (1986) Growth hormone release in man induced by galanin, a new hypothalamic peptide Lancet **ii**, 192–195

Beck, B. & Max, J. P. (1986) Increased effect of GIP on lipid metabolism in adipose tissue of obese Zucker (*fa/fa*) rats. In Proc. Int. Conf. Gastrointestinal Hormones, 6th, Vancouver, BC, p. 53, National Research Council of Canadian Research Journals, Ottawa

Bell, G. I., Sanchez-Pescador, R., Laybourn, P. J. & Najarian, R. C. (1983) Exon duplication and divergence in the human preproglucagon gene. Nature (London) **304**, 369–371

Berthoud, H. R. (1984) The relative contribution of the nervous system, hormones and metabolites to the total insulin response, during a meal in the rat. Metab. Clin. Exp. **33**, 18–25

Best, L. C., Atkins, T. W., Bailey, C. J., Flatt, P. R., Newton, D. F. & Matty, A. J. (1977) Increased activity of the enteroinsular axis in obese hyperglycaemic mice (*ob/ob*). J. Endocrinol. **72**, 44P

Blackburn, N. A., Redfern, J. S., Jarjis, H., Holgate, A. M., Hanning, I., Scarpello, J. H. B., Johnson, I. T. & Read, N. W. (1984) The mechanism of action of guar gum in improving glucose tolerance in man. Clin. Sci. **66**, 329–336

Brown, J. C., Dryburgh, J. R., Ross, S. A. & Dupré, J. (1975) Identification and actions of gastric inhibitory peptide. Recent Prog. Horm. Res. **31**, 487–532

Chan, C. B., Pederson, R. A., Buchan, A. M. J., Tubesing, K. B. & Brown, J. C. (1984) Gastric inhibitory polypeptide (GIP) and insulin release in the obese Zucker rat. Diabetes **33**, 536–542

Clark, J. D. A., Wheatley, T., Brons, I. G. M., Bloom, S. R. & Calne, R. Y. (1989) Studies of the enteroinsular axis following pancreas transplantation: neural or hormonal control? Diabetic Med. **6**, 813–817

Collier, G., McLean, A. & O'Dea, K. O. (1984) The effect of co-ingestion of fat on the metabolic responses to slowly and rapidly absorbed carbohydrate. Diabetologia **26**, 50–54

Committee on Medical Aspects of Food Policy (1984) Diet and cardiovascular disease. Report of the panel on diet in relation to cardiovascular disease. Report on Health & Social Subjects No. 28, H.M.S.O., London

Creutzfeldt, W. & Ebert, R. (1977) Release of gastric inhibitory polypeptide (GIP) to a test meal under normal and pathological conditions in man. In Diabetes, (Bajaj, J. S., ed.), pp. 53–75, Excerpta Medica, Amsterdam

Creutzfeldt, W., Ebert, R., Williams, B., Frerichs, H. & Brown, J. C. (1978) GIP and insulin in obesity: Increased response to stimulation and defective feedback control of serum levels. Diabetologia **14**, 15–24

Creutzfeldt, W., Ebert, R., Nauck, M. & Stöckmann, F. (1983) Disturbances of the enteroinsular axis. Scand. J. Gastroenterol. **18**, (Suppl. 83) 111

D'Alessio, D. A., Sieber, C., Beglinger, C. & Ensinck, J. W. (1989) A physiologic role for somatostatin-28 as a regulator of insulin secretion. J. Clin. Invest. **84**, 857–862

De Fronzo, R. A., Ferrannini, E. & Koivisto, V. (1983) New concepts in the pathogenesis and treatment of non-insulin-dependent diabetes mellitus. Am. J. Med. **74**, 52–81

Dockray, G. J. (1987) Physiology of enteric neuropeptides. In Physiology of the Gastrointestinal Tract (Johnson, L. R., ed.), vol. 1, pp. 41–66, Raven Press, New York

Dupré, J., Curtis, J. D., Waddell, R. W. & Beck, J. C. (1969) Effects of secretin, pancreozymin and gastrin on the response of the endocrine pancreas to administration of glucose or arginine in man. J. Clin. Invest. **48**, 745–757

Ebert, R. & Creutzfeldt, W. (1980) Hypo- and hyper-secretion of GIP in maturity onset diabetics. Diabetologia **19**, 271–272A

Ebert, R. & Creutzfeldt, W. (1982) Influence of gastric inhibitory polypeptide antiserum on glucose-induced insulin secretion in rats. Endocrinology **111**, 1601–1606

Ebert, R. & Creutzfeldt, W. (1989) Gastric inhibitory polypeptide (GIP) hypersecretion in obesity depends on meal size and is not related to hyperinsulinaemia. Acta Diabetol. Lat. **26**, 1–15

Ebert, R., Frerichs, H. & Creutzfeldt, W. (1979) Impaired feed-back control of fat-induced gastric inhibitory polypeptide secretion by insulin in obesity and glucose intolerance. Eur. J. Clin. Invest. **9**, 129–135

Ebert, R., Unger, R. H. & Creutzfeldt, W. (1983) Preservation of incretin activity after removal of gastric inhibitory polypeptide from rat gut extracts by immunoabsorption. Diabetologia **24**, 449–454

Eckel, R. H., Fujimoto, W. J. & Brunzell, J. D. (1978) Gastric inhibitory polypeptide enhances lipoprotein lipase activity in cultured pre-adipocytes. Diabetes **28**, 1141–1142

Elahi, D., Andersen, D. K., Muller, D. C., Tobin, J. D., Brown, J. C. & Andres, R. (1984)

The enteric enhancement of glucose-stimulated insulin release. The role of GIP in ageing, obesity and non-insulin dependent diabetes mellitus. Diabetes **33**, 950–957

Elahi, D., Meneilly, G. S., Hinaker, K. L., Rowe, J. W. & Andersen, D. K. (1986) Regulation of hepatic glucose production by gastric inhibitory polypeptide in man. In Proc. Int. Conf. Gastrointestinal Hormones, 6th, Vancouver, BC, p. 18, National Research Council of Canadian Research Journals, Ottawa

Elrick, H., Stimmler, L., Hlad, C. J. & Arai, Y. (1964) Plasma insulin responses to oral and intravenous glucose administration. J. Clin. Endocrinol. Metab. **24**, 1076–1082

Ensinck, J. W., Vogel, R. E., Laschansky, E. C. & Francis, B. H. (1990) Effect of ingested carbohydrate, fat and protein on the release of somatostatin-28 in humans. Gastroenterology **98**, 633–638

Faber, O., Kristensen, K., Kehlet, H., Madsbad, S. & Binder, C. (1981) Decreased insulin removal contributes to the hyperinsulinaemia in obesity. J. Clin. Endocrinol. Metab. **53**, 618–23

Fehmann, H.-C., Göke, R., Göke, M. E., Trautman, M. E. & Arnold, C. (1989) Synergistic stimulatory effect of glucagon-like peptide-1$_{(7-36)}$ amide and glucose dependent insulin-releasing polypeptide on the rat pancreas. FEBS Lett. **252**, 109–112

Flatt, P. R. & Bailey, C. J. (1981) Development of glucose intolerance and impaired plasma insulin response to glucose in obese hyperglycaemic (*ob/ob*) mice. Horm. Metab. Res. **13**, 556–560

Flatt, P. R. & Bailey, C. J. (1982) Role of dietary factors in the hyperinsulinaemia of genetically obese hyperglycaemic (*ob/ob*) mice. J. Nutr. **112**, 2212–2216

Flatt, P. R. & Bailey, C. J. (1984) Dietary components and plasma insulin responses to fasting and refeeding in genetically-obese hyperglycaemic (*ob/ob*) mice. Br. J. Nutr. **51**, 403–413

Flatt, P. R. & Bailey, C. J. (1987) Effects of cholecystokinin variants (CCK-8 and CCK-33) on insulin release and glucose homeostasis in obese-hyperglycaemic (*ob/ob*) mice. Med. Sci. Res. **15**, 495–496

Flatt, P. R., Bailey, C. J., Kwasowski, P., Swanston-Flatt, S. K. & Marks, V. (1983) Abnormalities of GIP in spontaneous syndromes of obesity and diabetes in mice. Diabetes **32**, 433–435

Flatt, P. R., Bailey, C. J., Swanston-Flatt, S. K., Best, L., Kwasowski, P., Buchanan, K. D. & Marks, V. (1984) Involvement of glucagon and GIP in the metabolic abnormalities of obese hyperglycaemic (*ob/ob*) mice. In Lessons from Animal Diabetes (Shafrir, E. & Renold, A. E., eds.), pp. 341–347, John Libbey & Co., London

Flatt, P. R., Bailey, C. J., Kwasowski, P., Swanston-Flatt, S. K. & Marks, V. (1985) Glucoregulatory effects of cafeteria feeding and diet restriction in genetically obese hyperglycaemic (*ob/ob*) mice. Nutr. Rep. Int. **32**, 847–854

Fried, M., Mayer, E. A., Bloom, S. R., Taylor, I. L. & Meyer, J. H. (1989) GIP and insulin release in relation to gastric emptying of a mixed meal in man. Regul. Pept. **26**, 305–312

Füessl, H. S., Yiangou, Y., Ghatei, M. A., Goebel, F. D. & Bloom, S. R. (1988) Effect of synthetic glucose-dependent insulinotropic polypeptide on insulin secretion in man. Diabetologia **31**, 492A

Gama, R. & Marks, V. (1989) The reduction of peripheral insulin concentrations in obese subjects following a hypocaloric diet: reduced pancreatic secretion or increased hepatic extraction? Ann. Clin. Biochem. **26**, 388–392

Gerich, J. E., Charles, M. A. & Grodsky, G. M. (1976) Regulation of pancreatic insulin and glucagon secretion. Annu. Rev. Physiol. **38**, 353–388

Gibby, O. M. & Hales, C. N. (1983) Oral glucose decreases hepatic extraction of insulin. Br. Med. J. **286**, 921–923

Groop, P. H. (1989) The influence of body weight, age and glucose tolerance on the relationship between GIP secretion and beta-cell function in man. Scand J. Clin. Lab. Invest. **49**, 367–379

Hallfrisch, J., Lazar, F. L., Jorgensen, C. & Reiser, S. (1979) Insulin and glucose responses in rats fed sucrose or starch. Am. J. Clin. Nutr. **32**, 787–793

Hampton, S. M., Kwasowski, P., Tan, K., Morgan, L. M. & Marks, V. (1983) Effect of pretreatment with a high fat diet on the gastric inhibitory polypeptide and insulin responses to oral triolein and glucose in rats. Diabetologia **24**, 278–281

Hampton, S. M., Morgan, L. M., Tredger, J. A., Cramb, R. & Marks, V. (1986) Insulin and C-peptide levels after oral and intravenous glucose; contribution of enteroinsular axis to insulin secretion. Diabetes **35**, 612–616

Hartmann, H., Ebert, R. & Creutzfeldt, W. (1986) Insulin-dependent inhibition of hepatic glycogenolysis by gastric-inhibitory polypeptide (GIP) in perfused rat liver. Diabetologia **29**, 112–114

Hermansen, K. (1984) Effects of cholecystokinin (CCK-4), non-sulphated CCK-8 and sulphated CCK-8 on pancreatic somatostatin, insulin and glucagon secretion in the dog; studies *in vitro*. Endocrinology **114**, 1770–1775

Holst, J. J., Ørskov, C., Nielson, O. V. & Schwartz, T. W. (1987) Truncated glucagon-like peptide I, an insulin releasing hormone from the distal gut. FEBS Lett. **211**, 169–174

Horwitz, D., Starr, J., Marks, M., Blankard, W. & Rubenstein, A. (1975) Proinsulin, insulin and C-peptide concentrations in human portal and peripheral blood. J. Clin. Invest. **55**, 1278–1286

Hunt, J. N., Smith, J. L. & Jiang, C. L. (1985) Effect of meal volume and energy density on the gastric emptying of carbohydrates. Gastroenterology **89**, 1326–1330

Jakob, A., Largiader, F. & Froesch, E. R. (1970) Glucose turnover and insulin secretion in dogs with pancreatic allografts. Diabetologia **6**, 441–444

Jenkins, D. J. A., Wolever, T. M. S., Leeds, A. R., Gassul, M. A., Haisman, P., Dilawari, J., Goff, D. V., Metz, G. L. & Alberti, K. G. M. M. (1978) Dietary fibres, fibre analogues and glucose tolerance: importance of viscosity. Br. Med. J. **1**, 1392–1394

Jones, I. R., Owens, D. R., Moody, A. J., Luzio, S. D., Morris, T. & Hayes, T. M. (1987) The effects of gastric inhibitory polypeptide infused at physiological concentrations in normal subjects and type 2 diabetics on glucose tolerance and insulin secretion. Diabetologia **30**, 707–712

Jorde, R., Amland, P. F., Burhol, P. G., Giercksky, K.-E. & Ebert, R. (1983) GIP and insulin responses to a test meal in healthy subjects. Scand. J. Gastroenterol. **18**, 1115–1119

Kergoat, M., Bailbe, D. & Portha, B. (1987) Effect of high sucrose diet on insulin secretion and insulin action. A study in the normal rat. Diabetologia **30**, 252–258

Krarup, T. (1988) Immunoreactive gastric inhibitory polypeptide. Endocr. Rev. **9**, 122–134

Krarup, T., Madsbad, S., Moody, A. J., Regeur, L., Faber, O. K., Holst, J. J. & Sestoft, L. (1983) Diminished immunoreactive gastric inhibitory polypeptide response to a meal in newly diagnosed Type I (insulin-dependent) diabetics. J. Clin. Endocrinol. Metab. **56**, 1306–1312

Krarup, T., Madsbad, S. & Moody, A. J. (1985) Immunoreactive gastric inhibitory polypeptide response to a meal during the first eighteen months after diagnosis of type I (insulin-dependent) diabetes mellitus. J. Clin. Endocrinol. Metab. **60**, 120–125

Krarup, T., Holst, J. J. & Madsbad, S. (1987) Heterogeneity of immunoreactive gastric inhibitory polypeptide in the plasma of newly diagnosed type 1 (insulin-dependent) diabetics. Acta Endocrinol. (Copenhagen) **114**, 74–83

Kreymann, B., Williams, G., Ghatei, M. A. & Bloom, S. R. (1987) Glucagon-like peptide-1 7–36: A physiological incretin in man. Lancet **2**, 1300–1304

Kreymann, B., Yiangou, Y., Kanse, S., Williams, G., Ghatei, M. A. & Bloom, S. R. (1988) Isolation and characterization of GLP-1$_{(7-36)}$ amide from rat intestine: Elevated levels in diabetic rats. FEBS Lett. **242**, 167–170

Kwasowski, P., Flatt, P. R., Bailey, C. J. & Marks, V. (1985) Effect of fatty acid chain length and saturation on gastric inhibitory peptide release in obese hyperglycaemic (*ob/ob*) mice. Biosci. Rep. **5**, 701–705

Lauritsen, K. B., Christensen, K. C. & Stockholm, K. H. (1980) Gastric inhibitory polypeptide (GIP) release and incretin effect after oral glucose in obesity and after jejunoileal bypass. Scand. J. Gastroenterol. **15**, 489–495

Lauritsen, K. B., Holst, J. J. & Moody, A. J. (1981) Depression of insulin release by anti-GIP antiserum after oral glucose in rats. Scand. J. Gastroenterol. **16**, 417–420

Levitt, N. S., Vinik, A. I. & Child, P. T. (1980) Glucose-dependent insulin-releasing peptide in non-insulin-dependent maturity-onset diabetes: effects of autonomic neuropathy. J. Clin. Endocrinol. Metab. **51**, 254–258

Lichtenstein, N. J., Yarnell, J. W. G., Elwood, P. C., Beswick, A. D., Sweetnam, P. M., Marks, V., Teale, D. & Riad-Fahny, D. (1987) Sex hormones, insulin, lipids and prevalent ischaemic heart disease. Am. J. Epidemiol. **126**, 647–657

Licinio-Paixao, J., Polonsky, K. S., Given, B. D., Pugh, W., Ostrega, D., Frank, B. F. & Rubenstein, A. H. (1986) Ingestion of a mixed meal does not affect the metabolic clearance rate of biosynthetic human C-peptide. J. Clin. Endocrinol. Metab. **63**, 401–403

Lindkaer Jensen, S., Vagn Nielson, O. & Kuhl, C. (1976) The enteral insulin stimulation after pancreas transplantation in the pig. Diabetologia **12**, 617–620

Low, A. G. (1991) Nutritional regulation of gastric secretion, digestion and emptying. Nutr. Res. Rev. **4**, in the press

Lucas, A., Sarson, D. L., Bloom, S. R. & Aynsley-Green, A. (1980) Developmental aspects of gastric inhibitory polypeptide (GIP) and its possible role in the entero-insular axis in neonates. Acta Paediatr. Scand. **69**, 321–325

McIntyre, N., Holdsworth, D. & Turner, D. S. (1964) New interpretation of oral glucose tolerance. Lancet **2**, 20–21

Mazzaferri, E. L., Starich, G. H. & St Joer, S. T. (1984) Augmented gastric inhibitory polypeptide responses to a meal after an increase in carbohydrate (sucrose) intake. J. Clin. Endocrinol. Metab. **58**, 640–645

Mazzaferri, E. L., Starich, G. H., Lardinois, C. K. & Bowen, G. D. (1985) Gastric inhibitory polypeptide responses to nutrients in Caucasians and American Indians with obesity and non insulin-dependent diabetes mellitus. J. Clin. Endocrinol. Metab. **61**, 313–321

Mojsov, S., Heinrich, G., Wilson, I. B., Ravazzola, M., Occi, L. & Habener, J. F. (1986) Preproglucagon gene expression in pancreas and intestine diversifies at the level of post-translational processing. J. Biol. Chem. **261**, 11880–11889

Mojsov, S., Weir, G. C. & Habener, J. F. (1987) Insulinotropin: glucagon-like peptide 1 (7–37) co-encoded in the glucagon gene is a potent stimulator of insulin release in the perfused rat pancreas J. Clin. Invest. **79**, 616–619

Moody, A. J., Holst, J. J., Thim, L. & Lindkaer Jensen, S. L. (1981) Relationship of glicentin to proglucagon and glucagon in the porcine pancreas. Nature (London) **289**, 514–516

Moody, A. J., Thim, L. & Valverde, I. (1984) The isolation and sequencing of human gastric inhibitory polypeptide (GIP). FEBS Lett. **172**, 142–148

Morgan, L. M. (1979) Immunoassayable gastric inhibitory polypeptide: Investigations into its role in carbohydrate metabolism. Ann. Clin. Biochem. **16**, 6–14

Morgan, L. M., Goulder, T. J., Tsiolakis, D., Marks, V. & Alberti, K. G. M. M. (1978) The effect of unabsorbable carbohydrate on gut hormones: Modification of post-prandial GIP secretion by guar. Diabetologia **17**, 85–89

Morgan, L. M., Lord, C., Wong, J. & Marks, V. (1980) Plasma GIP and motilin responses to oral lactose in human subjects with lactose intolerance. Regul. Pept. **1**, 77

Morgan, L. M., Tredger, J. A., Hampton, S. M., Kwasowski, P., Wright, J., Dunn, M. & Marks, V. (1983) Effect of diet upon response to oral fat and glucose in man: modification in control of the entero-insular axis. Scand. J. Gastroenterol. **18** (Suppl. 87), 99–101

Morgan, L. M., Tredger, J. A., Madden, A., Kwasowski, P. & Marks, V. (1985) The effect of guar-gum on carbohydrate, fat and protein stimulated gut hormone secretion. Br. J. Nutr. **53**, 467–475

Morgan, L. M., Flatt, P. R. & Marks, V. (1988a) Nutrient regulation of the enteroinsular axis and insulin secretion. Nutr. Res. Rev. **1**, 79–97

Morgan, L. M., Hampton, S. M., Tredger, J. A., Cramb, R. & Marks, V. (1988b) Modification of gastric inhibitory polypeptide (GIP) secretion in man by a high-fat diet. Br. J. Nutr. **59**, 373–380

Morgan, L. M., Tredger, J. A., Hampton, S. M., French, A. P., Peake, J. C. F. & Marks, V. (1988c) The effect of dietary modification and hyperglycaemia on gastric emptying and gastric inhibitory polypeptide (GIP) secretion. Br. J. Nutr. **60**, 29–37

Morgan, L. M., Tredger, J. A., Wright, J. & Marks, V. (1990) The effect of soluble and insoluble fibre supplementation on post-prandial glucose tolerance, insulin and gastric inhibitory polypeptide secretion in healthy subjects. Br. J. Nutr. **64**, 103–110

Morgan, L. M., Tredger, J. A., Wilkinson, J., Williams, C., Zampelas, A. & Marks, V. (1991) The effect of a low fat diet on hormone and metabolite concentrations following a mixed meal in healthy subjects. Proc. Nutr. Soc. in the press

Nauck, M., Van Hoorn, W., Gubernatis, G., Ebert, R., Stewert, J. R. & Creutzfeldt, W. (1985) Preserved incretin effect after complete surgical denervation of the pancreas in young pigs. Res. Exp. Med. **185**, 291–298

Nauck, M., Stockmann, F., Ebert, R. & Creutzfeldt, W. (1986) Reduced incretin effect in type II (non-insulin-dependent) diabetes. Diabetologia **29**, 46–52

Oben, J., Morgan, L., Fletcher, J. & Marks, V. (1991) Effect of entero-pancreatic hormones, gastric inhibitory polypeptide and glucagon-like polypeptide-1$_{(7-36)}$ amide on fatty acid synthesis in explants of rat adipose tissue. J. Endocrinol. **130**, 267–272

Okabayashi, Y., Otsuki, M., Ohki, A., Sakamoto, C. & Baba, S. (1983) Effects of C terminal fragments of cholecystokinin on exocrine and endocrine secretion from isolated perfused rat pancreas. Endocrinology **113**, 2210–2215

Ørskov, C., Holst, J. J., Knuhtsen, S., Baldiserra, F. G. A., Poulsen, S. S. & Vagn Nielsen, O. (1986) Glucagon-like peptides GLP-1 and GLP-2, predicted products of the glucagon gene, are secreted separately from pig small intestine but not pancreas. Endocrinology **119**, 1467–1475

Ørskov, C., Holst, J. J., Poulsen, S. S. & Kirkegaard, P. (1987) Pancreatic and intestinal processing of proglucagon in man. Diabetologia **30**, 874–881

Penman, E., Wass, J. A. H., Medback, S., Morgan, L. M., Lewis, J., Besser, G. M. & Rees, L. H. (1981) Response of circulating somatostatin to nutritional stimuli in normal subjects. Gastroenterology **81**, 692–699

Polak, J. M., Pearse, A. G. E., Grimelius, L. & Marks, V. (1975) Gastrointestinal apudosis in obese hyperglycaemic mice. Virchows Arch. B. **19**, 135–150

Ponter, A. A., Salter, D. N., Morgan, L. M. & Flatt, P. R. (1990) The effect of high fat diets on gastric inhibitory polypeptide (GIP) and insulin secretion in growing pigs. Anim. Prod. **50**, 571

Ponter, A. A., Salter, D. N., Morgan, L. M. & Flatt, P. R. (1991) The effect of energy source and feeding level on the hormones of the entero-insular axis and plasma glucose in the growing pig. Br. J. Nutr. **66**, 187–197

Reimers, J., Nauck, M., Creutzfeldt, W., Strietzel, J., Ebert, R., Cantor, P. & Hoffman, G. (1988) Lack of insulinotropic effect of endogenous and exogenous cholecystokinin in man. Diabetologia **14**, 271–280

Reiser, S., Michaelis, O. E., Cataland, S. & O'Dorisio, T. M. (1980) Effect of isocaloric exchange of dietary starch and sucrose in humans on the gastric inhibitory polypeptide response to a sucrose load. Am. J. Clin. Nutr. **33**, 1907–1911

Reynolds, C., Tronsgard, N., Gibbons, E., Blix, P. M. & Rubenstein, A. H. (1979) Gastric inhibitory polypeptide response to hyper- and hypoglycaemia in insulin-dependent diabetics. J. Clin. Endocrinol. Metab. **49**, 255–261

Roberts, F. G., Low, A. G., Young, S., Smith, H. A. & Ellis, P. R. (1991) The effect of high viscosity guar gum flow on the rate of glucose absorption and net insulin production in the portal blood of the pig. Proc. Nutr. Soc. in the press

Rushakoff, R. J., Goldfine, I. D., Carter, J. D. & Liddle, R. A. (1987) Physiological concentrations of cholecystokinin stimulate amino-acid induced insulin release in humans. J. Clin. Endocrinol. Metab. **65**, 395–401

Salera, M., Giacomoni, P., Pironi, L., Cornia, G., Capelli, M., Marini, A., Benfenati, F., Miglioli, M. & Barbara, L. (1982) GIP release after oral glucose: relationship to glucose intolerance, diabetes mellitus and obesity. J. Clin. Endocrinol. Metab. **55**, 329–336

Schmid, R., Schusdziarra, V., Schulte-Frohlinde, E., Maier, V. & Classen, M. (1989) Effect of CCK on insulin, glucagon and pancreatic polypeptide levels in humans. Pancreas **4**, 653–661

Service, F. J., Hall, L. D., Westland, R. E., O'Brien, P. C., Go, V. L. W., Matmond, M. W. & Rizza, R. A. (1983) Effects of size, time of day and sequence of meal ingestion on carbohydrate tolerance in normal subjects. Diabetologia **25**, 316–321

Service, F. J., Rizza, R. A., Westland, R. E., Hall, L. D., Gerich, J. E. & Go, V. L. W. (1984) Gastric inhibitory polypeptide in obesity and diabetes mellitus. J. Clin. Endocrinol. Metab. **58**, 1133–1140

Sheppard, M. C., Bailey, C. J., Flatt, P. R., Swanston-Flatt, S. K. & Shennan, K. I. J. (1985) Immunoreactive neurotensin in spontaneous syndromes of obesity and diabetes in mice. Acta Endocrinol. (Copenhagen) **108**, 532–536

Shima, K., Hirota, M. & Ohboshi, C. (1988) Effect of glucagon-like peptide-1 on insulin secretion. Regul. Pept. **22**, 245–252

Shuster, L. T., Go, V. L., Rizza, R. A., O'Brien, P. C. & Service, F. J. (1988a) Incretin effect due to increased secretion and decreased clearance of insulin in normal humans. Diabetes **37**, 200–203

Shuster, L. T., Go, V. L., Rizza, R. A., O'Brien, P. C. & Service, F. J. (1988*b*) Potential incretins. Mayo Clin. Proc. **63**, 794–800

Sykes, S., Morgan, L. M., English, J. & Marks, V. (1980) Evidence for preferential stimulation of gastric inhibitory polypeptide secretion in the rat by actively transported carbohydrates. J. Endocrinol. **85**, 201–207

Tajiri, Y., Sako, Y., Umeda, F., Hisatomi, A. & Nawata, H. (1990) Effect of galanin on arginine-stimulated pancreatic hormone release from isolated perifused rat islets. Horm. Metab. Res. **22**, 1–6

Takahashi, H., Manaka, H., Katsuyuki, S., Fukase, N., Tominaga, M., Sasaki, H., Kawai, K. & Ohashi, S. (1990) Radioimmunoassay for glucagon-like peptide-1 in human plasma using N-terminal and C-terminal antibodies: a physiologic insulinotropic role of GLP-1$_{(7-36)}$ amide. Biomed. Res. **11**, 99–108

Tan, K. S., Kwasowski, P. & Marks, V. (1987) Effects of high-fat cafeteria diet on plasma insulin (IRI) and gastric inhibitory polypeptide (IR-GIP) response to a glucose load in the rat. Clin. Sci. **73** (Suppl. 17), 57P

Thim, L. & Moody, A. J. (1981) The primary structure of porcine glicentin (proglucagon). Regul. Pept. **2**, 139–150

Tronier, B., Deigard, A., Andersen, T. & Madsbad, S. (1985) Absence of incretin effect in obese type II and diminished effect in lean type II and obese subjects. Diabetes Res. Clin. Pract. **1**, (Suppl. 1) S568

Unger, R. H. & Eisentraut, A. M. (1969) Entero insular axis. Arch. Intern. Med. **123**, 261–266

Uvnäs-Moberg, K. (1989) Gastrointestinal hormones in mother and infant. Acta Paediatr. Scand. **351**, Suppl. 88–93

Walsh, J. H. (1987) Gastrointestinal hormones. In Physiology of the Gastrointestinal Tract (Johnson, L. R., ed.), vol. 1, pp. 181–254, Raven Press, New York

Willms, B., Ebert, R. & Creutzfeldt, W. (1978) Gastric inhibitory polypeptide and insulin in obesity: II. Reversal of increased responses to stimulation by starvation or food restriction. Diabetologia **14**, 379–387

2

Role of classical and peptidergic neurotransmitters in insulin secretion

Jens J. Holst

Department of Medical Physiology C, Panum Institute, University of Copenhagen, DK-2200 Copenhagen N, Denmark

Introduction

Today it is generally accepted that the endocrine organ responsible for the secretion of insulin, the pancreatic islets, is regulated not only by the concentration of nutrients or metabolic fuels in the blood perfusing the organ, but also by gastrointestinal hormones and by the autonomic nervous system. The activity in the efferent autonomic nerves to the pancreatic islets may, in turn, be reflexly modified by the nutritional state of the organism. Apparently receptors both in the gastrointestinal tract and in the central nervous system may be activated by both low and high concentrations of nutrients. Hypothalamic centres integrate the incoming signals and adjust the secretory rate of the pancreatic islets via changes in the activity of the efferent autonomic nerves. It appears that both divisions of the autonomic nervous system, the sympathetic and the parasympathetic, may influence insulin secretion, generally in opposite directions. In agreement with this, both of the classical transmitters of the autonomic nerves, acetylcholine and noradrenaline, may strongly influence insulin secretion, the former being stimulatory and the latter inhibitory. However, most, if not all of the pancreatic nerves contain and produce neuropeptides, many of which may also influence insulin secretion. The neuropeptides are probably released from the pancreatic nerves in parallel with the classical neurotransmitters, and may therefore be responsible for some of the secretory effects observed in response to autonomic nervous activity.

It is the purpose of the present chapter to discuss the extent and importance of the peptidergic control of insulin secretion as compared with the regulation exerted by the classical transmitters of the autonomic nerves, acetylcholine and noradrenaline. For further aspects of the nervous control of pancreatic endocrine function, the reader is referred to several reviews (Woods & Porte, 1974; Smith & Porte, 1976; Gerich & Lorenzi, 1978; Miller, 1981; Rohner-Jeanrenaud *et al.*, 1983; Edwards, 1984; Ahren *et al.*, 1986; Havel & Taborsky, 1989). The mechanism of action of neurotransmitters at the pancreatic B-cell is considered in Chapter 14 by Berggren *et al.*

Reflexly regulated insulin secretion

As already mentioned, the transmitters of the autonomic nervous system, may very potently influence insulin secretion, when released in the vicinity of the pancreatic B-cells. It is also easy to demonstrate experimentally that insulin secretion may be influenced by stimulation of the autonomic nerves. But what is the role of the islet innervation under physiological circumstances? Recent advances in the field of organ transplantation may throw some light on this. Patients with insulin-dependent diabetes mellitus (IDDM) treated successfully by pancreas transplantation may be viewed as a model of total pancreatic denervation in man. Such patients may have normal fasting blood glucose concentrations and a normal tolerance to intravenous glucose. Characteristically, these patients have hyperinsulinaemia both in the fasting state and during stimulation (Diem *et al.*, 1990). However, their C-peptide concentrations both in the fasting state and during stimulation, and their urinary C-peptide excretion rates are normal, indicating that some insulin may escape the normal first-pass clearance in the liver, explaining the hyperinsulinaemia, while the secretory activity of the transplanted B-cells is normal. In fact, patients with grafts draining to the portal circulation had both normal C-peptide and insulin concentrations (Diem *et al.*, 1990). Haemoglobin A_{1c} concentrations were also normal suggesting that normal or near normal levels of glycaemia were present not only in the basal state, but, generally, throughout the day. Thus, it can be concluded that a normal secretion of insulin in the basal state and in response to intravenous glucose loads may be achieved in the absence of autonomic innervation of the islets.

The islets, however, do receive an abundant supply of nerve fibres (Smith & Davis, 1983). According to the classical concept (Honjin, 1956; Kamel *et al.*, 1979) three intrapancreatic plexuses are described: perivascular, peri-acinar and peri-insular. In addition, a 'neuro-insular complex' of collections of neurons associated with the islets has been described (Simard, 1937; Coupland, 1958). The latter neurons may belong to the parasympathetic division (Kamel *et al.*, 1979). Adrenergic fibres are found both to terminate on non-adrenergic nerve cell bodies of the intrapancreatic ganglia and to innervate endocrine cells and blood vessels of the islets (Legg, 1968). By light and electron microscopy, three types of nerve endings have been observed within the pancreatic islets (Smith & Davis, 1983; Forssmann & Greenberg, 1978), two of which exhibit characteristics of what have been believed to be sympathetic and parasympathetic nerve terminals. In addition, the islets may contain or receive an abundance of fibres that stain by immunohistochemistry with anti-bodies against various neuropeptides as discussed below (Larsson, 1979). It should be noted that some of the nerve fibres may be afferent (Forssmann & Greenberg, 1978).

The role of this dense autonomic innervation may be illustrated more clearly in situations of more severe adaptational stress. At this stage it will be necessary to distinguish between the two divisions of the system: (i) the parasympathetic being activated in situations of fuel abundancy, and (ii), the sympathetic, in situations of need. It will also be necessary to distinguish between studies performed in experimental animals and in man.

Glucose abundancy—cephalic-phase insulin secretion

The existence of a cephalic phase of insulin secretion, a reflexly stimulated secretion of insulin, induced by sensational stimuli, is well established in rats. Strubbe & Steffens (1975) noted that insulin levels in blood had risen already 1 min after start of food ingestion in rats. Berthoud et al. (1980) observed that oral administration of saccharin caused a glycaemia-independent increase in insulin secretion, and also showed that this response was abolished in streptozotocin-diabetic, islet-transplanted rats with normal insulin responses to glucose. Berthoud (1984) calculated that the neurally mediated insulin response to a liquid meal amounted to at least 26 % of the total insulin response. In further studies, Trimble et al. (1981) concluded that the neurally mediated insulin response was of great importance for glucose tolerance in rats. Also dogs show a clear-cut cephalic-phase insulin secretion (Hommel et al., 1972), that is abolished after pancreas transplantation or vagotomy (Freyse et al., 1982).

The afferent link of the cephalic phase of insulin secretion seems to include vagal afferents coming from intestinal glucoreceptors (Mei et al., 1981; Grill et al., 1984).

In humans it has been more difficult to demonstrate a cephalic-phase insulin secretion. Taylor & Feldman (1982) were unable to demonstrate an insulin response to so-called modified sham feeding, and Sjöström et al. (1980) were able to demonstrate a response to the sight and smell of food in obese subjects only. It should be noted, however, that modified sham feeding ('chew and spit') is a relatively weak stimulus as compared with the complete act of ingesting food, as clearly shown by Schwartz et al. (1979). They compared the pancreatic polypeptide responses to modified sham feeding with those obtained by 'adequate sham feeding', brought about by means of an occluding tube in the lower oesophagus introduced through a gastrostomy. In a more recent study, however, Bruce and colleagues (1987) found that a cephalic-phase insulin response could clearly be elicited in normal weight humans by a combination of food-associated stimuli. In studies performed in the author's laboratory modified sham feeding caused a significant increase in the concentration of insulin in peripheral venous plasma in parallel with increases in gastric acid secretion and peripheral concentrations of gastrin and pancreatic polypeptide (Loud *et al.*, 1988). As will be discussed below, activity in the sympathetic nervous system strongly inhibits insulin secretion, in man also. It is possible therefore, that anxiety or other discomfort associated with the laboratory manipulations involved in such studies could dampen or conceal the stimulatory effects of feeding, and thus explain the inability of some workers to demonstrate the cephalic-phase response in humans. Another line of evidence attests to the importance of vagal activity for insulin secretion. Some syndromes of obesity are claimed to be dependent on primary or secondary hyperinsulinism caused by a stimulatory vagal overactivity (Rohner-Jeanrenaud *et al.*, 1983). In agreement with this notion, vagotomy was successfully used in the treatment of certain patients with morbid obesity (Kral, 1978, 1983).

Glucose need—effects of sympathoadrenal discharge

As discussed above the endocrine pancreas is capable of adjusting its secretion to the prevailing blood glucose levels, but nervous mechanisms also contribute to the defence against hypoglycaemia by inhibiting insulin secretion and increasing glucagon secretion. It seems that all stressful situations that are accompanied by a sympathoadrenal discharge exhibit this characteristic pattern of pancreatic endocrine secretion (regardless of the blood glucose levels). Such stress situations include: acute psychological stress (Bloom *et al.*, 1973); strenuous muscular exercise (Galbo, 1983); hypoglycaemia (Oomura, 1983; Havel & Taborsky, 1989); haemorrhage leading to arterial hypotension (Järhult & Holst, 1978); hypoxia (Baum & Porte, 1980); surgical stress (Russel *et al.*, 1975); cold stress (Sasaki *et al.*, 1982); and water intoxication (Thurston *et al.*, 1978).

The inhibition of insulin secretion during muscular exercise in man is believed to be due to noradrenergic sympathetic inhibition of the islets, since adrenalectomy has no effect on the inhibition (Järhult & Holst, 1979) and since α-adrenergic blocking agents reduce the inhibition (Galbo *et al.*, 1977; Galbo, 1983). The reduction in insulin secretion (together with the increase in glucagon secretion) appears to be essential for proper adjustment of hepatic glucose production (Issekutz, 1980; Wolfe *et al.*, 1986) to the augmented needs. The inhibition of insulin secretion in response to haemorrhage is elicited reflexly through the arterial baroreceptors (Järhult & Holst, 1978) and is carried to the pancreas via the splanchnic nerves (Andersson *et al.*, 1979). The resulting increase in hepatic glucose production, because of the greatly increased molar glucagon/insulin ratio in the portal venous blood reaching the liver (Andersson *et al.*, 1979), is believed to serve, by its osmotic activity, as a substitute for the lost blood (Järhult, 1975).

The neurally mediated inhibition of insulin secretion in response to hypoglycaemia is probably elicited after activation of cerebral glucoreceptors (Rohner-Jeanrenaud *et al.*, 1983) and mediated through central noradrenergic pathways (McCaleb & Myers, 1982). It is suppressed by α-adrenergic blockade (Müller *et al.*, 1973) or spinal cord transection (Niijima, 1975) indicating that efferent sympathetic pathways are responsible (Havel & Taborsky, 1989). In this connection it is of interest that an α-adrenergic blockade, whereby the sympathetic inhibition of insulin secretion probably is attenuated, has been reported to improve glucose-potentiated insulin secretion in non-insulin-dependent diabetic patients (Broadstone *et al.*, 1987).

It may be concluded that while autonomic nervous regulation of insulin secretion may not be essential in the basal, post-absorptive state, such regulation is indeed important for adequate adaptation to environmental and nutritional stress.

Insulin secretion in response to stimulation of the pancreatic innervation

The pancreas is richly supplied with myelinated as well as non-myelinated nerve fibres, nerve trunks and intrapancreatic ganglia which are scattered throughout the tissue (Holst, 1986). The main sources are the vagus nerves and the splanchnic nerves. However, well-defined extrinsic nerve trunks ('a pancreatic nerve') do not exist. The superior pancreaticoduodenal vessels are generally accompanied by autonomic nerve fibres, but the majority of the supply enters the pancreas diffusely from the periphery. Many of the fibres either originate in, or pass, the coeliac ganglion on their way to the pancreas. Note that the nerve fibres that enter the pancreas are mixed nerves, composed of fibres from both divisions of the autonomic system. To distinguish between the two divisions, it is therefore necessary either to isolate the vagal or sympathetic contributions separately, or to try to separate out the two by pharmacological blockade.

Effects of vagus stimulation

Acetylcholine very efficiently stimulates insulin secretion in all preparations studied so far, including isolated islets (Malaisse *et al.*, 1967), isolated perfused canine pancreas (Iversen, 1973*a*), and pig pancreas (Holst *et al.*, 1981*c*). The B-cells appear to possess muscarinic cholinergic receptors

(Grill & Östenson, 1983). Also in intact animals, an insulin-stimulating effect of acetylcholine may be demonstrated, when it is infused into vessels supplying the pancreas (Kaneto & Kosaka, 1974; Holst et al., 1981c). Metacholine stimulates insulin secretion in man (Kajinuma et al., 1968). In agreement with these observations, electrical stimulation of the vagus nerves increases insulin secretion in dogs (Frohman et al., 1967), calves (Bloom & Edwards, 1981) and pigs (Holst et al., 1981a). The effect is direct and independent of changes in extrapancreatic factors such as blood flow, insulinotropic hormones or metabolites. Thus the response can be elicited in completely isolated perfused preparations of the pancreas with intact vagal nerve supply and perfused with a synthetic medium (Holst et al., 1986; Nishi et al., 1987). Both the effects of acetylcholine and vagus stimulation depend critically on blood glucose levels. The higher the glucose levels the larger the insulin response (Holst et al., 1981a). At concentrations below euglycaemia, there is no, or very little, insulin response. Glucagon secretion is also greatly increased by vagal stimulation but the glucagon responses increase proportionally to the degree of hypoglycaemia (Holst et al., 1981a). Thus, the net effect of the vagally stimulated secretion of the pancreatic glucoregulatory hormones is to restore blood glucose to euglycaemia whether glucose levels are high or low.

From these results it would be reasonable to assume that acetylcholine release from cholinergic parasympathetic fibres within or near the islets would be responsible for the effect of vagus stimulation on insulin secretion. In agreement with this, atropine has been reported to abolish the insulin response in dogs (Bergman & Miller, 1973; Kaneto et al., 1974). In pigs, however, the insulin response to vagus stimulation, particularly at high glucose levels, was remarkably resistant to the actions of atropine even in very high concentrations (Holst et al., 1981b). In further studies, using the completely isolated perfused pig pancreas with intact vagus supply, Holst et al. (1986) found that the choline esterase inhibitor, eserine, augmented the insulin response to vagus stimulation, while atropine at a concentration of 10^{-6} M inhibited the insulin response. Both results clearly point to an essential role for cholinergic fibres and muscarinic receptors in the insulin response in this species also. A substantial insulin response, however, remained in spite of excessive atropinization, and it was concluded that non-cholinergic mechanisms were also operative in this species, and that, primates apart, this presumably is the experimental animal whose nutritional physiology comes closest to human physiology (Miller & Ullrey, 1987). It is of interest that very similar results were recently obtained in a rat pancreas model by Nishi et al. (1987).

Sympathetic effects—effects of splanchnic nerve stimulation

The presence of adrenergic receptors on the B-cells is well established (Malaisse, 1972; Miller, 1981; Iversen, 1973b; Samols & Weir, 1979). The B-cells possess both α-adrenergic and β-adrenergic receptors. The broad spectrum β-agonist, isoprenaline, greatly enhances insulin secretion from the B-cells, and experiments with β_1- and β_2-antagonists and agonists have clearly shown that the stimulatory receptor can be characterized as belonging to the β_2-subtype.

Activation of the α-receptors on the B-cells, on the other hand, leads to inhibition of insulin secretion. Experiments with specific α_1- or α_2-agonists and antagonists have clearly established these inhibitory receptors as belonging to the α_2-subgroup. Administration of the natural sympathetic transmitter, noradrenaline, as well as the hormone adrenaline, brings about an inhibition of insulin secretion if the catecholamines are presented in physiological, rather high concentrations. In lower concentrations a stimulatory effect may be seen, apparently because the affinity of the catecholamines for the stimulatory β-receptors is higher than their affinity for the α-receptors.

In agreement with these findings, stimulation of the splanchnic nerves has been found to inhibit insulin secretion in dogs (Kaneto et al., 1975; Miller, 1975), calves (Bloom & Edwards, 1975), and cats (Andersson et al., 1982) and splanchnic nerve stimulation abolished the enhancing effect of simultaneous stimulation of the vagus nerves in pigs (Holst et al., 1981d). The nature of the transmitters involved was studied in more detail in experiments with a completely isolated perfused porcine pancreas with an intact splanchnic nerve supply (Holst et al., 1983; Holst et al., 1986). Electrical stimulation of the splanchnic nerves strongly inhibited insulin secretion. Administration of the α-blocker, phenoxybenzamine, in a concentration that was sufficient to abolish the vasoconstriction resulting from the stimulation, reversed the inhibition, resulting in a significantly increased insulin secretion. Administration of the broad spectrum β-antagonist, propranolol, decreased the basal release of insulin, but had no apparent effect on the inhibition resulting from splanchnic nerve stimulation. After combined α- and β-adrenergic blockade there was no change in insulin secretion in response to splanchnic nerve stimulation. It was concluded from these experiments that the inhibitory effect of splanchnic nerve stimulation could be fully explained by a release of noradrenaline from nerve endings, at or in the islets, with noradrenaline acting predominantly on inhibitory α-adrenergic receptors on the insulin-secreting cells. It may be noted that the secretion of somatostatin followed the same pattern as that of insulin (Holst et al., 1983). Paracrine, intra-islet effects of somatostatin, therefore, do not appear to be involved in the sympathetic inhibition of insulin secretion. On the other hand, it is not possible to conclude that other transmitters or modulators were not involved in these responses, because their role might be to potentiate or prolong the activity of noradrenaline. If this primary effect was lost, the effect of the co-transmitter or modulator might be lost as well. Furthermore, these results, although in agreement with results obtained in other species (e.g. cats, Andersson *et al.*, 1982) may not be applicable to all mammals, since differences between species may occur. For instance, very similar results to those presented above were obtained recently in rats (Kurose *et al.*, 1990). These authors, who used the α-adrenergic antagonist, phentolamine, were unable to abolish completely the inhibition of insulin secretion induced by splanchnic nerve stimulation and suggested that a neuropeptide could be involved. Similarly, Dunning *et al.* (1988) reported inhibition of insulin secretion in anaesthetized dogs by stimulation of pancreatic mixed nerves, in spite of a combined pharmacological α- and β-adrenergic blockade. In both of these studies, however, it is difficult to feel convinced that a complete adrenergic blockade was indeed obtained. Stimulation of mixed coeliac nerves in an isolated perfused human pancreas preparation was recently reported to produce inhibition of insulin secretion via an α-adrenergic effect (Brunicardi *et al.*, 1987).

Involvement of pancreatic neuropeptides

The morphological distribution and possible role of neuropeptides in the control of pancreatic exocrine secretion have been reviewed recently (Holst, 1986, 1990). Numerous neuropeptides have been reported to be present in pancreatic neurons or nerve fibres, including: vasoactive intestinal peptide (VIP); peptide histidine-isoleucinamide (PHI); gastrin-releasing polypeptide (GRP or mammalian bombesin); neuropeptide Y (NPY); galanin; cholecystokinin (CCK); calcitonin-gene-related peptide (CGRP); substance P; and opioid peptides (Larsson, 1979; Larsson & Rehfeld, 1979; Bishop *et al.*, 1980; Rehfeld *et al.*, 1980; Dunning *et al.*, 1986; Petterson *et al.*, 1986; Holst *et al.*, 1987; Knuhtsen *et al.*, 1987; Sheikh *et al.*, 1988; Messell *et al.*, 1990). Practically all of these peptides have been reported to have some effect on pancreatic endocrine secretion and could, therefore, if released at the islets during nerve stimulation, contribute to the secretory responses observed. To prove such functions for a neuropeptide is not a simple matter. In the author's laboratory a set of criteria have been proposed, the fulfilment of which strengthens the case for a physiological function of a neuropeptide (Holst *et al.*, 1990). According to these, it is required: (i) that the peptide is there; (ii) that the peptide is active in that system (implying that receptors are present and that the peptide is sufficiently potent); (iii) that the peptide is released from the nerves upon appropriate stimulation; (iv) that release of peptide and response parallel each other (e.g. under pharmacological blockade), and (v) that specific interference with peptide action/release influences responses. Such specific interference could consist of desensitization, administration of receptor antagonists or immunoneutralization. However, presently few peptides fulfil all of these criteria.

The most abundant pancreatic neuropeptide is VIP (Bishop *et al.*, 1980; Holst *et al.*, 1984, 1987). The related peptide, PHI, is a product of the same precursor as VIP, and immunoreactive PHI is therefore found in the same pancreatic neurons as VIP (Holst *et al.*, 1987). Some of the nerve fibres clearly reach the pancreatic islets. By vagus stimulation (but not by splanchnic nerve stimulation) a marked release of VIP from pancreatic neurons can be demonstrated (Holst *et al.*, 1984). This release is completely abolished by the actions of the nicotinic ganglionic blocker, hexamethonium, and is enhanced rather than inhibited by atropine. A peptide with PHI-like immunoreactivity is also released in parallel with VIP, but the peptide is larger than PHI. At the most, 25% of the immunoreactivity could be accounted for by authentic PHI (Holst *et al.*, 1987). In the pancreas, therefore, the VIP precursor is processed in a way that differs from that of the small intestine, from which PHI was isolated. Both VIP and PHI increase insulin secretion in a glucose-dependent manner just like the effect of vagus stimulation (Jensen *et al.*, 1978; Holst *et al.*, 1987), and both peptides may therefore be involved in the atropine-resistant part of the insulin response to vagus stimulation. The potent and efficient stimulatory effect of VIP on insulin secretion is not restricted to pigs; rats, mice and dogs react in a similar fashion (Ahren *et al.*, 1986). It is of considerable interest that VIP has been reported to coexist with acetylcholine in many nerves (Lundberg *et al.*, 1980). Although not specifically demonstrated for the pancreas such coexistence could occur in this organ as well. Indeed, a synergism between acetylcholine and VIP has been demonstrated for glucagon secretion in mice (Ahren & Lundquist, 1982). Unfortunately, substances that could antagonize the actions of VIP with sufficient potency are not yet available. In experiments with immunoneutralization, the pancreatic endocrine secretion was perturbed both during administration of a non-immune serum and specific antiserum, rendering a study of insulin release impossible (Holst *et al.*, 1984).

Another abundant pancreatic neuropeptide is GRP (mammalian bombesin). GRP-containing nerve fibres can be demonstrated to traverse the pancreatic islets (Knuhtsen *et al.*, 1987) and GRP (and bombesin) stimulate insulin secretion in a glucose-dependent manner (Ipp & Unger, 1979; Martindale *et al.*, 1982; Knuhtsen *et al.*, 1986; Hermansen & Ahren, 1990). Also GRP is released in an atropine-resistant manner during stimulation of the vagus nerves (Knuhtsen *et al.*, 1987), and a role for GRP in insulin release is therefore possible. A number of synthetic peptides that act as GRP-receptor antagonists are available, and one, [Leu^{13}-ψ-CH$_2$NH-Leu^{14}]bombesin was sufficiently potent to antagonize the actions of GRP in the antrum, where GRP functions to regulate gastrin secretion (Holst *et al.*, 1990). In fact, using this antagonist, it was possible to inhibit part of the insulin response to vagus stimulation, suggesting that GRP is indeed involved in the parasympathetic control of insulin secretion (Holst, 1990).

The third most abundant neuropeptide in the pancreas is NPY (Sheikh *et al.*, 1988). NPY has been reported to inhibit insulin secretion in rodents (Moltz & McDonald, 1985). NPY is stored in pancreatic nerve fibres from both the sympathetic and parasympathetic divisions and is released both in response to stimulation of the vagal and the splanchnic nerve supply to the pancreas (Sheikh *et al.*, 1988). In the porcine pancreas, however, this porcine peptide has no effect on insulin secretion, neither alone nor in combination with the sympathetic transmitter, noradrenaline (Holst *et al.*, 1989). NPY acted synergistically with noradrenaline in controlling pancreatic vasoconstriction, however, and might participate in secretory control through its effects on blood flow. Synergistic effects between NPY and the parasympathetic transmitters have not been reported.

Galanin is present in nerve fibres both in the canine and in the porcine pancreas (Dunning *et al.*, 1986; Messell *et al.*, 1990), and galanin is released from the canine pancreas in response to sympathetic neural activation (Dunning *et al.*, 1990). Galanin inhibits insulin secretion in both rodents and dogs, and Dunning & Taborsky (1988) have suggested that galanin acts as a sympathetic inhibitory transmitter for insulin secretion. Galanin, however, does not inhibit glucose-induced insulin secretion in man (Gilbey *et al.*, 1989), and porcine galanin actually increases insulin secretion in the isolated pig pancreas (Messell *et al.*, 1990). It is probable that differences between species amount for these discrepancies. It is suggested that galanin is not an important regulator of insulin secretion in humans (or pigs).

CGRP has been identified by immunohistochemistry in pancreatic islets (Fujimura *et al.*, 1988), both in endocrine cells and in nerve fibres (Su *et al.*, 1987; Sternini & Brecha, 1986). CGRP nerve fibres are generally associated with blood vessels, and may promote vasodilatation (Uddman *et al.*, 1986; Tippins, 1986). Extrapolating from other tissues, many of the CGRP-containing fibres would be expected to be afferent fibres often also containing substance P (Green & Dockray, 1987; Gibson *et al.*, 1984). CGRP has been reported to inhibit insulin secretion from individual rat B-cells (Lewis *et al.*, 1988) and also inhibits basal and glucose-induced insulin secretion when infused into the superior pancreatic artery of anaesthetized pigs (Ahren *et al.*, 1987). It has no conspicuous effects on the endocrine secretion of the isolated perfused porcine pancreas and a release of CGRP from the pancreas cannot be demonstrated in response to electrical stimulation of the autonomic nerves to the pancreas (J. J. Holst, unpublished work). Thus, its role in the control of islet function remains to be determined.

Substance P has been reported to stimulate the secretion of insulin from the perfused canine pancreas (Hermansen, 1980), but inhibits glucose-induced insulin secretion in mice *in vivo* (Ahren *et al.*, 1986). Substance P is present in the pig pancreas (Larsson, 1979), but in exceedingly low concentrations (around 0·1 pmol/g of tissue). Immuno-reactive substance P can just be detected in perfusate from perfused pancreases and the concentration increases slightly upon stimulation of the vagus supply. Substance P significantly stimulates insulin secretion, but it is neither very potent nor efficient (J. J. Holst, unpublished work). Thus it seems difficult to assign a prominent role for substance P in insulin secretion.

CCK-like immunoreactivity has been demonstrated in nerve fibres in relation to the pancreatic islets, and most of the *C*-terminal fragments of CCK stimulate insulin secretion (Rehfeld *et al.*, 1980). The exact chemical nature of the CCK-like peptide(s) contained in the pancreatic nerve fibres has not yet been established, however, and it is impossible to demonstrate a release of CCK-like immunoreactivity from pancreatic nerves upon electrical stimulation of either division of the pancreatic autonomic nerve supply. Thus, the role of CCK-like neuropeptides in the control of insulin secretion remains to be settled.

Immunoreactive [Leu]enkephalin has been reported to be present in the pancreas (Larsson, 1979) and so has β-endorphin (Feldman *et al.*, 1983) and other opioids (Pfeiffer & Herz, 1984). Both endorphins and enkephalins were found to stimulate insulin release (Ipp *et al.*, 1978; Hermansen, 1983), but inhibition and no effect have also been reported (Kanter *et al.*, 1980; Stubbs *et al.*, 1978). Naloxone, the antagonist, has no consistent effect on insulin secretion (Feldman *et al.*, 1983; Pfeiffer & Herz, 1984) and β-endorphin immunoneutralization does not affect insulin secretion (Tannenbaum *et al.*, 1979). Against this background it seems less likely that the opioid peptides are important for the regulation of insulin secretion.

Conclusion

There is as yet little solid proof that the neuropeptides are essential in the nervous regulation of insulin secretion. It seems probable, though, that VIP and GRP could act as transmitters in the parasympathetic pathway supply to the pancreas and thereby possibly explain the atropine-resistant effect of nerve stimulation. Likewise galanin may act as a sympathetic, inhibitory co-transmitter in dogs and rodents (but does not appear to do so in humans and pigs). It appears to be a general rule that the nerves of the peripheral autonomic system exhibit a coexistence of transmitters, both classical and peptidergic, and in more and more systems it is becoming evident that the peptides act as modulators of the response to the classical transmitter. This seems to apply to the endocrine pancreas as well.

References

Ahren, B. & Lundquist, I. (1982) Interaction of vasoactive intestinal peptide (VIP) with cholinergic stimulation glucagon secretion. Experientia **38**, 405–406

Ahren, B., Taborsky, G. J. & Porte, D., Jr (1986) Neuropeptidergic versus cholinergic and adrenergic regulation of islet hormone secretion. Diabetologia **29**, 827–836

Ahren, B., Mårtensson, H. & Nobin, A. (1987) Effects of calcitonin gene-related peptide (CGRP) on islet hormone secretion in the pig. Diabetologia **30**, 354–359

Andersson, P.-O., Holst, J. & Järhult, J. (1979) Role of the sympatho-adrenal system in the control of endocrine pancreas during haemorrhage in cats. Eur. Surg. Res. **11**, 409–422

Andersson, P.-O., Holst, J. J. & Järhult, J. (1982) Effects of adrenergic blockade on the release of insulin, glucagon and somatostatin from the pancreas in response to splanchnic nerve stimulation in cats. Acta Physiol. Scand. **116**, 403–409

Baum, D. & Porte, D., Jr (1980) Stress hyperglycemia and the adrenergic regulation of pancreatic hormones in hypoxia. Metabolism **29** (Suppl. 1), 1176–1185

Bergman, R. N. & Miller, R. E. (1973) Direct enhancement of insulin secretion by vagal stimulation of the isolated pancreas. Am. J. Physiol. **225**, 481–486

Berthoud, H. R. (1984) The relative contribution of the nervous system, hormones, and metabolites to the total insulin response during a meal in the rat. Metabolism **33**, 18–25

Berthoud, H. R., Trimble, E. R., Siegel, E. G., Bereiter, D. A. & Jeanrenaud, B. (1980) Cephalic-phase insulin secretion in normal and pancreatic islet-transplanted rats. Am. J. Physiol. **238**, E336–E340

Bishop, A. E., Polak, J. M., Green, I. C., Bryant, M. G. & Bloom, S. R. (1980) The location of VIP in the pancreas of man and rat. Diabetologia **18**, 73–78

Bloom, S. R. & Edwards, A. V. (1975) The release of pancreatic glucagon and inhibition of insulin in response to stimulation of the sympathetic innervation. J. Physiol. (London) **253**, 157–173

Bloom, S. R. & Edwards, A. V. (1981) The role of the parasympathetic system in the control of insulin release in the conscious calf. J. Physiol. (London) **314**, 37–46

Bloom, S. R., Daniel, P. M., Johnston, D. I., Ogawa, O. & Pratt, O. E. (1973) Release of glucagon induced by stress. Q. J. Exp. Physiol. **58**, 99–108

Broadstone, V. L., Pfeifer, M. A., Baja, V., Stagner, J. I. & Samols, E. (1987) α-Adrenergic blockade improves glucose-potentiated insulin secretion in non-insulin-dependent diabetes mellitus. Diabetes **36**, 932–937

Bruce, D. G., Storlien, L. H., Furler, S. M. & Chisholm, D. J. (1987) Cephalic phase metabolic responses in normal weight adults. Metabolism **36**, 721–725

Bruncardi, F. C., Sun, Y. S., Druck, P., Goulet, R. J., Elahi, D. & Andersen, D. K. (1987) Splanchnic neural regulation of insulin and glucagon secretion in the isolated perfused human pancreas. Am. J. Surg. **153**, 34–40

Coupland, R. E. (1958) The innervation of the pancreas of the rat, cat, and rabbit as revealed by the cholinesterase technique. J. Anat. **92**, 143–149

Diem, P., Abid, M., Redmon, B., Sutherland, D. E. R. & Robertson, R. P. (1990) Systemic venous drainage of pancreas allografts as independent cause of hyperinsulinemia in type I diabetic recipients. Diabetes **39**, 534–540

Dunning, B. E. & Taborsky, G. J., Jr (1988) Galanin—Sympathetic neurotransmitter in endocrine pancreas? Diabetes **37**, 1157–1162

Dunning, B. E., Ahren, B., Veith, R. C., Böttcher, G., Sundler, F. & Taborsky, G. J., Jr (1986) Galanin: A novel pancreatic neuropeptide. Am. J. Physiol. **251**, E127–E133

Dunning, B. E., Ahren, B., Veith, R. C. & Taborsky, G. J. (1988) Non-adrenergic sympathetic neural influences on basal pancreatic hormone secretion. Am. J. Physiol. **255**, E785–E792

Dunning, B. E., Havel, P. J., Veith, R. C. & Taborsky, G. J., Jr (1990) Pancreatic and extrapancreatic galanin release during sympathetic neural activation. Am. J. Physiol. **258**, E436–E444

Edwards, A. V. (1984) Neural control of the endocrine pancreas. Recent Adv. Physiol. **10**, 277–315

Feldman, M., Kiser, R. S., Unger, R. H. & Li, C. H. (1983) Beta-endorphin and the endocrine pancreas. Studies in healthy and diabetic human beings. N. Engl. J. Med. **308**, 349–353

Forssmann, W. G. & Greenberg, J. (1978) Innervation of the endocrine pancreas in primates. In Peripheral Neuroendocrine Interactions (Coupland, R. E. & Forssmann, W. G., eds.), pp. 124–143, Springer Verlag, New York

Freyse, E.-J., Kiene, S., Brinckmann, W. & Fischer, U. (1982) Plasma insulin and glucose tolerance in pancreatectomized dogs after autologous partial pancreas transplantation. Loss of the insulinogenic reflex after OGTT and meal feeding. Horm. Metab. Res. **14**, 521–525

Frohman, L. A., Ezdinli, E. Z. & Javid, R. (1967) Effect of vagotomy and vagal stimulation on insulin secretion. Diabetes **16**, 443–448

Fujimura, M., Greeley, G. H., Hancock, M. B., Alwmark, A., Santos, A., Cooper, C. W., Reumont, K. J., Ishizuka, J. & Thompson, J. C. (1988) Colocalization of calcitonin gene-related peptide and somatostatin in pancreatic islet cells and inhibition of insulin secretion by calcitonin gene-related peptide in the rat. Pancreas **3**, 49–52

Galbo, H. (1983) In Hormonal and Metabolic Adaptation to Exercise, pp. 1–116, Georg Thieme Verlag, New York

Galbo, H., Christensen, N. J. & Holst, J. J. (1977) Catecholamines and pancreatic hormones during autonomic blockade in exercising man. Acta Physiol. Scand. **101**, 428–437

Gerich, J. E. & Lorenzi, M. (1978) The role of the autonomic nervous system and somatostatin in the control of insulin and glucagon secretion. In Frontiers in Neuroendocrinology (Ganong, W. F. & Martini, L., eds.), vol. 5, pp. 265–287, Raven Press, New York

Gibson, S. J., Polak, J. M., Bloom, S. R., Sabate, I. M., Mulderry, P. M., Ghatei, M. A., McGregor, G. P., Morrison, J. F. B., Kelly, J. S., Evans, R. M. & Rosenfeld, M. G. (1984) Calcitonin gene-related peptide immunoreactivity in the spinal cord of man and eight other species. J. Neurosci. **4**, 3101–3111

Gilbey, S. G., Stephenson, J., O'Halloran, J., Burrin, J. M. & Bloom, S. R. (1989) High-dose porcine galanin infusion and effect on intravenous glucose tolerance in humans. Diabetes **38**, 1114–1116

Green, T. & Dockray, G. J. (1987) Calcitonin gene-related peptide and substance P in afferents to the upper gastrointestinal tract in the rat. Neurosci. Lett. **76**, 151–156

Grill, V. & Östenson, C.-G. (1983) Muscarinic receptors in pancreatic islets of the rat. Demonstration and dependence on long-term glucose environment. Biochim. Biophys. Acta **756**, 159–168

Grill, H. V., Berridge, K. C. & Ganster, D. J. (1984) Oral glucose is the prime elicitor of preabsorptive insulin secretion. Am. J. Physiol. **246**, R88–R95

Havel, P. J. & Taborsky, G. J. (1989) The contribution of the autonomic nervous system to changes of glucagon and insulin secretion during hypoglycemic stress. Endocr. Rev. **10**, 332–350

Hermansen, K. (1980) Effects of substance P and other peptides on the release of somatostatin, insulin and glucagon *in vitro*. Endocrinology **107**, 1469–1473

Hermansen, K. (1983) Enkephalins and the secretion of pancreatic somatostatin and insulin in dogs: Studies *in vitro*. Endocrinology **113**, 1149–1154

Hermansen, K. & Ahren, B. (1990) Gastrin-releasing peptide stimulates the secretion of insulin, but not that of glucagon or somatostatin, from the isolated perfused dog pancreas. Acta Physiol. Scand. **138**, 175–179

Holst, J. J. (1986) Neural regulation of pancreatic exocrine function. In The Exocrine Pancreas. Biology, Pathobiology and Diseases (Go, V. L. W., Gardner, J. D., Brooks, F. P., Lebenthal, E., DiMagno, E. P. & Scheele, G. A., eds.), pp. 287–300, Raven Press, New York

Holst, J. J. (1990) Peptidergic mechanisms in the pancreas. Arch Int. Pharmacodyn. Ther. **303**, 252–269

Holst, J. J., Grønholt, R., Schaffalitzky de Muckadell, O. B. & Fahrenkrug, J. (1981*a*) Nervous control of pancreatic endocrine secretion in pigs. I. Insulin and glucagon response to electrical stimulation of the vagus nerves. Acta Physiol. Scand. **111**, 1–7

Holst, J. J., Grønholt, R., Schaffalitzky de Muckadell, O. B. & Fahrenkrug, J. (1981*b*)

Nervous control of pancreatic endocrine secretion in pigs. II. The effect of pharmacological blocking agents on the response to vagal stimulation. Acta Physiol. Scand. **111**, 9–14

Holst, J. J., Schaffalitzky de Muckadell, O. B., Fahrenkrug, J., Lindkær, S., Nielsen, O. V. & Schwartz, T. W. (1981*c*) Nervous control of pancreatic endocrine secretion in pigs. III. The effect of acetylcholine on the pancreatic secretion of insulin and glucagon. Acta Physiol. Scand. **111**, 15–22

Holst, J. J., Grønholt, R., Schaffalitzky de Muckadell, O. B. & Fahrenkrug, J. (1981*d*) Nervous control of pancreatic endocrine secretion in pigs. V. Influence of the sympathetic nervous system on the pancreatic secretion of insulin and glucagon, and on the insulin and glucagon response to vagal stimulation. Acta Physiol. Scand. **113**, 279–283

Holst, J. J., Jensen, S. L., Knuhtsen, S. & Nielsen, O. V. (1983) Autonomic nervous control of pancreatic somatostatin secretion. Am. J. Physiol. **245**, E542–E548

Holst, J. J., Fahrenkrug, J., Knuhtsen, S., Jensen, S. L., Poulsen, S. S. & Nielsen, O. V. (1984) Vasoactive intestinal polypeptide (VIP) in the pig pancreas: role of VIPergic nerves in control of fluid and bicarbonate secretion. Regul. Pept. **8**, 245–259

Holst, J. J., Schwartz, T. W., Knuhtsen, S., Jensen, S. L. & Nielsen, O. V. (1986) Autonomic nervous control of the endocrine secretion from the isolated, perfused pig pancreas. J. Auton. Nerv. Syst. **17**, 71–84

Holst, J. J., Fahrenkrug, J., Knuhtsen, S., Jensen, S. L., Nielsen, O. V., Lundberg, J. M. & Hökfelt, T. (1987) VIP and PHI in the pig pancreas: coexistence, corelease and cooperative effects. Am. J. Physiol. **252**, G182–G189

Holst, J. J., Ørskov, C., Knuhtsen, S., Sheikh, S. & Nielsen, O. V. (1989) On the regulatory functions of neuropeptide Y (NPY) with respect to vascular resistance and exocrine and endocrine secretion in the pig pancreas. Acta Physiol. Scand. **136**, 519–526

Holst, J. J., Harling, H., Messell, T. & Coy, D. H. (1990) Identification of the neurotransmitter/neuromodulator functions of the neuropeptide gastrin-releasing peptide in the porcine antrum, using the antagonist (Leu^{13}-ψ-CH$_2$-Leu^{14})-bombesin. Scand. J. Gastroenterol. **25**, 89–96

Hommel, H., Fischer, U., Retzlaff, K. & Knöfler, K. (1972) The mechanism of insulin secretion after oral glucose administration. II. Reflex insulin secretion in conscious dogs bearing fistulas of the digestive tract by sham-feeding of glucose or tap water. Diabetologia **8**, 111–116

Honjin, R. (1956) The innervation of the pancreas of the mouse, with special reference to the structure of the peripheral extension of the vegetative nervous system. J. Comp. Neurol. **104**, 331–371

Ipp, E. & Unger, R. H. (1979) Bombesin stimulates the release of insulin and glucagon, but not pancreatic somatostatin from the isolated perfused dog pancreas. Endocr. Res. Commun. **6**, 37–42

Ipp, E., Dobbs, R. & Unger, R. H. (1978) Morphine and beta-endorphin influence the secretion of the endocrine pancreas. Nature (London) **276**, 190–191

Issekutz, B. (1980) The role of hypoinsulinemia in exercise metabolism. Diabetes **29**, 629–635

Iversen, J. (1973*a*) Effect of acetyl choline on the secretion of glucagon and insulin from the isolated, perfused canine pancreas. Diabetes **22**, 381–387

Iversen, J. (1973*b*) Adrenergic receptors and the secretion of glucagon and insulin from the isolated, perfused canine pancreas. J. Clin. Invest. **52**, 2102–2116

Järhult, J. (1975) Role of the sympatho-adrenal system in hemorrhagic hyperglycemia. Acta Physiol. Scand. **93**, 25–33

Järhult, J. & Holst, J. J. (1978) Reflex adrenergic control of endocrine pancreas evoked by unloading of carotid baroreceptors in cats. Acta Physiol. Scand. **104**, 188–202

Järhult, J. & Holst, J. J. (1979) The role of the adrenergic innervation to the pancreatic islets in the control of insulin release during exercise in man. Pfluegers Arch. **383**, 41–45

Jensen, S. L., Fahrenkrug, J., Holst, J. J., Nielsen, O. V. & Schaffalitzky de Muckadell, O. B. (1978) Secretory effects of VIP on isolated perfused porcine pancreas. Am. J. Physiol. **235**, E387–E391

Kajinuma, H., Kaneto, A., Kuzuya, T. & Nakao, K. (1968) Effects of metacholine on insulin secretion in man. J. Clin. Endocrinol. **28**, 1384–1388

Kamel, I., Mikhail, Y. & Beshir, S. (1979) Study on the innervation of the pancreas of the rat. Acta Anat. **104**, 237–241

Kaneto, A. & Kosaka, K. (1974) Stimulation of glucagon and insulin secretion by acetylcholine infused intrapancreatically. Endocrinology **95**, 676–681

Kaneto, A., Kajinuma, H. & Kosaka, K. (1975) Effect of splanchnic nerve stimulation on glucagon and insulin output in the dog. Endocrinology **96**, 143–150

Kaneto, A., Miki, E. & Kosaka, K. (1974) Effects of vagal stimulation on glucagon and insulin secretion. Endocrinology **95**, 1005–1009

Kanter, R. A., Ensinck, J. W. & Fujinoto, W. Y. (1980) Disparate effects of enkephalin and morphine upon insulin and glucagon secretion by islet cell cultures. Diabetes **29**, 84–86

Knuhtsen, S., Holst, J. J., Schwartz, T. W., Jensen, S. L. & Nielsen, O. V. (1986) The effect of gastrin-releasing peptide on the endocrine pancreas. Regul. Pept. **17**, 169–176

Knuhtsen, S., Holst, J. J., Baldissera, F. G. A., Skak-Nielsen, T., Poulsen, S. S., Jensen, S. L. & Nielsen, O. V. (1987) Gastrin-releasing peptide in the porcine pancreas. Gastroenterology **92**, 1153–1158

Kral, J. G. (1978) Vagotomy for the treatment of severe obesity. Lancet **i**, 307–308

Kral, J. G. (1983) Behavioral effects of vagotomy in humans. In Vagal Nerve Function: Behavioral and Methodological Considerations (Kral, J. G., Powley, T. L. & Brooks, C. McC., eds.), pp. 273–281, Elsevier, Amsterdam

Kurose, T., Seino, Y., Nishi, S., Tsuji, K., Taminato, T., Tsuda, K. & Imura, H. (1990) Mechanism of sympathetic neural regulation of insulin, somatostatin, and glucagon secretion. Am. J. Physiol. **258**, E220–E227

Larsson, L.-I. (1979) Innervation of the pancreas by substance P, Enkephalin, Vasoactive Intestinal Polypeptide and Gastrin/CCK immunoreactive nerves. J. Histochem. Cytochem. **27**, 1283–1284

Larsson, L.-I. & Rehfeld, J. F. (1979) Peptidergic and adrenergic innervation of pancreatic ganglia. Scand. J. Gastroenterol. **14**, 433–437

Legg, P. G. (1968) Fluorescence studies on neural structures and endocrine cells in the pancreas of the cat. Zeitschr. Zellforsch. **88**, 487–495

Lewis, C. E., Clark, A., Ashcroft, S. J. H., Cooper, G. J. S. & Morris, J. F. (1988) Calcitonin gene-related peptide and somatostatin inhibit insulin release from individual rat B cells. Mol. Cell. Endocrinol. **57**, 41–49

Loud, F. B., Holst, J. J., Christiansen, J. & Rehfeld, J. F. (1988) Effect of glucagon on vagally induced gastric acid secretion in humans. Dig. Dis. Sci. **33**, 405–408

Lundberg, J. M., Änggård, A., Fahrenkrug, J., Hökfelt, T. & Mutt, V. (1980) Vasoactive intestinal polypeptide in cholinergic neurons of exocrine glands: functional significance of coexisting transmitters for vasodilatation and secretion. Proc. Natl. Acad. Sci. U.S.A. **77**, 1651–1655

Malaisse, W. (1972) Hormonal and environmental modification of islet activity. In Handbook of Physiology. Endocrinology, vol. 1, The Endocrine Pancreas (Steiner, D. F. & Freinkel, N., eds.), pp. 237–260, American Physiological Society, Washington D.C.

Malaisse, W., Malaisse-Lagae, F., Wright, P. H. & Ashmore, J. (1967) Effects of adrenergic and cholinergic agents upon insulin secretion *in vivo*. Endocrinology **80**, 975–978

Martindale, R., Levin, S. & Alfin-Slater, R. (1982) Effects of caerulein and bombesin on insulin and glucagon secretion from the isolated, perfused rat pancreas. Regul. Pept. **3**, 313–324

McCaleb, M. L. & Myers, R. D. (1982) 2-Deoxy-D-glucose and insulin modify release of norepinephrine from rat hypothalamus. Am. J. Physiol. **242**, R596–R601

Mei, N., Arlhac, A. & Boyer, A. (1981) Nervous regulation of insulin release by the intestinal vagal glucoreceptors. J. Auton. Nerv. Syst. **4**, 351–363

Messell, T., Harling, H., Böttcher, G., Johnsen, A. H. & Holst, J. J. (1990) Galanin in the porcine pancreas. Regul. Pept. **28**, 161–176

Miller, E. R. & Ullrey, D. E. (1987) The pig as a model for human nutrition. Annu. Rev. Nutr. **7**, 361–382

Miller, R. E. (1975) Neural inhibition of insulin secretion from the isolated canine pancreas. Am. J. Physiol. **229**, 144–149

Miller, R. E. (1981) Pancreatic neuroendocrinology: peripheral neural mechanisms in the regulation of the islets of Langerhans. Endocr. Rev. **2**, 471–494

Moltz, J. H. & McDonald, J. K. (1985) Neuropeptide Y: Direct and indirect action on insulin secretion in the rat. Peptides **6**, 1155–1159

Müller, E. E., Frohman, L. A. & Cocchi, D. (1973) Drug control of hyperglycemia and inhibition of insulin secretion due to centrally administered 2-deoxy-D-glucose. Am. J. Physiol. **224**, 1210–1217

Niijima, A. (1975) The effect of 2-deoxy-D-glucose and D-glucose on the efferent discharge rate of sympathetic nerves. J. Physiol. (London) **251**, 231–243

Nishi, S., Seino, Y., Ishida, H., Seino, M., Taminato, T., Sakurai, H. & Imura, H. (1987) Vagal regulation of insulin, glucagon and somatostatin secretion *in vitro* in the rat. J. Clin. Invest. **79**, 1191–1196

Oomura, Y. (1983) Glucose as a regulator of neuronal activity. Adv. Metab. Disord. **10**, 31–65

Petterson, M., Ahren, B., Böttcher, G. & Sundler, F. (1986) Calcitonin-gene-related peptide: Occurrence in pancreatic islets in the mouse and the rat and inhibition of insulin secretion in the mouse. Endocrinology **119**, 865–869

Pfeiffer, A. & Herz, A. (1984) Endocrine actions of the opioids. Horm. Metab. Res. **16**, 386–397

Rehfeld, J. F., Larsson, L.-I., Goltermann, N. R., Schwartz, T. W., Holst, J. J., Jensen, S. L. & Morley, J. S. (1980) Neural regulation of pancreatic hormone secretion by the C-terminal tetrapeptide of CCK. Nature (London) **284**, 33–38

Rohner-Jeanrenaud, F., Bobbioni, E., Ionescu, E., Sauter, J.-F. & Jeanrenaud, B. (1983) Central nervous system regulation of insulin secretion. Adv. Metab. Disord. **10**, 193–220

Russel, R. C. G., Walker, C. J. & Bloom, S. R. (1975) Hyperglucagonaemia in the surgical patient. Br. Med. J. **i**, 10–12

Samols, E. & Weir, G. C. (1979) Adrenergic modulation of pancreatic A, B, and D cells. J. Clin. Invest. **63**, 230–238

Sasaki, Y., Takahashi, H., Aso, H., Ohneda, A. & Weekes, T. E. C. (1982) Effects of cold exposure on insulin and glucagon secretion in sheep. Endocrinology **111**, 2070–2075

Schwartz, T. W., Stenquist, B. & Olbe, L. (1979) Cephalic phase of pancreatic polypeptide secretion studied by sham feeding in man. Scand. J. Gastroenterol. **14**, 313–320

Sheikh, S. P., Holst, J. J., Skak-Nielsen, T., Knigge, U., Warberg, J., Theodorsson-Norheim, E., Hökfelt, T., Lundberg, J. M. & Schwartz, T. W. (1988) Release of NPY in pig pancreas: dual parasympathetic and sympathetic regulation. Am. J. Physiol. **255**, G46–G54

Simard, L. C. (1937) Les complexes neuro-insulaires du pancreas humain. Arch. Anat. Microsc. Morphol. Exp. **33**, 49–64

Sjöström, L., Garellick, G., Krotkiewski, M. & Luyckx, A. (1980) Peripheral insulin in response to the sight and smell of food. Metabolism **29**, 901–909

Smith, P. H. & Davis, B. J. (1983) Morphological and functional aspects of pancreatic islet innervation. J. Auton. Nerv. Syst. **9**, 53–66

Smith, P. H. & Porte, D. (1976) Neuropharmacology of the pancreatic islets. Annu. Rev. Pharmacol. Toxicol. **16**, 269–285

Sternini, C. & Brecha, N. (1986) Immunocytochemical identification of islet cells and nerve fibers containing calcitonin gene-related peptide-like immunoreactivity in the rat pancreas. Gastroenterology **90**, 1155–1163

Strubbe, J. H. & Steffens, A. B. (1975) Rapid insulin release after ingestion of a meal in the unanesthetized rat. Am. J. Physiol. **229**, 1019–1022

Stubbs, W. A., Jones, A., Edwards, C. R. W., Delitala, G., Jeffcoate, W. J., Ratter, S. J., Besser, G. M., Bloom, S. R. & Alberti, K. G. M. M. (1978) Hormonal and metabolic responses to an enkephalin analogue in normal man. Lancet **ii**, 1225–1227

Su, H. C., Bishop, A. E., Power, R. F., Hamada, Y. & Polak, J. M. (1987) Dual intrinsic and extrinsic origins of CGRP- and NPY-immunoreactive nerves of rat gut and pancreas. J. Neurosci. **7**, 2674–2687

Tannenbaum, G. S., Panerai, A. E. & Friesen, H. G. (1979) Failure of β-endorphin antiserum, naloxone, and naltrexone to alter physiologic growth hormone and insulin secretion. Life Sci. **25**, 1983–1990

Taylor, I. L. & Feldman, M. (1982) Effect of cephalic-vagal stimulation on insulin, gastric inhibitory polypeptide, and pancreatic polypeptide release in humans. J. Clin. Endocrinol. Metab. **55**, 1114–1117

Thurston, J. H., Hauart, R. E. & Dirgo, J. A. (1978) Hyperglycemia, hypoinsulinemia, and hyperglucagonemia in acute water intoxication. Diabetes **27**, 61–63

Tippins, J. R. (1986) CGRP: A novel neuropeptide from the calcitonin gene is the most potent vasodilator known. J. Hypertens. **4**, S102–S105

Trimble, E. R., Berthoud, H. R., Siegel, E. G., Jeanrenaud, B. & Renold, A. E. (1981) Importance of cholinergic innervation of the pancreas for glucose tolerance in the rat. Am. J. Physiol. **241**, E337–E341

Uddman, R., Edvinsson, L., Ekblad, E., Håkanson, R. & Sundler, F. (1986) Calcitonin gene-related peptide (CGRP): perivascular distribution and vasodilatory effects. Regul. Pept. **15**, 1–23

Wolfe, R. F., Nadel, E. R., Shaw, J. H. F., Stephenson, L. A. & Wolfe, M. H. (1986) Role of changes in insulin and glucagon in glucose homeostasis in exercise. J. Clin. Invest. **77**, 900–907

Woods, S. C. & Porte, D. (1974) Neural control of the endocrine pancreas. Physiol. Rev. **54**, 596–619

3

Intra-islet interactions

Vincent Marks,* Ellis Samols† and John Stagner†

*Department of Biochemistry, University of Surrey, Guildford GU2 5XH, U.K., and †Department of Medicine, University of Louisville, Louisville, Kentucky 40203, U.S.A.

Introduction

The isolation of insulin from extracts of dog and beef pancreas fulfilled expectations that they would contain a hypoglycaemic agent, the lack of which was held to be the cause of hyperglycaemia in diabetic subjects (Loubatieres, 1970). The discovery by Murlin, barely a year after the purification of insulin, of a hyperglycaemia-producing substance in the very same pancreatic extracts as contained insulin was totally unexpected and received little attention from either the medical or scientific communities for nigh on a quarter of a century.

Though named for its hyperglycaemic action, glucagon remained largely uninvestigated until it was purified and subsequently characterized by chemists working in the laboratories of Eli Lilly in Indianapolis. The demonstration that glucagon produced its hyperglycaemic effects by activating adenylate cyclase with the formation of cyclic AMP acting as a second messenger, was a major factor in the award of the Nobel Prize for Medicine to Earl Sutherland.

That the two hormones, insulin and glucagon, might have a more intimate relationship with one another than was suggested by their seemingly diametrically opposed actions on the blood glucose concentration was first suggested as a result of the discovery that glucagon is one of the most potent stimulators of insulin secretion known (Marks, 1962; Samols *et al.*, 1965, 1966). This action of glucagon is a direct one upon the pancreatic B-cell and is not mediated by a rise in blood glucose concentration as had originally been thought. Nevertheless, glucose does play an important and probably, under physiological conditions, an essential role in the overall stimulatory process of insulin secretion.

In this chapter, the nature of the relationship between the various cellular elements that make up the islets of Langerhans will be examined in the light of what is now known about the structure and function not only of the cells that constitute the islets but of the islets themselves.

Historical perspective

The belief that the cells responsible for the secretion of the hypothetical hypoglycaemic agent of the pancreas, and whose absence caused diabetes, were contained within the islets of Langerhans rather than the pancreas as a whole antedated, by many years, the actual isolation of insulin (Loubatieres, 1970). These small collections of cells, which had first been identified by Langerhans while still a medical student, were looked upon initially as mere curiosities of no particular physiological significance. The subsequent discovery of the role of the pancreas in the pathogenesis of diabetes changed all that.

Islets are found scattered throughout the pancreas of all mammalian and avian species, but appear not to have a uniform anatomy either across or within species (Hellman & Lernmark, 1970). They show, for example, great variation in size in all species in which they have been studied—including man—even within a single pancreas. They are, on average, 250 μm in diameter and contain somewhere in the region of 3000 cells. Between them the islets account for 1.0–1.5 % of the volume of the pancreas, but 10 % of the blood flow (Lifson *et al.*, 1980).

Mammalian islets consist of at least four distinct types of cell. These are distinguished from one another on the basis of their histological, morphological, tinctural, immunocytochemical and functional properties. They are referred to nowadays as A-, B-, D- and PP-cells, respectively, though in the older literature they are referred to by a variety of names, some of which are still used. Ever since their discovery, the islets have been known to be richly innervated by autonomic nerve fibres, but these were largely ignored until comparatively recently (Woods & Porte, 1974). They are now thought to play an important role in the modulation of hormone secretion as considered in detail in Chapter 2 by Holst. This is in contrast to the blood vessels of the islets, the anatomical significance of which has only very recently been appreciated (Bonner-Weir & Orci, 1982). While it is possible that the nervous system exerts at least some of its regulatory functions on hormone secretion through its ability to influence blood flow through the islets this must, at the present time, be considered no more than speculative.

Before 1964, the islets were considered to be simple collections of cells, albeit important ones. They were thought to consist mainly, though not exclusively, of A- and B-cells that functioned completely independently of one another. The B-cells were known to be the sole source of insulin while the A-cells, though not the exclusive source of glucagon, were nevertheless its most important one.

The discovery that glucagon stimulated insulin secretion by direct action on the B-cells and conversely that insulin inhibited glucagon secretion by the A-cells led us to suggest that, far from being random collections of cells, the islets were complex micro-organs consisting of interactive cells whose main function was to secrete exactly the right amount of insulin in response to ingestion of a meal (Marks & Samols, 1968; Samols *et al.*, 1972). This would permit the constituents of the meal to be disposed of into the tissues without producing too large a perturbation in the concentration of metabolites in the blood or their wasteful loss into the urine.

The hypothesis that an important function of pancreatic glucagon is to amplify the insulin secretory response to food gained credibility from the demonstration by McIntyre *et al.* (1964)—and made more or less contemporaneously—that whereas hyperglycaemia produced by the intravenous injection of glucose is a comparatively poor stimulus to insulin secretion, that produced by oral ingestion of glucose is much more potent. This phenomenon—which is now known to be at least in part due to the secretion, from the gut, of powerful insulinotropic hormones—is referred to as the incretin effect of the entero-insular axis and of which glucose-dependent insulinotropic polypeptide (GDIP) and truncated glucagon-like peptide (GLP-$1_{(7-36)}$) are currently its best characterized members (see Morgan *et al.*, 1988 and Chapter 1 by Morgan). It is of some interest that while GDIP is both glucagonotrophic and insulinotrophic *in vivo* and *in vitro*, its insulinotrophic effect is exerted independently of glucagon (Tan *et al.*, 1984), unlike that of arginine which is seemingly partly mediated through its ability to stimulate glucagon release from the A-cells (Tan *et al.*, 1985*a,b*).

We originally proposed that A- and B-cells might communicate with one another through diffusion of their respective hormonal secretions in the interstitial fluid in which both types of cell are bathed. This hypothesis, which postulated a paracrine interrelationship between A- and B-cells was, however, slow to gain acceptance (Samols *et al.*, 1972). It had to be extended to include the D-cells (Reichlin, 1983) after these were shown to be the exclusive source of pancreatic somatostatin, a potent inhibitor of both insulin and glucagon secretion. Its participation in the inhibition of insulin secretion had been anticipated by Hellman on purely morphological grounds (Hellman & Lernmark, 1970) several years before somatostatin itself was isolated. The extended paracrine hypothesis proposed that A-, B- and D-cells regulate one anothers' secretions through the intra-islet interstitial fluid they all share; inhibition of both insulin and glucagon by somatostatin being its main feature (Reichlin, 1983).

Since it was first suggested (Samols *et al.*, 1966), an extensive literature has accumulated to support the hypothesis of a complex intra-islet relationship between the different islet cell types. More recent observations, especially on the structure and function of islet vasculature, have, however, made it less likely than formerly that the paracrine hypothesis is capable of providing a complete and totally satisfactory explanation of all of the major intra-islet cellular relationships (Samols, 1983; Samols *et al.*, 1983; Samols & Stagner, 1988; Marks *et al.*, 1990).

Microstructure and vasculature of islets

Mammalian islets of Langerhans can be shown, by a variety of techniques, to be remarkably sophisticated micro-organs, each with its own individual morphology and vasculature. The anatomical details differ depending upon the species from which the islets are derived (Hellman & Lernmark, 1970), as well as from which part of the pancreas they are harvested (Orci, 1985). The islets of most species appear to have certain features in common in so far as they consist of a central core of more or less pure B-cells surrounded by a mantle of D-cells and either A-, or PP-cells, depending upon whether they are of dorsal or ventral lobe origin. Birds show a completely different pattern of islet structure, however, and in the horse, the typical islet consists of a core of A-cells surrounded by a ring of more or less pure B-cells, around which the D-cells are scattered.

   In the human and rat islet, the mantle of A-cells and D-cells is perforated by one or more arterioles carrying blood from the pancreatic artery into the islets. This splits up into capillaries which traverse the islet tissue and eventually emerge as a venule which drains into the pancreatic vein. This arrangement does not necessarily exist in all species, the horse for example, where the A-cells are at the core of the islet.

   Relative to the rest of the pancreas, the islets of Langerhans are extremely well supplied with blood, making them among the most highly vascularized organs of the body (Lifson *et al.*, 1980). These facts, together with the observation that the capillaries of the islets are generally impervious to proteins (Kvietys *et al.*, 1983) as large as most of the immunoglobulins led one of us (E. S.) to question the total correctness of the 'paracrine' theory of intra-islet interaction. Much of the supporting evidence for such interaction comes from perifusion and other *in vitro* techniques for studying islet function, which exclude the circulation from consideration.

   On the basis of new information on the microvasculature of the islets of Langerhans, we proposed the existence of an intra-islet portal system wherein blood perfusing the central core of B-cells picks up insulin (Samols *et al.*, 1983). This is then delivered downstream to the A- and D-cells, constituting the mantle, where it serves to regulate the secretion of glucagon and somatostatin, respectively.

   This hypothesis was subsequently subjected to rigorous investigation, the results of which have served to substantiate it. The proposition that the vasculature of individual islets does indeed constitute a tiny intra-islet portal system and that blood flows progressively past B-, A- and finally D-cells is consistent with all the observations that have been made to date (Stagner *et al.*, 1988; Samols *et al.*, 1988; Stagner *et al.*, 1989). The evidence obtained in this way provides little support for the 'paracrine' hypothesis, but does not demolish it. The evidence in favour of the 'paracrine' hypothesis itself will be considered in greater detail later in this Chapter, especially in so far as it relates to the stimulation of insulin secretion or its facilitation by endogenous glucagon secretion.

Pancreatic islet perfusion

Although the anatomy of the islet microvasculature is now more or less established, the direction of blood flow within the blood vessels is still controversial, just as it was many years ago after the discovery of the hypothalamico-pituitary portal system.

It was originally believed that blood in the intra-islet blood vessels flowed in the direction of mantle to core, but this view was challenged by Bonner-Weir & Orci (1982). They suggested that, in the rat at least, the flow of blood was from core to mantle; in other words, that the core of B-cells was perfused before the mantle of A- and D-cells whose vascular relationship to one another, if indeed there was one, could not be determined by the purely morphological techniques available to them.

The investigative system developed by Samols and co-workers to test which of the two views of the intra-islet blood flow represents the true situation utilizes the perfused isolated pancreas preparation with or without concomitant immunoneutralization. A novel twist introduced by them to expand the usefulness of traditional pancreas perfusion experiments was the decision to perfuse through both the pancreatic artery, i.e. anterograde, and through the pancreatic vein, i.e. retrograde (Stagner & Samols, 1986) sequentially. In this way it should prove possible to see whether changes in direction of flow of the perfusate affected output of the various islet hormones. No changes would be expected if intra-islet cellular interactions occurred solely, or mainly, as a result of changes in the composition of the interstitial fluid whereas they might be if they were mediated via an intra-islet 'endocrine' mechanism.

Although the effects, both stimulatory and inhibitory, of insulin, C-peptide (Flatt *et al.*, 1986), glucagon and somatostatin upon the secretory function of the various pancreatic cell types can be deduced from observations made *in vivo*, as well as *in vitro*, it is often very difficult—and in some cases impossible—to distinguish direct from indirect effects mediated by nearby or contiguous cells. Mechanically separated islet cells, and those grown in monoculture, have been used to try and overcome some of the problems, but techniques employing these preparations are not entirely free from difficulties, since cells do not necessarily behave normally under these unphysiological circumstances. We and other authors have employed immunoneutralization techniques to try and overcome some of the difficulties but in doing so have created others (Schatz & Kullek, 1980; Fujimoto et al., 1983; Tan et al., 1985a,b).

Details of the methods employed in many of the pancreas perfusion experiments, the results of which are summarized here, are described elsewhere and will not be repeated. Suffice to say that only high avidity, very specific and purified immunoglobulins with neutralizing antibody activity were employed (Stagner & Samols, 1986; Samols et al., 1988; Stagner et al., 1988, 1989).

It could be computed from the known (pharmacological) effects of the various islet hormones upon the different islet endocrine cells that: (i) if intra-islet interactions are mediated largely or entirely through paracrine mechanisms, i.e. those involving only the interstitial fluid, then no differences would be observed in the amount of hormones secreted in response to perfusion with a fluid of fixed composition, regardless of whether the perfusion was made in the anterograde or in the retrograde direction; (ii) if all, or most, of the interactions between islet cells of similar or different cell types are mediated by intra-islet capillaries carrying hormones from one cell type to another through a micro-portal system, then profound differences would be observed depending on whether the perfusion was in one direction or the other.

The importance, in immunoneutralization experiments—especially those involving immunoperfusion—of using only purified, high-affinity and specific antibodies cannot be over-emphasized. These requirements were not always appreciated by earlier authors whose results must therefore be considered with some degree of circumspection.

Capillary permeability

Because islet capillaries are ordinarily impermeable to injected immuno-globulins (Kvietys et al., 1983) they are excluded, during perfusion experiments, from the interstitial fluid shared by the islet cells. Consequently antibodies to insulin, glucagon and somatostatin that are added to the perfusion fluid remain exclusively within the intra-islet vasculature during perfusion experiments, and any effect they exert must be through their ability to react with, and neutralize, any of the hormones against which they have been raised that have actually entered the blood vessels. Immunoglobulins, therefore, provide an excellent means of distinguishing events that can only be attributed to things happening within, or as a result of, the vasculature rather than as a consequence of inter-cell reactions mediated by the interstitial fluid or by mere juxtaposition. Thus while any insulin that gains entry to the circulation is completely neutralized during a perfusion experiment in which insulin antibodies are present in the perfusion fluid—providing they have a sufficiently high binding affinity—insulin that is already in, or is subsequently released into, the interstitium remains unneutralized and consequently available for interaction with any A- or D-cells with which it comes into contact.

Under 'ordinary' conditions *in vitro*, using isolated pancreatic islets or pancreas slices, exclusion of immunoglobulins from the interstitium does not occur; indeed, if immunoglobulin penetration of the interstitium did not occur under these circumstances the results of experiments in which they were used would be worthless. Preparations of this type, therefore, provide pharmacological rather than physiological information and results obtained with them should be interpreted accordingly.

Pancreatic perfusion and immunoglobulins

What follows is a summary of the results we have obtained to date using the isolated perfused pancreas preparation.

Anti-insulin immunoglobulins

Anterograde perfusion of the isolated dog or rat pancreas with anti-insulin immunoglobulins, in the presence of a perfusate glucose concentration of 5·0 mM produced a prompt rise in glucagon secretion as judged from the increased concentration of glucagon in the effluent (Fig. 1). No such rise was observed when the perfusion was made in the reverse or retrograde direction through the pancreatic vein (Samols *et al.*, 1986, 1988).

These results are exactly what would be expected if insulin secreted by the core of B-cells was exerting a tonic inhibition on glucagon secretion by the mantle A-cells and from which these cells were released as soon as the intravascular insulin was neutralized by anti-insulin immunoglobulins (Fig. 2).

Retrograde infusion of anti-insulin immunoglobulins had no effect upon somatostatin secretion, as reflected by its output in the effluent, whereas anterograde perfusion was attended by a proportionately very much greater increase than was observed with glucagon (Fig. 3). A small increase in somatostatin secretion might have been anticipated as a result of release from the presumed tonic inhibition exerted by the insulin secreted by the core B-cells; the very large rise that was observed was unexpected and raises the possibility that blood circulation through the mantle is, instead of being entirely random, more orderly than has been

Fig. I.   Effect of anti-insulin antibodies on glucagon concentrations in emerging perfusion fluid from the perfused rat pancreas

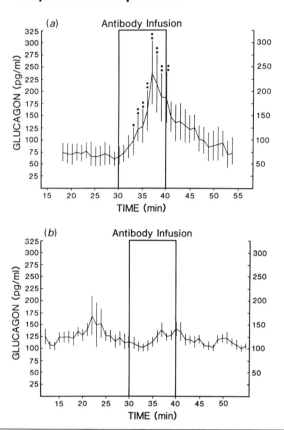

(a) shows the effect when perfusions were made in the anterograde direction, (b) when made in the retrograde direction. All other conditions were identical (Reproduced from Samols et al. (1988) with permission).

supposed: going first past the A-cells—where glucagon is added to it—and then past the D-cells which respond to the increase in endogenous glucagon secretion by increasing their own secretion of somatostatin.

Anti-glucagon immunoglobulins

This explanation of the observed findings is entirely consistent with perfusion experiments using anti-glucagon immunoglobulins. When perfused in the retrograde direction anti-glucagon immunoglobulins have no effect upon somatostatin output by the isolated rat pancreas, but

Fig. 2. Postulated mechanism of enhanced glucagon output by rat pancreas perfused *in vitro* with and without insulin antibodies in (*a*) the anterograde, and (*b*) the retrograde direction

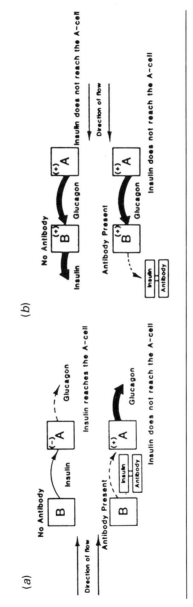

(*a*)

(*b*)

Reproduced from Samols et al. (1988)

modestly, though significantly, reduce its insulin secretion (Fig. 4). When perfused in the anterograde direction, on the other hand, they cause a moderate, but significant, fall in somatostatin secretion without affecting insulin output (Stagner *et al.*, 1989).

Fig. 3.   Effect of anti-insulin antibodies infused in anterograde and retrograde directions on the integrated glucagon and somatostatin output by the perfused rat pancreas *in vitro*

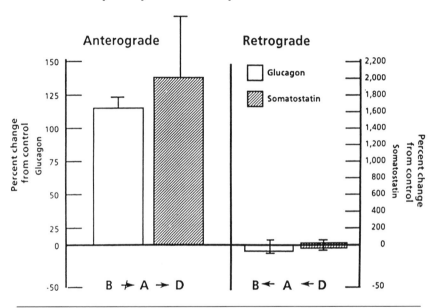

The diagram shows the percentage change in output from zero which represents the values observed during control perfusions before and after the addition of immunoglobulins to the perfusate (Reproduced from Samols et al. (1988) with permission).

Anti-somatostatin immunoglobulins

Anti-somatostatin immunoglobulins infused in the anterograde direction do not affect insulin or glucagon output in marked contrast with what occurred when they were infused retrogradely (Fig. 5). Under these circumstances there was a moderate, but significant, rise in glucagon and a very much larger and highly significant rise in insulin output. These results are exactly what would be expected if glucagon secretion by pancreatic A-cells had been released from tonic inhibition by somatostatin secreted by the D-cells, and had then become available to stimulate the core B-cells to secrete insulin (Samols *et al.*, 1988).

The results of these perfusion experiments strongly suggest that under ordinary conditions of blood flow there is an orderly progression of blood past the B-cell core—where it picks up insulin secreted in response to the prevailing concentration of glucose and other stimulatory

---

Fig. 4.   Effect of anti-glucagon antibodies infused in the anterograde and retrograde directions on the integrated insulin and somatostatin output by the perfused rat pancreas *in vitro*

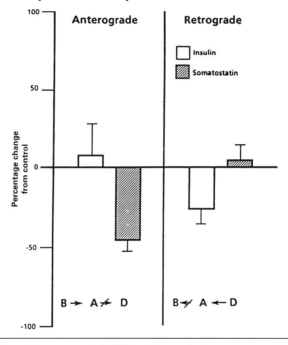

Reproduced from Stagner et al. (1989) with permission.

---

metabolites, as well as any gut hormones that may have been secreted in response to the ingestion of a meal—and then on past the A-cells in the islet mantle. There it gives up some of its insulin and picks up glucagon. Finally, it goes past the D-cells whose level of secretory activities are affected by both the prevailing insulin and glucagon concentrations as well as by any other regulators.

Support for the role of the islet vasculature in the regulation of islet function comes from morphological studies which indicate a distinct polarity of the B-cells with one pole facing a 'venous' and the other an 'arterial' capillary (Weir & Bonner-Weir, 1990). The B-cells, themselves, are separated from one another by canaliculi which span the space between the 'arterial' and 'venous' capillaries and into which microvilli—rich in B-cell-specific glucose transporter—protrude. These are thought to play an important role in the response of the B-cells to nutrients. Less is known about polarity of the A-cells—though most are thought to face two

---

Fig. 5.   **Effect of anti-somatostatin antibodies infused in the anterograde or retrograde directions on the integrated insulin and glucagon outputs by the perfused rat pancreas *in vitro***

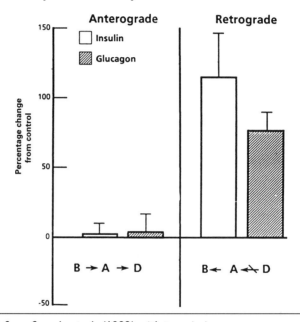

Reproduced from Samols et al. (1988) with permission.

---

separate blood vessels just like the B-cells. Virtually nothing is known about the polarity of D-cells, although they have been described as having dendritic extensions penetrating into the outer layers of the core B-cells, which could fit them for a local paracrine regulatory role; on the other hand their micro-anatomy has been said to suggest that they fulfil an endocrine rather than a paracrine function (Aponte *et al.*, 1985).

Intra-islet paracrine and autocrine interactions

Evidence for the existence of an intra-islet portal system, which has been outlined above, is not incompatible with some measure of paracrine interaction between islet cells as previously suggested (Samols *et al.*, 1966; Samols *et al.*, 1972). This would seem to be especially likely with respect to the A- and B-cells (and even the D-cells) where they abut one another towards the periphery of the B-cell core. Such an interaction would fulfil the insulin amplification role first assigned to glucagon after the discovery of its potent insulinotrophic properties. It is, however, difficult to reconcile the evidence we have now obtained with the theory, held by many, that somatostatin released by D-cells is one, if not the main, mechanism by which hyperglycaemia inhibits glucagon secretion. It is, of course, entirely compatible with the view that hyperglycaemia, by stimulating insulin secretion, produces a reciprocal inhibition of glucagon release.

Stimulation of insulin secretion by endogenous glucagon

The evidence for stimulation or, at the very least, the facilitation of glucose-stimulated insulin secretion by endogenous glucagon through a paracrine mechanism—or possibly even by temporary reversal of blood flow within the islet—is still largely indirect, but nevertheless substantial (Samols, 1983; Tan *et al.*, 1985*b*).

Arginine is a potent stimulator of both insulin and glucagon secretion *in vivo* and *in vitro*. In this respect, as in many others, it is unlike leucine which is almost a pure insulin secretagogue and is alone among amino acids in being able to substitute for glucose in insulin secretion studies *in vitro*. It has long been recognized that the insulin stimulatory effects of arginine are abolished, or greatly attenuated, by prolonged fasting which also diminishes or abolishes the insulinotropic effect of exogenous glucagon, but not that of glucose. Insulin release promoted by arginine *in vitro* can be suppressed by the addition of anti-glucagon immunoglobulins to the incubation or perfusion fluid and *in vivo* by either active or passive immunization (Tan *et al.*, 1985*b*). This inhibition is not always observed, however, when, for example, low-avidity antisera are used to achieve immunoneutralization or during single-pass pancreas perfusion experiments where access to the paracrine or interstitial space is denied or at best incomplete.

In elegant studies using purified A-, B- and D-cells from rat pancreases, Pipeleers and co-workers (1982) reported that single B-cells responded 2–4-fold more effectively to glucose when they were perfused with exogenous glucagon or when they were incubated with purified A-cells than when they were incubated alone. It would appear from these experiments that an optimum glucagon concentration in the vicinity of the B-cells is necessary for effective insulin secretion.

Trimble and co-workers (1982) took advantage of the fact that islets from the dorsal pancreas are much richer in A-cells than those from the ventral part, where PP-cells predominate, to show that under identical perfusion conditions and despite similar insulin contents, glucose-induced insulin secretion was some 50% greater from dorsal than from ventral islets. Radioleucine incorporation into proinsulin was also higher in the dorsal islets.

Tolbutamide which stimulates insulin secretion *in vivo* and *in vitro* is also capable of stimulating or inhibiting glucagon secretion—depending on the circumstances (Samols & Harrison, 1976). In insulin-dependent diabetic subjects, for example, in whom the insulinotropic effect of tolbutamide is lacking, its administration produces a rise in plasma glucagon concentration in contrast with normal healthy subjects, in whom it causes a fall. The normal response can be attributed to the inhibitory effect of the increased amount of insulin delivered to the A-cells via the intra-islet portal system, which is more than sufficient to overcome the presumably weak, but direct, stimulatory effect of tolbutamide on the A-cells themselves.

The insulin stimulatory effect of tolbutamide is greatly attenuated, at least in rats, by prior passive immunization with potent anti-glucagon immunoglobulins (Marks *et al.*, 1990). These must presumably have had sufficient time to diffuse into the intercellular fluid of the islets in amounts that are adequate to interfere with any glucagon-mediated actions upon the nearby B-cells.

Suppression of glucagon secretion by insulin

In view of what is now known about the nature and direction of blood flow in the intra-islet portal system, and clear evidence of the ability of insulin to inhibit glucagon secretion, it is no longer necessary to postulate a direct paracrine effect of B-cells on A-cell function without, however, disproving it (Samols & Harrison, 1976).

Inhibition of insulin and glucagon secretion by somatostatin

Somatostatin is a potent inhibitor of both insulin and glucagon secretion under all conditions that have been studied. Soon after its discovery in the pancreas it was assigned a paracrine role in the regulation of both insulin and glucagon secretion, although it is some 50–500 times more effective (Madarino *et al.*, 1981; Schuit *et al.*, 1989) as a suppressor of glucagon than of insulin secretion. This has led to the suggestion that negative feedback of glucagon secretion may be the main function of somatostatin at the level of the pancreatic islets (Reichlin, 1983).

As with the postulated A-cell:B-cell paracrine relationship within the islet, the evidence supporting a D-cell:A-cell and a D-cell:B-cell paracrine relationship is not only indirect but even more tenuous. It is, moreover, difficult to reconcile with new information on the intra-islet portal system which puts the D-cells at the end of the endocrine cascade and histological evidence that pancreatic D-cells are orientated towards the capillaries and consequently endocrine release of somatostatin (Aponte *et al.*, 1985).

Apart from the arguments based upon the pharmacology of somatostatin and morphological considerations, almost the sole evidence for a paracrine relationship, under physiological conditions, of the somatostatin-secreting D-cells to either the A-cells or the B-cells comes from the use of a non-immunoreactive somatostatin analogue in the canine pancreas. It is a feature of the islets of the dog that they appear to have D-cells scattered throughout the B-cell core of some islets. Use of the analogue, in low dosage, in perfusion experiments in the dog pancreas was associated with suppression of endogenous pancreatic somatostatin and an increase in both insulin and glucagon secretion. This was interpreted as demonstrating the release from tonic inhibition by endogenous somato-statin of both A- and B-cells (Taborsky, 1983). This explanation is open to the objection, however, that in higher doses the analogue suppresses insulin and glucagon release. Moreover, we have been unable to reproduce the stimulatory effect of the analogue on insulin and glucagon secretion in the rat pancreas in which there are no D-cells in the islet core and which, in this respect, resembles the islets of humans and other primates. We suggest that the result obtained with the somatostatin analogue in the dog pancreas could be owing to a stimulation–suppression dose effect, such as is sometimes seen with other peptides on the islet cells, or to the special anatomical arrangements of D-cells within the canine islets.

Physiological and pathological relevance of intra-islet interrelationships

Reams have been written on the possible relevance of intra-islet cellular relationships ever since the concept was first introduced some 25 years ago. Almost all of what has been written is speculative, however, and it is not our intention to discuss the subject in any detail here. A flavour of the debate (Samols, 1983; Samols *et al.*, 1983) can be obtained by reference to our earlier reviews which were written before the case for an intra-islet portal system had been fully established.

Conclusions

We believe that a better understanding of the way that the cells of the islets interact with one another, both in health and in disease, will have important therapeutic implications, especially if further work confirms the importance of the A-cells in determining the size and speed of the insulinaemic response to certain drugs and metabolites.

References

Aponte, G., Gross, D. & Yamada, T. (1985) Capillary orientation of rat pancreatic D-cell processes: evidence for endocrine release of somatostatin. Am. Physiol. Soc. **249**, G599–G606

Bonner-Weir, S. & Orci, L. (1982) New perspectives on the microvasculature of the islets of Langerhans in the rat. Diabetes **31**, 833–839

Flatt, P. R., Swanston-Flatt, S. K., Hampton, S. M., Bailey, C. J. & Marks, V. (1986) Feedback inhibition of insulin release: a physiological role for proinsulin C-peptide? Biochem. Soc. Trans. **14**, 781–782

Fujimoto, W. Y., Kawazu, S., Ikeuchi, M. & Kanazawa, Y. (1983) *In vitro* paracrine regulation of islet B-cell function by A and D cells. Life Sci. **32**, 1873–1878

Hellman, B. & Lernmark, A. (1970) A possible role of the pancreatic A_1 and A_2 cells as local regulators of insulin secretion. In The Structure and Metabolism of the Pancreatic Islets: A centennial of Paul Langerhans' discovery (Falkmer, S., Mellan, B. & Taljedal, I.-B., eds.), pp. 453–462, Pergamon, Oxford

Kvietys, P. R., Perry, M. A. & Granger, D. N. (1983) Permeability of pancreatic capillaries to small molecules. Am. J. Physiol. **8**, G519–G524

Lifson, N., Kraminger, K. G., Mayrand, R. R. & Lander, E. J. (1980) Blood flow to the rabbit pancreas with special reference to the islets of Langerhans. Gastroenterology **79**, 466–473

Loubautieres, A. (1970) Paul Langerhans: A memorial lecture. In The Structure and Metabolism of the Pancreatic Islets: A centennial of Paul Langerhans' discovery (Falkmer, S., Mellan, B. & Taljedal, I. B., eds.), pp. 5–21, Pergamon, Oxford

Mandarino, L., Stenner, D., Blanchard, W., Nissen, S., Gerich, J., Ling, N., Brazeau, P., Bohlen, P., Esch, F. & Guillemin, R. (1981) Selective effects of somatostatin-14, -25, and -128 on *in vitro* insulin and glucagon secretion. Nature (London) **291**, 76–77

Marks, V. (1962) The investigation of hypoglycaemia. In Disorders of Carbohydrate Metabolism (Pyke, D. A., ed.), pp. 229–239, Pitman, London

Marks, V. & Samols, E. (1968) Glucose homeostasis. In: Recent Advances in Endocrinology, 8th edn., (James, V. H. T., ed.), pp. 111–138, J. & A. Churchill, Edinburgh

Marks, V., Tan, K. S., Stagner, J. I. & Samols, E. (1990) Intra-islet cellular interrelationships. Biochem. Soc. Trans. **18**, 103–104

McIntyre, N., Holdsworth, D. & Turner, D. S. (1964) New interpretation of oral glucose tolerance. Lancet **ii**, 20–21

Morgan, L. M., Flatt, P. R. & Marks, V. (1988) Nutrient regulation of the entero-insular axis and insulin secretion. Nutr. Res. Rev. **1**, 79–97

Orci, L. (1985) The insulin factory: a tour of the plant surroundings and a visit to the assembly line: The Minkowski lecture 1973 revisited. Diabetologia **28**, 528–546

Pipeleers, D. G., In't Veld, P., Maes, E. & van de Winkel, M. (1982) Glucose-induced insulin release depends on functional co-operation between islet cells. Proc. Natl. Acad. Sci. U.S.A., **70**, 7322–7325

Reichlin, S. (1983) Somatostatin. N. Engl. J. Med. **309**, 1495–1501

Samols, E. (1983) Glucagon and insulin secretion. In Handbook of Experimental Pharmacology (Lefebvre, P. J., ed.), vol. 66/I, pp. 485–518, Springer-Verlag, Berlin

Samols, E. & Harrison, J. (1976) Remarkable potency of somatostatin as a glucagon suppressant. Metabolism (Suppl. 1) **25**, 1495–1497

Samols, E. & Stagner, J. I. (1988) Intra-islet regulation. Am. J. Med. **85** (5A), 31–35

Samols, E., Marri, G. & Marks, V. (1965) Promotion of insulin secretion by glucagon. Lancet **ii**, 415–416

Samols, E., Marri, G. & Marks, V. (1966) The interrelationship of glucagon, insulin and glucose. Diabetes **15**, 855–866

Samols, E., Tyler, J. & Marks, V. (1972) Glucagon–insulin interrelationships. In Glucagon. Molecular Physiology: Clinical and Therapeutic Implications. (Lefebvre, P. J., ed.), pp. 151–173, Pergamon, Oxford

Samols, E., Weir, G. C. & Bonner-Weir, S. (1983) Intra-islet insulin–glucagon–somatostatin relationships. In Handbook of Experimental Pharmacology (Lefebvre, P. J., ed.), vol. 66/II, pp. 153–173, Springer-Verlag, Berlin

Samols, E., Stagner, J. I. & Marks, V. (1986) Determination of flow-dependent intra-islet interactions of retrograde infusion of anti-insulin serum. Clin Res. **36**, 627A

Samols, E., Stagner, J., Ewart, R. B. L. & Marks, V. (1988) The order of islet cellular perfusion is B-A-D in the perfused rat pancreas. J. Clin. Invest. **82**, 350–354

Schatz, H. & Kullek, U. (1980) Studies on the local (paracrine) actions of glucagon, somatostatin and insulin in isolated islets of rat pancreas. FEBS Lett. **122**, 207–210

Schuit, F. C., Derde, M. P. & Pipeleers, D. G. (1989) Sensitivity of rat pancreatic A- and B-cells to somatostatin. Diabetologia **32**, 207–212

Stagner, J. I. & Samols, E. (1986) Retrograde perfusion as a model for testing the relative effects of glucose versus insulin on the A-cell. J. Clin. Invest. **77**, 1035–1037

Stagner, J. I., Samols, E. & Bonner-Weir, S. (1988) B > A > D pancreatic islet cellular perfusion in dogs. Diabetes **37**, 1715–1721

Stagner, J. I., Samols, E. & Marks, V. (1989) The anterograde and retrograde infusion of glucagon antibodies suggests that A-cells are vascularly perfused before D-cells within the rat islet. Diabetologia **32**, 203–206

Taborsky, G. J. (1983) Evidence of a paracrine role for pancreatic somatostatin *in vivo*. Am. J. Physiol. **245**, E598–603

Tan, K. S., Atabani, G. & Marks, V. (1984) Glucagon antibodies do not modify GIP-stimulated insulin secretion. Dig. Dis. Sci. **29**, 87S

Tan, K. S., Tsiolakis, D. & Marks, V. (1985a) Effect of glucagon antibodies on plasma glucose, insulin and somatostatin in the fasting and fed rat. Diabetologia **28**, 435–440

Tan, K. S., Atabani, G. & Marks, V. (1985b) Divergent effect of glucagon antibodies on arginine and glucose-stimulated insulin secretion in the rat. Diabetologia **28**, 441–444

Trimble, E. R., Hallban, P. A., Wollheim, C. B. & Renold, A. E. (1982) Functional differences between rat islets of dorsal and ventral pancreatic origin. J. Clin. Invest. **69**, 405–413

Weir, G. C. & Bonner-Weir, S. (1990) Islets of Langerhans: The puzzle of intraislet interactions and their relevance to diabetes. J. Clin. Invest. **85**, 983–987

Woods, S. C. & Porte, D. (1974) Neural control of the endocrine pancreas. Physiol. Rev. **54**, 596–619

4

Biosynthesis of insulin secretory granule proteins

Paul C. Guest and John C. Hutton

Department of Clinical Biochemistry, Addenbrooke's Hospital,
Cambridge CB2 2QR, U.K.

Introduction

The cytoplasmic granules of the pancreatic B-cells are the major source of secreted insulin in the acute response of the cell to hyperglycaemic stimuli. There are approximately 13 000 granules per cell, amounting to some 10 % of the cell volume (Dean, 1973). The granule contents are released from the cell by regulated exocytotic events, and during active periods of secretion more than 10 % of the granule population may turn over each hour. This process is dependent on the co-ordinated synthesis and precise segregation of a large number of proteins and lipids which are specifically required for granule formation and function.

Two dimensional gel electrophoretograms of purified insulin granules reveal the presence of more than 100 polypeptides (Hutton *et al.*, 1982). Many of these are related, and are differentially glycosylated forms of the same protein or various intermediates and products of post-translational proteolysis of precursor proteins. Nevertheless, the number of independent gene products in the granule is of the order of 30 or more. These include the proteases involved in propolypeptide conversion (endopeptidases, carboxypeptidases and amidating enzymes), co-secreted regulatory factors (islet amyloid polypeptide, chromogranin A and thyrotropin-releasing hormone), ion-translocating proteins which regulate the intragranular environment (proton-translocating ATPase), and extrinsic membrane proteins involved in intracellular granule movement and exocytosis.

This Chapter considers a number of these proteins with emphasis on the interdependence of their activities, and how this contributes to the co-ordination and integration of insulin granule function. Recent data will be presented describing post-translational modifications of these proteins and their segregation to the secretory granule compartment. Finally, we will address the question of how the granule composition and function are maintained in the face of changing rates of secretion.

The insulin secretory granule

Insulin secretory granules are characterized at the ultrastructural level as membrane-bound spheres 200–300 nm in diameter, containing an electron-opaque core surrounded by a mantle of translucent material. The morphology of the granule core, which consists mostly of crystalline insulin (Michael *et al.*, 1987), is distinctive and species specific (Greider *et al.*, 1969; Lange, 1974). The insulin crystals of most vertebrate species are composed of arrays of insulin hexamers with two centrally co-ordinated zinc atoms stabilizing each hexameric subunit (Blundell *et al.*, 1971).

In addition to insulin, the secretory granules contain the excised proinsulin connecting peptide (C-peptide), in amounts equimolar with insulin (Rubenstein *et al.*, 1977). Accordingly, the C-peptide is secreted from B-cells in amounts equivalent to insulin (Rubenstein *et al.*, 1969). These two peptides alone account for approximately 75 % of the granule protein mass (Hutton *et al.*, 1982). The remaining 25 % of the protein is distributed among 100 or more different granule matrix and membrane constituents of various molecular sizes and isoelectric points (Hutton *et al.*, 1982).

Insulin gene expression

Tissue–specific expression

In adult mammals, the insulin gene is expressed solely in pancreatic B-cells. Several lines of evidence have demonstrated that B-cell specific expression is controlled by transcriptional enhancer and promoter sequence elements in the 5′ flanking DNA of the gene (Edlund *et al.*, 1985). Mutational studies have defined regions within the rat insulin-1 gene enhancer which are important for transcriptional activity, including two structurally related sequence elements lying between positions -112 and -104 and -241 and -233 (relative to the transcription start site), which interact with a single protein (insulin enhancer binding factor 1) (Karlsson *et al.*, 1987, 1989; Ohlsson *et al.*, 1988). Deletion of either of these sequences greatly reduced expression of the gene, and a double mutation eliminated enhancer activity (Karlsson *et al.*, 1987). Another sequence element located between positions -100 and -91 of the rat insulin-2 gene enhancer is controlled by both positive- and negative-acting cellular transcriptional factors (Whelan *et al.*, 1989). The positive-acting factor appeared to be uniquely active in B-cells. In contrast with the enhancer, the rat insulin-2 gene promoter sequence did not appear to interact with cell-specific transcription factors and was constitutively active in both insulin-producing and non-insulin-producing cells (Whelan *et al.*, 1989). Regulatory sequences have also been identified within the 5' flanking DNA of the human insulin gene, which are regulated by positive- and negative-acting transcription factors (Boam et al., 1990). Several of these factors appeared to be uniquely active in insulin-producing cells.

Regulation of insulin gene transcription

Insulin gene transcription is regulated by specific hormones and nutrient secretagogues (for review see Steiner et al., 1985). Early studies in isolated rat islets suggested that glucose induced a specific increase in the synthesis of insulin mRNA relative to other cellular RNAs (Permutt & Kipnis, 1972). Direct evidence for such regulation has been obtained in more recent investigations by Brundstedt & Chan (1982) and by Nielsen and co-workers (1985). The insulin mRNA content of islets was reduced by culture in low glucose (0–3·3 mM) compared with islets cultured in high glucose (17–20 mM), which maintained the insulin mRNA content at a level similar to that in freshly isolated islets. In addition, the rate of insulin gene transcription was approximately 3-fold higher in islets cultured in 17 mM-glucose compared with 3·3 mM-glucose, an effect which could be mimicked partially by the addition of dibutryl cyclic AMP (Nielsen et al., 1985). Since glucose indirectly increases islet cyclic AMP levels (Charles et al., 1975), this mechanism may be of physiological importance.

The long-term regulation of insulin gene transcription by glucose also occurs by specific inhibition of insulin mRNA degradation. Studies have shown that the half-life of insulin mRNA was 2·6-fold greater in islets cultured in 17 mM-glucose compared with 3·3 mM-glucose (Welsh et al., 1985). Cholera toxin produced a similar effect in the insulin-producing RINm5F cells, indicating that the stabilizing effect of glucose on insulin mRNA may also be mediated by cyclic AMP (Welsh et al., 1985).

Translation of insulin mRNA

The initial translation product of insulin mRNA is pre-proinsulin, which consists of an N-terminal signal peptide linked to proinsulin (Chan et al., 1976). Like most nascent secretory proteins, translocation of pre-proinsulin across the rough endoplasmic reticulum (RER) membrane commences by interaction of the signal sequence with the 54 kDa polypeptide component of the signal recognition particle (SRP) (Kurzchalia et al., 1986), an event which retards further elongation of the peptide chain (Gilmore et al., 1982; Meyer et al., 1982). Association of this complex with the RER membrane is mediated by the affinity of the SRP for the SRP receptor (also called the 'docking protein'), an integral component of the membrane (Gilmore et al., 1982; Meyer et al., 1982). This interaction results in the release of SRP from both the ribosome (Gilmore & Blobel, 1983) and the signal sequence (Wiedmann et al., 1987a). The signal sequence is then transferred to the signal sequence receptor (SSR), a glycosylated, integral membrane protein

(Wiedmann *et al.*, 1987*b*). Photo-cross-linking studies have shown that both the signal sequence and the succeeding part of nascent pre-prolactin are closely associated with the SSR during translocation (Wiedmann *et al.*, 1989), a finding which suggests that the SSR may be a component of the putative proteinaceous translocation pore in the membrane (Blobel & Dobberstein, 1975).

Newly synthesized pre-proinsulin is rapidly cleaved to free proinsulin during or shortly after its translocation across the RER membrane (Patzelt *et al.*, 1978). This cleavage is mediated by the signal peptidase localized on the luminal surface of the membrane (Jackson & Blobel, 1977). Within the lumen of the RER, proinsulin rapidly folds forming the three disulphide bridges of native insulin, a process which may involve the luminal enzyme protein disulphide isomerase (Tager *et al.*, 1980).

Regulation of insulin mRNA translation

The biosynthesis and secretion of insulin by the islets of Langerhans are regulated by many circulating factors including glucose, certain amino acids, neurotransmitters and hormones [for reviews see Hedeskov, 1980; Permutt, 1981 and the Chapters 1, 2, 5 & 14 by Morgan, Holst, Malaisse and Berggren *et al*]. The metabolism of glucose is generally required for the stimulation of both processes since only metabolizable analogues of glucose and other sugars of amino acids are effective (Ashcroft *et al.*, 1978). Insulin biosynthesis and secretion are stimulated by mannose (Lin & Haist, 1969) and leucine (Andersson, 1976), but not by fructose, xylitol or ribose (Lin & Haist, 1969). The glucose-induced stimulation of both processes is inhibited by mannoheptulose (Lin & Haist, 1969), which blocks glucose metabolism in islets by inhibiting its phosphorylation to glucose 6-phosphate (Ashcroft & Randle, 1970).

The biosynthesis and secretion of insulin are not obligatorily coupled since these processes can be dissociated under certain conditions. Glucose-stimulated insulin release is inhibited in a Ca^{2+}-free medium, whereas synthesis is still activated (Pipeleers *et al.*, 1973*a*). Phosphodi-esterase inhibitors such as isobutylmethylxanthine (IBMX) and caffeine potentiate glucose-stimulated insulin release by increasing islet cyclic AMP levels (Howell & Montague, 1973), but do not significantly affect insulin biosynthesis (Ashcroft *et al.*, 1978). In addition, the threshold for glucose-induced activation of insulin synthesis (2·5–3·9 mM) is lower than that for insulin secretion (4·2–5·6 mM) [Pipeleers *et al.*, 1973*b*; Maldonato *et al.*, 1977].

Although glucose is known to stimulate islet insulin mRNA levels over long periods of exposure (2–72 h), blot-hybridization studies using cDNA probes have demonstrated that there is no significant increase in islet insulin mRNA after a 1 h exposure to the sugar (Itoh & Okamoto, 1980).

Over the same time period, incorporation of radiolabelled amino acids into proinsulin is increased (10–20)-fold (Howell & Taylor, 1966; Morris & Korner, 1970; Lin *et al.*, 1972; Ashcroft *et al.*, 1978). This effect does not require the synthesis of new mRNA as indicated by the rapidity of the response and the lack of effect of transcriptional inhibitors such as actinomycin D (Morris & Korner, 1970; Permutt & Kipnis, 1972). Thus, the initial stimulation of insulin biosynthesis, which occurs within 20 min of exposure to glucose (Permutt & Kipnis, 1972; Ashcroft *et al.*, 1978), must utilize pre-existing mRNA and involve translational regulation.

Analysis of the subcellular distribution of insulin mRNA in isolated rat islets suggests that glucose increases the rate of translational initiation (Itoh & Okamoto, 1980; Welsh *et al.*, 1986). Exposure of islets to glucose concentrations above 3.3 mM, resulted in an increased transfer of cytoplasmic insulin mRNA to subcellular fractions containing ribosomes and larger polysomes (Welsh *et al.*, 1986). The same response was achieved by pre-incubation of islets with the phosphodiesterase inhibitor theophylline and a combination of 10 mM-L-leucine and 3.3 mM-glucose (Welsh *et al.*, 1987). However, similar effects on distribution have been observed on total islet mRNA which suggest that altered rates of initiation may be a general response to glucose (Permutt & Kipnis, 1975).

Glucose also increases the transfer of initiated insulin mRNA from free to membrane-bound polysomes (Welsh *et al.*, 1986), consistent with SRP-mediated transfer of ribosomes bearing nascent pre-proinsulin from the cytoplasm to the RER. This effect could be mimicked by 10 mM-L-leucine in combination with 3.3 mM-glucose although, in contrast with effect on initiation, not by theophylline (Welsh *et al.*, 1987). These findings indicate that the metabolizable B-cell substrate L-leucine stimulates insulin biosynthesis by a mechanism similar to that of glucose, whereas agents which increase the B-cell cyclic AMP content, such as theophylline, act only to stimulate translational initiation rates.

Investigations involving *in vitro* translation of islet homogenates indicate that glucose stimulation of pre-proinsulin synthesis might be the result of an increased association of the SRP initiation complex with the SRP receptor (Welsh *et al.*, 1986). Addition of the SRP receptor to the islet homogenates increased the run-off incorporation of ^{125}I-tyrosine into pre-proinsulin. This response was more pronounced when islets were pre-incubated in 16·7 mM-glucose, indicating that in glucose-stimulated islets the SRP may be altered structurally, enhancing its interaction with the SRP receptor. In addition, recent studies on the distribution of translating ribosomes on insulin mRNA have demonstrated an increase in ribosomal pausing, under conditions of low glucose, after approximately 70 amino acids of pre-proinsulin had been synthesized (Wolin & Walter, 1988). This was consistent with the site of SRP-mediated arrest on the nascent peptide chain.

The rate of translational elongation of pre-proinsulin may be regulated specifically by glucose in the range of 0–5·6 mM. This has been assessed in experiments estimating rates of insulin synthesis in the presence of low concentrations of cycloheximide, under which conditions elongation is the rate-limiting step in translation (Welsh *et al.*, 1986). In the presence of cycloheximide, insulin synthesis was stimulated by glucose at concentrations up to 5·6 mM, whereas non-insulin protein synthesis was not significantly affected by glucose. In addition, this stimulation was observed without any change in the intracellular distribution of insulin mRNA and was thus interpreted to result from an increase in the elongation rate of pre-proinsulin.

Molecular sorting and secretory granule formation

Newly synthesized proteins destined for the plasma membrane, lysozomes and secretory granules traverse the same intracellular pathway from the RER to the Golgi complex (Palade, 1975). These proteins exit the RER in transport vesicles which bud from transitional elements of the RER membrane and are delivered to the *cis* region of the Golgi complex and on through the Golgi cisternae by repeated cycles of vesicle budding and fusion (Rothman *et al.*, 1984). Studies using tripeptides containing the Asn-X-Ser/Thr acceptor sequence for *N*-linked glycosylation have demonstrated the existence of a non-selective bulk flow of proteins to the cell surface, which suggests that proteins which do not contain specific signals for retention or diversion are secreted from the cell by default (Wieland *et al.*, 1987). Known signals which divert proteins from this pathway include the *C*-terminal peptide -Lys-Asp-Glu-Leu, which causes retention of resident luminal proteins of the RER (Munro & Pelham, 1987), and the mannose-6-phosphate marker which directs soluble lysozomal enzymes to lysozomes (for review see Kornfeld & Mellman, 1989).

The nature of the putative signal for diversion to the secretory granules is unknown. However, the observed association of proinsulin (Orci *et al.*, 1984), pro-opiomelanocortin (Loh & Tam, 1985) and proenkephalin (Birch *et al.*, 1986) with Golgi and secretory granule membranes may indicate that it is a receptor-mediated process. Alternatively, sorting may occur through the specific condensation of secretory granule proteins, as suggested by studies *in vitro* of purified human secretogranin II (Gerdes *et al.*, 1989). This protein formed aggregates in the presence of 10 mM-calcium at pH 5·2, conditions characteristic of the neuroendocrine secretory granule matrix, while no aggregation of constitutive secretory proteins such as immunoglobulin G and serum albumin, was observed. In addition, the packaging *in vivo* of newly synthesized secretogranin II into secretory granules was inhibited by ammonium chloride, which is known to neutralize the pH of acidic intracellular compartments.

Morphological (Orci *et al.*, 1987*a*; Tooze *et al.*, 1987) and biochemical studies (Tooze & Huttner, 1990) have shown that segregation of regulated secretory proteins in endocrine and neutral cells occurs upon exit from the *trans* Golgi network (TGN). In the case of the insulin granule in the pancreatic B-cell, condensing secretory material buds from distinct clathrin-coated regions of the TGN to yield immature coated granules (Orci, 1985). Subsequent maturation of the granule involves further condensation of the matrix constituents, reduction in granule size and dissociation of the coat proteins.

Insulin secretory granule proteins

The proton-translocating ATPase

Early investigations of intact insulinoma secretory granules revealed the presence of an ATPase activity (Hutton & Peshavaria, 1982) and a pH gradient of 1–1·5 units (acidic inside) across the granule membrane (Hutton, 1982). This indicated that the membrane contains a catalytic activity which, at the expense of ATP hydrolysis, transports protons from the cytosol into the granule interior. The properties of the insulin granule proton-translocating ATPase were indistinguishable from those of the adrenal chromaffin granule enzyme, and from similar enzymic activities in the intracellular vesicles of distantly related organisms (Al-Awqati, 1986; Mellman *et al.*, 1986). The finding, that antibodies raised against the beetroot tonoplast membrane proton pump cross-reacted with the chromaffin and insulin granule enzymes, further indicated the highly conserved nature of this catalytic activity.

Functional studies of the insulin granule ATPase have been performed at light microscopic level using fluorescent probes (Abrahamsson & Gylfe, 1980), and at the ultrastructural level using antibodies raised to permeant dinitrophenol congeners (Orci, 1986), to determine the pH of the granule interior relative to the cytoplasm. Newly formed clathrin-coated granules appeared to have a neutral internal pH environment, whereas mature non-coated granules were relatively acidic. Since newly formed granules are rich in proinsulin and mature granules contain predominantly insulin (Orci, 1986), it follows that acidification is an important event in the initiation of prohormone conversion. It is not known whether this occurs through the activation of existing proton translocases or as a result of their insertion into the membrane at a late stage in granule development.

The pH of the granule interior (5·0–5·5) corresponds to the

isoelectric point of insulin and as such will promote the formation of insulin crystals (Tanford & Epstein, 1954a,b). In addition, the proinsulin converting enzymes are maximally active in this pH range (Davidson & Hutton, 1987; Davidson et al., 1988). Acidification may also cause dissociation of metal ion complexes within the granule (Tanford & Epstein, 1954a), and the transmembrane potential may account for the accumulation of biogenic amines such as 5-hydroxytryptamine and dopamine in the granule interior (Ekholm et al., 1971; Owman et al., 1973).

Proinsulin-converting endopeptidases

Pulse-chase radiolabelling studies in isolated islets indicate that the proteolytic conversion of proinsulin to insulin may commence within the terminal regions of the Golgi apparatus, although the major conversion occurs shortly after secretory granule formation (Sorenson et al., 1970; Docherty & Steiner, 1982; Davidson et al., 1988). This process involves initial cleavage by trypsin-like endopeptidases on the C-terminal side of two dibasic sequences in the precursor. The exposed basic residues are then removed by a carboxypeptidase B-like enzyme to generate native insulin, C-peptide and free arginine and lysine residues (Fig. 1) [for review see Docherty & Steiner, 1982].

Two distinct endopeptidase activities are thought to be involved in the conversion process (Davidson et al., 1988). One of these (type I) cleaves exclusively after the Arg^{31}-Arg^{32} sequence at the proinsulin B–C chain junction, and the other (type II) cleaves preferentially after the Lys^{64}-Arg^{65} sequence at the C–A chain junction (although it will also cleave the Arg^{31}-Arg^{32} site to a minor extent). The optimum pH for both activities is 5·5, although their pH profiles differ slightly. The type I enzyme is virtually inactive at the neutral pH values typical of the Golgi complex (Orci et al., 1987b), while under these conditions the type II enzyme retains 30–40 % of its maximum activity.

The enzymes also have different Ca^{2+} requirements. The type I activity is half maximal at 2·5 mM-Ca^{2+} while the type II activity requires only 100 μM-Ca^{2+}. Since the free Ca^{2+} content of the insulin granule is estimated to be 1–10 mM (Hutton et al., 1983), it follows that the granule is capable of supporting the maximum activity of both enzymes. However, at the lower free Ca^{2+} content of the Golgi complex (Herman et al., 1973) the type I activity is likely to exhibit a reduced activity.

Control exerted by pH and the free Ca^{2+} concentration ensures that the production of insulin does not occur until the precursor is segregated to the granule compartment (important since insulin is considerably less soluble than proinsulin). In addition, the less stringent Ca^{2+} and pH requirements of the type II enzyme may enable it to play an additional role in the processing of other non-granule proteins during their passage through the Golgi complex.

Fig. I. Pathway of conversion of proinsulin to insulin

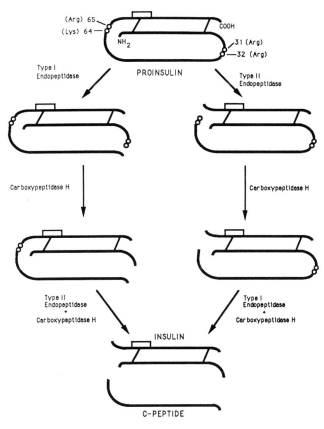

Carboxypeptidase H

The carboxypeptidase B-like activity involved in proinsulin conversion was demonstrated originally in crude rat islet secretory granule preparations (Kemmler *et al.*, 1973), and purified subsequently from rat insulinoma tissue (Davidson & Hutton, 1987). The enzyme was found to be indistinguishable from carboxypeptidase H (also termed carboxypeptidase E and enkephalin convertase; EC 3.4.17.10) which is present in many endocrine and neural tissues (Fricker & Snyder, 1982, 1983; Docherty & Hutton, 1983). Carboxypeptidase H activity is localized to secretory granules, where the enzyme exists in soluble and membrane-bound forms which differ in molecular mass by 2–3 kDa (Supattapone *et al.*, 1984). In the pancreatic B-cell it constitutes 2–5% of the total protein of the granule (Hutton, 1984), and is present mostly as a soluble constituent with an apparent molecular mass of 53–54 kDa (Davidson & Hutton, 1987).

The purified enzyme is capable of removing basic amino acids from the C-terminus of trypsinized proinsulin to generate insulin (Davidson & Hutton, 1987). The pH optimum of conversion is sharp in the range of 5–6, compatible with the intragranular environment. Conversion can be stimulated 5-fold by $CoCl_2$, while it is inhibited by guanidinomercaptosuccinic acid (an active-site-directed inhibitor) and chelating agents such as 1,10-phenanthroline and EDTA.

A series of related cDNA clones encoding the enzyme have been obtained from rat islet and insulinoma libraries (J. C. Hutton, unpublished work), and from rat hippocampal and hypothalamic libraries (Fricker et al., 1989). The nucleotide sequences of these clones suggest that they were derived from an identical mRNA species encoding a protein of 476 amino acids (Fricker et al., 1989). Northern blot analyses of rat tissues indicated the presence of a single carboxypeptidase H mRNA, with the highest levels found in tissues of endocrine and neural origin.

The carboxypeptidase H N-terminus contains a stretch of 16 hydrophobic amino acids which probably serves as a signal peptide for translocation of the enzyme into the lumen of the RER. Five dibasic amino acid sites are present in the molecule including a sequence consisting of five Arg residues at amino acid positions 38–42. This sequence may constitute a possible site of cleavage for endopeptidases during passage of the enzyme along the secretory pathway. In addition, an Arg-Lys sequence at amino acid positions 436–437 precedes a stretch of 11 residues at the molecule's C-terminus. This C-terminal sequence is predicted to form an amphiphilic α-helix, which had been postulated to be a membrane anchor for a higher molecular mass form of the enzyme (Fricker et al., 1990). It has been proposed in the case of the bovine pituitary carboxypeptidase H that cleavage at this dibasic site produces the soluble form of the enzyme (Fricker et al., 1990).

The predicted amino acid sequence of rat carboxypeptidase H shows an overall similarity of more than 90 % with the bovine (Fricker et al., 1986) and the human (Manser et al., 1990) enzymes, indicating that it has been highly conserved during evolution. A similar enzyme has been detected in mouse, amphibian and mollusc endocrine tissues (Fricker & Herbert, 1988; Mackin & Noe, 1987). The carboxypeptidase H sequence also shows a substantial degree of similarity with the exocrine pancreatic carboxypeptidases A (20 %) and B (17 %) particularly in regions thought to be important for Zn binding and catalytic function. The observation that the overall similarity between carboxypeptidases A and B (48 %) is greater than the similarity of these proteins to carboxypeptidase H, indicates that the exocrine and endocrine enzymes diverged from a common precursor.

Chromogranin A

Another insulin granule protein termed betagranin was first distinguished as a peptide of 20–21 kDa co-secreted with insulin from isolated rat islets and insulinoma cells (Sopwith *et al.*, 1984). Three molecular forms of the protein have been purified and found to possess identical *N*-termini and amino acid compositions (Hutton *et al.*, 1985). In addition the *N*-terminal sequence of these proteins was found to be highly similar to that of chromogranin A, a larger co-secreted protein of the adrenal chromaffin cell (Streider *et al.*, 1968).

Pulse-chase radiolabelling studies in rat insulinoma cells have shown that betagranin is synthesized initially as a larger precursor, of the same size as rat adrenal chromogranin A (100 kDa by SDS/PAGE), which is converted into the mature 21 kDa peptide (Hutton *et al.*, 1987*a*). This conversion paralleled that of proinsulin to insulin indicating that chromogranin A tranverses the same intracellular pathway as insulin, and is subjected to similar post-translational proteolytic events. The proteolytic activities were localized to secretory granules by *in vitro* conversion assays using a biosynthetically labelled chromogranin A-like precursor and rat insulinoma subcellular fractions (Hutton *et al.*, 1987*b*). Inhibitor and ion-dependency analyses indicated that, like proinsulin, conversion of chromogranin A required endopeptidase and carboxypeptidase H activities.

Immunoblot analyses using antibodies raised to insulinoma betagranin revealed the presence of the 20–21 kDa peptides in both rat insulinoma and islet tissue (Hutton *et al.*, 1988*a*). In islets, immuno-reactivity was present in most endocrine cells, although subpopulations of B- and A-cells appeared to be more reactive. In insulinoma cells, immunoreactivity was confined principally to the secretory granules and co-localized with insulin. Rat pituitary and adrenal tissues were also immunoreactive for betagranin, but in this case higher molecular mass forms of 65, 85 and 100 kDa were mostly apparent.

Several cDNA clones have been obtained from rat insulinoma and islet libraries encoding the complete 448 amino acid sequence of the precursor protein (Hutton *et al.*, 1988*b*). Northern blot analyses revealed the presence of a single mRNA species of approximately 2·0 kb in insulinoma tissue, pituitary and adrenal. This finding indicated that the rat molecule is the product of a single gene and mRNA transcript, and tissue variations are most likely due to post-translational proteolysis.

Analysis of the deduced amino acid sequence of rat chromogranin A revealed several unusual features including a high content of acidic amino acids with a stretch of 20 consecutive Gln residues. Predictions of its tertiary structure indicate that it is mostly a randomly coiled protein, which is supported by the findings of studies *in vivo* and *in vitro* using n.m.r. spectroscopy (Daniels *et al.*, 1978). The molecule also contains 10 dibasic amino acid sequences. One of these, Lys^{129}-Arg^{130}, is located just two residues beyond the most C-terminal peptide fragment sequenced from betagranin (Hutton *et al.*, 1988*b*), indicating that this is a likely site of proteolytic cleavage.

The insulinoma chromogranin A cDNA sequence shows substantial similarity with the bovine (Iacangelo *et al.*, 1986) and human (Konecki *et al.*, 1987) sequences, indicating that it has been highly conserved. In addition, chromogranin A-like immunoreactivity has been detected in tissues of vertebrates such as the pig, horse, chicken and frog (Rieker *et al.*, 1988), and invertebrates such as the ciliated protozoan *Paramecium tetraurelia* (Peterson *et al.*, 1987).

The precise physiological function of chromogranin A has remained unknown in spite of more than 20 years of intensive investigation. However, the observation that it contains the coding sequence for pancreastatin (amino acids 267–314 of the rat sequence), a peptide which inhibits insulin and somatostatin secretion from the perfused rat pancreas (Tatemoto *et al.*, 1987; Efendic *et al.*, 1987), suggests that it may serve as a precursor of bioactive peptides in the endocrine pancreas [see Chapter 14 by Berggren *et al.*, for further details]. The finding that chromogranin A is a competitive inhibitor of the porcine pituitary endopeptidase, IRCM-serine protease 1, suggests that it might be involved in the regulation of post-translational proteolysis of prohormones (Seidah *et al.*, 1987). However, this is not likely to occur in the case of islet-cell hormones since chromogranin A is only a minor constituent of normal islet tissue (0.1–0.3 % of insulin) (P. C. Guest & J. C. Hutton, unpublished work). The appearance of the fibronectin cell-binding domain sequence (Arg-Gly-Asp) in chromogranin A, suggests that it may also be involved in the segregation of proteins to secretory granules (Benedum *et al.*, 1986).

Islet amyloid polypeptide

Amyloid deposits have been found in the islets of Langerhans of more than 90 % of non-insulin-dependent diabetes mellitus (NIDDM) patients (Clark *et al.*, 1987; Westermark *et al.*, 1987*a*). The close proximity of these deposits to insulin-producing B-cells suggests that their accumulation may impair the normal secretory capacity of the B-cell, leading to hyper-glycaemia and the diseased state. The major component of islet amyloid has been isolated from a human insulinoma (Westermark *et al.*, 1987*b*) and from the pancreata of NIDDM patients (Cooper *et al.*, 1987*a*). Sequence analysis revealed a 37 amino acid peptide, termed islet amyloid polypeptide (IAPP), which has 43 % and 46 % amino acid sequence similarity with calcitonin-gene-related peptides (CGRP) I and II. Examination of the cDNA sequence encoding human IAPP showed that it contains a signal peptide of 22 amino acids followed by an 11 amino acid propeptide, which terminates in a Lys-Arg sequence at the N-terminus of the mature peptide (Sanke *et al.*, 1988). The IAPP C-terminus is followed by the proteolysis/amidation signal, Gly-Lys-Arg, and another propeptide of 16 amino acids.

Immunolocalization studies have shown that like insulin, IAPP is localized to the central region of human B-cell secretory granules, and is thus likely to be co-secreted with the hormone (Lukinius *et al.*, 1989). Indeed, studies with isolated rat islets have shown that IAPP secretion is stimulated by glucose and that the levels of IAPP released amount to approximately 5% of that observed for insulin (Kanatsuka *et al.*, 1989). These findings suggest that IAPP may have an extracellular function, perhaps in the modification of insulin action.

Synthetic amidated IAPP has been reported to inhibit insulin secretion from isolated rat islets, although the doses required for this effect were extremely high (10^{-5} M) (Ohsawa, *et al.*, 1989). Other studies suggest that IAPP may be a potent inhibitor of basal and insulin-stimulated rates of glycogen synthesis in muscle, an effect it shares with CGRP (Leighton & Cooper, 1988; Cooper *et al.*, 1988). Both amidated and non-amidated forms of IAPP have been shown to reduce serum calcium levels *in vivo* and *in vitro* (Datta *et al.*, 1989; MacIntyre, 1989). In addition, IAPP may have a direct effect on calcium uptake in bone tissue, but it is not clear whether this effect is exerted through IAPP or calcitonin receptors (Datta *et al.*, 1989). Further studies are required to establish the mechanism of islet amyloid formation, and the reason for its accumulation in the islets of some diabetic subjects.

Granule membrane proteins

The membrane of the insulin granule may contain up to 100 different polypeptides (Hutton *et al.*, 1982). Unlike insulin, these proteins are not necessarily lost from the cell by exocytosis but may be recycled. Morphologically studies of pancreatic B-cells (Orci, 1974) and other secretory cells (for review see Farquhar, 1985) suggest that granule membrane proteins are retrieved from the plasma membrane to the Golgi apparatus and used in the formation of new granules. Immunoprecipitation studies have shown that the adrenal-chromaffin-granule enzyme dopamine-beta-hydroxylase is cleared quantitatively from the plasma membrane to granule membranes within 4 h of Ba^{2+}-stimulated secretion (Hunter & Phillips, 1989).

Monoclonal antibodies raised against insulinoma granule membrane antigens have been used to characterize and investigate the synthesis of two glycoproteins of 80 kDa (SGM 80) and 110 kDa (SGM 110) in the insulin granule membrane (Grimaldi *et al.*, 1987*a,b*). Antibody binding to these components paralleled the distribution of insulin in insulinoma subcellular fractions, thus confirming their localization in secretory granules (Grimaldi *et al.*, 1987*b*). Both antigens were found to be integral components of the granule membrane since the antibodies bound preferentially to salt-washed granule membranes, with little or no binding to granule matrix constituents. In addition, the antigenic determinants of these proteins appeared to be located on the internal face of the membrane, since granule disruption was required for maximal binding (Grimaldi *et al.*, 1987*a*).

Pulse-chase radiolabelling studies using [^{35}S]methionine have shown that SGM 110 is synthesized initially as a 97 kDa protein which migrated as a narrow band upon SDS/polyacrylamide-gel electrophoresis (Grimaldi *et al.*, 1987*b*). This form was transformed after 30–60 min to a more diffuse component of approximately 110 kDa, a change attributed to extensive glycosylation in the Golgi apparatus. The observation that this change in size occurred at about the same time newly synthesized proinsulin passes from the site of terminal glycosylation in the *trans* Golgi to the secretory granules suggests that SGM 110 and proinsulin traverse the secretory pathway at approximately the same rate. However, unlike proinsulin and chromogranin A, SGM 110 did not appear to undergo proteolytic conversion during its segregation to the secretory granule compartment.

Immunofluorescence studies have shown that SGM 80 and SGM 110 are present in normal rat islets, and immunoblot analysis has demonstrated the presence of components of similar molecular size in anterior pituitary secretory granules and adrenal medullary chromaffin granules (Grimaldi *et al.*, 1987*a*). Immunologically related peptides of distinct molecular size were also detected in rat liver vesicles, suggesting that these antigens are restricted in subcellular localization but widespread in tissue distribution.

Other granule proteins

Besides the proteins already considered, a number of other proteins and activities can be assigned to the insulin granule. These include a Ca^{2+}-stimulated ATPase (Formby *et al.*, 1976), an adenine nucleotide transporter (Sussman & Leitner, 1977), a Ca^{2+}-sensitive phosphatidylinositol kinase activity (Tooke *et al.*, 1984) and thyrotropin-releasing hormone (Leduque *et al.*, 1989). Other proteins may be extrinsically associated with the granule, such as tubulin (Suprenant & Dentler, 1982), actin and myosin (Bendayan, 1981; Howell & Tyhurst, 1982).

Regulation of insulin secretory granule biogenesis

Since the matrix constituents of the insulin secretory granule are presumably lost during exocytosis the question is raised of how the composition and function of the granule is maintained in the face of changing rates of secretion.

To address the question of whether the biosynthesis of different insulin granule proteins is co-ordinated with that of insulin, biosynthetic

Fig. 2. **Biosynthetic response of different insulin secretory granule proteins in glucose-stimulated islets**

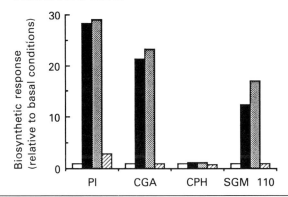

Batches of 100–200 isolated rat islets were incubated for 20 min in 100 μl of Krebs buffer containing 100 μCi of [^{35}S]methionine, then lysed and the indicated proteins immunoprecipitated and electrophoresed. The gels were subjected to fluorography and the incorporation of [^{35}S]methionine into specific proteins determined by densitometry (Grimaldi et al., 1987b; Guest et al., 1989). The results are expressed relative to the incorporation under basal conditions (□, 2·8 mM-glucose); ■, 16·7 mM-glucose; ▨, 16·7 mM-glucose plus 1 mM-EGTA (no calcium); ▨, 16·7 mM-glucose plus 20 mM-mannoheptulose. Abbreviations used: PI, proinsulin; CGA, chromogranin A; CPH, carboxypeptidase H.

studies were conducted on the secretory granule membrane antigen SGM 110 (Grimaldi *et al.*, 1987*a*), and the granule matrix components chromogranin A and carboxypeptidase H (Guest *et al.*, 1989). Isolated rat islets of Langerhans were radiolabelled with [^{35}S]methionine and the incorporation into individual proteins was determined by immunoprecipitation, followed by polyacrylamide-gel electrophoresis, fluorography and densitometric analysis. Glucose stimulation produced an increase in the synthesis of chromogranin A and SGM 110 to an extent similar to that observed for proinsulin (Fig. 2). In contrast, the same conditions produced little or no effect on carboxypeptidase H synthesis. The stimulatory effect of glucose on the biosynthesis of proinsulin, chromogranin A and SGM 110, required the metabolism of glucose, as indicated by the inhibitory effect of mannoheptulose. The finding that removal of Ca^{2+} from the medium did not affect the biosynthetic responses of proinsulin, chromogranin A and SGM 110 to glucose, indicated that activation of the synthesis of these proteins was not strictly coupled to exocytosis but occurred as a primary response to a signal generated by the secretagogue.

Investigations using two-dimensional electrophoretic analysis of [35S]methionine-labelled islets have yielded the surprising finding that

Fig. 3.   Two-dimensional gel electrophoretic analysis of the effect of glucose on islet secretory granule proteins

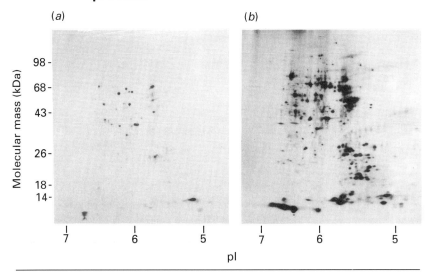

Batches of 500 isolated rat islets were labelled for 1 h in 500 μl of Krebs buffer containing 500 μCi of [35S]methionine and either (a) 2·8 mm-glucose or (b) 16·7 mm-glucose, then incubated for a further 3 h in 1 ml of non-radioactive medium containing 2·8 mm-glucose. Subcellular fractions were prepared on Nycodenz density gradients, and those enriched in insulin (secretory granules) were subjected to two-dimensional gel electrophoresis and fluorography.

glucose exerts a similar stimulatory effect on the biosynthesis of more than 100 islet polypeptides (Guest *et al.*, 1991). Subcellular fractionation of these islets revealed that the majority of glucose-stimulated proteins were localized in fractions enriched in secretory granules (Fig. 3), although a small proportion were also present in cytoplasmic fractions. It is unlikely that release of SRP-mediated arrest is the only mechanism involved in the biosynthetic response of islet proteins to glucose since not all proteins which are co-translationally inserted into the RER lumen, such as secretory and plasma membrane proteins, responded in an equivalent manner. In addition, a small number of cytoplasmic proteins, which are synthesized on free ribosomes, exhibited a large stimulation.

Since the biosynthetic regulation of this glucose-stimulated subset of proteins paralleled that of insulin it is tempting to conclude that control is exerted at the translational level. It is conceivable that the mRNAs encoding these proteins contain common structural elements which allow their selective recognition by the translational machinery. Regulation of translation via the 5' non-coding region of eukaryotic mRNAs is thought to occur due to the ability of these sequences to form secondary structures, and modulate the accessibility of the 5'-cap (for review see Clemens, 1989). However, such elements are not readily discernible by direct comparison of the linear cDNA sequences encoding insulin and chromogranin A (Hutton et al., 1990).

Conclusions

It is clear that the biogenesis of the insulin secretory granule requires the co-ordinate synthesis and assembly of more than 100 different proteins. The essential functions of many of these proteins are in turn regulated by other components of the granule. For example, the proton pump is a key component in the production of a suitable ionic environment in the granule interior, leading to the activation of intragranular proteases, crystallization of the hormone, production of autocrine regulators and accumulation of biogenic amines.

It is conceivable that aberrations in the synthesis of one or more of these insulin granule proteins might result in the defective storage or secretion of insulin. The presence of high circulating levels of proinsulin and processing intermediates in NIDDM subjects and non-diabetic twins of insulin-dependent diabetes mellitus IDDM subjects (Ward et al., 1987; Heaton et al., 1987), might reflect alterations in the biosynthesis of the proinsulin-converting enzymes. Perturbations in the biosynthesis of IAPP may lead to increased amyloid deposition in the islets of NIDDM subjects (Westermark et al., 1986; Cooper et al., 1987b). Thus there is considerable scope for further studies of insulin-secretory-granule biogenesis in the diseased state. Studies involving alterations in the structure of secretory granule proteins and in the overall protein composition of the granule, might provide a means of determining the roles of individual proteins in insulin secretory granule morphogenesis and function. Such investigations will become more practicable with time as antibodies and cDNA probes to other secretory granule components become available.

Work from our laboratory which is described above was supported by the M.R.C. of Great Britain, the British Diabetic Association and the Wellcome Trust.

References

Abrahamsson, H. & Gylfe, E. (1980) Demonstration of a proton gradient across the insulin granule membrane. Acta Physiol. Scand. **109**, 113–114

Al-Awqati, Q. (1986) Proton-translocating ATPases. Annu. Rev. Cell. Biol. **2**, 179–200

Andersson, A. (1976) Stimulation of insulin biosynthesis in isolated mouse islets by L-leucine, 2-aminoarboinane-2-carboxylic acid and alpha-ketoisocaproic acid. Biochim. Biophys. Acta **437**, 345–353

Ashcroft, S. J. H. & Randle, P. J. (1970) Enzymes of glucose metabolism in normal mouse pancreatic islets. Biochem. J. **119**, 5–15

Ashcroft, S. J. H., Bunce, J., Lowry, M., Hansen, S. E. & Hedeskov, C. J. (1978) The effect of sugars on (pro)insulin biosynthesis. Biochem. J. **174**, 517–526

Bendayan, M. (1981) Ultrastructural localization of actin in insulin-containing granules. Biol. Cell **41**, 157–160

Benedum, U. M., Baeuerle, P. A., Konecki, D. S., Frank, R., Powell, J., Mallet, J. & Huttner, W. B. (1986) The primary structure of bovine chromogranin A: A representative of a class of acidic secretory proteins common to a variety of peptidergic cells. EMBO J. **5**, 1495–1502

Birch, N. P., Davies, A. D. & Christe, D. L. (1986) Identification of a 27 kDa enkephalin-containing protein associated with bovine adrenal medullary chromaffin granule membranes by immunoblotting. FEBS Lett. **197**, 173–178

Blobel, G. & Dobberstein, B. (1975) Transfer of proteins across membranes. II. Reconstitution of functional rough microsomes from heterologous components. J. Cell Biol. **67**, 852–862

Blundell, T. L., Dodson, G. G., Dodson, E., Hodgekin, D. C. & Vijayan, M. (1971) X-ray analysis and the structure of insulin. Recent Prog. Horm. Res. **27**, 1–40

Boam, D. S. W., Clark, A. R. & Docherty, K. (1990) Positive and negative regulation of the human insulin gene by multiple trans-acting factors. J. Biol. Chem. **265**, 8285–8296

Brundstedt, J. & Chan, S. J. (1982) Direct effect of glucose on the preproinsulin mRNA level in isolated pancreatic islets. Biochem. Biophys. Res. Commun. **106**, 1383–1389

Chan, S. J., Keim, P. & Steiner, D. F. (1976) Cell-free synthesis of rat preproinsulins: characterization and partial amino acid sequence determination. Proc. Natl. Acad. Sci. U.S.A. **73**, 1964–1968

Charles, M. S., Lawecki, J., Pictet, R. & Grodski, G. M. (1975) Insulin secretion: inter-relationships of glucose, cyclic adenosine 3′, 5′-monophosphate and calcium. J. Biol. Chem. **250**, 6134–6140

Clark, A., Cooper, G. J. S., Lewis, C. E., Morris, J. F., Willis, A. C., Reid, K. B. M. & Turner, R. C. (1987) Islet amyloid formed from diabetes-associated peptide may be pathogenic in type-2 diabetes. Lancet **ii**, 231–234

Clemens, M. J. (1989) Regulatory mechanisms in translational control. Curr. Opinion Cell Biol. **1**, 1160–1167

Cooper, G. J. S., Willis, A. C., Clark, A., Turner, R. C., Sim, R. B. & Reid, K. B. M. (1987a) Purification and characterization of a peptide from amyloid-rich pancreases of type-2-diabetic patients. Proc. Natl. Acad. Sci. U.S.A. **84**, 8628–8632

Cooper, G. J. S., Willis, A. C., Reid, K. B. M., Clark, A., Baker, C. A., Turner, R. C., Lewis, C. E., Morris, J. F., Howland, K. & Rothbard, J. B. (1987b) Diabetes-associated peptide. Lancet **ii**, 966–969

Cooper, G. J. S., Leighton, B., Dimitriadis, G. D., Parry-Billings, M., Kowalchuk, J. M., Howland, K., Rothbard, J. B., Willis, A. C. & Reid, K. B. M. (1988) Amylin found in amyloid deposits in human type 2 diabetes mellitus may be a hormone that regulates glycogen metabolism in skeletal muscle. Proc. Natl. Acad. Sci. U.S.A. **85**, 7763–7766

Daniels, A. J., Williams, R. J. P. & Wright, P. E. (1978) The character of the stored molecules in chromaffin granules of the adrenal medulla: a nuclear magnetic resonance study. Neuroscience **3**, 573–585

Datta, H. K., Saidi, M., Wimalawansa, S. J., Ghatei, M. A., Beacham, J. L., Bloom, S. R. & MacIntyre, I. (1989) In vivo and in vitro effects of amylin and amylin-amide on calcium metabolism in the rat and rabbit. Biochem. Biophys. Res. Commun. **162**, 876–881

Davidson, H. W. & Hutton, J. C. (1987) The insulin secretory granule carboxypeptidase H: Purification and demonstration of proinsulin processing activity. Biochem. J. **245**, 575–582

Davidson, H. W., Rhodes, C. J. & Hutton, J. C. (1988) Intraorganellar Ca and pH control proinsulin cleavage in the pancreatic beta-cell via Arg.Arg and Lys.Arg-specific endopeptidases. Nature (London) **333**, 93–96

Dean, P. M. (1973) Ultrastructural morphometry of the pancreatic beta-cell. Diabetologia **9**, 115–119

Docherty, K. & Hutton, J. C. (1983) Carboxypeptidase activity in the insulin secretory granule. FEBS Lett. **162**, 137–141

Docherty, K. & Steiner, D. F. (1982) Post-translational proteolysis in polypeptide hormone biosynthesis. Annu. Rev. Physiol. **44**, 625–638

Edlund, T., Walker, M. D., Barr, P. J. & Rutter, W. J. (1985) Cell specific expression of the rat insulin I gene. Evidence for roles of two distinct 5′-flanking elements. Science **230**, 912–916

Efendic, S., Tatemoto, K., Mutt, V., Quan, C., Chang, D. & Ostenson, C. G. (1987) Pancreastatin and islet hormone release. Proc. Natl. Acad. Sci. U.S.A. **84**, 7257–7260

Ekholm, R., Ericson, L. E. & Lundquist, J. (1971) Monoamines in the pancreatic islets of the mouse. Subcellular localization of 5-hydroxytryptamine by electron microscopic autoradiography. Diabetologia **7**, 339–348

Farquhar, J. G. (1985) Progress in unraveling pathways of Golgi traffic. Annu. Rev. Cell. Biol. **1**, 447–488

Formby, B., Capito, K., Egeberg, J. & Hedeskov, C. J. (1976) Ca-activated ATPase activity in subcellular fractions of mouse pancreatic islets. Am. J. Physiol. **230**, 441–448

Fricker, L. D. & Herbert, E. (1988) Comparison of a carboxypeptidase E-like enzyme in human, bovine, mouse, Xenopus, shark, and Aplysia neural tissue. Brain Res. **453**, 281–286

Fricker, L. D. & Snyder, S. H. (1982) Enkephalin convertase: purification and characterization of a specific enkephalin-synthesizing carboxypeptidase localized to adrenal chromaffin granules. Proc. Natl. Acad. Sci. U.S.A. **79**, 3886–3890

Fricker, L. D. & Snyder, S. H. (1983) Purification and characterization of enkephalin convertase, an enkephalin-synthesizing carboxypeptidase. J. Biol. Chem. **258**, 10950–10955

Fricker, L. D., Evans, C. H., Esch, F. S. & Herbert, E. (1986) Cloning and sequence analysis of cDNA for bovine carboxypeptidase E. Nature (London) **323**, 461–464

Fricker, L. D., Adelman, J. P., Douglass, J., Thompson, R. C., von Strandmann, R. P. & Hutton, J. C. (1989) Isolation and sequence analysis of cDNA for rat carboxypeptidase E [EC 3.4.17.10], a neuropeptide processing enzyme. Mol. Endocrinol. **3**, 666–673

Fricker, L. D., Das, B. & Hogue-Angeletti, R. (1990) Identification of the pH dependent membrane anchor of carboxypeptidase E [EC 3.4.17.10]. J. Biol. Chem. **265**, 2476–2482

Gerdes, H.-H., Rosa, P., Phillips, E., Baeuerle, P. A., Frank, R., Argos, P. & Huttner, W. (1989) The primary structure of human secretogranin II, a widespread tyrosine-sulphated secretory granule protein and exhibits low pH- and calcium-induced aggregation. J. Biol. Chem. **264**, 12009–12015

Gilmore, R. & Blobel, G. (1983) Transient involvement of signal recognition particle and its receptor in the microsomal membrane prior to protein translocation. Cell (Cambridge, Mass.) **35**, 677–685

Gilmore, R., Walter, P. & Blobel, G. (1982) Protein translocation across the endoplasmic reticulum I. Detection in the microsomal membrane of a receptor for the signal recognition particle. J. Cell Biol. **95**, 463–469

Greider, M. H., Howell, S. L. & Lacy, P. E. (1969) Isolation and properties of secretory granules from rat islets of Langerhans. J. Cell Biol. **41**, 162–166

Grimaldi, K. A., Hutton, J. C. & Siddle, K. (1987a) Production and characterization of monoclonal antibodies to the insulin secretory granule membrane. Biochem. J. **245**, 557–566

Grimaldi, K. A., Siddle, K. & Hutton, J. C. (1987b) Biosynthesis of insulin secretory granule membrane proteins: control by glucose. Biochem. J. **245**, 567–573

Guest, P. C., Rhodes, C. J. & Hutton, J. C. (1989) Regulation of the biosynthesis of insulin-secretory-granule proteins: Co-ordinate translational control is exerted on some, but not all, granule matrix constituents. Biochem. J. **257**, 431–437

Guest, P. C., Bailyes, E. M., Rutherford, N. G. & Hutton, J. C. (1991) Insulin secretory granule biogenesis: Co-ordinate regulation of the biosynthesis of the majority of constituent proteins. Biochem. J. **274**, 73–78

Heaton, D. A., Millward, B. A., Gray, I. P., Tun, Y., Hales, C. N., Pyke, D. A. & Leslie,

R. D. G. (1987) Evidence for beta-cell dysfunction which does not lead to diabetes: a study of identical twins of insulin dependent diabetics. Br. Med. J. **294**, 145–146

Hedeskov, C. J. (1980) Mechanisms of glucose-induced insulin secretion. Physiol. Rev. **60**, 442–509

Herman, L., Sato, T. & Hales, C. N. (1973) The electron microscopic localization of cations to the islets of Langerhans and their possible role in insulin secretion. Ultrastruct. Res. **42**, 298–311

Howell, S. L. & Montague, W. (1973) Adenylate cyclase activity in isolated rat islets of Langerhans. Effects of agents which alter insulin secretion. Biochim. Biophys. Acta **320**, 44–52

Howell, S. L. & Taylor, K. W. (1966) Effects of glucose concentration on incorporation of (^{3}H) leucine into insulin using isolated mammal islets of Langherhans. Biochim. Biophys. Acta **130**, 519–521

Howell, S. L. & Tyhurst, M. (1982) Actomyosin interactions with insulin storage granules *in vitro*. Biochem. J. **206**, 157–160

Hunter, A. & Phillips, J. H. (1989) The recycling of a secretory granule membrane protein. Exp. Cell Res. **182**, 445–460

Hutton, J. C. (1982) The internal pH and membrane potential of the insulin secretory granule. Biochem. J. **204**, 171–178

Hutton, J. C. (1984) Secretory granules. Experentia **40**, 1091–1097

Hutton, J. C. & Peshavaria, M. (1982) Proton-translocating Mg^{2+}-dependent ATPase in insulin secretory granules. Biochem. J. **204**, 161–170

Hutton, J. C., Penn, E. J. & Peshavaria, M. (1982) Isolation and characterisation of insulin secretory granules from a rat islet cell tumour. Diabetologia **23**, 365–373

Hutton, J. C., Penn, E. J. & Peshavaria, M. (1983) Low molecular weight constituents of isolated insulin secretory granules: Divalent cations, adenine nucleotides and inorganic phosphate. Biochem. J. **210**, 297–305

Hutton, J. C., Hansen, F. & Peshavaria, M. (1985) Betagranins: 21 kDa co-secreted peptides of the insulin granule closely related to adrenal medullary chromogranin A. FEBS Lett. **188**, 336–340

Hutton, J. C., Davidson, H. W., Grimaldi, K. A. & Peshavaria, M. (1987*a*) Biosynthesis of betagranin in pancreatic beta cells: Identification of a chromogranin A-like precursor and its parallel processing with proinsulin. Biochem. J. **244**, 449–456

Hutton, J. C., Davidson, H. W. & Peshavaria, M. (1987*b*) Proteolytic processing of chromogranin A in purified insulin granules. Formation of a 20000 dalton fragment (betagranin) by the concerted action of a Ca^{2+}-dependent endopeptidase and carboxypeptidase H. Biochem. J. **244**, 457–464

Hutton, J. C., Peshavaria, M., Johnston, C. F., Ravazzola, M. & Orci, L. (1988*a*) Immunolocalization of betagranin: a chromogranin A related protein of the pancreatic B-cell. Endocrinology **122**, 1014–1020

Hutton, J. C., Nielson, E. & Kastern, W. (1988*b*) Molecular cloning of the chromogranin A-like precursor to betagranin and pancreastatin from the endocrine pancreas. FEBS Lett. **236**, 269–274

Hutton, J. C., Bailyes, E. M., Rhodes, C. J., Rutherford, N. G., Arden, S. A. & Guest, P. C. (1990) Biosynthesis and storage of insulin. Biochem. Soc. Trans. **18**, 122–124.

Iacangelo, A., Affolter, H. U., Eiden, L. E., Herbert, E. & Grimes, M. (1986) Bovine chromogranin A sequence and distribution of its mRNA in endocrine tissues. Nature (London) **323**, 82–86

Itoh, N. & Okamoto, H. (1980) Translational control of proinsulin synthesis by glucose. Nature (London) **283**, 100–102

Jackson, R. C. & Blobel, G. (1977) Post-translational cleavage of presecretory proteins with an extract of rough microsomes from dog pancreas containing signal peptidase activity. Proc. Natl. Acad. Sci. U.S.A. **74**, 5598–5602

Kanatsuka, A., Makino, H., Ohsawa, H., Tokuyama, Y., Yamaguchi, T., Yoshida, S. & Adachi, M. (1989) Secretion of islet amyloid polypeptide in response to glucose. FEBS Lett. **259**, 199–201

Karlsson, O., Edlund, T., Barnett-Moss, J., Rutter, W. J. & Walker, M. D. (1987) A mutational analysis of the insulin gene transcriptional control region: expression in beta cells is dependent on two related sequences within the enhancer. Proc. Natl. Acad. Sci. U.S.A. **84**, 8819–8823

Karlsson, O., Walker, M. D., Rutter, W. J. & Edlund, T. (1989) Individual protein-binding domains of the insulin gene enhancer positively activate beta-cell-specific transcription. Mol. Cell. Biol. **9**, 823–827

Kemmler, W., Steiner, D. F. & Borg, J. (1973) Studies on the conversion of proinsulin to insulin. III. Studies *in vitro* with crude secretion granule fraction isolated from rat islets of Langerhans. J. Biol. Chem. **248**, 4544–4551

Konecki, D. S., Benedum, U. M., Gerdes, H. H. & Huttner, W. B. (1987) The primary structure of human chromogranin A and pancreastatin. J. Biol. Chem. **262**, 17026–17030

Kornfeld, S. & Mellman, I. (1989) The biogenesis of lysozomes. Annu. Rev. Cell Biol. **5**, 483–525

Kurzchalia, T. V., Wiedmann, M., Girshovich, A. S., Bochkareva, E. S., Bielka, H. & Rapoport, T. A. (1986) The signal sequence of nascent preprolactin interacts with the 54 kDa polypeptide of the signal recognition particle. Nature (London) **320**, 634–636

Lange, R. H. (1974) Crystalline islet B-granules in the grass snake *Natrix natrix* (L.): tilting experiments in the electron microscope. J. Ultrastruct. Res. **46**, 301–307

Leduque, P., Aratan-Spire, S., Scharfmann, R., Basmaciogullari, A., Czernichow, P. & Dubois, P. M. (1989) Coexistence of thyrotropin-releasing hormone and insulin in cultured fetal rat islets: a light and electron microscopic immunocytochemical study during islet neoformation. Biol. Cell **66**, 291–296

Leighton, B. & Cooper, G. J. S. (1988) Pancreatic amylin and calcitonin-gene related peptide cause resistance to insulin in skeletal muscle *in vitro*. Nature (London) **335**, 632–635

Lin, B. J. & Haist, R. E. (1969) Insulin biosynthesis: effects of carbohydrates and related compounds. Can. J. Physiol. Pharmacol. **47**, 791–801

Lin, B. J., Nagy, B. R. & Haist, R. E. (1972) Effect of various concentrations of glucose on insulin biosynthesis. Endocrinology **91**, 309–311

Loh, Y. P. & Tam, W. W. H. (1985) Association of newly synthesized pro-opiomelanocortin with secretory granule membranes in pituitary pars intermedia cells. FEBS Lett. **184**, 40–43

Lukinius, A., Wilander, E., Westermark, G. T., Engstrom, U. & Westermark, P. (1989) Co-localization of islet amyloid polypeptide and insulin in the B-cell secretory granules of the human pancreatic islets. Diabetologia **32**, 240–244

MacIntyre, I. (1989) Amylin amide, bone conservation and pancreatic B cells. Lancet **ii**, 1026–1027

Mackin, R. B. & Noe, B. D. (1987) Characterization of an islet carboxypeptidase B involved in prohormone processing. Endocrinology **120**, 457–468

Maldonato, A., Renold, A. E., Sharp, G. W. G. & Cerasi, E. (1977) Glucose-induced proinsulin biosynthesis: role of cyclic AMP. Diabetes **26**, 538–545

Manser, E., Fernandez, D., Loo, L., Goh, P. Y., Monfries, C., Hall, C. & Lim, L. (1990) Human carboxypeptidase E. Isolation and characterization of the cDNA, sequence conservation, expression and processing *in vitro*. Biochem. J. **267**, 517–525

Mellman, I., Fuchs, R. & Helenius, A. (1986) Acidification of the endocytotic and exocytotic pathways. Annu. Rev. Biochem. **55**, 663–700

Meyer, D. I., Krause, E. & Dobberstein, B. (1982) Secretory protein translocation across membranes—the role of the "docking protein". Nature (London) **297**, 647–650

Michael, J., Carroll, R., Swift, H. H. & Steiner, D. F. (1987) Studies on the molecular organization of rat insulin secretory granules. J. Biol. Chem. **262**, 16531–16535

Morris, G. E. & Korner, A. (1970) The effect of glucose on insulin biosynthesis by isolated islets of Langerhans in the rat. Biochim. Biophys. Acta **208**, 404–413

Munro, S. & Pelham, H. R. B. (1987) A *C*-terminal signal prevents secretion of luminal ER proteins. Cell (Cambridge, Mass.) **48**, 899–907

Nielsen, D. A., Welsh, M., Casadaban, M. J. & Steiner, D. F. (1985) Control of insulin gene expression in pancreatic beta-cells and in an insulin-producing cell line, RIN-5F cells I. Effects of glucose and cyclic AMP on the transcription of insulin mRNA. J. Biol. Chem. **260**, 13585–13589

Ohlsson, H., Karlsson, O. & Edlund, T. (1988) A beta-cell-specific protein binds to the two major regulatory sequences of the insulin gene enhancer. Biochemistry **85**, 4228–4231

Ohsawa, H., Kanatsuka, A., Yamaguchi, T., Makino, H. & Yoshida, S. (1989) Islet amyloid polypeptide inhibits glucose-stimulated insulin secretion from rat pancreatic islets. Biochem. Biophys. Res. Commun. **160**, 961–967

Orci, L. (1974) A portrait of the pancreatic B-cell. Diabetologia **10**, 163–187

Orci, L. (1985) The insulin factory: a tour of the plant surroundings and a visit to the assembly line. Diabetologia **28**, 528–546

Orci, L. (1986) The insulin cell: Its cellular environment and how it processes (pro)insulin. Diabetes/Metab. Rev. **2**, 71–106

Orci, L., Ravazzola, M. & Perrelet, A. (1984) (Pro)insulin associates with Golgi membranes of pancreatic B cells. Proc. Natl. Acad. Sci. U.S.A. **81**, 6743–6746

Orci, L., Ravazzola, M., AmHerdt, M., Perrelet, A., Powell, S. K., Quinn, D. L. & Moore, H.-P. H. (1987a) The *trans*-most cisternae of the Golgi complex: A compartment for sorting of secretory and plasma membrane proteins. Cell (Cambridge Mass.) **51**, 1039–1051

Orci, L., Ravazzola, M., Storch, M.-J., Anderson, R. G. W., Vassalli, J.-D. & Perrelet, A. (1987b) Proteolytic maturation of insulin is a post-Golgi event which occurs in acidifying clathrin-coated secretory vesicles. Cell (Cambridge, Mass.) **49**, 865–868

Owman, C., Hoakanson, R. & Sandler, F. (1973) Occurrence and function of amines in endocrine cells producing polypeptide hormones. Fed. Proc. Fed. Am. Soc. Exp. Biol. **32**, 1785–1791

Palade, G. (1975) Intracellular aspects of the process of protein synthesis. Science **189**, 347–358

Patzelt, C., Labrecque, A. D., Duguid, J. R., Carroll, R. J., Keim, P. S., Heinrikson, R. L. & Steiner, D. F. (1978) Detection and kinetic behavior of preproinsulin in pancreatic islets. Proc. Natl. Acad. Sci. U.S.A. **75**, 1260–1264

Permutt, M. A. (1981) Biosynthesis of insulin. In the Islets of Langerhans (Cooperstein, S. J. & Watkins, D., eds.), pp. 75–95, Academic Press, New York

Permutt, M. A. & Kipnis, D. M. (1972) On the mechanism of glucose stimulation. J. Biol. Chem. **247**, 1194–1199

Permutt, M. A. & Kipnis, D. M. (1975) Insulin biosynthesis and secretion. Fed. Proc. Fed. Am. Soc. Exp. Biol. **34**, 1549–1555

Peterson, J. B., Nelson, D. L., Ling, E. & Hogue-Angeletti, R. (1987) Chromogranin A-like proteins in the secretory granules of a protozoan, *Paramecium tetraurelia*. J. Biol. Chem. **262**, 17264–17267

Pipeleers, D. G., Marichal, M. & Malaisse, W. J. (1973a) The stimulus-secretion coupling of glucose-induced insulin release. XIV. Glucose regulation of insulin biosynthetic activity. Endocrinology **93**, 1001–1011

Pipeleers, D. G., Marichal, M. & Malaisse, W. J. (1973b) The stimulus-secretion coupling of glucose-induced insulin release. XV. Participation of cations in the recognition of glucose by the beta-cell. Endocrinology **93**, 1012–1018

Rieker, S., Fischer-Colbrie, R., Eiden, L. E. & Winkler, H. (1988) Phylogenetic distribution of peptides related to chromogranins A and B. J. Neurochem. **50**, 1066–1073

Rothman, J. E., Urbani, L. J. & Brands, R. (1984) Transport of proteins between cytoplasmic membranes of fused cells: correspondence to processes reconstituted in a cell-free system. J. Cell Biol. **99**, 248–259

Rubenstein, A. H., Clark, J. L., Melani, F. & Steiner, D. F. (1969) Secretion of proinsulin C-peptide by pancreatic beta cells and its circulation in blood. Nature (London) **224**, 697–699

Rubenstein, A. H., Steiner, D. F., Horwitz, D. L., Mako, M. E., Block, M. B., Starr, J. I., Kuzuya, J. & Melani, F. (1977) Clinical significance of circulating proinsulin and C-peptide. Recent Prog. Horm. Res. **33**, 435–475

Sanke, T., Bell, G. I., Sample, C., Rubenstein, A. H. & Steiner, D. F. (1988) An islet amyloid peptide is derived from an 89 amino acid precursor by proteolytic processing. J. Biol. Chem. **262**, 17243–17246

Seidah, N. G., Hendy, G. N., Hamelin, J., Paquin, J., Lazure, C., Metters, K. M., Rossier, J. & Chretien, M. (1987) Chromogranin A can act as a reversible processing enzyme inhibitor. FEBS Lett. **211**, 144–150

Sopwith, A. M., Hales, C. N. & Hutton, J. C. (1984) Pancreatic beta-cells secrete a range of novel proteins besides insulin. Biochim. Biophys. Acta **803**, 342–345

Sorenson, R. L., Steffes, M. W. & Lindall, A. W. (1970) Subcellular localization of proinsulin to insulin conversion in isolated rat islets. Endocrinology **86**, 88–96

Steiner, D. F., Chan, S. J., Welsh, J. M. & Kwok, S. C. M. (1985) Structure and evolution of the insulin gene. Annu. Rev. Genet. **19**, 463–484

Streider, N. E., Ziegler, E., Winkler, H. & Smith, A. D. (1986) Some properties of soluble proteins from chromaffin granules of different species. Biochem. Pharmacol. **17**, 1553–1556

Supattapone, S., Fricker, L. D. & Snyder, S. H. (1984) Purification and characterization of a membrane-bound enkephalin-forming carboxypeptidase, 'enkephalin convertase.' J. Neurochem. **42**, 1017–1023

Suprenant, K. A. & Dentler, W. L. (1982) Association between endocrine pancreatic secretory granules and *in vitro* assembled microtubules is dependent on microtubule associated proteins. J. Cell Biol. **93**, 164–174

Sussman, K. E. & Leitner, J. W. (1977) Conversion of ATP to other adenine nucleotides within isolated islet secretory vesicles. Effect of cyclic AMP on phosphate translocation. Endocrinology **101**, 694–701

Tager, H. S., Patzelt, C., Assoian, R. K., Chan, S. J., Duguid, J. R. & Steiner, D. F. (1980) Biosynthesis of islet cell hormones. Ann. N.Y. Acad. Sci. **343**, 133–147

Tanford, C. & Epstein, J. (1954*a*) The physical chemistry of insulin. I Hydrogen ion titration curve of Zn-free insulin. J. Am. Chem. Soc. **76**, 2163–2169

Tanford, C. & Epstein, J. (1954*b*) The physical chemistry of insulin. II Hydrogen ion titration curve of crystalline Zn insulin. J. Am. Chem. Soc. **76**, 2170–2176

Tatemoto, K., Efendic, S., Mutt, V., Makk, G., Feistner, G. & Barchas, J. D. (1987) Pancreastatin, a novel pancreatic peptide that inhibits insulin secretion. Nature (London) **324**, 476–478

Tooke, N. E., Hales, C. N. & Hutton, J. C. (1984) Ca^{2+}-sensitive phosphatidyl 4-phosphate metabolism in a rat beta-cell tumour. Biochem. J. **219**, 471–480

Tooze, S. A. & Huttner, W. B. (1990) Cell-free sorting to the regulated and constitutive secretory pathways. Cell (Cambridge, Mass.) **60**, 837–847

Tooze, J., Tooze, S. A. & Fuller, S. D. (1987) Sorting of progeny coronavirus from condensed secretory proteins at the exit from the *trans*-Golgi network of AtT20 cells. J. Cell Biol. **105**, 1215–1226

Ward, W. K., LaCava, E. C., Paquette, T. L., Beard, J., Wallum, B. J. & Porte, D., Jr. (1987) Disproportionate elevation of immunoreactive proinsulin in type 2 (non-insulin-dependent) diabetes mellitus and in experimental insulin resistance. Diabetologia **30**, 698–702

Welsh, M., Nielson, D. A., MacKrell, A. J. & Steiner, D. F. (1985) Control of insulin gene expression in pancreatic beta-cells and in an insulin-producing cell line, RINM5F cells. II. Regulation of insulin mRNA stability. J. Biol. Chem. **260**, 13590–13594

Welsh, M., Scherberg, N., Gilmore, R. & Steiner, D. F. (1986) Translational control of insulin biosynthesis. Evidence for regulation of elongation, initiation and signal-recognition-particle-mediated translational arrest by glucose. Biochem. J. **235**, 459–467

Welsh, N., Welsh, M., Steiner, D. F. & Hellerstrom, C. (1987) Mechanisms of leucine- and theophylline-stimulated insulin biosynthesis in isolated rat pancreatic islets. Biochem. J. **246**, 245–248

Westermark, P., Wernstedt, C., Wilander, E. & Sletten, K. (1986) A novel peptide in the calcitonin gene related peptide family as an amyloid fibril protein in the endocrine pancreas. Biochem. Biophys. Res. Commun. **140**, 827–831

Westermark, P., Wilander, E., Westermark, G. T. & Johnson, K. H. (1987*a*) Islet amyloid polypeptide-like immunoreactivity in the islet B cells of type 2 (non-insulin-dependent) diabetic and non-diabetic individuals. Diabetologia **30**, 887–892

Westermark, P., Wernstedt, C., Wilander, E., Hayden, D. W., O'Brian, T. D. & Johnson, K. H. (1987*b*) Amyloid fibrils in human insulinoma and islets of Langerhans of the diabetic cat are derived from a neuropeptide-like protein also present in normal islet cells. Proc. Natl. Acad. Sci. U.S.A. **84**, 3881

Whelan, J., Poon, D., Weil, P. A. & Stein, R. (1989) Pancreatic beta-cell-type-specific expression of the rat insulin II gene is controlled by positive and negative cellular transcriptional elements. Mol. Cell. Biol. **9**, 3253–3259

Wiedmann, M., Kurzchalia, T. V., Bielka, H. & Rapoport, T. A. (1987*a*) Direct probing of the interaction between the signal sequence of nascent preprolactin and the signal recognition particle by specific cross-linking. J. Cell Biol. **104**, 201–208

Wiedmann, M., Kurzchalia, T. V., Hartmann, E. & Rapoport, T. A. (1987*b*) A signal sequence receptor in the endoplasmic reticulum membrane. Nature (London) **328**, 830–833

Wiedmann, M., Goerlich, D., Hartmann, E., Kurzchalia, T. V. & Rapoport, T. A. (1989) Photocrosslinking demonstrates proximity of a 34 kDa membrane protein to different portions of preprolactin during translocation through the endoplasmic reticulum. FEBS Lett. **257**, 263–268

Wieland, F. T., Gleason, M. L., Serafini, T. A. & Rothman, J. E. (1987) The rate of bulk flow from the endoplasmic reticulum to the cell surface. Cell (Cambridge, Mass) **50**, 289–300

Wolin, S. L. & Walter, P. (1988) Ribosome pausing and stacking during translation of a eucaryotic mRNA. EMBO J. **7**, 3559–3569

5

Regulation of insulin secretion by nutrients: the fuel concept

Willy J. Malaisse

Laboratory of Experimental Medicine, Brussels Free University, B-1000, Brussels, Belgium

Introduction

The fuel concept for the process of nutrient-induced insulin release postulates that the stimulation of insulin release by nutrient secretagogues results from their ability to augment ATP generation rate in the pancreatic B-cell. As reviewed in prior reports (Malaisse *et al.*, 1979*a*; Malaisse, 1984), this fuel concept received considerable support from studies aimed at elucidating the biochemical determinants of (i) the anomeric specificity of the B-cell secretory response to D-glucose and D-mannose (Malaisse *et al.*, 1976*a*; Sener *et al.*, 1982*a*), (ii) the insulinotropic action of a non-metabolized analogue of L-leucine, 2-aminobicyclo[2,2,1]heptane-2-carboxylic acid (BCH) (Sener & Malaisse, 1980; Sener *et al.*, 1981), and (iii) the release of insulin provoked by the poorly metabolized 2-keto acid 3-phenylpyruvate (Sener *et al.*, 1983; Malaisse *et al.*, 1983*a*). In these three instances, the view had been first expressed that the stimulation of insulin secretion may be accounted for by the interaction of the nutrient under consideration with a stereospecific receptor, rather than by its metabolic fate in the B-cell. Yet, in each case, the secretory response was eventually found to coincide with a commensurate increase in the rate of exogenous and/or endogenous nutrient catabolism in the islet cells.

The fuel concept for nutrient-stimulated insulin secretion, if correct, raises the immediate question as to the identity of the factors which might couple the accelerated utilization of nutrients to more distal events in the secretory sequence, such as the remodelling of cationic fluxes resulting from the decrease in K^+ conductance and subsequent gating of voltage-sensitive Ca^{2+} channels (Malaisse & Herchuelz, 1982). A multifactorial coupling mechanism was here proposed, which might include changes in the generation rate of reducing equivalents, high-energy phosphate intermediates and protons (Malaisse *et al.*, 1979*b*, 1984).

Emphasis is currently placed, however, on an increase in the cytosolic ATP/ADP ratio leading to the closure of ATP-responsive K^+ channels (Malaisse & Sener, 1987; see also Chapter 10 by Ashcroft *et al.*). This concept does not rule out a contribution of other coupling factors.

The fuel concept for insulin release also implies that the magnitude of the secretory response to nutrient secretagogues is tightly dependent on the regulation of metabolic events in the pancreatic B-cell. In this respect, equal attention should be paid to the fate of exogenous nutrients, such as D-glucose (Sener & Malaisse, 1984), L-leucine (Malaisse, 1986) or ketone bodies (Malaisse *et al.*, 1990*a*), and that of endogenous nutrients, especially amino acids and fatty acids (Malaisse *et al.* 1983*b*, 1985*a*). Because of limitation in space and in view of the essential role of D-glucose in the regulation of insulin release, the present review is restricted to the regulation of D-glucose metabolism in pancreatic islets, with emphasis on recent acquisitions.

Regulation of D-glucose transport across the B-cell plasma membrane

The transport of D-glucose into the B-cell is mediated by the liver-type glucose transporter, which is preferentially located in microvilli rather than on the flat regions of the plasma membrane (Orci *et al.*, 1990). This carrier is sufficiently efficient to allow virtually immediate equilibration of extracellular and cytosolic D-glucose concentrations.

As reviewed elsewhere (Malaisse, 1988), a site-specific defect in D-glucose transport was first identified in tumoral islet cells of the RINm5F line (Malaisse *et al.*, 1986). These cells are apparently devoid of the liver-type hexose carrier. Whether D-glucose transport is also altered in other instances of B-cell dysfunction, e.g. in diabetes, remains a matter of debate (Marynissen *et al.*, 1988). In this perspective, it might be underlined that, on theoretical grounds, the efficiency of the glucose transport system in the B-cell should be decreased by at least one order of magnitude to become a rate-limiting step in the control of D-glucose catabolism (Malaisse *et al.*, 1976*b*).

Fate and role of intracellular D-glucose

The equilibration of D-glucose concentration across the B-cell plasma membrane, in the physiological range of hexose concentrations, is of major significance to its phosphorylation by hexokinase isoenzymes. This topic will be considered in the next section of the present review.

It should be realized, however, that the presence of D-glucose inside the B-cell may have several other implications than its regulatory role in hexose phosphorylation. Three examples will be given here.

First, D-glucose modulates in islet cells, like in hepatocytes, the activity of glycogen phosphorylase. This is discussed below in the section devoted to the regulation of glycogen synthesis and breakdown.

Secondly, D-glucose serves as a precursor of sorbitol in the reaction catalysed by aldose reductase. The conversion of D-glucose to sorbitol might be coupled with the generation of NADPH in the pentose phosphate pathway (Malaisse *et al.*, 1976a). A rise in extracellular D-glucose concentration provokes a rapid and sizeable increase in sorbitol production. Little sorbitol accumulates in islet cells, however, even under conditions of sustained hyperglycaemia (Sener & Malaisse, 1990). This appears attributable to a large release of sorbitol by the islet cells (Malaisse *et al.*, 1974).

Thirdly, in situations of sustained hyperglycaemia, the presence of D-glucose inside the B-cell could lead to the non-enzymic glycation of cytosolic proteins, including glycolytic enzymes, in a manner comparable with that recently documented in hepatocytes (Zähner *et al.*, 1990).

Regulation of D-glucose phosphorylation

The phosphorylation of D-glucose is catalysed in the B-cell by both a high-affinity hexokinase and a low-affinity glucokinase (Malaisse *et al.*, 1976c; see also Chapter 6 pp. 101–124). The K_m of the former enzyme for D-glucose does not exceed 50 μM, so that its maximal velocity is reached at low concentrations of the hexose well below the physiological value. The contribution of the low-K_m hexokinase to the overall rate of glucose phosphorylation is much lower in intact islets than in islet homogenates, because of inhibition of the enzyme by D-glucose 6-phosphate and, to a lesser extent, D-glucose 1,6-bisphosphate (Giroix *et al.*, 1984a). The high-K_m glucokinase thus plays an essential role in allowing an increase in D-glucose phosphorylation rate to take place in the physiological range of hexose concentrations.

The rate of D-glucose phosphorylation by intact islet cells does not depend solely, however, on the intracellular concentration of D-glucose. There are at least four other factors which participate in the regulation of hexose phosphorylation in islet cells.

First, the availability of ATP might exert a synarchistic regulation of the sequential type upon the phosphorylation of D-glucose (Carpinelli *et al.*, 1987).

Secondly, in islet cells, the hexokinase isoenzymes are largely bound to mitochondria and this binding is itself modulated, in a phenomenon of ambiquity, by factors such as the concentration of D-glucose 6-phosphate, the pH and the presence of polyamines (Sener *et al.*, 1986; Malaisse-Lagae & Malaisse, 1988). The binding of hexokinase isoenzymes may have several implications. Bound hexokinase is more resistant than the free enzyme to inhibition by D-glucose 6-phosphate (Sener *et al.*, 1986), preferentially uses mitochondrial rather than extramitochondrial ATP as a substrate for hexose phosphorylation (Rasschaert & Malaisse, 1990), and provides a direct pathway for coupling

Fig. I.   **Schematic view for the role of a regulatory protein mediating the antagonistic effects of D-fructose I-phosphate (FIP) and D-fructose 6-phosphate (F6P), generated respectively in the fructokinase (FK) and hexokinase (HK) reaction, on glucokinase (GK) activity**

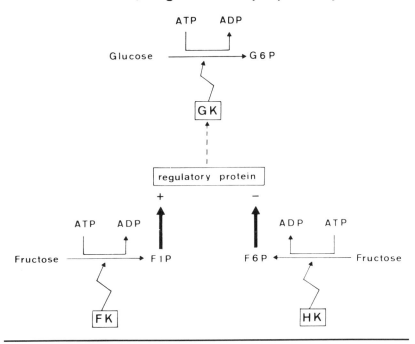

hexose phosphorylation to mitochondrial respiration (Rasschaert *et al.*, 1990).

Thirdly, the glucokinase content of islet cells is regulated in a long-term manner, through induction-repression, by the glycaemic level. For instance, the activity of glucokinase is severely decreased in fasted animals (Malaisse *et al.*, 1976c). It is also conceivable that, as in hepatocytes, the turnover of glucokinase in islet cells, as dictated by its rate of biosynthesis, affects some of its intrinsic properties (Zähner & Malaisse, 1990).

Lastly, it was recently demonstrated (Malaisse *et al.*, 1990b) that, in islet cells like in hepatocytes, the activity of glucokinase is modulated by a regulatory protein which mediates the antagonistic effects of D-fructose 1-phosphate and D-fructose 6-phosphate upon D-glucose phosphorylation (Fig. 1). Since islets were found to display limited but sizeable fructokinase activity (Malaisse *et al.*, 1989), the generation of D-fructose 1-phosphate from exogenous D-fructose could conceivably favour, to a limited extent, D-glucose phosphorylation by glucokinase. Moreover, D-fructose 1-phosphate may also be generated in islet cells from a triose and triose phosphate, e.g. from D-glyceraldehyde and glycerone-3-phosphate (Malaisse *et al.*, 1990*b*).

Regulation of glycogen synthesis and glycogenolysis

Normal B-cells are devoid of glycogen. In islets, the deposition of glycogen formed from exogenous D-glucose accounts for only a minor fraction of the hexose phosphorylation rate (Malaisse *et al.*, 1977). Nevertheless, sustained hyperglycaemia may lead to the accumulation of a significant amount of glycogen in the B-cell (Marynissen *et al.*, 1990).

Like in hepatocytes, the rate of glycogenolysis appears to be regulated by the concentration of both cyclic AMP and D-glucose in the islet cell. Thus, agents raising the cyclic AMP content of cells stimulate glycogenolysis (Malaisse *et al.*, 1977), whereas a rise in extracellular, and hence intracellular, D-glucose concentration suppresses glycogenolysis in glycogen-rich islets (Malaisse, 1991). As is the case with purified enzymes, the activation of phosphorylase phosphatase and concomitant inactivation of phosphorylase *a* by D-glucose in intact B-cells may display an anomeric preference for α-D-glucose (Malaisse, 1991; Bollen *et al.*, 1990). This would result in a more severe inhibition of glycogenolysis in response to α- rather than β-D-glucose in glycogen-rich islets and, as such, may account for the anomeric malaise in insulin release often found in non-insulin-dependent diabetic subjects or experimental models of sustained hyperglycaemia (Malaisse, 1990; 1991).

The glucose 6-phosphatase riddle

Conflicting data were recently reported concerning the presence of glucose-6-phosphatase in pancreatic islets (Giroix *et al.*, 1987; Waddell & Burchell, 1988). This refers to an issue of more than academic interest. Thus, glucose-6-phosphatase was both speculated to play a role in the storage of Ca^{2+} by the endoplasmic reticulum in islet cells (Waddell & Burchell, 1988), and claimed to participate in a futile cycling between D-glucose and D-glucose 6-phosphate, which would account for up to 40% of the rate of glucose phosphorylation in intact islets from *ob/ob* mice (Kahn *et al.*, 1989).

In a recent study, we have re-investigated the presence of glucose 6-phosphatase activity in rat liver or pancreatic islet crude homogenates and microsomes (Perales *et al.*, 1990). In the islets, the hydrolysis of D-glucose 6-phosphate by disrupted microsomes represented, when expressed relative to protein content, less than 2% of the value recorded in liver microsomes. Moreover, no phosphotransferase activity was detected in islets. These findings impose reservations on both the presence of glucose 6-phosphatase in rat islets and its participation in stimulus-secretion coupling.

Regulation of circulation in the pentose phosphate pathway

Only a modest fraction of D-glucose 6-phosphate generated from exogenous D-glucose is channelled into the pentose phosphate pathway. The fractional contribution of this pathway to the overall rate of triose phosphate generation is not increased when the concentration of extracellular D-glucose is raised (Giroix *et al.*, 1985*a*). The β-anomer of D-glucose 6-phosphate is preferentially oriented into the pentose phosphate pathway (Malaisse *et al.*, 1985*b*). The fractional channelling of hexose 6-phosphate into the latter pathway is not identical in islets exposed to D-glucose and D-fructose, respectively, and, in the latter case, is apparently modulated by the presence of the aldohexose (Sener & Malaisse, 1988). The mechanism(s) responsible for these differences and changes remain(s) to be elucidated.

Regulation of D-glucose 6-phosphate and D-fructose 6-phosphate interconversion

In islets, the frequency of back-and-forth interconversion of hexose 6-phosphates in the phosphoglucoisomerase reaction, as estimated from both the activity of the enzyme in islet homogenates and the steady-state concentrations of D-glucose 6-phosphate and D-fructose 6-phosphate in intact cells exceeds by one to two orders of magnitude the net glycolytic flux (Malaisse & Bodur, 1991). This would imply a virtually complete detritiation of hexose 6-phosphates generated from D-[2-^{3}H]glucose, even if allowance is made for both the isotopic discrimination in reaction velocity towards the tritiated esters and the intramolecular transfer of tritium between D-[2-^{3}H]glucose 6-phosphate and D-[1-^{3}H]fructose 6-phosphate (Liemans *et al.*, 1990). Yet the rate of ^{3}H$_2$O production from D-[2-^{3}H]glucose underestimates by about 25% the true rate of glycolysis in intact islets (Malaisse *et al.*, 1988*a*). To reconcile experimental and theoretical values for ^3H_2O production from both D-[2-^{3}H]glucose and D-[5-^{3}H]glucose, enzyme-to-enzyme tunnelling of hexose 6-phosphates in the hexokinase/phosphoglucoisomerase/phosphofructokinase sequence was recently postulated (Malaisse & Bodur, 1991). In this respect, the most

---

Fig. 2.   Model for the metabolism of unlabelled D-glucose (upper panel) and D-[2-^{3}H]glucose (lower panel) in pancreatic islets exposed to 16.7 mM-D-glucose

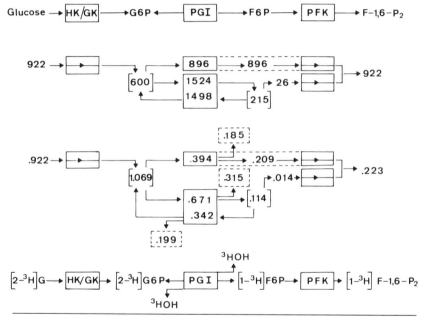

Flow rates (expressed per min) and pool sizes (indicated in brackets) are shown as μmol/l of islet intracellular water. For illustrative purpose, the tracer amount of D-[2-^{3}H]glucose is taken as 0.1% of that of unlabelled D-glucose. The production of ^3HOH is indicated in the dotted rectangles. In this model, the fractional contribution of the non-tunnelled pathway to the net generation of F-1,6-P$_2$, i.e. 2.8%, is identical to the activity of free phosphoglucoisomerase (PGI) relative to that measured in islet homogenates.

---

satisfactory model was restricted to the channelling of hexose 6-phosphates in the phosphoglucoisomerase/phosphofructokinase couple, as illustrated in Fig. 2 This enzyme-to-enzyme tunnelling of early glycolytic intermediates may favour the expression of the anomeric specificity or preference of the concerned enzymes. This is most relevant to the phosphoglucoisomerase/phosphofructokinase couple, since we recently observed (Hallenga *et al.*, 1990) that phosphoglucoisomerase, which is known to display strict α-stereospecificity towards D-glucose 6-phosphate, also displays β-stereospecificity towards D-fructose 6-phosphate, so that the enzyme would convert α-D-glucose 6-phosphate to β-D-fructose 6-phosphate, which is the preferred substrate for phosphofructokinase.

Regulation of D-fructose 6-phosphate and D-mannose 6-phosphate interconversion

Taking advantage of the opposite diastereomeric specificity of phospho-glucoisomerase and phosphomannoisomerase, respectively, we have attempted, by measuring the generation of ^3H_2O from D-[1-^{3}H]glucose, D-[5-^{3}H]glucose and D-[6-^{3}H]glucose, to estimate the extent of interconversion of D-[1-^{3}H]fructose 6-phosphate and D-[2-^{3}H]mannose 6-phosphate in intact islets. Relative to glycolytic flux, such an interconversion was quite elevated in normal islet cells (Malaisse-Lagae *et al.*, 1989).

Regulation of D-fructose 6-phosphate phosphorylation

To keep pace with the rate of hexose phosphorylation, the conversion of fructose 6-phosphate to fructose 1,6-bisphosphate requires activation of phosphofructokinase (Malaisse *et al.*, 1981). This is mediated by both glucose 1,6-bisphosphate and fructose 2,6-bisphosphate (Sener *et al.*, 1982*b*; 1984*a*). In islet cells, as distinct from hepatocytes, fructose 6-phosphate 2-kinase does not appear to be inactivated by cyclic AMP (Malaisse *et al.*, 1982). Full activation of phosphofructokinase does not occur in tumoral islet cells of the RINm5F line exposed to a high concentration of D-glucose (Malaisse *et al.*, 1988*b*). An impaired activation of phosphofructokinase apparently also participates in the fasting-induced alteration of glycolysis in pancreatic islets (Giroix *et al.*, 1984*b*).

Regulation of aerobic glycolysis

Part of the NADH generated in the reaction catalysed by glyceraldehyde-3-phosphate dehydrogenase is re-oxidized to NAD^+ through the conversion of pyruvate to lactate. The production of lactate from exogenous D-glucose indeed accounts for a large fraction of the glycolytic flux (Sener *et al.*, 1976). However, part of the pyruvate derived from exogenous D-glucose is not converted into L-lactate and, instead, is either released as pyruvate, converted into L-alanine, oxidized in the pyruvate dehydrogenase reaction or carboxylated in the reaction catalysed by pyruvate carboxylase (Sener & Malaisse, 1987). In these four instances, the re-oxidation of NADH generated at the glyceraldehyde-3-phosphate level is mediated to a large extent through the transfer of reducing equivalents into mitochondria.

Fig. 3. **Effect of increasing concentrations of ᴅ-glucose on the ratio between ᴅ-[3,4-^{14}C]glucose oxidation and ᴅ-[5-^{3}H]glucose utilization by rat pancreatic islets**

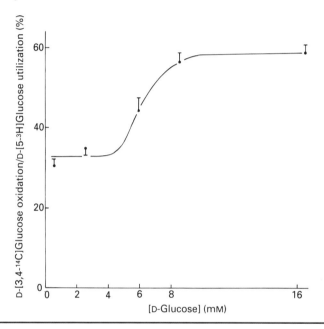

There is evidence to suggest that such a transfer is itself mediated to a large extent by the glycerol phosphate shuttle (Sener *et al.*, 1988). The activity of the FAD-linked mitochondrial glycerophosphate dehydrogenase, which is often looked upon as a rate-limiting factor in this shuttle, is much higher in pancreatic islets than in other cell types (Giroix *et al.*, 1991). The enzyme is activated by Ca^{2+} and its activity is severely impaired in the islets of adult rats injected with streptozotocin during the neonatal period (Giroix *et al.*, 1991).

A rise in extracellular ᴅ-glucose concentration causes, in islets, preferential stimulation of aerobic glycolysis relative to total glycolysis (Sener & Malaisse, 1987). The concentration dependency for such a preferential effect displays a sigmoidal pattern (Fig. 3). The preferential stimulation of aerobic glycolysis might be due, in part at least, to activation of the enzyme in response to a rise in cytosolic Ca^{2+} concentration. It should be noted, however, that the preferential stimulation of aerobic glycolysis is not abolished in the absence of extracellular Ca^{2+} and not mimicked by non-glucidic nutrient secretagogues such as 4-methyl-2-oxo-pentanoate or 3-phenylpyruvate (Malaisse *et al.*, 1991). In glucose-stimulated islets, however, the ratio between D-[3,4-^{14}C]glucose oxidation and D-[5-^{3}H]glucose utilization is decreased in the presence of cyclo-heximide or ouabain, suggesting that aerobic glycolysis may be regulated by factors affecting the consumption of ATP, in such processes as the biosynthesis of protein and the active pumping of monovalent cations by Na^+,K^+-ATPase.

Regulation of triose phosphate catabolism

The lower segment of glycolysis leading to the stepwise conversion of D-glyceraldehyde 3-phosphate to pyruvate is susceptible to regulation at several sites. For instance, the islet content in 2,3-diphosphoglycerate appears essential for full activation of phosphoglycerate 2,3-mutase (Malaisse-Lagae *et al.*, 1984). Likewise, the maintenance of a sufficient K^+ islet content is required to ensure adequate activity of pyruvate kinase (Sener *et al.*, 1980).

Regulation of pyruvate decarboxylation

A rise in extracellular D-glucose concentration preferentially stimulates the oxidation of D-[3,4-^{14}C]glucose relative to the utilization of D-[5-^{3}H]glucose. At the first glance, this might suggest that the hexose causes activation of pyruvate dehydrogenase. McCormack *et al.* (1990) recently reported that D-glucose indeed causes a rapid and concentration-related increase of the active, non-phosphorylated, form of pyruvate dehydro-genase in cultured rat pancreatic islets.

Some caution should be exerted, however, in considering these proposals. First, in a previous study conducted in freshly isolated islets, active pyruvate dehydrogenase represented about 94 % of the total activity measured after phosphatase treatment (Paxton *et al.*, 1988). Secondly, the oxidation of D-[3,4-^{14}C]glucose is tightly coupled to the generation of pyruvate by aerobic glycolysis, since little ^{14}C-labelled pyruvate or alanine accumulates in the islets and incubation media (Sener & Malaisse, 1987). Thirdly, dichloroacetate fails to augment glucose-stimulated insulin release (Sener *et al.*, 1978). Lastly, as already mentioned, the oxidation of D-[3,4-^{14}C]glucose is little affected by changes in extracellular Ca^{2+} availability and is not stimulated by non-glucidic nutrient secretagogues such as BCH or 3-phenylpyruvate. All these findings argue against the view that activation of pyruvate dehydrogenase, e.g. as a result of Ca^{2+} accumulation in mitochondria, represents a major feature of the islet cell metabolic response to D-glucose.

Regulation of acetyl-CoA oxidation

A rise in extracellular D-glucose concentration stimulates preferentially the oxidation of D-[6-^{14}C]glucose relative to the utilization of D-[5-^{3}H]glucose (Sener & Malaisse, 1987). Such a preferential stimulation displays a sigmoidal dependence on hexose concentration and an exponential time course tending towards a saturation value during prolonged exposure to a high concentration of the hexose (Malaisse & Sener, 1988).

Although these findings could suggest activation of the Krebs cycle in glucose-stimulated islets, it should be emphasized that the ratio between D-[3,4-^{14}C]glucose and D-[6-^{14}C]glucose oxidation is not significantly affected by a rise in hexose concentration (Sener & Malaisse, 1987). As judged from such a ratio, about half of the acetyl residues generated from exogenous D-glucose in the pyruvate dehydrogenase reaction escape oxidation in the Krebs cycle. The two processes, i.e. pyruvate decarboxylation and acetyl coenzyme A oxidation can be dissociated from one another, however, by inhibiting ATP-requiring functional events, e.g. by incubating islets in the presence of cycloheximide and/or absence of extracellular Ca^{2+}. In this case, the oxidation of D-[6-^{14}C]glucose is more severely inhibited than that of D-[3,4-^{14}C]glucose (Malaisse & Sener, 1988).

To distinguish between a mere mass action phenomenon and a true activation of the Krebs cycle, we have recently investigated the effect of non-glucidic nutrient secretagogues, upon the paired ratio between D-[3,4-^{14}C]glucose or D-[6-^{14}C]glucose oxidation and D-[5-^{3}H]glucose utilization in islets exposed to a low concentration of the hexose (Malaisse & Sener, 1990). As shown in Fig. 4, BCH preferentially stimulated D-[6-^{14}C]glucose oxidation relative to either D-[5-^{3}H]glucose utilization or D-[3,4-^{14}C]glucose oxidation. Comparable results were obtained with 4-methyl-2-oxo-pentanoate, L-leucine and 3-phenylpyruvate. In each case, the activation of the Krebs cycle was shown to represent a Ca^{2+}-dependent process. Incidentally, the relative extent of stimulation of the Krebs cycle may well be underestimated in these experiments, since ^{14}C-labelled acetyl residues generated from exogenous D-glucose may undergo isotopic dilution by unlabelled acetyl residues generated in response to the exposure of the islets to the non-glucidic nutrient secretagogues. Control experiments indicated that the activation of the Krebs cycle did not occur when the secretory response to D-glucose was enhanced by non-nutrient secretagogues.

Regulation of circulation in the Krebs cycle

The findings just evoked unambiguously document that nutrient secretagogues activate circulation in the Krebs cycle. This could well be due to activation of 2-ketoglutarate dehydrogenase, e.g. as a result of the

Fig. 4.   Effect of BCH on D-glucose metabolism in islet cells

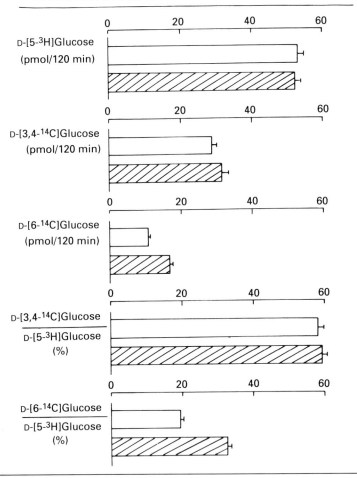

Effect of BCH (10 mM) on the metabolism of D-Glucose (6 mM)

Cells were incubated in the absence (open columns) or presence (hatched columns) of BCH.

mitochondrial accumulation of Ca^{2+} in nutrient-stimulated islets (Sener *et al.*, 1990). Such an activation appears to depend not solely on facilitated Ca^{2+} influx into the islet cells but also on an increase in ATP availability and, possibly, a change in mitochondrial redox state (Malaisse & Sener, 1990).

Like in other tissues, 2-ketoglutarate dehydrogenase activity in islet homogenates or isolated islet mitochondria displays exquisite Ca^{2+}-sensitivity, the divalent Ca^{2+} increasing the affinity of the enzyme for 2-ketoglutarate (Sener *et al.*, 1990). The view that D-glucose causes activation of the enzyme is supported by the finding that the rate of $[1\text{-}^{14}C]2$-ketoglutarate decarboxylation is increased when the mitochondrial suspension is prepared from islets pre-incubated in the presence, as distinct from absence, of D-glucose. The absence of extracellular Ca^{2+} impairs, but does not totally suppress, such a memory phenomenon (Sener *et al.*, 1990).

At this point, it should be emphasized that the preferential stimulation by D-glucose of mitochondrial oxidative events — such as circulation in the glycerol phosphate shuttle, pyruvate decarboxylation and oxidation of acetyl residues in the Krebs cycle — is obviously well suited to optimalize the fuel-sensor function of islet cells (Malaisse, 1987). It is indeed these mitochondrial reactions which provide the major fraction of ATP generated by the catabolism of D-glucose.

Regulation of anabolic processes

D-glucose, in high concentrations, exerts a modest but significant sparing action upon the production of $^{14}CO_2$ by islets prelabelled with [U-^{14}C]palmitate (Malaisse *et al.*, 1979*b*). D-glucose and several other nutrient secretagogues also increase the rate of synthesis of acyl residues in islet cells (Sener *et al.*, 1978). This coincides with an increased content of islet cells in malonyl coenzyme A (Matschinsky *et al.*, 1989). The fraction of acetyl coenzyme A generated from exogenous D-glucose and escaping oxidation in the Krebs cycle could thus be used, in part at least, to support the synthesis of fatty acids (Sener & Malaisse, 1987). In this case, the NADH generated in the glyceraldehyde-3-phosphate dehydrogenase reaction could be re-oxidized to NAD^+ in the reaction catalysed by a cytosolic NAD-specific malate dehydrogenase. According to this scheme, the synthesis of palmitate from D-glucose would also involve the formation of oxaloacetate from pyruvate in the reaction catalysed by pyruvate carboxylase. Indirect evidence to support the participation of the latter enzyme in islet mitochondrial metabolism was found in the generation of ^{14}C-labelled amino acids other than L-alanine in islets exposed to D-[3,4-^{14}C]glucose (Sener & Malaisse, 1987). Likewise, the presence in islets of malic enzyme activity and the generation of pyruvate from malate, itself derived from mitochondrial ^{14}C-labelled metabolites, were both previously documented (Sener *et al.*, 1984*b*).

Conclusions

The present review on the regulation of D-glucose metabolism in pancreatic islets should be considered as exemplative rather than exhaustive. Even if restricted, the information provided convincingly documents, in my opinion, that the metabolism of D-glucose is indeed regulated at a great number of distinct levels from its transport across the plasma membrane to the oxidation in the Krebs cycle of acetyl residues derived from the exogenous hexose. Moreover, the majority of these regulatory steps were found to be affected by site-specific defects in models of B-cell dysfunction. The present review could thus be considered as a working framework for further investigations on several essential aspects of insulin release: (i) its physiologic regulation by D-glucose, as ruled by the catabolism of the hexose in islet cells, (ii) its modulation by ontogenic and environmental factors, as exemplified by the altered features of D-glucose metabolism in islets removed from newborn (Boschero *et al.*, 1990) or fasted (Levy *et al.*, 1976) animals, and (iii) its perturbation in a number of distinct pathologic situations, such as encountered in tumoral islet cells (Giroix *et al.*, 1985*b*), after cytotoxic insults (Giroix *et al.*, 1991) or in situations of B-cell glucotoxicity (Malaisse, 1991; Chapter 16 by Flatt *et al.*).

The experimental work here under review was supported by grants from the Belgian Foundation for Scientific Medical Research and Belgian Prime Minister's Office-Science Policy Programming. I am most grateful to C. Demesmaeker for secretarial help.

References

Bollen, M., Malaisse-Lagae, F., Malaisse, W. J. & Stalmans, W. (1990) The interaction of phosphorylase a with D-glucose displays α-stereospecificity. Biochim. Biophys. Acta **1038**, 141–145

Boschero, A. C., Bordin, S., Sener, A. & Malaisse, W. J. (1990) D-glucose and L-leucine metabolism in neonatal and adult cultured rat pancreatic islets. Mol. Cell. Endocrinol., **73**, 63–71

Carpinelli, A. R., Sener, A. & Malaisse, W. J. (1987) Positive feedback effect of ATP on glucose phosphorylation in pancreatic islets. Med. Sci. Res. **15**, 481–482

Giroix, M.-H., Sener, A., Pipeleers, D. G. & Malaisse, W. J. (1984*a*) Hexose metabolism in pancreatic islets. Inhibition of hexokinase. Biochem. J. **223**, 447–453

Giroix, M.-H., Dufrane, S. P., Malaisse-Lagae, F., Sener, A. & Malaisse, W. J. (1984*b*) Fasting-induced impairment of glucose-1,6-bisphosphate synthesis in pancreatic islets. Biochem. Biophys. Res. Commun. **119**, 543–548

Giroix, M.-H., Sener, A. & Malaisse, W. J. (1985*a*) Pentose cycle pathway in normal and tumoral islet cells. FEBS Lett. **185**, 1–3

Giroix, M.-H., Sener, A., Dufrane, S. P., Malaisse-Lagae, F. & Malaisse, W. J. (1985*b*) Glucose metabolism in insulin-producing tumoral cells. Arch. Biochem. Biophys. **241**, 561–570

Giroix, M.-H., Sener, A. & Malaisse, W. J. (1987) Hexose metabolism in pancreatic islets. Absence of glucose 6-phosphatase in rat islet cells. Mol. Cell. Endocrinol. **49**, 219–225

Giroix, M.-H., Rasschaert, J., Bailbe, D., Leclercq-Meyer, V., Sener, A., Portha, B. & Malaisse, W. J. (1991) Impairment of the glycerol phosphate shuttle in islets from rats with diabetes induced by neonatal streptozotocin. Diabetes **40**, 227–232

Hallenga, K., Malaisse-Lagae, F., Malaisse, W. J. & Willem, R. (1990) 2D Phase sensitive EXSY ^{13}C N.M.R. on ^{13}C-enriched substrates for the elucidation of the anomeric specificity of fructose 6-phosphate in the phosphoglucoisomerase reaction. Abstracts 10th Europe. Exp. N.M.R. Conference, pp. 59–60, Veldhoven, The Netherlands

Khan, A., Chandramouli, V., Östenson, C.-G., Ahren, B., Schumann, W. C., Löw, H., Landau, B. R. & Efendic, S. (1989) Evidence for the presence of glucose cycling by pancreatic islets of the *ob/ob* mouse. J. Biol. Chem. **264**, 9732–9733

Levy, J., Herchuelz, A., Sener, A. & Malaisse, W. J. (1976) The stimulus-secretion coupling of glucose-induced insulin release. XX. Fasting: a model for altered glucose recognition by the B-cell. Metabolism **25**, 538–591

Liemans, V., Bodur, H., Malaisse-Lagae, F. & Malaisse, W. J. (1990) Phosphoglucoisomerase-catalyzed interconversion of hexose phosphates: a model for the interconversion of D-[2-^{3}H]glucose 6-phosphate and D-[1-^{3}H]fructose 6-phosphate. Biochimie **72**, 251–258

Malaisse, W. J. (1984) Insulin release: the fuel concept. Diabete Métab. **9**, 313–320

Malaisse, W. J. (1986) Branched-chain amino and keto acid metabolism in pancreatic islets. Adv. Enzyme Regul. **25**, 203–217

Malaisse, W. J. (1987) Insulin release: the glucoreceptor myth. Med. Sci. Res. **15**, 65–67

Malaisse, W. J. (1988) Possible sites for deficient glucose recognition in islet cells. In The Pathology of the Endocrine Pancreas in Diabetes (Lefebvre, P. J. & Pipeleers, D. G., eds.), pp. 219–232, Springer Verlag, Berlin

Malaisse, W. J. (1990) Physiology and pathology of the pancreatic B-cell glucose-sensor device. The Morgagni Prize Lecture. In Diabetes, Obesity and Hyperlipidemias (Crepaldi, G., Tiengo, A. & Enzi, G., eds.), pp. 3–22, Elsevier Science Publishers, Amsterdam

Malaisse, W. J. (1991) Physiology of insulin secretion and its alteration in diabetes: the concept of glucotoxicity. In Diabetic Complications: Epidemiology and Pathogenetic Mechanisms (Andreani, D., Gueriguian, J. L. & Striker, G. E., eds.), pp. 3–23, Raven Press, New York

Malaisse, W. J. & Bodur, H. (1991) Hexose metabolism in pancreatic islets. Enzyme-to-enzyme tunnelling of hexose 6-phosphates. Int. J. Biochem., in the press

Malaisse, W. J. & Herchuelz, A. (1982) Nutritional regulation of K^+ conductance: an unsettled aspect of pancreatic β-cell physiology. In Biochemical Actions of Hormones (Litwack, G., ed.), vol. 9, pp. 69–72, Academic Press, New York

Malaisse, W. J. & Sener, A. (1987) Glucose-induced changes in cytosolic ATP content in pancreatic islets. Biochim. Biophys. Acta **927**, 190–195

Malaisse, W. J. & Sener, A. (1988) Hexose metabolism in pancreatic islets. Feedback control of D-glucose oxidation by functional events. Biochim. Biophys. Acta **971**, 246–254

Malaisse, W. J. & Sener, A. (1990) Calcium-dependent activation of the Krebs cycle in islets stimulated by non-glucidic nutrient secretagogues. Diabetelogia **33** (Suppl), A88 (abstract)

Malaisse, W. J., Sener, A. & Mahy, M. (1974) The stimulus-secretion coupling of glucose-induced insulin release. XVIII. Sorbitol metabolism in isolated islets. Eur. J. Biochem. **47**, 365–370

Malaisse, W. J., Sener, A., Koser, M. & Herchuelz, A. (1976*a*) The stimulus-secretion coupling of glucose-induced insulin release. XXIV. The metabolism of α- and β-D-glucose in isolated islets. J. Biol. Chem. **251**, 5936–5943

Malaisse, W. J., Sener, A., Levy, J. & Herchuelz, A. (1976*b*) The stimulus-secretion coupling of glucose-induced insulin release. XXII. Qualitative and quantitative aspects of glycolysis in isolated islets. Acta Diabetol. Lat. **13**, 202–215

Malaisse, W. J., Sener, A. & Levy, J. (1976*c*) The stimulus-secretion coupling of glucose-induced insulin release. XXI. Fasting-induced adaptation of key glycolytic enzymes in isolated islets. J. Biol. Chem. **251**, 1731–1737

Malaisse, W. J., Sener, A., Koser, M., Ravazzola, M. & Malaisse-Lagae, F. (1977) The stimulus-secretion coupling of glucose-induced insulin release. XXV. Insulin release due to glycogenolysis in glucose-deprived islets. Biochem. J. **164**, 447–454

Malaisse, W. J., Sener, A., Herchuelz, A. & Hutton, J. C. (1979a) Insulin release: the fuel hypothesis. Metabolism **28**, 373–386

Malaisse, W. J., Hutton, J. C., Kawazu, S., Herchuelz, A., Valverde, I. & Sener, A. (1979b) The stimulus-secretion coupling of glucose-induced insulin release. XXXV. The links between metabolic and cationic events. Diabetologia **16**, 331–341

Malaisse, W. J., Malaisse-Lagae, F., Sener, A., Van Schaftingen, E. & Hers, H.-G. (1981) Is the glucose-induced stimulation of glycolysis in pancreatic islets attributable to activation of phosphofructokinase by fructose 2,6-bisphosphate? FEBS Lett. **25**, 217–219

Malaisse, W. J., Malaisse-Lagae, F. & Sener, A. (1982) The glycolytic cascade in pancreatic islets. Diabetologia **23**, 1–5

Malaisse, W. J., Sener, A., Welsh, M., Malaisse-Lagae, F., Hellerström, C. & Christophe, J. (1983a) Mechanism of 3-phenylpyruvate-induced insulin release. Metabolic aspects. Biochem. J. **210**, 921–927

Malaisse, W. J., Best, L., Kawazu, S., Malaisse-Lagae, F. & Sener, A. (1983b) The stimulus-secretion coupling of glucose-induced insulin release. LV. Fuel metabolism in islets deprived of exogenous nutrient. Arch. Biochem. Biophys. **224**, 102–110

Malaisse, W. J., Malaisse-Lagae, F. & Sener, A. (1984) Coupling factors in nutrient-induced insulin release. Experientia **40**, 1035–1043

Malaisse, W. J., Malaisse-Lagae, F., Sener, A. & Hellerström, C. (1985a) Participation of endogenous fatty acids in the secretory activity of the pancreatic B-cell. Biochem. J. **227**, 995–1002

Malaisse, W. J., Giroix, M.-H. & Sener, A. (1985b) Anomeric specificity of glucose metabolism in the pentose cycle. J. Biol. Chem. **260**, 14630–14632

Malaisse, W. J., Giroix, M.-H., Malaisse-Lagae, F., Leclercq-Meyer, V. & Sener, A. (1986) Hexose transport and metabolism in tumoral insulin-producing cells. In Diabetes 1985 (Serrano-Rios, M. & Lefèbvre, P. J., eds.), ICS 700, pp. 169–172, Excerpta Medica, Amsterdam, New York, Oxford

Malaisse, W. J., Yilmaz, M. T., Malaisse-Lagae, F. & Sener, A. (1988a) Underestimation of D-glucose phosphorylation as measured by ^3H_2O production from D-[2-^{3}H]glucose. Biochem. Med. Metab. Biol. **40**, 35–41

Malaisse, W. J., Rasschaert, J., Zähner, D. & Sener, A. (1988b) Hexose metabolism in pancreatic islets: The Pasteur effect. Diabetes Res. **7**, 53–58

Malaisse, W. J., Malaisse-Lagae, F., Davies, D. R. & Van Schaftingen, E. (1989) Presence of fructokinase in pancreatic islets. FEBS Lett. **255**, 175–178

Malaisse, W. J., Lebrun, P., Rasschaert, J., Blachier, F., Yilmaz, T. & Sener, A. (1990a) Ketone bodies and islet function: ^{86}Rb handling and metabolic data. Am. J. Physiol. **259**, E129–E130

Malaisse, W. J., Malaisse-Lagae, F., Davies, D. R., Vandercammen, A. & Van Schaftingen, E. (1990b) Regulation of glucokinase by a fructose-1-phosphate-sensitive protein in pancreatic islets. Eur. J. Biochem. **190**, 539–545

Malaisse, W. J., Rasschaert, J., Conget, I. & Sener, A. (1991) Hexose metabolism in pancreatic islets. Regulation of aerobic glycolysis and pyruvate decarboxylation. Int. J. Biochem. **23**, 955–959

Malaisse-Lagae, F. & Malaisse, W. J. (1988) Hexose metabolism in pancreatic islets. Regulation of mitochondrial hexokinase binding. Biochem. Med. Metab. Biol. **39**, 80–89

Malaisse-Lagae, F., Sener, A. & Malaisse, W. J. (1984) Hexose metabolism in pancreatic islets: phosphoglucose 2,3-mutase and enolase activities in rat islets. Biochimie **66**, 723–726

Malaisse-Lagae, F., Liemans, V., Yaylali, B., Sener, A. & Malaisse, W. J. (1989) Phosphoglucoisomerase-catalysed interconversion of hexose phosphates: comparison with phosphomannoisomerase. Biochim. Biophys. Acta **998**, 118–125

Marynissen, G., Sener, A. & Malaisse, W. J. (1988) D-glucose uptake by pancreatic islets from normal and hyperglycemic rats. Med. Sci. Res. **16**, 1181–1182

Marynissen, G., Leclercq-Meyer, V., Sener, A. & Malaisse, W. J. (1990) Perturbation of pancreatic islet function in glucose-infused rats. Metabolism **39**, 87–95

Matschinsky, F. M., Corkey, B. E., Prentki, M., Meglasson, M. E., Erecinska, M., Shimizu,

T., Ghosh, A. & Parker, J. (1989) Metabolic connectivity and signalling in pancreatic B-cells. In Diabetes 1988 (Larkins, R. G., Zimmet, P. Z. & Chisholm, D. J., eds.), ICS 800, pp. 17–26, Excerpta Medica, Amsterdam, New York, Oxford

McCormack, J. G., Longo, E. A. & Corkey, B. E. (1990) Glucose-induced activation of pyruvate dehydrogenase in isolated rat pancreatic islets. Biochem. J. **267**, 527–530

Orci, L., Thorens, B., Ravazzola, M. & Lodish, H. F. (1990) Localization of the pancreatic beta cell glucose transporter to specific plasma membrane domains. Science **245**, 295–297

Paxton, R., Harris, R. A., Sener, A. & Malaisse, W. J. (1988) Branched-chain α-ketoacid dehydrogenase and pyruvate dehydrogenase activity in isolated rat pancreatic islets. Horm. Metab. Res. **20**, 317–322

Perales, M.-A., Sener, A. & Malaisse, W. J. (1990) Hexose metabolism in pancreatic islets. The glucose-6-phosphate riddle. Mol. Cell. Biochem. **101**, 67–71

Rasschaert, J. & Malaisse, W. J. (1990) Hexose metabolism in pancreatic islets. Preferential utilization of mitochondrial ATP for glucose phosphorylation. Biochim. Biophys. Acta **1015**, 353–360

Rasschaert, J., Sener, A. & Malaisse, W. J. (1990) Hexose metabolism in pancreatic islets: the coupling between hexose phosphorylation and mitochondrial respiration. Biochem. Med. Metab. Biol. **44**, 84–95

Sener, A. & Malaisse, W. J. (1980) L-leucine and a non-metabolized analogue activate pancreatic islet glutamate dehydrogenase. Nature (London) **288**, 187–189

Sener, A. & Malaisse, W. J. (1984) Nutrient metabolism in islet cells. Experimentia **40**, 1026–1035

Sener, A. & Malaisse, W. J. (1987) Stimulation by D-glucose of mitochondrial oxidative events in islet cells. Biochem. J. **246**, 89–95

Sener, A. & Malaisse, W. J. (1988) Hexose metabolism in pancreatic islets. Metabolic and secretory responses to D-fructose. Arch. Biochem. Biophys. **261**, 16–26

Sener, A. & Malaisse, W. J. (1990) A sensitive radioisotopic method for the measurement of NAD(P)H: Its application to the assay of metabolites and enzymatic activities. Anal. Biochem. **186**, 236–242

Sener, A., Levy, J. & Malaisse, W. J. (1976) The stimulus-secretion coupling of glucose-induced insulin release. XXIII. Does glycolysis control calicum transport in the B-cell? Biochem. J. **156**, 521–525

Sener, A., Kawazu, S., Hutton, J. C., Boschero, A. C., Devis, G., Somers, G., Herchuelz, A. & Malaisse, W. J. (1978) The stimulus-secretion coupling of glucose-induced insulin release. XXXIII. Effect of exogenous pyruvate on islet function. Biochem. J. **176**, 217–232

Sener, A., Kawazu, S. & Malaisse, W. J. (1980) The stimulus-secretion coupling of glucose-induced insulin release. XXXVII. Metabolism of glucose in K$^+$ deprived islets. Biochem. J. **186**, 183–190

Sener, A., Malaisse-Lagae, F. & Malaisse, W. J. (1981) Stimulation of islet metabolism and insulin release by a non-metabolizable amino acid. Proc. Natl. Acad. Sci. U.S.A. **78**, 5460–5464

Sener, A., Malaisse-Lagae, F., Lebrun, P., Herchuelz, A., Leclercq-Meyer, V. & Malaisse, W. J. (1982a) Anomeric specificity of D-mannose metabolism in pancreatic islets. Biochem. Biophys. Res. Commun. **108**, 1567–1573

Sener, A., Malaisse-Lagae, F. & Malaisse, W. J. (1982b) Glucose-induced accumulation of glucose-1,6-bisphosphate in pancreatic islets: its possible role in the regulation of glycolysis. Biochem. Biophys. Res. Commun. **104**, 1033–1040

Sener, A., Welsh, M., Lebrun, P., Garcia-Morales, P., Saceda, M., Malaisse-Lagae, F., Herchuelz, A., Valverde, I., Hellerström, C. & Malaisse, W. J. (1983) Mechanism of 3-phenylpyruvate-induced insulin release. Secretory, ionic and oxidative events. Biochem. J. **210**, 913–919

Sener, A., Van Schaftingen, E., Van de Winkel, M., Pipeleers, D. G., Malaisse-Lagae, F., Malaisse, W. J. & Hers, H.-G. (1984a) Effects of glucose and glucagon on the fructose 2,6-bisphosphate content of pancreatic islets and purified pancreatic B-cells. Biochem. J. **221**, 759–764

Sener, A., Malaisse-Lagae, F., Dufrane, S. P. & Malaisse, W. J. (1984b) The coupling of metabolic to secretory events in pancreatic islets. The cytosolic redox state. Biochem. J. **220**, 433–440

Sener, A., Malaisse-Lagae, F., Giroix, M.-H. & Malaisse, W. J. (1986) Hexose metabolism in pancreatic islets: compartmentation of hexokinase in islet cells. Arch. Biochem. Biophys. **251**, 61–67

Sener, A., Rasschaert, J., Zähner, D. & Malaisse, W. J. (1988) Hexose metabolism in pancreatic islets. Stimulation by D-glucose of [2-^{3}H]glycerol detritiation. Int. J. Biochem. **20**, 595–598

Sener, A., Rasschaert, J. & Malaisse, W. J. (1990) Hexose metabolism in pancreatic islets. Participation of Ca^{2+}-sensitive 2-ketoglutarate dehydrogenase in the regulation of mitochondrial function. Biochim. Biophys. Acta **1019**, 42–50

Waddell, I. D. & Burchell, A. (1988) The microsomal glucose-6-phosphatase enzyme of pancreatic islets. Biochem. J. **255**, 471–476

Zähner, D. & Malaisse, W. J. (1990) Kinetic behaviour of liver glucokinase in insulinopenic situations: effect of fructose 1-phosphate in fed and starved rats. Biochimie, **72**, 715–718

Zähner, D., Ramirez, R. & Malaisse, W. J. (1990) Non-enzymatic glycation of liver cytosolic proteins in diabetic rats. Med. Sci. Res. **18**, 33–34

6

Glucokinase: signal recognition enzyme for glucose-induced insulin secretion

Sigurd Lenzen

Institute of Pharmacology and Toxicology, University of Göttingen,
Göttingen, Germany

Introduction

A unique characteristic of the pancreatic B-cell is the dual function that glucose plays in this cell. Glucose is both a fuel and, at millimolar concentrations, a physiological stimulus for insulin secretion and insulin biosynthesis (Hedeskov, 1980; Ashcroft, 1981; Permutt, 1981; Malaisse *et al.*, 1983; see also Chapters 4 and 5 of this book by Guest and Hutton, and Malaisse, respectively). This dual function of glucose has been the theoretical basis for the concept of a signal function of fuel metabolism for the initiation of insulin secretion by glucose (Grodsky *et al.*, 1963; Coore & Randle, 1964; Randle *et al.*, 1968). For such a mechanism to be functional in the B-cell, the system requires a device to translate changes in the millimolar blood glucose concentration into corresponding signal-generating metabolic flux rates for initiation of insulin secretion. In B-cells, a facilitative plasma membrane glucose transporter isoform is expressed which corresponds to the transporter isoform in hepatocytes. This has a high K_m for glucose in the range of at least 15–20 mM and a high V_{max}. (Bell *et al.*, 1990; Johnson *et al.*, 1990; Mueckler, 1990). Glucose uptake by the B-cells via facilitated diffusion is usually not rate limiting for glucose utilization and cannot serve a signal-generating function for initiation of insulin secretion. However, glucokinase is a glucose phosphorylating enzyme in the B-cell which can fulfil the function of the so-called signal recognition enzyme for the initiation of glucose-induced insulin secretion.

Pancreatic islet research has elucidated three sites of major importance for coupling changes in the blood glucose concentration to corresponding changes in the rate of insulin secretion. These are glucokinase (Meglasson & Matschinsky 1984; Lenzen & Panten 1988*a*; Lenzen, 1990), the ATP-sensitive potassium channel (Ashcroft, 1988; Petersen, 1988; Panten, 1987; Quast & Cook, 1989; see also Chapter 10 of this book by Ashcroft *et al.*) and the voltage-sensitive calcium channel

---

Fig. 1.   Schematic model of the pancreatic B-cell depicting the mechanisms of glucose signal recognition and insulin exocytosis

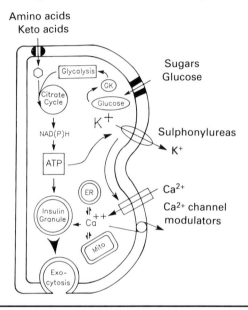

(Wollheim & Sharp, 1981; Bechem *et al.*, 1988; see also Chapter 11 of this book by Hellman *et al.*) (Fig. 1). The organ distribution of glucokinase and the two types of channel is different. Thus, while glucokinase is expressed only in pancreatic B-cells and hepatocytes (Lenzen & Panten, 1988*a*), the ATP-sensitive potassium channel is present also in neuronal and muscle tissues (Ashcroft, 1988; Quast & Cook, 1989), and the L-type voltage-sensitive calcium channel is found in many secretory and contractile tissues (Bechem *et al.*, 1988).

The glucose concentration in the B-cell reflects the glucose concentration in the extracellular space (Matschinsky & Ellerman, 1968; Malaisse *et al.*, 1976*b*) and closely follows the blood glucose concentration. An increase in the extracellular glucose concentration is immediately effective on glucokinase in the pancreatic B-cell. This permits an increased rate of glucose phosphorylation by glucokinase and an increased rate of metabolic flux through glycolysis (Lenzen & Panten, 1988*a*), leading to substrate pressure at the respiratory chain and the ATP generation like other fuel insulin secretagogues, such as leucine and 2-ketoisocaproic acid which do not enter intermediary metabolism via glycolysis (Panten, 1987; Panten & Lenzen, 1988) (Fig. 1).

ATP acting as a second messenger by interaction with ATP-sensitive potassium channels depolarizes the plasma membrane through reduction of the potassium permeability (Henquin & Meissner, 1984; Panten, 1987; Ashcroft, 1988; Petersen, 1988). The result is an opening of voltage-sensitive calcium channels through which calcium enters the pancreatic B-cell. In addition to glucose, other fuel secretagogues, including the hexose mannose, the triose glyceraldehyde, the amino acid leucine and the keto acid 2-ketoisocaproic acid, achieve this depolarization through an increase in ATP at the cytoplasmic side of the ATP-sensitive potassium channel (Henquin & Meissner, 1984; Panten, 1987; Ashcroft, 1988; Petersen, 1988). In contrast, hypoglycaemic sulphonylurea drugs, tolbutamide and glibenclamide, depolarize the B-cell through direct interaction with the ATP-sensitive potassium channel from the extra-cellular side. Calcium-channel modulators affect insulin secretion through interaction with the calcium channel of the B-cell. Fig. 1 presents a schematic model of the pancreatic B-cell depicting the mechanisms of glucose signal recognition and insulin exocytosis. Detailed consideration of ionic events leading to insulin secretion is given in Chapters 8–11 of this book.

Characteristics of pancreatic B-cell glucokinase

In addition to three hexokinase isoenzymes (hexokinases I, II, and III) with high affinity for glucose, the B-cell is the only cell other than the hepatocyte which contains an isoenzyme with low affinity for glucose, called glucokinase (hexokinase IV; hexokinase D; EC 2.7.1.2) (for review see Lenzen & Panten, 1988a). Glucokinase phosphorylates glucose to yield glucose 6-phosphate and mannose to yield mannose 6-phosphate.

Glucokinase antibodies raised against liver glucokinase have recognized a protein in the B-cell cytosol (Iynedjian et al., 1986; Lenzen et al., 1987a). This has a single protein subunit with immunological characteristics and an apparent molecular mass of 56500 Da (Iynedjian et al., 1986) similar to liver glucokinase (Pollard-Knight & Cornish-Bowden, 1982). The primary structure of rat liver glucokinase was deduced recently from a rat liver glucokinase cDNA (Andreone et al., 1989). The enzyme was found to be composed of 465 amino acids with a molecular mass of 51914 Da. Liver glucokinase has 53% and 33% amino acid sequence identities with the C-terminal domains of rat brain hexokinase I and yeast hexokinase, respectively. On the basis of a sequence analysis of a B-cell glucokinase cDNA, the structure of the pancreatic B-cell isoenzyme was predicted to be different from the liver isoenzyme by 15 amino acids at the N-terminus (Milburn et al., 1989; Magnuson, 1990). Thus the molecular mass of B-cell glucokinase is also around 52000 Da (Magnuson, 1990).

While the hexokinases (types I–III) exhibiting low K_m values have molecular masses of more than 100000 Da, glucokinase, with a molecular mass somewhat greater than 50000 Da, more closely resembles yeast hexokinase (Anderson et al., 1978; Lenzen & Panten, 1988a,b; Magnuson, 1990). The structure of mammalian type I hexokinase, as recently determined by cDNA cloning, was found to consist of two halves with considerable sequence similarity (Nishi et al., 1988; Schwab & Wilson, 1989). This confirms the classical view that, in contrast to mammalian glucokinase and yeast hexokinase, which are monomers, the hexokinases (types I–III) with low K_m values are dimers which arise from gene duplication and fusion involving an ancestral gene similar to that of yeast hexokinase, and the glucokinase in hepatocytes and pancreatic B-cells (Anderson et al., 1978; Lawrence & Trayer, 1984; Ureta, 1982). Significant expression of the glucokinase gene is apparently restricted to these two tissues (Iynedjian et al., 1989; Lenzen & Panten, 1988a).

The contribution of glucokinase to total glucose phosphorylation capacity has been found to be in the range of 50% in pancreatic islet homogenates (Lenzen & Panten, 1988a). The comparable figure for liver homogenates is around 70% (Lenzen & Panten, 1988a). These percentages are roughly 20% lower than in cytoplasmic fractions (Lenzen & Panten, 1988a), because hexokinase is partially bound to the particulate fraction (Lenzen & Panten, 1988a; Malaisse et al., 1990).

Percentages for glucokinase contribution to total glucose phosphorylation capacity in this range have been found by several groups (for review see Lenzen & Panten, 1988a), including Malaisse and collaborators, who have been critics of the concept of a signal-generating function of glucokinase in the initiation of insulin secretion by glucose (Malaisse & Sener, 1985). Matschinsky and collaborators have often reported lower percentages which would in fact exclude a role for glucokinase as a signal recognition enzyme (reviewed by Lenzen & Panten, 1988a).

For the concept of glucokinase as the signal recognition enzyme for glucose-induced insulin secretion to be valid, a harmony between the characteristics of glucose-induced insulin secretion and those of glucokinase is necessary. Experimental evidence is available to support this concept. The following are characteristics of pancreatic B-cell glucokinase (Lenzen & Panten, 1988a,b): (i) a narrow substrate specificity; (ii) high K_m values for the two substrates, D-glucose and D-mannose, of the order of 10 mM and 20 mM, respectively; (iii) a slight preference for the α-anomers of these two aldohexoses; (iv) $V_{max.}$ values for D-glucose which are 4–5 times higher than those for D-mannose; (v) lack of product inhibition by glucose 6-phosphate; (vi) inhibition of glucokinase activity by a specific glucokinase antibody; (vii) inhibition of glucokinase activity by D-mannoheptulose and some other sugars; (viii) inhibition of glucokinase activity by alloxan and some other pyrimidine derivatives; and (ix) inhibition of glucokinase activity by ninhydrin and some derivatives.

These characteristics are completely identical with those of liver glucokinase (Lenzen & Panten, 1988a) and correspond to the well-known features of hexose-induced insulin biosynthesis and secretion (Hedeskov, 1980; Ashcroft, 1981; Permutt, 1981; Malaisse et al., 1983). In contrast, the characteristics of the hexokinases with low K_m values are at variance with those of glucokinase. These would not allow transmission of a millimolar change of circulating glucose to a change of signal-generating metabolic flux in the B-cell for initiation of glucose-induced insulin secretion (Lenzen & Panten, 1988a). On the other hand, though the characteristics of pancreatic B-cell and liver glucokinase are virtually identical, the possibility of a signal-generating function of liver glucokinase has never been considered.

Regulation of glucokinase enzyme activity

The glucokinase of pancreatic B-cells is a monomer. This can help to explain why B-cell glucokinase is remarkably free from complex regulation. The only major factor that determines the activity level of glucokinase during short-term regulation is the concentration of glucose (Lenzen & Panten, 1988a). In the millimolar concentration range, substrate phosphorylation increases with K_m values for glucose and mannose of the order of 10 mM and 20 mM, respectively. In addition, glucose phosphorylation by glucokinase in hepatocytes has recently been shown to be stimulated by fructose through formation of fructose 1-phosphate (Van Schaftingen & Vandercammen, 1989). However, regulation of pancreatic B-cell glucokinase by fructose is apparently not important for regulation of insulin secretion (Lenzen, 1990). In contrast with hexokinase, glucokinase from pancreatic islets and liver is not inhibited by glucose 6-phosphate (Lenzen & Panten 1988a). This provides an explanation for the observation that the fractional contribution of glucokinase to the total glucose phosphorylation in intact islet cells (Malaisse et al., 1990) exceeds the value of 50% registered in pancreatic islet homogenates (Lenzen & Panten 1988a). Thus hexokinase is largely inhibited by endogenous glucose 6-phosphate and probably, to a lesser extent, by glucose 1,6-phosphate (Malaisse et al., 1990). For ATP, a K_m value (versus glucose) of 0.5 mM has been reported for rat pancreatic islet glucokinase (Meglasson et al., 1983) similar to that for rat liver. Glucokinase in the pancreatic B-cell is not likely, therefore, to be affected by variations in physiological concentrations of ATP, ADP, and glucose 6-phosphate. The enzyme is also remarkably free of allosteric effects. Hill coefficients of glucokinase from islets somewhat greater than 1.0 for glucose and mannose (Meglasson *et al.*, 1983; Miwa *et al.*, 1983; Meglasson & Matschinsky, 1984) are indicative of some degree of co-operativity. A useful consequence of the co-operativity is a particular sensitivity of the reaction, owing to a sigmoidal shape of the saturation curve, to small changes in the glucose concentration in the range of 5–10 mM (Pollard-Knight & Cornish-Bowden, 1982).

Glucokinase in insulin-secreting tumour cells

In a number of situations, a correlation has been observed between glucokinase activity and the degree of insulin secretory responsiveness to glucose. In normal pancreatic B-cells, at least 50% of the glucose phosphorylating enzyme capacity is glucokinase activity (Lenzen & Panten, 1988a). In rat insulinoma cells, insulin secretory responsiveness to glucose and glucokinase activity are inversely correlated with the extent of dedifferentiation and the rate of cellular growth. Slowly growing streptozotocin-induced rat islet cell tumours, which are moderately dedifferentiated insulinomas, lose their insulin secretory responsiveness to glucose stimulation (Lenzen *et al.*, 1985a). This occurs in parallel with loss of glucokinase activity (Lenzen *et al.*, 1987b) and with increasing tumour size, but hexokinase activity is not increased (Lenzen *et al.*, 1987b). In rapidly growing, radiation-induced, transplantable rat islet cell tumours, which are highly dedifferentiated insulinomas and do not exhibit glucose stimulation of insulin secretion (Chick *et al.*, 1977; Sopwith *et al.*, 1981; Flatt *et al.*, 1986), glucokinase activity is lost virtually completely and replaced by high hexokinase activity (Lenzen *et al.*, 1987b). The high hexokinase activity in poorly differentiated insulinomas might help these tumour cells to meet the high energy demand via glycolysis in order to maintain a high growth rate. At the same time, the high hexokinase activity may partly explain the occurrence of basal hyperinsulinaemia and fatal hypoglycaemia in rats bearing large poorly differentiated insulinomas (Lenzen *et al.*, 1987b). This is because the increased glycolytic flux rate at low glucose concentrations corresponds to the optimal range for phosphorylation by hexokinase, providing a signal-generating function for insulin secretion from the tumour. However, this signal-generating function of hexokinase does not only result in a high rate of insulin secretion at micromolar concentrations of glucose. This continual stimulation of insulin secretion by unphysiologically low glucose concentrations also makes it impossible for the tumour cell to store insulin for release when challenged by a millimolar concentration of glucose. Thus increased hexokinase activity alone may be sufficient to abolish the response of such tumour cells to physiological glucose stimulation independent of the glucokinase activity level.

This picture may be similar for insulin-secreting tumour lines maintained in tissue culture. In the RINm5F cell line, which is derived from rapidly growing radiation-induced islet cell tumours (Chick *et al.*, 1977), loss of insulin content and insulin secretory responsiveness to glucose is accompanied by a corresponding loss of glucokinase activity, while hexokinase activity is increased (Praz *et al.*, 1983; Halban *et al.*, 1983; Vischer *et al.*, 1987; Shimizu *et al.*, 1988*a,b*; Lenzen, 1990). Cells of the RINm5F$_{S2}$ sub-line contain more and release somewhat more insulin than tumour cells of the RINm5F$_{D2}$ sub-line (Flatt *et al.*, 1987*a,b*; P. R. Flatt, personal communication). In the RINm5F$_{S2}$ and the RINm5F$_{D2}$ tumour cell sub-lines, glucokinase activity comprises only 24% and 11%, respectively of the total glucose phosphorylating enzyme capacity (Lenzen, 1990). However, insulin-producing hamster tumour cells of the HIT cell line which are weakly sensitive to glucose stimulation of insulin secretion still contain glucokinase (Shimizu *et al.*, 1988*a,b*).

Loss of a certain distinct distribution of hexokinases with high and low affinity for glucose in insulin-producing tumour cells therefore represents an example of how such a metabolic derangement can affect cell function. On the other hand, it must be born in mind when considering studies with insulin-producing tumour cells that these cells generally contain multiple defects and that altered glucokinase activity is not the sole determinant of defects in insulin biosynthesis or secretion in response to glucose stimulation. Defects related to other important events in the regulation of insulin secretion, such as ion and glucose transport, may add up to a complex picture which is ultimately responsible for defective insulin secretion in insulin-producing tumour cells (see also Chapter 16 of this book by Flatt *et al.*).

Inhibitors of glucokinase

Glucose and mannose are the sole substrates for the pancreatic B-cell glucokinase, but a number of other sugars reversibly inhibit this enzyme through competition for the sugar-binding site. These sugars are not usually phosphorylated, but prevent access of glucose to the sugar-binding site of the enzyme. These inhibitory sugars include mannoheptulose, glucosamine, *N*-acetylglucosamine and 5-thioglucose (Lenzen *et al.*, 1988*a*). Other sugars, in particular 3-O-methylglucose and 2-deoxyglucose, are neither substrates nor inhibitors because they do not bind to the sugar-binding site of the enzyme (Lenzen *et al.*, 1988*a*).

Mannoheptulose has always been of particular interest in pancreatic islet research. This sugar inhibits glucose-induced insulin secretion and glucose oxidation through inhibition of B-cell glucokinase (Coore & Randle, 1964; Ashcroft *et al.*, 1970; Lenzen *et al.*, 1987*a*, 1988*a*). This prevents the generation of increased metabolic flux through glycolysis, the citric acid cycle and the respiratory chain, thereby preventing an increase in ATP concentration at the cytoplasmic side of the ATP-sensitive potassium channel (Fig. 1).

Alloxan, a well-known pancreatic B-cell toxin and diabetogenic agent (see Chapter 17 by Okamoto in this book), is also an inhibitor of glucose-induced insulin secretion (Cooperstein & Watkins, 1981). As this agent inhibits pancreatic B-cell glucokinase (Lenzen *et al.*, 1987*a*, 1988*a,b*), it has been postulated that this represents the mechanism through which alloxan inhibits glucose-induced insulin secretion (Lenzen & Panten, 1988*b*).

Experimental evidence supports this assumption. Alloxan inhibits glucokinase from pancreatic B-cells (Lenzen *et al.*, 1987*a*) and liver (Miwa *et al.*, 1984; Meglasson *et al.*, 1986; Lenzen *et al.*, 1987*a*). The half-maximal inhibitory concentration of alloxan is around 5 µM (Lenzen *et al.*, 1987*a*). The sensitivity of glucokinase to inhibition by alloxan is remarkably selective. Other glycolytic enzymes such as hexokinase, phosphofructokinase, pyruvate kinase or glucose-6-phosphate dehydrogenase are either not affected or they are much less sensitive to inhibition by alloxan (Miwa *et al.*, 1984; Lenzen *et al.*, 1990). Sensitivity of pancreatic B-cell hexokinase to inhibition by alloxan is one hundred times lower than that of the glucokinase (Lenzen *et al.*, 1990).

Hexokinase from insulin-producing tumour cells is thirty times less sensitive to inhibition by alloxan (Lenzen *et al.*, 1990). This provides an explanation for the reduced susceptibility of insulin-producing tumour cells from radiation-induced insulinomas to the toxic effect of alloxan. These tumours have low levels of glucokinase, such that the glucose metabolism primarily depends on high-affinity glucose phosphorylating isoenzymes (Praz *et al.*, 1983; Halban *et al.*, 1983; Lenzen *et al.*, 1987*b*; Vischer *et al.*, 1987; Shimizu *et al.*, 1988*a,b*).

Only D-glucose and D-mannose protect B-cell glucokinase against inhibition by alloxan (Lenzen *et al.*, 1987*a*, 1988*a*). The α-anomers of these two aldohexoses provide significantly greater protection than the β-anomers (Lenzen *et al.*, 1987*a*). L-Glucose, D-fructose, D-galactose and 3-O-methyl-D-glucose do not protect glucokinase against inhibition by alloxan (Lenzen *et al.*, 1987*a*). However, 3-O-methyl-D-glucose can indirectly protect glucokinase in the intact cell through inhibition of alloxan uptake (Lenzen *et al.*, 1987*a*). Thus, in contrast with D-glucose, 3-O-methyl-D-glucose provides protection only through inhibition of alloxan transport and not through interference of alloxan interaction with the enzyme itself (Lenzen *et al.*, 1987*a*). Glucokinase activity is also protected by D-mannoheptulose (Lenzen *et al.*, 1987*a*, 1988*a*), which itself inhibits glucose-induced insulin secretion (Coore & Randle, 1964), D-glucose metabolism (Ashcroft *et al.*, 1970) and glucokinase activity (Meglasson *et al.*, 1983; Lenzen *et al.*, 1987*a*, 1988*a*). This observation indicates that

D-glucose, D-mannose, D-mannoheptulose and alloxan interact with the same site of the glucokinase, i.e. its active site (Lenzen *et al.*, 1987*a*, 1988*a*; Lenzen & Panten, 1988*a,b*). The alternative view, expressed by Meglasson *et al.* (1986), that the sugar-binding site was not the site for interaction of alloxan with the enzyme, is not supported by these data (for review see Lenzen & Panten, 1988*a,b*).

The underlying molecular mechanism of glucokinase inhibition by alloxan is the oxidation of two adjacent SH groups in the sugar-binding site of the enzyme (Lenzen & Panten, 1988*b*; Lenzen *et al.*, 1988*b*). Glucose, through binding to this site protects the SH groups against oxidation by alloxan and thereby guards glucose-induced insulin secretion against inhibition by alloxan (Lenzen & Panten, 1988*b*; Lenzen *et al.*, 1988*a*). Besides alloxan, only uramil inhibited glucokinase (Lenzen *et al.*, 1988*a*). This agent was less potent and a variety of other pyrimidine derivatives and related substances were ineffective (Lenzen *et al.*, 1988*a*). This points to the central importance of the 5-CO group of alloxan for interaction with the SH-groups in the sugar-binding site of glucokinase (Lenzen *et al.*, 1988*a*; Lenzen & Panten, 1988*b*). All of the characteristics of glucokinase inhibition by alloxan and the protective effects of various sugars are consistent with inhibition of insulin secretion by alloxan (Cooperstein & Watkins, 1981). Thus, alloxan has proved to be a valuable tool in the definition of the role of glucokinase as a signal recognition enzyme for initiation of glucose-induced insulin secretion (Lenzen & Panten, 1988*a,b*; Lenzen, 1990).

In addition to its ability to inhibit glucose-induced insulin secretion, alloxan is a selective pancreatic B-cell toxic agent (see Cooperstein & Watkins, 1981 and Chapter 17 by Okamoto in this book). The resulting necrosis of the B-cells is the morphological substrate of the diabetogenic action of alloxan. However, inhibition of glucokinase is not responsible for the cytotoxic action which may be attributed to cytotoxic intermediates generated from alloxan partly as a result of interaction with glucokinase (S. Lenzen, unpublished work). The other well-known diabetogenic agent, streptozotocin, does not inhibit glucokinase (S. Lenzen, unpublished work) and has another mechanism of cytotoxic action. The diabetes syndromes produced by alloxan and streptozotocin are considered in Chapter 16 of this book by Flatt *et al.*

Ninhydrin also inhibits B-cell glucokinase with a half-maximal inhibitory concentration of around 5 μM (Lenzen *et al.*, 1988*a*). The molecular mechanism underlying this inhibition also involves oxidation of two adjacent SH groups in the sugar-binding site of the enzyme (Lenzen *et al.*, 1988*b*). Thus, glucokinase inhibition can be regarded as the primary reason for the ability of ninhydrin to inhibit glucose-induced insulin secretion. However, as glucose is neither able to significantly protect insulin secretion (Cooperstein & Watkins, 1981) nor glucokinase from inhibition by ninhydrin (Lenzen *et al.*, 1988*b*), this agent must have other sites of action in the B-cell. These may concern virtually any adjacent SH groups which owing to different physicochemical properties (S. Lenzen, unpublished work) are accessible for ninhydrin, but not alloxan. A good example are the SH groups in the sugar-binding site of the B-cell hexokinase. This enzyme is inhibited by ninhydrin with a half-maximal inhibitory concentration only three times greater than that for ninhydrin inhibition of glucokinase (Lenzen *et al.*, 1990). Thus, it is not surprising that ninhydrin, in contrast with alloxan, is not selectively toxic for the pancreatic B-cell, but rather systemically toxic, because these interactions can take place with a great number of thiol structures in virtually any cell (S. Lenzen, unpublished work).

It can be concluded therefore that all agents which inhibit glucose-induced insulin secretion via inhibition of glucokinase achieve this effect through interference with the inhibition of the signal-generating fuel metabolism of glucose in the pancreatic B-cell. The molecular mechanism underlying glucokinase inhibition by sugars and agents such as alloxan is not identical.

Regulation of glucokinase gene expression

Comparison of the rat liver, islet, and insulinoma glucokinase cDNAs indicates that different glucokinase isoforms are generated through alternate splicing of the glucokinase gene product (Magnuson, 1990). These glucokinase isoforms are specific for liver (Andreone *et al.*, 1989; Magnuson *et al.*, 1989), pancreatic B-cells (Magnuson & Shelton, 1989; Milburn *et al.*, 1989), and insulinoma cells (Magnuson & Shelton, 1989). The glucokinase isoform generated in the liver apparently differs from the isoforms in pancreatic B-cells and insulinomas by sequences in the *N*-terminal (Magnuson & Shelton, 1989). This difference accounts for no more than 15 amino acids and has a negligible effect on the molecular mass. The exact sequence of the *N*-terminus is still unknown (Magnuson, 1990). In liver and pancreatic B-cells, the glucokinase gene uses different first exons. Thus different transcription initiation sites, promotors and regulatory elements are functional. Different transcription units give rise to different tissue-specific glucokinase mRNAs (Iynedjian *et al.*, 1989; Magnuson & Shelton, 1989) and to tissue-specific glucokinase isoforms (Andreone *et al.*, 1989; Magnuson & Shelton, 1989). The glucokinase isoform in insulinoma cells is generated by the use of an alternate splice acceptor site in the fourth exon of the gene. Deletion of 51 nucleotides from the mRNA results in a glucokinase isoform in these insulinoma cells where 17 amino acids in a region of the protein situated between the putative ATP- and glucose-binding domains are missing (Magnuson & Shelton, 1989). At present, it is not known whether these differences are

functionally significant. It is unlikely that a few different amino acids at the
N-terminus have dramatic effects (Magnuson, 1990). This assumption is
supported by the fact that the glucokinase isoforms in pancreatic B-cells
and in liver have enzymic properties which are completely identical
(Lenzen & Panten, 1988a,b; Lenzen, 1990). Deletion of 17 amino acids in
the region of the insulinoma glucokinase isoform between the putative
ATP- and glucose-binding domains is more likely to have some effect
(Magnuson, 1990). The enzymic properties of the insulinoma glucokinase
isoform have not been studied in detail. However, the difference between
the pancreatic B-cell and insulinoma isoform may be of relevance for a
possible regulatory effect of insulin or glucose on glucokinase enzyme
activity. At present it is not clear whether expression of the B-cell and
insulinoma glucokinase isoform is restricted or if the two isoforms may be
present with a different ratio in the two types of insulin-producing cells
(Magnuson & Shelton, 1989; Milburn et al., 1989; Magnuson, 1990).

  The different transcription control regions allow the gene to be
regulated differently (Granner & Pilkis 1990; Magnuson, 1990). Different
promotors in the glucokinase gene provide a genetic basis for possible
differential regulation of this enzyme in liver and pancreatic B-cells.
Glucokinase synthesis in B-cells could be affected both by a transcriptional
mechanism involving the upstream glucokinase transcription control
region or by a translational mechanism involving the different 5'-non-
coding mRNA sequences (Magnuson, 1990). The existence of different
transcription control regions in a gene is not without precedent
(Magnuson, 1990), but different transcription control regions do not
necessarily imply a different regulation of gene translation product in vivo.
In addition to the generation of glucokinase isoforms with different N-
terminals, the use of alternate first exons in the glucokinase gene results in
different 5'-non-coding sequences in the mRNAs. The B-cell and
insulinoma glucokinase mRNA 5'-non-coding sequence is around 400
nucleotides long and thus is about 200 nucleotides longer than that of liver
glucokinase mRNA (Magnuson & Shelton, 1989; Magnuson, 1990).
These differences in the sequences preceding the reading frame for the
enzyme may affect the translational efficiency of the different glucokinase
mRNA templates. A less efficient translation of pancreatic B-cell
glucokinase mRNA, or in particular of insulinoma glucokinase mRNA,
than of liver glucokinase mRNA may result.

Long-term regulation of glucokinase activity

Two factors determine the activity of glucokinase. These are the
concentration of glucose (see above) and the activity of the enzyme. The
activity state of glucokinase in pancreatic B-cells (Meglasson &
Matschinsky, 1984; Lenzen & Panten, 1988a) as in liver (Sharma et al.,

1964; Walker, 1966; Pilkis, 1970; Niemeyer *et al.*, 1976; Weinhouse, 1976; Lenzen & Panten, 1988*a*), is modulated by prior dietary history and hormonal status. As the long-term regulation of insulin secretion is also under dietary and hormonal control, it is reasonable to assume that changes in glucokinase activity may be of importance for long-term regulation of insulin secretion (Lenzen & Panten, 1988*a*). This would provide the pancreatic B-cell with a mechanism for adaptation of its secretory function to the varying nutritional and metabolic demands.

Fasting decreases glucokinase activity in a time-dependent manner in pancreatic B-cells, whereas re-feeding induces the enzyme (Malaisse *et al.*, 1976*a*; Burch *et al.*, 1981; Bedoya *et al.*, 1986; Lenzen *et al.*, 1986, 1987*b*). The situation in the liver is identical (Lenzen & Panten, 1988*a*). Reduction of glucokinase activity during starvation is more pronounced than the decrease of hexokinase activity (Malaisse *et al.*, 1976*a*; Bedoya *et al.*, 1986; Lenzen *et al.*, 1986, 1987*b*). However, during starvation, deterioration of insulin secretion can become evident somewhat earlier than the reduction of glucokinase activity (Lenzen & Panten, 1988*a*). Thus, although control of the flux rate through glycolysis is achieved at the glucose phosphorylation step by glucokinase—the first non-equilibrium step of this pathway—adjacent regulatory steps further down in the glycolytic chain can contribute to the regulatory control of the flux rate through this pathway (Lenzen & Panten, 1988*a*). Modulation at such secondary control points (Lenzen & Panten, 1988*a*) may reduce the signal-generating flux rate and thus contribute to the regulation of glucose-induced insulin secretion during starvation.

Long-term hyperglycaemia may also affect the regulation of glycolytic flux rate at sites other than the initial glucose phosphorylation. Normally the amount of glucose 6-phosphate dephosphorylated by pancreatic B-cells is negligible and glucose-6-phosphate dehydrogenase does not apparently contribute significantly to flux rate regulation (Ashcroft *et al.*, 1970). However, when islets have been exposed for a long period to high glucose concentrations *in vivo*, the rate of glucose cycling in pancreatic B-cells can increase through an increased rate of glucose-6-phosphate dephosphorylation (see Khan *et al.*, 1990 and Chapter 5 by Malaisse in this book). This may represent a safety device to avoid over-production of ATP and hence over-stimulation of the insulin secretory apparatus of the pancreatic B-cell.

At present, however, the central question is whether induction of glucokinase during re-feeding in pancreatic B-cells like in the liver is primarily brought about by endogenous insulin (Lenzen *et al.*, 1986, 1987*b*) or by glucose (Bedoya *et al.*, 1986; Liang *et al.*, 1990). Insulin treatment can prevent the starvation-induced fall of glucokinase activity in islets (Lenzen *et al.*, 1987*a*) and in liver (Sharma *et al.*, 1964; Pilkis, 1970; Niemeyer *et al.*, 1976; Weinhouse, 1976; Lenzen *et al.*, 1987*b*). This occurs despite the fact that blood glucose levels are lowered during the period of insulin treatment (Lenzen *et al.*, 1987*a*). Glibenclamide, a sulphonylurea drug which lowers blood glucose, can, like insulin, prevent the starvation-induced fall of glucokinase activity in both pancreatic islets and liver (Lenzen *et al.*, 1986). Glibenclamide increases circulating insulin levels through stimulation of secretion and decreases blood glucose concentrations (Lenzen *et al.*, 1986). Treatment of fed rats with glucocorticoids or thyroid hormones did not significantly affect glucokinase activities in B-cells or liver (Lenzen & Panten, 1988*a*). Starvation, re-feeding, insulin and glibenclamide treatment can also affect other cellular functions, such as protein synthesis, and enzyme activities are usually expressed per milligram of islet protein (Lenzen & Panten, 1988*a*). However, the observation that insulin, as well as glibenclamide, have no concomitant effects on hexokinase activities in pancreatic islets and liver (Lenzen *et al.*, 1986; 1987*b*) indicates that their effects on glucokinase are not secondary to other changes.

Thus, it is evident that the starvation-induced decrease and the re-feeding-induced restoration of glucokinase activity correlates in all situations with corresponding changes of circulating insulin, but not with changes in blood glucose concentration. Induction of glucokinase by insulin in pancreatic islets (Lenzen *et al.*, 1986; 1987*b*) and liver (Sharma *et al.*, 1964; Pilkis, 1970; Niemeyer *et al.*, 1976; Weinhouse, 1976; Lenzen *et al.*, 1987*b*) could be mediated through the insulin receptor. Thus, the slower decrease of glucokinase activity during starvation in pancreatic islets (Lenzen *et al.*, 1986; 1987*b*), might reflect the fact that the islet cell membrane is exposed to higher insulin concentrations *in vivo* than the liver cell membrane. However, even if insulin is the primary determinant, glucose may play a facilitative role in the induction of glucokinase in B-cells as well as in liver (Pilkis, 1970). On the basis of studies with insulinoma-bearing rats Bedoya *et al.* (1986) assigned glucose the primary role in the regulation of glucokinase in pancreatic islets, but not in liver which was dependent on insulin. However, Bedoya *et al.* (1986) used an experimental design which cannot exclude the possibility that increased plasma glucose concentrations released sufficient endogenous insulin from the B-cells to raise their glucokinase activity. The concentrations of insulin necessary to induce glucokinase in islets and liver are far lower than those required for inhibition of insulin secretion from pancreatic islets by insulin (Verspohl *et al.*, 1982).

Insulinoma cells have lost their sensitivity to glucokinase modulation by dietary or hormonal factors. The substantial loss of glucokinase activity in the poorly differentiated radiation-induced rat insulinomas (Lenzen *et al.*, 1987*b*), which do not respond to glucose with insulin secretion, shows that the glucokinase in these tumour cells is insensitive to physiological changes in circulating glucose and insulin concentrations. The same phenomenon has been observed in poorly differentiated hepatocarcinomas (Sato *et al.*, 1969; Shatton *et al.*, 1969). However, in addition, the glucokinase of the Kirkman tumour, a transplantable hamster insulinoma which contains much more glucokinase than transplantable rat insulinomas, was found not to be dependent on plasma glucose or plasma insulin concentrations (Shimizu & Matschinsky, 1988).

Whether this long-term regulation of pancreatic B-cell glucokinase is achieved on a transcriptional or translational level is essentially unsettled at present. In the liver, it is well established that glucokinase mRNA levels are reduced by starvation and increased by re-feeding or insulin treatment (Iynedjian *et al.*, 1987, 1989; Magnuson & Shelton, 1989; Granner & Pilkis, 1990). With respect to regulation of B-cell glucokinase mRNA, only one study has addressed this topic so far (Iynedjian *et al.*, 1989). These authors, at variance to the situation in the liver, observed no changes of mRNA levels when animals were fasted or re-fed (Iynedjian *et al.*, 1989). Results of more recent experiments show that pancreatic B-cell glucokinase mRNA concentrations, like liver mRNA concentrations, are dependent on the nutritional status of the animal (Tiedge & Lenzen, 1991).

Other mechanisms for initiation of insulin secretion via pancreatic B-cell metabolism

Changes of circulating glucose provide the physiological signal for initiation of insulin secretion. Insulin-secreting tumour cells have lost this responsiveness in parallel with the loss of glucokinase activity (see above). However, tumour cells from poorly differentiated rat insulinomas have high hexokinase activities required to fulfil the high energy demands of fast-growing tumour cells (Lenzen *et al.*, 1987*b*). As these insulinoma cells show high rates of basal insulin release in the presence of low glucose concentrations (Giroix *et al.*, 1985), glucose phosphorylation through hexokinase apparently causes an increased signal-generating metabolic flux rate. This is an alternative, albeit unphysiological, mechanism for increased ATP generation as the prerequisite for initiation of fuel-induced insulin secretion.

In addition to the hexoses glucose and mannose, the triose glyceraldehyde is a potent insulin secretagogue (Hedeskov, 1980; Ashcroft, 1981). Glyceraldehyde also enters the glycolytic chain through initial phosphorylation, albeit at a lower point. Triokinase is the enzyme which can phosphorylate glyceraldehyde and thus feed glyceraldehyde into B-cell metabolism via glycolysis at the triose phosphate level, finally resulting in increased ATP formation. Triokinase has a high affinity for glyceraldehyde as is evident from its K_m value in the micromolar range. Its activity in pancreatic B-cells is apparently considerably lower than the glucose phosphorylating enzyme capacity of the B-cell (MacDonald, 1989).

However, another enzyme present in the pancreatic B-cell, glyceraldehyde phosphate dehydrogenase, can phosphorylate glyceraldehyde (MacDonald, 1989). The K_m of this enzyme with respect to glyceraldehyde is around 5 mM, which is within the range of the half-maximal effective concentration of glyceraldehyde for initiation of insulin secretion (Hedeskov, 1980; Ashcroft, 1981). This reaction leads to an increase of reduced pyridine nucleotides and finally an increase of ATP formation by feeding H^+ ions from reduced pyridine nucleotides through shuttle mechanisms into the respiratory chain. An insulin secretory response, as well as the closure of ATP-sensitive potassium channels, in response to glyceraldehyde, is also evident in insulin-secreting tumour cells (Ashcroft, 1988) indicating that the signal recognition mechanism for glyceraldehyde is not disturbed in these cells.

Several insulin secretagogues with an exclusively intramitochondrial metabolic fate, e.g. the amino acid leucine and the keto acid 2-ketoisocaproic acid, bypass an ATP-consuming, and possibly rate-limiting, flux through the glycolytic chain and directly enhance the mitochondrial fuel supply. Various enzymes with K_m values in the micromolar and millimolar range feed the different amino and keto acids into intramitochondrial metabolism (Lenzen et al., 1985b), thereby providing the basis for initiation and maintenance of insulin secretion by these fuel secretagogues.

Thus, enzymes in addition to glucokinase can function as signal recognition enzymes for initiation of insulin secretion by other fuel secretagogues.

Experimental evidence supporting an association between initial glucose phosphorylation by glucokinase and regulation of the rate of insulin secretion

If the concept of glucokinase as the signal recognition enzyme for initiation of glucose-induced insulin secretion is valid, it should be possible to demonstrate a close correlation between ATP-generating and ATP-consuming situations on the one hand and a concomitant increase or decrease of the rate of insulin secretion on the other. This is in fact possible in a variety of experimental situations.

Increase of insulin secretion
An increase in the rate of glucose-induced insulin secretion is evident when the rate of ATP generation is increased through feeding of metabolic intermediates from the glycolytic degradation of glucose into the citric acid cycle and respiratory chain. This can be shown under the following situations.

**Table 1.   Effect of various substances in the pre-
            perfusion medium on the delay (latent period
            in seconds) between exposure to glucose
            (16.7 mM) or other insulin secretagogues and the
            appearance of the peak of the insulin secretory
            response of the perfused rat pancreas**

Pre-perfusion medium	Concn. (mM)	Perfusion medium	Concn. (mM)	Latent period (s)
Glucose	0	Glucose	16.7	100
Glucose	0	Mannose	16.7	130
Glucose	0	Glyceraldehyde	10	70
Glucose	0	2-Ketoisocaproic acid	10	70
Glucose	0	Tolbutamide	0.8	10
Glucose	0	Glucose	16.7	100
Glucose	5.5	Glucose	16.7	30
Glucose	8.3	Glucose	16.7	10
Glucose + mannoheptulose (1 mM)	5.5	Glucose	16.7	80
Glucose	0	Glyceraldehyde	10	70
Glucose	5.5	Glyceraldehyde	10	20
Glucose	0	Tolbutamide	0.8	10
Glucose	5.5	Tolbutamide	0.8	10
Glucose	8.3	Tolbutamide	0.8	0
Mannose	16.7	Glucose	16.7	15
Glyceraldehyde	10.0	Glucose	16.7	45
Leucine	20.0	Glucose	16.7	40
Tolbutamide	0.6	Glucose	16.7	130
3-O-Methylglucose	16.7	Glucose	16.7	100

Data are adapted from Lenzen (1978).

1. The increase in the rate of glucose-induced insulin secretion is virtually immediate and without delay (Table 1) when the glucose concentration is increased from a high sub-stimulatory to a stimulatory concentration (i.e. 8.3 mM to 16.7 mM) (Lenzen, 1978) (Fig. 2).

2. The increase in the rate of insulin secretion is evident with a delay of around 100 s (Table 1) when the glucose concentration is increased from zero to a stimulatory concentration (i.e. 16.7 mM) (Fig. 2) (Bennett *et al.*, 1973; Lenzen, 1975, 1978; Vague *et al.*, 1975).

3. This delay decreases with increasing glucose concentrations in the pre-perfusion medium (Table 1) (Matschinsky *et al.*, 1971; Lenzen, 1978).

4. Mannoheptulose suppresses the ability of glucose in the pre-

stimulatory extracellular medium to decrease this delay (Table 1) (Lenzen, 1978).

5. Sub-stimulatory concentrations of mannose, glyceraldehyde, or leucine can replace glucose as a source of metabolic energy and thus can

Fig. 2. **Reduction of the delay (latent period in seconds) between the arrival of a stimulatory glucose concentration at pancreatic B-cells and the appearance of the peak of the insulin secretory response of the perfused rat pancreas after pre-perfusion with a sub-stimulatory glucose concentration**

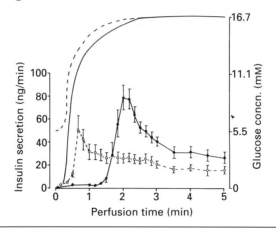

The stimulatory glucose concentration was 16.7 mM (upper curves); the sub-stimulatory glucose concentration was 5.5 mM (O---O), compared with controls in the absence of glucose (●---●). Mean ± s.e.m. Taken from Lenzen (1978) with permission.

also decrease the delay before appearance of an insulin secretory response to glucose stimulation (i.e. 16.7 mM) (Table 1) (Lenzen, 1978).

6. This delay increases on the other hand to 130 s (Table 1) when tolbutamide is present in the pre-stimulatory extracellular medium (Lenzen, 1978). This relates to the fact that sulphonylurea drugs are not fuels, but rather induce energy-consuming activities, such as the release of insulin, thereby decreasing intracellular ATP levels (Panten et al., 1986).

7. The immediate insulin secretory response to glyceraldehyde or 2-ketoisocaproic acid appears after a shorter delay than the response to glucose (Vague et al., 1975; Lenzen, 1978), because these secretagogues increase intracellular ATP levels faster than glucose.

8. In contrast to glucose, tolbutamide induces insulin secretion

with a delay of only 10 s (Table 1) (Lenzen, 1978). This is because sulphonylurea drugs induce insulin secretion via interaction with an ATP-sensitive potassium channel in the B-cell membrane (see Ashcroft, 1988 and Chapter 15 by Nelson *et al.* in this book). These drugs have direct

Fig. 3.   The peak insulin secretory response of the perfused rat pancreas to simultaneous stimulation by tolbutamide and glucose

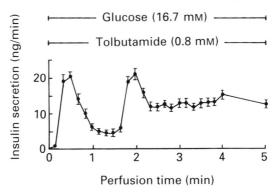

The first peak is due to tolbutamide (0.8 mM), the second peak is due to glucose (16.7 mM) stimulation. Mean ± s.e.m. Taken from Lenzen (1978) with permission.

access to this channel from the extracellular space and thereby bypass the various steps required for glucose to affect this channel by ATP generation.

9. However, even this short delay in the initiation of insulin secretion by tolbutamide disappears when a sub-stimulatory glucose concentration is present in the pre-perfusion medium (Table 1) (Lenzen, 1978). This is because glucose has filled up intracellular ATP stores before exposure to the sulphonylurea drug.

10. Even when tolbutamide and glucose are administered together in stimulatory concentrations, the secretory response to tolbutamide appears around 90 s earlier than the secretory response to glucose (Fig. 3) (Lenzen, 1975, 1978). However, a combination of tolbutamide and glucose does not release more insulin than glucose alone because both secretagogues compete for the same rapidly available hormone pool (Lenzen, 1978).

Decrease of insulin secretion
A transient decrease of the rate of insulin secretion is evident when ATP is consumed for the initial extra mitochondrial phosphorylation of the fuel secretagogue.

1. This occurs when the fuel secretagogue is glucose or glyceraldehyde (Panten *et al.*, 1988). The phenomenon is particularly easy to demonstrate when endogenous ATP stores have been lowered by prior exposure to a sulphonylurea drug such as glibenclamide (Panten *et al.*,

Fig. 4. **Effect of glucose on insulin secretion by isolated mouse pancreatic islets**

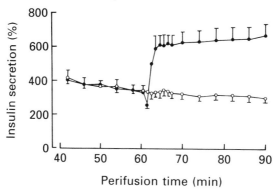

All media contained glibenclamide (0.1 μM) throughout the experiments and, in addition, glucose (10 mM) during the pre-perifusion period from time zero to 60 min. From 60 min to 92 min, perifusion media contained glucose (10 mM) (O----O) or glucose (40 mM) (●----●). Taken from Panten et al. (1988) with permission.

1988) (Fig. 4). The transient decrease in the rate of insulin secretion is accompanied by an opening of ATP-sensitive potassium channels with a resultant transient repolarization of the B-cell membrane and a concomitant decrease in the cytoplasmic ATP and free Ca^{2+} concentration (Arkhammar *et al.*, 1987; Corkey *et al.*, 1988).

2. This is not the case when a fuel insulin secretagogue has an exclusively intra mitochondrial metabolic fate such as 2-ketoisocaproic acid, which immediately raises the intramitochondrial fuel supply without an initial energy-consuming step (Panten *et al.*, 1988).

Inhibition of insulin secretion

Inhibition of glucose-induced insulin secretion is evident when glucose phosphorylation by glucokinase is inhibited.

1. The most prominent selective inhibitors of glucokinase are mannoheptulose and alloxan (see above). Inhibition of insulin secretion is not evident if the secretagogue is not dependent on glucokinase to enter signal-generating intermediary metabolism (i.e. as for glyceraldehyde,

leucine or 2-ketoisocaproic acid) or if the effects are independent of changes in intermediary metabolism (i.e. as for sulphonylurea drugs which interact with ATP-sensitive potassium channels) (Panten, 1987; Ashcroft, 1988).

Thus, to a very limited extent, both glycolytic ATP utilization and generation contribute to the regulation of the glucose-induced insulin secretory rate. The major source of ATP, however, is, of course, the citric acid cycle and respiratory chain.

Conclusions

The function of the glucokinase in the pancreatic B-cell is that of the so-called signal recognition enzyme for the initiation of glucose-induced insulin secretion. This couples changes in the millimolar glucose concentration in the extracellular space to corresponding changes in the signal-generating metabolic flux rate through glycolysis, the citric acid cycle and the respiratory chain for initiation of insulin biosynthesis and secretion. This concept is supported by far-reaching correlations between the characteristics of glucose-induced insulin secretion and those of the pancreatic B-cell glucokinase. It also explains the mechanisms underlying certain well-known distinct insulin secretory patterns.

The author's research cited in this chapter was supported by the Deutsche Forschungsgemeinschaft.

References

Anderson, C. M., Stenkamp, R. E. & Steitz, T. A. (1978) Sequencing a protein by X-ray crystallography. II. Refinement of yeast hexokinase B co-ordinates and sequence at 2.1 Å resolution. J. Mol. Biol. **123**, 15–33

Andreone, T. L., Printz, R. L., Pilkis, S. J., Magnuson, M. A. & Granner, D. K. (1989) The amino acid sequence of rat liver glucokinase deduced from cloned cDNA. J. Biol. Chem. **264**, 363–369

Arkhammar, P., Nilsson, T., Rorsman, P. & Berggren, P.-O. (1987) Inhibition of ATP-regulated K^+ channels precedes depolarization-induced increase in cytoplasmic free Ca^{2+} concentration in pancreatic beta-cells. J. Biol. Chem. **262**, 5448–5454

Ashcroft, F. M. (1988) Adenosine 5'-triphosphate-sensitive potassium channels. Annu. Rev. Neurosci. **11**, 97–118

Ashcroft, S. J. H. (1981) Metabolic controls of insulin secretion. In The Islet of Langerhans (Cooperstein, S. J. & Watkins, D., eds.), pp. 117–148, Academic Press, New York

Ashcroft, S. J. H., Hedeskov, C. J. & Randle, P. J. (1970) Glucose metabolism in mouse pancreatic islets. Biochem. J. **118**, 143–154

Bechem, M., Hebisch, S. & Schramm, M. (1988) Ca^{2+} antagonists: New sensitive probes for Ca^{2+} channels. Trends Pharmacol. Sci. **9**, 257–261

Bedoya, F. J., Matschinsky, F. M., Shimizu, T., O'Neil, J. J. & Appel, M. C. (1986) Differential regulation of glucokinase activity in pancreatic islets and liver of the rat. J. Biol. Chem. **261**, 10760–10764

Bell, G. I., Kayano, T., Buse, J. B., Burant, C. F., Takeda, J., Lin, D., Fukumoto, H. & Seino, S. (1990) Molecular biology of mammalian glucose transporters. Diabetes Care **13**, 198–208

Bennett, L. L., Curry, D. L. & Curry, K. (1973) Differences in insulin release in response to glucose and tolbutamide stimulation. Proc. Soc. Exp. Biol. Med. **144**, 436–439

Burch, P. T., Trus, M. D., Berner, D. K., Leontoire, A., Zawalich, K. C. & Matschinsky, F. M. (1981) Adaption of glycolytic enzymes. Glucose use and insulin release in rat pancreatic islets during fasting and refeeding. Diabetes **30**, 923–928

Chick, W. L., Waren, S., Chute, R. N., Like, A. A., Lauris, V. & Kitchen, K. C. (1977) A transplantable insulinoma in the rat. Proc. Natl. Acad. Sci. U.S.A. **74**, 628–632

Cooperstein, S. J. & Watkins, D. (1981) Action of toxic drugs on islet cells. In The Islet of Langerhans (Cooperstein, S. J. & Watkins, D., eds.), pp. 387–425, Academic Press, New York

Coore, H. G. & Randle, P. J. (1964) Regulation of insulin secretion studied with pieces of rabbit pancreas incubated *in vitro*. Biochem. J. **93**, 66–78

Corkey, B. E., Deeney, J. T., Glennon, M. C., Matschinsky, F. M. & Prentki, M. (1988) Regulation of steady-state free Ca^{2+} levels by the ATP/ADP ratio and orthophosphate in permeabilized RINm5F insulinoma cells. J. Biol. Chem. **263**, 4247–4253

Flatt, P. R., Bailey, C. J., Gray, C. & Swanston-Flatt, S. K. (1986) Metabolic effects of radiation-induced rat insulinoma at pancreatic, hepatic and subscapular transplantation sites. Comp. Biochem. Physiol. **85A**, 183–186

Flatt, P. R., DeSilva, M. G., Swanston-Flatt, S. K., Powell, C. J. & Marks, V. (1987a) Tumour formation and insulin secretion by clonal RINm5F cells following repeated subcutaneous transplantation in NEDH rats. J. Endocrinol. **118**, 429–437

Flatt, P. R., DeSilva, M., Swanston-Flatt, S. K. & Marks, V. (1987b) Insulin secretion in vivo and in vitro from transplantable NEDH rat insulinoma and derived clonal RINm5F cell line. Diabetes Res. **6**, 85–90

Giroix, M. H., Sener, A., Dufrane, S. P., Malaisse-Lagae, F. & Malaisse, W. J. (1985) Glucose metabolism in insulin-producing tumoral cells. Arch. Biochem. Biophys. **241**, 561–570

Granner, D. & Pilkis, S. (1990) The genes of hepatic glucose metabolism. J. Biol. Chem. **265**, 10173–10176

Grodsky, G. M., Batts, A. A., Bennett, L. L., Vcella, C., McWilliams, N. B. & Smith, D. F. (1963) Effects of carbohydrates on secretion of insulin from isolated rat pancreas. Am. J. Physiol. **205**, 638–644

Halban, P. A., Praz, G. A. & Wollheim, C. B. (1983) Abnormal glucose metabolism accompanies failure of glucose to stimulate insulin release from a rat pancreatic cell line (RINm5F). Biochem. J. **212**, 439–443

Hedeskov, C. J. (1980) Mechanism of glucose-induced insulin secretion. Physiol. Rev. **60**, 442–509

Henquin, J. C. & Meissner, H. P. (1984) Significance of ionic fluxes and changes in membrane potential for stimulus–secretion coupling in pancreatic B-cells. Experientia **40**, 1043–1052

Iynedjian, P. B., Möbius, G., Seitz, H. J., Wollheim, C. B. & Renold, A. E. (1986) Tissue-specific expression of glucokinase: identification of the gene-product in liver and pancreatic islets. Proc. Natl. Acad. Sci. U.S.A. **83**, 1998–2001

Iynedjian, P. B., Ucla, C. & Mach, B. (1987) Molecular cloning of glucokinase cDNA. Developmental and dietary regulation of glucokinase mRNA in rat liver. J. Biol. Chem. **262**, 6032–6038

Iynedjian, P. B., Pilot, P. R., Nouspikel, T., Milburn, J. L., Quaade, C., Hughes, S., Ucla, C. & Newgard, C. B. (1989) Differential expression and regulation of the glucokinase gene in liver and islets of Langerhans. Proc. Natl. Acad. Sci. U.S.A. **86**, 7838–7842

Johnson, J. H., Newgard, C. B., Milburn, J. L., Lodish, H. F. & Thorens, B. (1990) The high K_m glucose transporter of islets of Langerhans is functionally similar to the low affinity transporter of liver and has an identical primary sequence. J. Biol. Chem. **265**, 6548–6551

Khan, A., Chandramouli, V., Östenson, C.-G., Berggren, P.-O., Löw, H., Landau, B. R. & Efendic, S. (1990) Glucose cycling is markedly enhanced in pancreatic islets of obese hyperglycemic mice. Endocrinology **126**, 2413–2416

Lawrence, G. M. & Trayer, I. P. (1984) Hexokinase isoenzymes: antigenic cross reactivities and amino acid compositional relatedness. Comp. Biochem. Physiol. **79B**, 233–238

Lenzen, S. (1975) The immediate insulin secretory response of the isolated perfused rat pancreas to tolbutamide and glucose. FEBS Lett. **49**, 407–408

Lenzen, S. (1978) The immediate insulin-secretory response of the rat pancreas to glucose compared with tolbutamide and other secretagogues. Diabetes **27**, 27–34

Lenzen, S. (1990) Hexose recognition mechanisms in pancreatic B-cells. Biochem. Soc. Trans. **18**, 105–107

Lenzen, S. & Munday, R. (1991) Thiol-group reactivity, lipophilicity and stability of alloxan, its reduction products and its N-methyl derivatives and a comparison with ninhydrin. Biochem. Pharmacol. **42**, 1385–1391

Lenzen, S. & Panten, U. (1988*a*) Signal recognition by pancreatic B-cells. Biochem. Pharmacol. **37**, 371–378

Lenzen, S. & Panten, U. (1988*b*) Alloxan: history and mechanism of action. Diabetologia **31**, 337–342

Lenzen, S., Klöppel, G., Zielmann, S. & Panten, U. (1985*a*) Secretory, enzymatic and morphological characterization of rat pancreatic endocrine tumours induced by streptozotocin and nictotinamide. Acta Endocrinol. **109**, 361–368

Lenzen, S., Schmidt, W. & Panten, U. (1985*b*) Transamination of neutral amino acids and 2-keto acids in pancreatic B-cell mitochondria. J. Biol. Chem. **260**, 12629–12634

Lenzen, S., Tiedge, M. & Panten, U. (1986) Glibenclamide induces glucokinase in rat pancreatic islets and liver. Biochem. Pharmacol. **35**, 2841–2843

Lenzen, S., Tiedge, M. & Panten, U. (1987*a*) Glucokinase in pancreatic B-cells and its inhibition by alloxan. Acta Endocrinol. **115**, 21–29

Lenzen, S., Tiedge, M., Flatt, P. R., Bailey, C. J. & Panten, U. (1987*b*) Defective regulation of glucokinase in rat pancreatic islet cell tumours. Acta Endocrinol. **115**, 514–520

Lenzen, S., Brand, F. H. & Panten, U. (1988*a*) Structural requirements of alloxan and ninhydrin for glucokinase inhibition and of glucose for protection against inhibition. Br. J. Pharmacol. **95**, 851–859

Lenzen, S., Freytag, S. & Panten, U. (1988*b*) Inhibition of glucokinase by alloxan through interaction with SH groups in the sugar-binding site of the enzyme. Mol. Pharmacol. **34**, 395–400

Lenzen, S., Freytag, S., Panten, U., Flatt, P. R. & Bailey, C. J. (1990) Alloxan and ninhydrin inhibition of hexokinase from pancreatic islets and tumoural insulin-secreting cells. Pharmacol. Toxicol. **66**, 157–162

Liang, Y., Najafi, H. & Matschinsky, F. M. (1990) Glucose regulates glucokinase activity in cultured islets from rat pancreas. J. Biol. Chem. **265**, 16853–16866

MacDonald, M. J. (1989) Does glyceraldehyde enter pancreatic islet metabolism via both the triokinase and the glyceraldehyde phosphate dehydrogenase reactions? A study of these enzymes in islets. Arch. Biochem. Biophys. **270**, 15–22

Magnuson, M. A. (1990) Glucokinase gene structure. Functional implications of molecular genetic studies. Diabetes **39**, 523–527

Magnuson, M. A. & Shelton, K. D. (1989) An alternate promoter in the glucokinase gene is active in the pancreatic beta cell. J. Biol. Chem. **264**, 15936–15942

Magnuson, M. A., Andreone, T. L., Printz, R. L., Koch, S. & Granner, D. K. (1989) Rat glucokinase gene: structure and regulation by insulin. Proc. Natl. Acad. Sci. U.S.A. **86**, 4838–4842

Malaisse, W. J. & Sener, A. (1985) Glucokinase is not the pancreatic B-cell glucoreceptor. Diabetologia **28**, 520–527

Malaisse, W. J., Sener, A. & Levy, J. (1976*a*) The stimulus–secretion coupling of glucose-induced insulin release. Fasting-induced adaptation of key glycolytic enzymes in isolated islets. J. Biol. Chem. **251**, 1731–1737

Malaisse, W. J., Sener, A., Levy, J. & Herchuelz, A. (1976*b*) The stimulus–secretion coupling of glucose-induced insulin release. XXII. Qualitative and quantitative aspects of glycolysis in isolated islets. Acta Diabetol. Lat. **13**, 202–215

Malaisse, W. J., Malaisse-Lagae, F. & Sener, A. (1983) Anomeric specificity of hexose metabolism in pancreatic islets. Physiol. Rev. **63**, 773–786

Malaisse, W. J., Malaisse-Lagae, F., Rasschaert, J., Zähner, D., Sener, A., Davies, D. R. & Van Schaftingen, E. (1990) The fuel concept for insulin release: regulation of glucose phosphorylation in pancreatic islets. Biochem. Soc. Trans. **18**, 107–108

Matschinsky, F. M. & Ellerman, J. E. (1968) Metabolism of glucose in the islets of Langerhans. J. Biol. Chem. **243**, 2730–2736

Matschinsky, F. M., Landgraf, R., Ellerman, J. E. & Kotler-Brajtburg, J. (1971) Effects of glucose on insulin release and the metabolite pattern of islets of Langerhans of the perfused rat pancreas. Diabetes **20**, 327–328

Meglasson, M. D. & Matschinsky, F. M. (1984) New perspectives on pancreatic islet glucokinase. Am. J. Physiol. **246**, E1–E13

Meglasson, M. D., Burch, P. T., Berner, D. K., Najafi, H., Vogin, A. P. & Matschinsky, F. M. (1983) Chromatographic resolution and kinetic characterization of glucokinase from islets of Langerhans. Proc. Natl. Acad. Sci. U.S.A. **80**, 85–89

Meglasson, M. D., Burch, P. T., Berner, D. K., Najafi, H. & Matschinsky, F. M. (1986) Identification of glucokinase as an alloxan-sensitive glucose sensor of the pancreatic beta-cell. Diabetes **35**, 1163–1173

Milburn, J. L., Quaade, C., Iynedjian, P., Alam, T. & Newgard, C. B. (1989) Expression of a unique islet glucokinase mRNA in islets, islet cell tumors, and rat insulinoma cell lines. Diabetes **38**, 6A

Miwa, I., Inagaki, K. & Okuda, J. (1983) Preference of glucokinase for the alpha anomer of hexose: relation to alpha anomer preference in hexose-induced insulin release by pancreatic islets. Biochem. Int. **7**, 449–454

Miwa, I., Hara, H., Matsunaga, H. & Okuda, J. (1984) Inhibition of glucokinase in hepatocytes by alloxan. Biochem. Int. **9**, 595–602

Mueckler, M. (1990) Family of glucose-transporter genes. Implications for glucose homeostasis and diabetes. Diabetes **39**, 6–11

Niemeyer, H., Ureta, T. & Clark-Tarri, L. (1976) Adaptive character of liver glucokinase. Mol. Cell. Biochem. **6**, 109–126

Nishi, S., Susumu, S. & Bell, G. I. (1988) Human hexokinase sequences of amino- and carboxyl-terminal halves are homologous. Biochem. Biophys. Res. Commun. **157**, 937–943

Panten, U. (1987) Rapid control of insulin secretion from pancreatic islets. ISI Atlas Sci. **1**, 307–310

Panten, U. & Lenzen, S. (1988) Alterations in energy metabolism of secretory cells. In Energetics of Secretion Responses (Akkerman, J.-W., ed.), vol. 2, pp. 109–123, CRC Press, Boca Raton, FL

Panten, U., Zünkler, B. J., Scheit, S., Kirchhoff, K. & Lenzen, S. (1986) Regulation of energy metabolism in pancreatic islets by glucose and tolbutamide. Diabetologia **29**, 648–654

Panten, U., Schwanstecher, M., Wallasch, A. & Lenzen, S. (1988) Glucose both inhibits and stimulates insulin secretion from isolated pancreatic islets exposed to maximally effective concentrations of sulfonylureas. Naunyn-Schmiedeberg's Arch. Pharmacol. **338**, 459–462

Permutt, M. A. (1981) Biosynthesis of insulin. In The Islet of Langerhans (Cooperstein, S. J. & Watkins, D., eds.), pp. 75–95, Academic Press, New York

Petersen, O. H. (1988) Control of potassium channels in insulin-secreting cells. ISI Atlas Sci. **1**, 144–149

Pilkis, S. J. (1970) Hormonal control of hexokinase activity in animal tissues. Biochim. Biophys. Acta **215**, 461–476

Pollard-Knight, D. & Cornish-Bowden, A. (1982) Mechanism of liver glucokinase. Mol. Cell. Biochem. **44**, 71–80

Praz, G. A., Halban, P. A., Wollheim, C. B., Blondel, B., Strauss, A. J. & Renold, A. E. (1983) Regulation of immunoreactive-insulin release from a rat cell line (RINm5F). Biochem. J. **210**, 345–352

Quast, U. & Cook, N. S. (1989) Mowing together: K^+ channel openers and ATP-sensitive K^+ channels. Trends Pharmacol. Sci. **10**, 431–435

Randle, P. J., Ashcroft, S. J. H. & Gill, J. R. (1968) Carbohydrate metabolism and release of hormones. In Carbohydrate Metabolism and Its Disorders (Dickens, F., Randle, P. J. & Whelan, W. J., eds.), vol. 1, pp. 427–447, Academic Press, New York–London

Sato, S., Matsushima, T. & Sugimura, T. (1969) Hexokinase isoenzyme patterns of experimental hepatomas of rats. Cancer Res. **29**, 1437–1443

Schwab, D. A. & Wilson, J. E. (1989) Complete amino acid sequence of rat brain hexokinase, deduced from the cloned cDNA, and proposed structure of a mammalian hexokinase. Proc. Natl. Acad. Sci. U.S.A. **86**, 2563–2567

Sharma, C., Manjeshwar, R. & Weinhouse, S. (1964) Hormonal and dietary regulation of hepatic glucokinase. Adv. Enzyme Regul. **2**, 189–200

Shatton, J. B., Morris, H. P. & Weinhouse, S. (1969) Kinetic, electrophoretic and chromatographic studies on glucose-ATP-phosphotransferases in rat hepatomas. Cancer Res. **29**, 1161–1172

Shimizu, T. & Matschinsky, F. M. (1988) Characteristics of glucokinase of the Kirkman insulinoma. Metabolism **37**, 631–634

Shimizu, T., Knowles, B. B. & Matschinsky, F. M. (1988a) Control of glucose phosphorylation and glucose usage in clonal insulinoma cells. Diabetes **37**, 563–568

Shimizu, T., Parker, J. C., Najafi, H. & Matschinsky, F. M. (1988b) Control of glucose metabolism in pancreatic beta-cells by glucokinase, hexokinase, and phosphofructokinase. Model study with cell lines derived from beta-cells. Diabetes **37**, 1524–1530

Sopwith, A. M., Hutton, J. C., Naber, S. P., Chick, W. L. & Hales, C. N. (1981) Insulin secretion by a transplantable rat islet cell tumour. Diabetologia **21**, 224–229

Tiedge, M. & Lenzen, S. (1991) Regulation of glucokinase and GLUT-2 glucose-transporter gene expression in pancreatic B-cells. Biochem. J. **279**, 899–901

Ureta, T. (1982) The comparative isoenzymology of vertebrate hexokinases. Comp. Biochem. Physiol. **71B**, 549–555

Vague, P., Ramahandridona, G., Di Campo-Rougerie, C. & Mahmoud, F. (1975) Kinetics of the early insulin response of the perfused rat pancreas to various metabolites and tolbutamide. Diabete Metabolisme **1**, 185–189

Van Schaftingen, E. & Vandercammen, A. (1989) Stimulation of glucose phosphorylation by fructose in isolated rat hepatocytes. Eur. J. Biochem. **179**, 173–177

Verspohl, E. J., Händel, M., Hagenloh, I. & Ammon, H. P. T. (1982) In vitro effect of exogenous insulin on insulin secretion. Studies with glucose, leucine, arginine, aminophylline and tolbutamide. Acta Diabetol. Lat. **19**, 303–317

Vischer, U., Blondel, B., Wollheim, C. B., Höppner, W., Seitz, H. J. & Iynedjian, P. B. (1987) Hexokinase isoenzymes of RIN-m5F insulinoma cells. Expression of glucokinase gene in insulin-producing cells. Biochem. J. **241**, 249–255

Walker, D. G. (1966) The nature and function of hexokinases in animal tissues. Essays Biochem. **2**, 32–67

Weinhouse, S. (1976) Regulation of glucokinase in liver. Curr. Top. Cell. Regul. **11**, 1–50

Wollheim, C. B. & Sharp, G. W. G. (1981) Regulation of insulin release by calcium. Physiol. Rev. **61**, 914–973

7

Phospholipids and insulin secretion

Noel G. Morgan† and William Montague‡

†Department of Biological Sciences, University of Keele,
Keele ST5 5BG, U.K. and
‡Department of Biochemistry, Faculty of Medicine, P.O. Box 17666,
U.A.E. University, Al Ain, United Arab Emirates

Introduction

The first experimental evidence that phospholipids might be involved in the secretion of insulin from the B-cells of the pancreatic islets of Langerhans came from the studies of Fex & Lernmark (1972). They demonstrated that there was an increased turnover of specific phospholipids in B-cells when insulin secretion was stimulated by glucose. These original observations have been confirmed and extended by many other workers and it is now clear that phospholipids play a number of important roles in the insulin secretory process (Prentki & Matschinsky, 1987; Turk et al., 1987; Metz, 1988a).

The involvement of phospholipids in the insulin secretory process is not altogether surprising, since it is a process which involves both the phospholipid-rich plasma membrane of the B-cell and the phospholipid-rich membrane of the insulin storage granules. The plasma membrane is the first site of interaction between the B-cell and controlling factors present extracellularly, and as such it plays an important role in the stimulus–secretion coupling mechanism. In addition, it is also the final barrier through which insulin must pass on its way out of the B-cell, and its interaction with the membrane of the insulin storage granule is a key event in the secretory process. To date, phospholipids have been shown to play important roles both in the stimulus–secretion coupling mechanism and in the final exocytotic stage of the secretory process itself. In addition, it is likely that the endocytotic recovery of excess plasma membrane accumulated during secretion also involves alterations to the phospholipid component of the membrane.

This article attempts to review recent knowledge about the possible roles of membrane phospholipids and their metabolism in the stimulus–secretion coupling mechanism of the B-cell, and in the exocytotic secretory process itself.

Studies on the roles of phospholipids in the B-cell

The limited amount of tissue available when studying insulin secretion, using islets of Langerhans, has made it difficult to measure by direct chemical analysis the concentrations of individual phospholipids in B-cells. Studies on the roles of phospholipids in the B-cell have therefore usually been based on the use of radioactive precursors such as $[^{32}P]$ortho-phosphate, $[^{3}H]$glycerol, $[^{3}H]$inositol and both ^{14}C- and ^{3}H-labelled fatty acids to label the cellular phospholipids. Measurement of the rate of incorporation of a precursor into B-cell phospholipids in the presence and absence of a stimulus has often been used as an index of phospholipid synthesis. Phospholipid breakdown has usually been assessed by following the loss of radioactivity, in the presence and absence of a stimulus, from phospholipids prelabelled to isotopic equilibrium. Developments in analytical techniques such as h.p.l.c. have enabled certain of the metabolic products of phospholipids to be measured directly in B-cells and attempts have been made to measure the activities of the enzymes involved in B-cell phospholipid metabolism. The results of these various approaches can be summarized and integrated to give an overview of the possible roles of phospholipids in the secretion of insulin.

Phospholipids and the insulin secretory process

In ultrastructural terms the secretion of insulin can be considered as a two-stage process (Lacy, 1961; Orci, 1974). The initial stage (margination) involves the movement of insulin storage granules through the cytoplasm of the cell to the plasma membrane, where the final stage (exocytosis) occurs. In this stage, the membrane of the insulin storage granule fuses with the plasma membrane of the B-cell and the granule contents are released from the cell at the site of membrane fusion. The membrane of the insulin storage granule and the plasma membrane of the B-cell must undergo extensive biochemical modification before they can fuse, since cell membranes are inherently non-fusagenic. In addition, there must be extensive remodelling of the plasma membrane following exocytosis, as excess membrane added to the plasma membrane from the insulin storage granules has to be removed by endocytosis. One of the major barriers to membrane fusion may be the polar head-groups on the membrane phospholipids, since conversion of membrane phospholipids to diacyl-glycerols, after the removal of these head-groups by the enzyme phospholipase C, has been shown to promote membrane fusion (Allan &

Michell, 1975). Increased production of diacylglycerols has been demonstrated in the B-cell during insulin secretion (Montague & Parkin, 1980; Peter-Reisch *et al.*, 1988) and this may in part be related to the exocytotic process. In addition, a number of other phospholipid metabolites including lysophospholipids and phosphatidic acid may play a role in the membrane remodelling events related to the exocytotic process (Metz, 1988*a*).

The ultrastructural studies of Orci (1974) have shown that before membrane fusion during exocytosis, there is a movement of protein particles away from areas of the plasma membrane that subsequently fuse with the membrane of the insulin storage granule. This movement may be associated with the increase in membrane fluidity that occurs during insulin secretion (Deleers *et al.*, 1981). The biochemical basis of this change in membrane fluidity is unknown, but it may be related to an increase in the degree of unsaturation of the fatty acid component of membrane phospholipids which has been observed in the B-cell during insulin secretion (Montague & Parkin, 1980).

Phospholipids and the regulation of insulin secretion

The rate of insulin secretion from the B-cell is determined by the relative concentrations of a number of controlling factors present in the extracellular medium. These factors include nutrients such as glucose, hormones, regulatory peptides, local mediates, neurotransmitters and drugs (see Chapters 1, 2, 3, 5, 14 and 15 for further details). Some of these factors exert their effects on the secretory process by interaction with receptors on the plasma membrane of the cell. Such receptor interaction leads to the production of messenger molecules intracellularly which act to control the secretory process. Various classes of phospholipids have been shown to play a role in this type of stimulus–secretion coupling mechanism.

Inositol lipid turnover and insulin secretion
Much attention has been given to the possible role of inositol lipids as precursors of intracellular messengers in the pancreatic B-cell. This is due in part to the importance of this signalling system in the stimulus–response coupling mechanism of a multiplicity of cell types. In addition, a large amount of data have been obtained which indicate that rates of phosphatidylinositol (PtdIns) metabolism are increased in glucose-stimulated islets.

Uptake and metabolism of inositol in islet cells
Maintenance of the functional integrity of islet cells in tissue culture requires an adequate supply of inositol in the culture medium (Pace &

Clements, 1981). Inositol deprivation results in failure of glucose to stimulate either insulin secretion or insulin biosynthesis suggesting that compounds containing inositol are important in the mediation of both responses. In common with many cell types, rat islets possess an active transport mechanism for inositol accumulation (Biden & Wollheim, 1986a). This is independent of the glucose-uptake mechanism and is probably driven by the transmembrane Na^+ gradient, since inositol accumulation is inhibited under conditions when this gradient is compromised.

The major fate of intracellular inositol in the B-cell is the membrane phospholipid pool, where it can be readily incorporated into PtdIns and the polyphosphoinositides (Clements et al., 1981; Laychock, 1983a; Montague et al., 1985). Evidence from direct measurements of PtdIns mass supports the view that glucose stimulation leads to a net increase in PtdIns synthesis, probably resulting from increased substrate availability owing to enhanced glycolytic flux under these conditions (Farese et al., 1986). In most mammalian cells, the formation of PtdIns appears to take place in the endoplasmic reticulum, with subsequent translocation of the product to the plasma membrane occurring as a prerequisite to further modification. However, studies on subcellular fractions from rat islets have indicated that the majority of CDP-diacylglycerolinositol transferase activity is present in the secretory granule fraction (Rana et al., 1986a). Further work is required to examine the functional significance of this distribution.

Islet cell plasma membranes contain a resident PtdIns kinase activity which phosphorylates PtdIns to yield phosphatidylinositol 4-phosphate [PtdIns4P; Tooke et al., 1984; Rana & MacDonald, 1986; Dunlop & Malaisse, 1986]. This enzyme is inhibited by Ca^{2+} over the range 1–10 μM, suggesting that its activity might be regulated by stimulus-induced increases in cytosolic free Ca^{2+}, as part of a feedback control mechanism. The enzyme has also been reported to reside in secretory granule membranes (Tooke et al., 1984; Rana & MacDonald, 1986), although its role here has not been defined. B-cell plasma membranes also contain a second kinase activity capable of catalysing the formation of phosphatidylinositol 4,5-bisphosphate [PtdIns(4,5)P_2; Dunlop & Malaisse, 1986] and a Ca^{2+}-activated phosphomonoesterase responsible for PtdIns(4,5)P_2 degradation (Tooke et al., 1984).

Most of the studies designed to examine PtdIns metabolism in islets have employed isotopic methods to label the phospholipid pool. This approach provides a convenient means to identify islet PtdIns and its derivatives, but the validity of the methodology has been brought into question by evidence indicating that the precise labelling conditions used can markedly influence the results obtained. Thus, some studies suggest that islets are equipped with sub-pools of PtdIns which can become differentially labelled upon incubation with radioactive precursors (Rana et al., 1985). Furthermore, nutrient stimuli have been reported to provoke selective changes in the extent of labelling of these pools (Rana et al., 1986a,b). However, the evidence is conflicting, since some groups report that glucose stimulation fails to induce Ptd[³H]Ins turnover if islets are prelabelled under resting conditions (Rana et al., 1986b), whereas others find that stimulation of Ptd[³H]Ins metabolism can still be measured after labelling in the presence of sub-stimulatory glucose concentrations (Zawalich et al., 1989).

Inositol lipid turnover in glucose-stimulated islets

Despite the unresolved discrepancies, there is general agreement that stimulation of islet cells with nutrient stimuli or muscarinic agonists (e.g. carbachol) results in rapid hydrolysis of inositol-containing phospholipids. This was originally attributed to breakdown of PtdIns (Axen et al., 1983), but has subsequently been shown to reflect a primary hydrolysis of $PtdIns(4,5)P_2$ (Laychock, 1983a; Best & Malaisse, 1984; Montague et al., 1985).

Activation of phospholipase C

A phospholipase C activity capable of hydrolysing inositol-containing phospholipids has been described in guinea-pig (Schrey & Montague, 1983) and rat (Dunlop & Larkins, 1986) islets. In the former case the activity was primarily cytosolic, whereas in the latter it could be measured in a plasma membrane preparation. In both cases the activity was dependent on the presence of Ca^{2+}, and the current consensus indicates that, in contrast to the situation in many cells, islet phospholipase C may be directly activated by Ca^{2+}. Thus, in an isolated membrane preparation, raising the Ca^{2+} concentration from 1 μM to 10 μM resulted in a significant increase in enzyme activity (Dunlop & Malaisse, 1986). This observation raises important questions about the control of phospholipase C activity in the B-cell.

    Early studies indicated that hydrolysis of phosphoinositides in stimulated islets was dependent on the presence of extracellular Ca^{2+} (Clements et al., 1981; Axen et al., 1983; Laychock 1983a). In contrast, a number of other reports have indicated that glucose-stimulated $PtdIns(4,5)P_2$ hydrolysis can still proceed in the absence of extracellular Ca^{2+} (Best & Malaisse, 1983a; Dunlop & Larkins, 1984; Montague et al., 1985; Biden et al., 1987a). Part of the discrepancy between these observations may lie in the extent of Ca^{2+} depletion achieved, since it is clear that islet phospholipase C requires some Ca^{2+} for activity. However, the crucial aspect of these experiments relates to the time course of events which follow glucose stimulation. In particular, whether the activation of phospholipase C in glucose-stimulated islets precedes the rise in cytosolic Ca^{2+} concentration or whether it follows from this.

Treatment of rat islets with depolarizing concentrations of K^+ provoked a significant rise in inositol phosphate generation (Mathias *et al.*, 1985*a,b*; Best *et al.*, 1987; Biden *et al.*, 1987*a*), consistent with enhanced degradation of $PtdIns(4,5)P_2$ under these conditions, although this has not always been demonstrable in short-term incubations (Montague *et al.*, 1985). Studies with ionophores and sulphonylureas have also proved equivocal. Thus, ionomycin was reported to induce $PtdIns(4,5)P_2$ hydrolysis in rat islets (Laychock, 1983*a*), whereas A23187 was ineffective (Best & Malaisse, 1983*a*). Moreover, tolbutamide has been shown to elicit a Ca^{2+}-dependent hydrolysis of $PtdIns(4,5)P_2$ (Laychock, 1983*a*), but glibenclamide was reported to be ineffective (Best & Malaisse, 1983*b*). All of these agents increase islet cell Ca^{2+} influx, and it is surprising that the results obtained have not provided an unequivocal conclusion. Overall, it does appear that the B-cell phospholipase C can be activated by a rise in cytosolic Ca^{2+} under certain conditions. It remains possible, however, that nutrient stimuli such as glucose exert both Ca^{2+}-dependent and Ca^{2+}-independent effects on phospholipase C activity (Biden *et al.*, 1987*a*).

It is evident from the foregoing discussion that the mechanisms involved in stimulation of phospholipase C by glucose remain controversial. Direct activation resulting from enhanced Ca^{2+} influx may represent at least part of the mechanism, but other suggestions have also been advanced. A number of studies have provided evidence that glucose metabolism is an important component of the mechanism of enzyme activation in the B-cell. Thus, mannoheptulose is an effective inhibitor of glucose-induced $PtdIns(4,5)P_2$ breakdown (Laychock, 1983*a*; Montague *et al.*, 1985), and other nutrient substrates, such as mannose, glyceraldehyde (Montague *et al.*, 1985), leucine and certain intermediates of the tricarboxylic acid cycle (MacDonald *et al.*, 1989*a*) also increase inositol phosphate formation. These data do not directly clarify the mechanism involved in phospholipase C activation, since catabolism of each compound leads to membrane depolarization and enhanced Ca^{2+} influx. However, they do suggest that stimulation of polyphosphoinositide metabolism in the endocrine pancreas by nutrients results from metabolic events and not from surface receptor activation. This is a very different situation from that in most other cells where the system is activated primarily by agents acting at cell-surface receptors (Morgan, 1989). It should be emphasized, however, that the receptor mechanism can operate in the B-cell, since muscarinic cholinergic agonists (Morgan *et al.*, 1987*a,b*; Morgan & Hurst, 1988; Morgan, 1989), cholecystokinin (Zawalich *et al.*, 1987) and ATP (Blachier & Malaisse, 1988) all stimulate polyphosphoinositide hydrolysis as a consequence of binding to surface receptors.

Despite the strong body of evidence outlined above, certain recent results have introduced a measure of uncertainty concerning the mechanisms involved in regulation of islet phospholipase C by glucose.

This derives from studies undertaken in digitonin-permeabilized islets where glucose cannot be metabolized but has been reported to activate phospholipase C and to generate inositol phosphates (Wolf *et al.*, 1988). This effect was stereospecific and could not be reproduced by glucose 6-phosphate or by manipulating the cytosolic free Ca^{2+} concentration. The authors interpret the data as indicating the existence of a cell-surface receptor through which glucose mediates its effects. Using a similar approach, MacDonald *et al.* (1989*b*) failed to observe any stimulation of inositol phosphate formation upon addition of glucose to permeabilized islets. In contrast, they reported significant stimulation by glyceraldehyde 3-phosphate under these conditions. This agent also induced phospholipase C activation in intact islets (to a similar extent to glucose) and the authors propose that it may act directly to enhance $PtdIns(4,5)P_2$ hydrolysis. They attribute this to an interaction on the inner face of the plasma membrane rather than to receptor binding on the outer surface.

Clearly, there remain several unresolved issues, but the weight of current evidence still lies in favour of metabolic control of inositol lipid hydrolysis in the B-cell. The simplest model for nutrient regulation would then be that Ca^{2+} influx resulting from membrane depolarization leads to phospholipase C activation and inositol lipid hydrolysis. In this scheme there is no requirement for any coupling protein to activate the enzyme, since Ca^{2+} itself fulfils this role. This may, perhaps, be an over-simplification, since there is accumulating evidence that guanine nucleotides can be involved in phospholipase C activation in the pancreatic B-cell. This has been demonstrated in the insulin-secreting cell line RINm5F (Blachier & Malaisse, 1987; Vallar *et al.*, 1987; Wollheim *et al.*, 1987) and has also been reported in preparations of plasma membranes from neonatal islets (Dunlop & Larkins, 1986). Furthermore, Berggren *et al.* (1989) have demonstrated that over-expression of the guanine-nucleotide-binding protein C-Ha-ras leads to enhanced activation of phospholipase C in RIN cells. The data are not totally conclusive, however, since Best (1986) was unable to demonstrate any increase in inositol phosphate production upon addition of GTP analogues to permeabilized rat islets.

It is significant that treatment of islets with maximal stimulatory concentrations of glucose and carbachol simultaneously is associated with an additive increase in inositol triphosphate production (Morgan *et al.*, 1985*a*). This implies that these two agents utilize different mechanisms to stimulate polyphosphoinositide hydrolysis. Therefore, on balance, it seems probable that a G-protein is involved in receptor-mediated activation of phospholipase C in islets, but it remains possible that an alternative system of activation (possibly via Ca^{2+}) mediates the effect of glucose.

Inositol phosphates and islet cell Ca^{2+} handling

Hydrolysis of $PtdIns(4,5)P_2$ located in the inner leaflet of the plasma membrane leads to the release of inositol 1,4,5-triphosphate [$Ins(1,4,5)P_3$] into the cytosol. This agent then induces release of Ca^{2+} from membrane-bound stores and thereby promotes a rise in the cytosolic free Ca^{2+} concentration (Wollheim & Biden 1986a; Chapter 11 by Hellman et al.). Studies with digitonin-permeabilized rat islets have confirmed that $Ins(1,4,5)P_3$ can cause the release of Ca^{2+} from internal pools (Wolf et al., 1985; Hellman et al., 1986; Rana et al., 1987; Nilsson et al., 1987), but there is evidence that this may be a transient effect and that the newly released Ca^{2+} is rapidly accumulated into a second pool which is insensitive to $Ins(1,4,5)P_3$ (Nilsson et al., 1987).

The location of the $Ins(1,4,5)P_3$-sensitive Ca^{2+} pool in islet cells has been investigated in studies using mitochondrial inhibitors and ionophores. Pretreatment of $^{45}Ca^{2+}$-loaded islets with ionophore resulted in the release of label from intracellular stores and inhibited the subsequent effects of agents that raise $Ins(1,4,5)P_3$ levels (Morgan et al., 1989). Such evidence confirms the view that the target pool is membrane bound, and incubation of permeabilized islets with inhibitors of mitochondrial function supports the view that these organelles do not form part of the labile Ca^{2+} store (Nilsson et al., 1987). Rather, it appears that Ca^{2+} release is elicited from portions of the endoplasmic reticulum (Prentki et al., 1984, 1985; Wolf et al., 1987) which may be physically associated with specialized regions of the plasma membrane (Dunlop & Larkins, 1988).

It is beyond dispute that islet cells are equipped with a system to generate $Ins(1,4,5)P_3$ and that glucose stimulation does lead to $Ins(1,4,5)P_3$ generation (Montague et al., 1985; Biden et al., 1987a; Morgan et al., 1989). On this basis, it has been assumed that a rise in glucose concentration elicits $Ins(1,4,5)P_3$-induced intracellular Ca^{2+} mobilization in the B-cell (Biden et al., 1984; Rana et al., 1987) and that this contributes to the increase in cytosolic free Ca^{2+} necessary for increased secretion (Metz, 1988a). This hypothesis appears logical, but it remains unproven, and it does not accord with much of the experimental evidence. For example, addition of glucose to islets preloaded with $^{45}Ca^{2+}$ does not lead to any diminution of the extent of mobilization of intracellular Ca^{2+} stores upon subsequent addition of carbachol (Morgan et al., 1989). Since glucose elicits $Ins(1,4,5)P_3$ generation under these conditions, this suggests that the production of $Ins(1,4,5)P_3$ is not sufficient to activate the intracellular release mechanism or that the response to $Ins(1,4,5)P_3$ is negated. Since carbachol can still induce intracellular Ca^{2+} mobilization from islets incubated in the continued presence of 20 mM-glucose, the latter hypothesis seems unlikely. Therefore, it remains uncertain whether glucose can directly induce significant intracellular Ca^{2+} release in islet cells (Prentki & Matschinsky, 1987).

These conclusions bring into question the hypothesis that the first phase of glucose-induced insulin secretion may reflect mobilization of intracellular Ca^{2+} (Wollheim & Sharp, 1981; Joseph et al., 1984; Metz, 1988a). Indeed, this seems extremely unlikely for a number of reasons. Thus, glucose is unable to induce significant Ca^{2+} release from the $Ins(1,4,5)P_3$-sensitive pool in intact islets. Furthermore, stimulation of $Ins(1,4,5)P_3$ production in response to high glucose concentration probably does not precede, but rather results from a prior rise in cytosolic Ca^{2+}, mediated by increased Ca^{2+} influx. In addition, large-scale mobilization of intracellular Ca^{2+} via increased production of $Ins(1,4,5)P_3$ is not sufficient to initiate insulin secretion (Morgan et al., 1987b; Morgan & Hurst, 1988) even in the presence of elevated cyclic AMP (Morgan et al., 1989). Therefore, the function of inositol lipid hydrolysis in nutrient-stimulated islets is unlikely to be primarily related to Ca^{2+} handling, but must play a different role, perhaps to generate diacylglycerol in the plasma membrane. Indeed, there is evidence from human insulinoma cells (Chiba et al., 1987) and cultured mouse islets (Hallberg, 1986) that glucose can stimulate insulin secretion without eliciting any change in the rate of inositol lipid turnover.

Metabolism of inositol phosphates in glucose-stimulated islets

Despite the apparent lack of a functional role for $Ins(1,4,5)P_3$ in glucose-stimulated insulin secretion, the control of metabolism of this compound in islet cells is complex. H.p.l.c. analysis of islet extracts has revealed that glucose stimulation leads to the production of two isomers of inositol trisphosphate: $Ins(1,4,5)P_3$ and $Ins(1,3,4)P_3$ (Turk et al., 1986a; Best et al., 1987). Production of both compounds is rapid, and within 2 min of glucose stimulation the 1,3,4-isomer is the predominant form (Turk et al., 1986a). It is likely that there is a precursor–product relationship between these isomers and that a more highly phosphorylated derivative, inositol 1,3,4,5-tetrakisphosphate [$Ins(1,3,4,5)P_4$], is produced as an intermediate. Evidence for production of $Ins(1,3,4,5)P_4$ in rat islets has been presented (Best et al., 1987; Biden et al., 1987a) and detailed time-course analyses have been reported (Biden et al., 1987a). $Ins(1,4,5)P_3$ levels were elevated within 10 s in glucose-stimulated islets and this was followed by a rise in $Ins(1,3,4)P_3$ some 20 s later. Surprisingly, elevation of $Ins(1,3,4,5)P_4$ was the most rapid response measured and occurred within 2 s of exposure of islets to glucose (Biden et al., 1987a). All of these responses were significantly inhibited under conditions designed to minimize Ca^{2+} influx, consistent with the idea that they result from Ca^{2+} activation of phospholipase C. One problem with this interpretation, however, is that studies of the time course of increases in cytosolic free Ca^{2+} in single B-cells have revealed a lag of some 60 s before detectable increases (Pralong et al., 1990). At present there is no clear explanation for this discrepancy, apart from the obvious possibility that the rise in inositol phosphate levels is not dependent on Ca^{2+} entry. Further studies are still required to resolve this point.

Removal of extracellular Ca^{2+} has a different effect on inositol phosphate generation in islets treated with muscarinic agonists (Biden & Wollheim, 1986b), since, rather than preventing inositol trisphosphate formation, as in the case of glucose, this manoeuvre amplifies $Ins(1,4,5)P_3$ levels. This reflects the activation of phospholipase C by a Ca^{2+}-independent mechanism, and also the Ca^{2+} dependence of the enzyme inositol-1,4,5-trisphosphate-3-kinase. This enzyme is activated by increases in free Ca^{2+} between 0·1 and 10 μM (Biden & Wollheim, 1986b; Biden et $al.$, 1987b). Thus, when Ca^{2+} levels are not elevated, $Ins(1,4,5)P_3$ will tend to accumulate, but a rise in cytosolic Ca^{2+} will divert $Ins(1,4,5)P_3$ towards $Ins(1,3,4,5)P_4$ formation by activating the kinase. Hydrolysis of $Ins(1,3,4,5)P_4$ by an inositol-phosphate-5-phosphatase can then yield $Ins(1,3,4)P_3$, thus providing an explanation for the route and time course of its synthesis in islet cells.

The inositol-phosphate-5-phosphatase responsible for hydrolysis of $Ins(1,3,4,5)P_4$ may also be the same enzyme as that which degrades $Ins(1,4,5)P_3$ to yield $Ins(1,4)P_2$. The activation of this enzyme appears to be regulated by products of glucose metabolism in the B-cell. In particular, several diphosphorylated intermediates (2,3-bisphosphoglycerate, fructose 1,6-bisphosphate and glucose 1,6-bisphosphate) significantly inhibited the enzyme in islet extracts (Rana et $al.$, 1986c) and reduced the extent of inositol trisphosphate degradation in permeabilized islets (Rana et $al.$, 1987). These metabolites also potentiated inositol trisphosphate-induced $^{45}Ca^{2+}$ release in permeabilized islets, although, as indicated above, it is unclear whether this effect would be of any significance in intact cells.

Overall, it seems likely that catabolism of glucose plays a dual role in directing inositol trisphosphate metabolism in the B-cell. Generation of certain metabolites directly inhibits trisphosphate breakdown by reducing the activity of inositol-phosphate-5-phosphatase, and the rise in Ca^{2+} influx which follows membrane depolarization leads to activation of $Ins(1,4,5)P_3$-kinase and formation of $Ins(1,3,4,5)P_4$.

Studies with other cell types have revealed a still more complex pattern of inositol phosphate products, including further isomers of inositol tetrakisphosphate. Whether these molecules are present in islets remains to be established, as does the answer to a still more fundamental question—do these molecules have any functional significance in the regulation of insulin secretion from the B-cell by nutrients? It is clear that their function is not related to intracellular Ca^{2+} mobilization in response to nutrient stimuli, but one possibility that warrants further investigation is that they may be involved in the process of 'time-dependent potentiation'. It is well known that sequential stimulation of islets with glucose can induce potentiation of the secretory response. Recently, this has been correlated with prolonged activation of inositol lipid turnover in response to nutrients (Zawalich et al., 1989). These experiments utilize very indirect methods to estimate inositol lipid hydrolysis, and the conclusions must be considered speculative at the present time. Nevertheless, they do offer a possible new perspective on the function of the inositol signalling system in islets.

Diacylglycerol formation in islet cells

One of the consequences of phospholipase-C-catalysed phospholipid breakdown is the generation of diacylglycerol. This is significant, since diacylglycerol may be an important signal molecule in the pancreatic B-cell for several reasons. First, it could be involved in stimulating the activity of protein kinase C by lowering the Ca^{2+} sensitivity of the enzyme. Secondly, increased production of diacylglycerol can increase the fusogenic potential of biological membranes, which may be important for exocytosis. Thirdly, it can serve as a substrate for diacylglycerol lipase, an enzyme which is involved in the liberation of arachidonic acid from the sn-2 position of the molecule.

Addition of exogenous diacylglycerol can induce insulin secretion from isolated islets (Malaisse et al., 1985) and incubation of islets with stimulatory concentrations of glucose in the presence of isobutylmethyl-xanthine has been shown to result in increased labelling of diacylglycerol, when islets were prelabelled with [³H]glycerol (Montague & Parkin, 1980). A similar effect was also observed when incorporation of [¹⁴C]glucose was used as an index of diacylglycerol formation in islets stimulated with glucose (Wolf et al., 1990), although an earlier study had failed to demonstrate the response, except in the presence of exogenous palmitic acid (Vara & Tamarit-Rodriguez, 1986). Incorporation of radiolabelled glucose into diacylglycerol occurred within 1 min of stimulation in both rat (Peter-Reisch et al., 1988) and human (Wolf et al., 1990) islets. However, there is no clear consensus as to whether this represents a true increase in diacylglycerol mass under these conditions. Peter-Reisch et al. (1988) reported a 60% increase in islet diacylglycerol mass after glucose stimulation, whereas the more recent study by Wolf et al. (1990) found no evidence for a net increase during acute stimulation. The latter observation seems inconsistent with the view that phospholipid synthesis, which is stimulated by glucose (Hallberg, 1984), occurs as a result of formation of diacylglycerol from triose phosphates produced during glycolysis. However, evidence from neonatal islets suggests that phospholipids can be synthesized from glucose without the need to generate diacylglycerol as an intermediate. This is owing to the presence, in the B-cell, of an enzyme which can directly acylate dihydroxyacetone phosphate to yield lysophosphatidic acid (Dunlop & Larkins, 1985).

However, despite the existence of this pathway, it is noteworthy that neonatal islets still synthesized significant amounts of diacylglycerol from glucose (Dunlop & Larkins, 1985).

In principle, diacylglycerol can be generated by two major pathways after incubation of B-cells with glucose. In the first pathway, glucose is metabolized via glycolysis to generate triose phosphates which can then serve as precursors for *de novo* synthesis of diacylglycerol. In the second pathway, hydrolysis of inositol phospholipids by phospholipase C yields diacylglycerol as one of the products. Analysis of the fatty acid composition of diacylglycerol after glucose stimulation has revealed a marked difference compared with that observed after carbachol treatment (Peter-Reisch *et al.*, 1988). The significance of this observation lies in the fact that the rapid generation of diacylglycerol in response to carbachol reflects phospholipid breakdown, but not synthesis *de novo*. Thus there appears to be a difference between the pathways used for diacylglycerol synthesis in response to nutrient and neurotransmitter stimuli. Furthermore, the difference in fatty acid composition of the diacylglycerol produced in each of these circumstances suggests that the molecule may play a different role in each case.

Islets stimulated with glucose generate diacylglycerol that is enriched in palmitic acid, suggesting that the primary route of formation is via synthesis *de novo* (Peter-Reisch *et al.*, 1988). If the diacylglycerol were produced as a result of PtdIns(4,5)P_2 hydrolysis, it would be expected to contain a significant proportion of arachidonic acid, since inositol phospholipids are enriched in this fatty acid. In support of this, treatment of islets with carbachol resulted in rapid production of diacylglycerol which was enriched in arachidonic acid (Peter-Reisch *et al.*, 1988). These data, therefore, suggest that diacylglycerol is unlikely to be a primary source of arachidonic acid in glucose-stimulated islets. This, in turn, indicates that activation of diacylglycerol lipase may not contribute significantly to the generation of arachidonic acid during glucose stimulation.

These data also have implications for the activation of protein kinase C by glucose. Diacylglycerol production is an essential step in this process and activation is most effective when the diacylglycerol species has an unsaturated fatty acid (e.g. arachidonic acid) at position 2 of the glycerol backbone (Morgan, 1989). Palmitic acid is fully saturated and, as a result, it seems likely that diacylglycerol enriched in this fatty acid will not be an efficient activator of the enzyme.

In summary, diacylglycerol does appear to be generated as an early response to glucose in pancreatic islets, but the possibility that this may then serve as a signal molecule for insulin secretion requires further evaluation. Diacylglycerol and protein kinase C are discussed further in Chapters 11 and 12 by Hellman *et al.* and Persuad *et al.*

Phospholipid methylation in pancreatic islets

It has been evident for a number of years that many cells contain methyltransferase enzymes capable of methylating membrane phospholipid species. Indeed, formation of phosphatidylcholine (PtdCho) from phosphatidylethanolamine (PtdEtn) occurs by methylation. Lipid methylation may be of importance in secretory cells, since changes in the extent of methylation can lead to alteration in parameters such as membrane fluidity and receptor–effector coupling (Hirata & Axelrod, 1978), as well as changes in ion transport and in the activity of membrane-bound enzymes (Hirata & Axelrod, 1980; Navarro *et al.*, 1984).

Treatment of isolated rat islets with high glucose concentrations has been shown to induce a significant increase in membrane phospholipid methylation (Kowluru *et al.*, 1984; Saceda *et al.*, 1985). This effect could not be reproduced with non-metabolizable sugars (Kowluru *et al.*, 1984), indicating that it results from stimulation of glucose metabolism in the B-cell. Moreover, the dose–response curve relating glucose concentration to phospholipid methylation revealed that stimulation occurs over an equivalent range of concentrations to those required for stimulation of insulin secretion (Kowluru *et al.*, 1984). In addition, stimulation of insulin secretion by glucose was significantly impaired in the presence of inhibitors of phospholipid methylation (Best *et al.*, 1984*a*).

Islet extracts contain a phosphatidylethanolamine-*N*-methyltransferase activity which could be responsible for lipid methylation in the B-cell (Laychock, 1985), but the mechanism of regulation of this enzyme requires clarification. One possibility is that it is activated by the rise in cytosolic free Ca^{2+} that follows from glucose stimulation (Kowluru *et al.*, 1984; Saceda *et al.*, 1985). Alternatively, Laychock (1985) has presented evidence that it can be activated by the β-agonist isoprenaline, presumably as a result of adenylate cyclase activation. However, this conclusion requires confirmation, since the concentration of isoprenaline used was extremely high (100 μM) and neither 8-bromo-cyclic AMP (Laychock, 1985) nor dibutyryl cyclic AMP (Kowluru *et al.*, 1984) were effective. It also remains to be established whether phospholipid methylation plays any direct regulatory role in the pancreatic B-cell. Subcellular fractionation studies have indicated that the methyltransferase enzyme may be localized to the secretory granule (Kowluru *et al.*, 1984), raising the possibility that it could be involved in altering the membrane microenvironment to facilitate exocytotic release of insulin.

Arachidonic acid as a component of islet lipids

Arachidonic acid is a long-chain unsaturated fatty acid containing twenty carbon atoms and four double bonds. This fatty acid is important, since it has been implicated as a signal molecule which can exert a variety of effects in cells. In the resting state, most cellular arachidonic acid is esterified to membrane lipids and the intracellular free concentration is very low (Irvine, 1982). Under stimulating conditions the molecule can be released in the free form, and this can then affect several processes including activation of protein kinase C (McPhail *et al.*, 1984) and mobilization on intracellular Ca^{2+} (Kolesnik *et al.*, 1984). It can be metabolized to yield a plethora of potential signalling molecules (Needleman *et al.*, 1986), some of which are likely to be important in control of insulin secretion (see below).

Analysis of islet lipid components by g.l.c. has confirmed the presence of esterified arachidonic acid (Montague & Parkin, 1980; Cortizo *et al.*, 1987) and isotope-labelling experiments have revealed that glucose stimulation leads to enhanced incorporation of exogenous arachidonic acid into islet phospholipids (Evans *et al.*, 1983; Laychock, 1983*b*). Arachidonic acid comprises approximately 17% of the total fatty acid content of rat islets (Turk *et al.*, 1986*b*) and can become incorporated into several different phospholipid species (Morgan *et al.*, 1985*b*; Turk *et al.*, 1986*b*). An increase in the extent of this incorporation has been demonstrated after glucose stimulation, and the major effect of glucose was to increase the extent of labelled arachidonic acid associated with PtdIns and PtdCho (Laychock, 1983*b*). Indeed, PtdCho appears to be a major source of arachidonic acid in rat islets (Morgan *et al.*, 1985*b*), accounting for up to 43% of the total phospholipid-bound arachidonic acid (Turk *et al.*, 1986*b*).

At first sight, the observation that glucose induced a significant increase in incorporation of radiolabelled arachidonic acid into islet PtdCho, seems at odds with phospholipid mass determinations which have revealed a decrease in the amount of arachidonic acid associated with PtdCho under these conditions (Turk *et al.*, 1986*b*). This discrepancy can be resolved on the basis that the primary effect of glucose is to enhance the turnover of islet PtdCho, and the increase in radiolabel then reflects rapid reacylation of lyso-PtdCho. Thus, a rise in glucose concentration leads to release of fatty acid from phospholipids.

The mechanism of this release has not been unequivocally resolved and two major routes are possible: phospholipase-A_2-mediated hydrolytic cleavage of arachidonic acid from the C-2 position of the glycerol backbone of phospholipids and phospholipase-C-mediated removal of the polar head-groups of phospholipid leaving diacylglycerol which is subsequently hydrolysed by diacylglycerol lipase to release arachidonic acid. Diacylglycerol lipase activity has been described in guinea-pig islets (Schrey & Montague, 1983) and it is clear that activation of phospholipase C can occur in islets incubated in the presence of high concentrations of glucose. However, while the major source of free arachidonic acid is PtdCho, the activation of phospholipase C leads to hydrolysis of the polar head-group of inositol-containing phospholipids. Thus, it seems unlikely that the combined action of phospholipase C and diacylglycerol lipase represents the major pathway for release of arachidonic acid in islets stimulated with nutrients, although this pathway has been demonstrated in neonatal islets (Dunlop & Larkins, 1984).

Phospholipase A$_2$ activity in islet cells

Studies with guinea-pig islets failed to provide evidence for the presence of significant phospholipase A$_2$ activity under basal conditions (Schrey & Montague, 1983), but the enzyme does appear to be present in rat islets (Laychock, 1982). Its biochemical properties have not been well defined and it is not clear whether a single protein accounts for the activity or whether multiple forms are present, as in other tissues (Chang et al., 1987). The mechanism of regulation of the enzyme is also a matter of dispute.

In common with many phospholipase A$_2$ enzymes, the activity present in rat islets requires Ca^{2+} for activity, has an alkaline pH optimum and may be localized to cellular membranes (Laychock, 1982; Best et al., 1984b). Studies by Malaisse and colleagues (Best et al., 1984b; Mathias et al., 1985b), have indicated that activation of phospholipase A$_2$ follows from glucose stimulation of rat islets, but they could find no evidence for stable activation of the enzyme by glucose. On the basis of this evidence, it was proposed that the enzyme activity may be controlled by the cytosolic free Ca^{2+} concentration of the B-cell. This is at variance with the results of Laychock (1982) and Tadayyon et al. (1990) who observed that activation of phospholipase A$_2$ by glucose persisted in islet homogenates. This discrepancy has not yet been satisfactorily resolved.

It has become evident that regulation of phospholipase A$_2$ activity may be mediated by several factors in cells (Chang et al., 1987). One of these is the regulator protein lipocortin which acts to repress phospholipase A$_2$ under resting conditions. Relief of this inhibition leads to enzyme activation and lipocortin appears to be under agonist regulation in many cells. To our knowledge, no study has evaluated whether islet cells contain lipocortin, and this possibility deserves further attention. Evidence for metabolic regulation of islet phospholipase A$_2$ has recently emerged from results indicating that starvation leads to a significant reduction in islet phospholipase A$_2$ activity (Tadayyon et al., 1990). This was not associated with any reduction in the capacity of glucose to induce enzyme activation, but was manifest as a 50% decrease in total activity.

Recently, Yokokawa et al. (1989) have suggested that islet phospholipase A$_2$ activity may be subject to regulation by a G-protein. This conclusion derives from evidence that treatment of rat islets with the wasp venom protein mastoparan (which is purported to activate certain G-proteins) induced an insulin secretory response that could be inhibited by bromophenacyl bromide, an inhibitor of phospholipase A$_2$. Control of the enzyme by G-proteins has been described in other tissues (Fain et al., 1988), but further evidence is required to substantiate this in islets. Indeed, bromophenacyl bromide acts in a very non-specific manner in islets (Best *et al.*, 1984*c*; Metz, 1988*a*) and caution must be exercised when interpreting results obtained with this compound.

Involvement of phospholipid A_2 in insulin secretion

The evidence that phospholipase A_2 may play a direct regulatory role in the control of insulin secretion has come largely from studies with activators and inhibitors of the enzyme. All such studies suffer from the possible lack of specificity of the pharmacological agents used, but the overall consensus supports the view that this enzyme is important.

One agent that has been employed in a number of studies is the bee venom polypeptide, melittin. This protein is capable of activating phospholipase A_2 and readily stimulates insulin secretion from islet cells (Morgan & Montague, 1984; Dunlop *et al.*, 1984; Metz, 1986*a*). Stimulation was associated with significant mobilization of arachidonic acid from phospholipids, but not from diacylglycerol (Morgan *et al.*, 1985*b*), indicating that activation of phospholipase A_2 had occurred after addition of melittin to islets. One problem with such data relates to the observation that preparations of melittin may contain contaminating exogenous phospholipase A_2, making interpretation of the results difficult, since exogenous phospholipase A_2 can promote insulin release (Metz, 1986*a*). Nevertheless, the fact that the effects of melittin on insulin secretion could be inhibited by agents expected to alter the rate of metabolism of endogenous arachidonic acid (Dunlop *et al.*, 1984; Morgan *et al.*, 1985*b*) supports the view that phospholipase A_2 activation can promote insulin secretion. In addition to melittin, activation of islet phospholipase A_2 by Δ^9-tetrahydrocannabinol has also been shown to be associated with stimulation of insulin secretion (Laychock *et al.*, 1986).

Several agents believed to inhibit the activity of endogenous phospholipase A_2 have been reported to inhibit glucose-induced insulin secretion. These include quinacrine or mepacrine (Best *et al.*, 1984*c*; Morgan *et al.*, 1985*b*) and bromophenacyl bromide (Best *et al.*, 1984*c*; Walsh & Pek, 1984*a*). In one report, however, mepacrine was found to promote further enhancement of glucose-stimulated insulin secretion, while melittin was inhibitory (Tanaka *et al.*, 1983). These results led the authors to the conclusion that activation of phospholipase A_2 is associated with inhibition of insulin secretion.

On balance, most studies have produced results that are consistent with the involvement of phospholipase A_2 in stimulation of insulin secretion. However, the situation would be further clarified if more specific activators/inhibitors of the enzyme were available.

Metabolism of arachidonic acid in islets

Studies of the routes by which free arachidonic acid can be metabolized in the B-cell have revealed two major pathways. A cyclo-oxygenase pathway, which results in the formation of prostaglandin (PG) products, and a lipoxygenase pathway, responsible for the formation of hydroperoxy- and hydroxylated derivatives.

Islet PG synthesis

Using both radioisotopic and mass spectrometric techniques, it has been possible to demonstrate that islets synthesize PGs (Kelly & Laychock, 1981, 1984; Metz et al., 1981; Turk et al., 1984a; Tadayyon et al., 1990). These studies have revealed that islets can produce a variety of cyclo-oxygenase products from arachidonic acid, although the major product observed in labelling experiments appeared to be 6-keto-PGF$_{1\alpha}$ (Kelly & Laychock, 1981; Tadayyon et al., 1990) which is produced by spontaneous degradation of prostacyclin (PGI$_2$). Synthesis of smaller amounts of thromboxane B$_2$, PGs A$_2$, B$_2$, D$_2$, E$_2$, F$_{2\alpha}$ and hydroxyheptadecatrienoic acid have also been reported (Evans et al., 1983; Turk et al., 1987; Tadayyon et al., 1990). Recent studies suggest that human islets produce a range of cyclo-oxygenase products similar to those previously described in islets from other species (Turk et al., 1988).

There is good evidence that glucose stimulation of islets leads to increased production of cyclo-oxygenase-derived products of arachidonic acid (Evans et al., 1983; Kelly & Laychock, 1984; Yamamoto et al., 1985; Tadayyon et al., 1990). Under basal conditions, the availability of arachidonic acid is likely to be rate limiting for PG synthesis, therefore, the increase in synthesis seen after glucose stimulation probably reflects an increase in availability of the substrate, rather than any intrinsic change in cyclo-oxygenase activity. Despite evidence that 6-keto-PGF$_{1\alpha}$ is a major cyclo-oxygenase product in islets, the primary effect of glucose was to increase the production of PGE$_2$. This has been demonstrated by use of radiolabelled arachidonic acid (Kelly & Laychock, 1984), by direct mass spectrometric quantification (Turk et al., 1984b) and by radioimmunoassay (Morgan & Pek, 1984; Yamamoto et al., 1985; Tadayyon et al., 1990).

Quantitative analysis of cyclo-oxygenase products in islets, by direct mass measurements and by the use of radioactive substrates (Turk et al., 1984a,b), has revealed that there may be multiple pools of arachidonic acid which are selectively mobilized in response to glucose. This observation implies that caution must be exercised when examining islet arachidonic acid metabolism, and that prelabelling experiments may lead to underestimation of arachidonic acid release (Turk et al., 1984b).

Effects of cyclo-oxygenase products on insulin secretion

Two basic approaches have been employed to study the possible involvement of cyclo-oxygenase products in regulation of insulin secretion, involving either addition of exogenous PGs to islets or treatment of cells with cyclo-oxygenase inhibitors. The results obtained have not always been consistent (Robertson, 1983), but the consensus that has emerged is that cyclo-oxygenase products tend to inhibit glucose-induced insulin secretion, but do not significantly affect the basal secretory rate (Robertson, 1986).

Two drugs, indomethacin and flurbiprofen, which have been claimed to be selective inhibitors of cyclo-oxygenase enzymes, have been used extensively in such studies. Surprisingly, flurbiprofen was found to inhibit the first phase of glucose-induced insulin secretion in perfused pancreas preparations (Walsh & Pek, 1984b) and indomethacin inhibited insulin secretion *in vivo* (Schmitt *et al.*, 1980). These data could be taken as evidence that islet cyclo-oxygenase products are important for stimulation of insulin secretion. However, indomethacin may exert other, non-specific, effects in islets (Turk *et al.*, 1984b), which could account for the very inconsistent results obtained with this compound (Robertson, 1986) and the effects of flurbiprofen are variable according to the concentration used (MacAdams *et al.*, 1984).

Experiments with isolated islet preparations are less subject to possible indirect effects of PGs or inhibitors than studies *in vivo* or experiments with perfused pancreas preparations, and should be more useful for studies on the control of insulin secretion. A variety of studies using this system have revealed that cyclo-oxygenase inhibitors induce net stimulation of glucose-induced insulin secretion (Robertson, 1986, 1988). Thus, overall, it appears that at least one product derived from arachidonic acid is inhibitory to insulin secretion.

An important question which then arises relates to the nature of this product and the extent to which it is synthesized in nutrient-stimulated islets. As indicated above, isotopic studies have suggested that 6-keto-$PGF_{1\alpha}$ (derived from PGI_2) is a major islet cyclo-oxygenase product, whereas glucose stimulation leads to enhanced formation of PGE_2. This is significant, since these two compounds exert opposite effects on insulin secretion. For example, in one study PGI_2 (and its breakdown product, 6-keto-$PGF_{1\alpha}$) were observed to directly increase insulin secretion from rat islets (Heaney & Larkins, 1981). Whereas, the effects of PGI_2 were complex, with stimulation, no effect, or inhibition being observed under different incubation conditions. In contrast, a study in human subjects *in vivo* suggested that PGI_2 did not affect insulin secretion (Patrono *et al.*, 1981).

The reported effects of PGE_2 on glucose-induced insulin secretion have also been inconsistent. Early studies indicated that addition of PGE to islets was associated with stimulation of insulin secretion (Pek *et al.*, 1975, 1978). In an attempt to clarify the situation, Robertson (1983) has critically examined the accumulated data from experiments performed between 1976 and 1981. He drew the conclusion that the consensus favours the view that E-series PGs cause inhibition of glucose-induced insulin secretion.

The physiological importance of the inhibitory effects of PGs on nutrient-stimulated insulin secretion remains to be determined. It has been suggested (Evans *et al.*, 1983) that they may play an important role in controlling the time course of insulin secretion and that synthesis of PGs is necessary for generation of a biphasic secretory response. However, certain nutrients, such as glyceraldehyde and 4-methyl-2-oxopentanoate may stimulate insulin secretion without enhancing PG production (Dunlop *et al.*, 1984). Thus, it seems unlikely that formation of PGs is fundamental to the process of stimulus–secretion coupling in the B-cell.

The mechanism by which PGE_2 inhibits insulin secretion is also a matter of controversy. Studies with hamster insulinoma cells have implicated a cell-surface receptor in the action of PGE_2, and suggest that this may be coupled to a pertussis-toxin-sensitive G-protein (Robertson *et al.*, 1987). Treatment of insulin-secreting cells with PGE_2 was associated with inhibition of cyclic AMP generation, which would be consistent with coupling of the receptor to one of the G_i-proteins. Whether this mechanism can entirely explain inhibition of glucose-induced insulin secretion in islets is open to question, since cyclic AMP is not the primary coupling factor in normal B-cells. In this context, Laychock (1989*a*,*b*) has recently presented evidence for coupling of PGE_2 receptors to a pertussis-toxin-sensitive G-protein in rat islets. In this preparation, addition of PGE_2 resulted in inhibition of glucose oxidation, impaired phospho-inositide hydrolysis and reduced accumulation of inositol phosphates. These responses were not secondary to lowered cyclic AMP, but exhibited an unexplained latency which required pre-exposure of the cells to PGE_2 for manifestation of the effects. It is also unclear, therefore, whether these effects are primary components of the inhibitory mechanism.

In summary, it appears that PGE_2 is an inhibitor of glucose-induced insulin secretion. Synthesis of this agent is increased by glucose stimulation, suggesting that it could act as a feedback inhibitor of B-cell secretory activity. For this to happen, it must be released from the cell to interact with surface receptors on the same, or neighbouring cells. The effects of PGE_2 on islet function are complex, and control of several different intracellular processes may contribute to inhibition of insulin release.

Synthesis of lipoxygenase products by islet cells

In contrast with the situation with cyclo-oxygenase products, there is much less variability in the experimental data relating to the synthesis and function of lipoxygenated arachidonic acid derivatives in islets. Metz *et al.* (1983) reported that [^{3}H]arachidonic acid could be converted into 12-hydroxyeicosatetraenoic acid (12-HETE) by rat islets, and this has been confirmed by several groups using isotopic and direct mass measurements (Turk *et al.*, 1984*a*,*b*). Although a range of different lipoxygenase enzymes have been described in mammalian cells, which incorporate O_2 at different positions within the structure of arachidonic acid, it appears that islets contain only a single major enzyme activity, with specificity for C-12 of arachidonic acid (Turk *et al.*, 1987). The first product of this enzyme is a hydroperoxy-derivative of arachidonic acid 12-hydroperoxyeicosatetra-enoic acid (12-HPETE), but this rapidly and spontaneously rearranges to form 12-HETE. This product has been shown to represent the most abundant metabolite of arachidonic acid in both rat (Turk *et al.*, 1984*a*) and human (Turk *et al.*, 1988) islets. In the case of rat islets, levels of 12-HETE were estimated to be approximately 2 pg/islet (Turk *et al.*, 1985), whereas human islets contained 0·37 pg/islet (Turk *et al.*, 1988).

The production of trace quantities of 15-HETE has also been described in rat islets (Turk *et al.*, 1985; Metz, 1988*a*), although the levels were so low that it seems extremely unlikely that this metabolite could be of major significance to islet function. Its presence does indicate, however, that islets may contain small amounts of a 15-lipoxygenase.

As is the case for islet cyclo-oxygenase, the activity of the 12-lipoxygenase is probably regulated by the availability of free arachidonic acid, rather than by direct control of the enzyme itself. Production of 12-HETE (and/or other products) will, therefore, be increased by any stimulus which promotes liberation of arachidonic acid from membrane lipid. Indeed, enhanced production of 12-HETE has been described in islets incubated in the presence of stimulatory glucose concentrations (Turk *et al.*, 1984*b*; Metz, 1985; Laychock *et al.*, 1986).

The lipoxygenase-derived intermediate 12-HPETE can also be rearranged to form a different series of compounds which are hydroxy-epoxides of arachidonic acid. These have been termed hepoxilins and Pace-Asciak & Martin (1984) first reported the synthesis of two such compounds (hepoxilins A and B) by rat islets. These were originally identified by radioisotope labelling techniques, but their synthesis by islets was subsequently confirmed by mass spectrometry (Pace-Asciak *et al.*, 1985).

Effects of lipoxygenase products on insulin secretion

A large number of reports have now been published describing the effects of lipoxygenase inhibitors on insulin secretion, and they have produced a surprisingly uniform picture. A range of different agents have been employed, the most popular being nordihydroguaiaretic acid (NDGA), BW755c and 5,8,11,14-eicosatetraynoic acid (ETYA). In addition to these, at least seven other compounds have been used (Turk *et al.*, 1987; Metz, 1988*a*), and all of them have been found to inhibit glucose-induced insulin secretion (Metz *et al.*, 1982; Walsh & Pek, 1984*b*). Since this range of compounds comprises reagents which lack structural similarity and which inhibit the lipoxygenase by separate mechanisms, there seems little alternative but to draw the conclusion that at least one lipoxygenase product is important for stimulation of insulin secretion. Indeed, it has been argued that a lipoxygenase-derived metabolite of arachidonic acid may control a distal event in the secretory process (Yamamoto *et al.*, 1985; Metz, 1987*a*, 1988*a*).

Since 12-HPETE is the major product of lipoxygenase activity in islets, and its synthesis is increased by glucose, this would seem a likely candidate for the putative signalling intermediate. Addition of exogenous 12-HPETE or 12-HETE to isolated rat islets did not lead to any direct stimulation of insulin secretion (Turk *et al.*, 1985), although 12-HETE (but not 12-HPETE) partially reversed the inhibitory effect of lipoxygenase inhibition at certain concentrations (Turk *et al.*, 1985). In contrast, Metz *et al.* (1984) observed that exogenous 12-HPETE could potentiate glucose-induced insulin secretion in monolayer cultures of neonatal islets. Thus, there is no strong evidence to implicate either 12-HPETE or 12-HETE as mediators of nutrient-stimulated insulin secretion. Indeed, Metz (1985) has shown that stimulation of insulin secretion by mannose was not associated with increased 12-HETE production, which casts doubt on the likelihood that this compound or its immediate precursor could play any central role in stimulus–secretion coupling.

This latter observation is surprising since triose sugars did facilitate 12-HETE formation in the B-cell (Metz, 1985), and the stimulatory effect of glucose was susceptible to inhibition by manno-heptulose. Since mannose (like glucose) is readily metabolized in the B-cell, this implies that stimulation of 12-HETE formation is uniquely coupled to an early event associated with activation of some particular metabolic pathway. If true, this then suggests that liberation of arachidonic acid from membrane lipids must be controlled by this same pathway, rather than by the intracellular free Ca^{2+} concentration, which would be raised equally well by either glucose or mannose. This aspect of the control of arachidonic acid metabolism remains to be defined in detail.

The possibility that the hepoxilins may be important mediators of glucose-induced insulin secretion has not been critically examined, but it has been reported that exogenous hepoxilin A can potentiate insulin secretion induced by glucose in perifused rat islets (Pace-Asciak & Martin, 1984). Recent data have provided evidence that cell-surface receptors for hepoxilin A are present on human neutrophils, and that this agent can activate intracellular signalling processes in these cells (Dho *et al.*, 1990). It remains to be established whether similar mechanisms are operative in the B-cell, but if so, this might provide one mechanism by which 12-HETE (and hence hepoxilin A) formation could be coupled to insulin secretion.

Some studies have shown that insulin secretion can be enhanced by exogenous leukotrienes (Pek & Walsh, 1984), although this is not a universal observation (Turk *et al.*, 1985). Moreover, since islets do not appear to synthesize 5-HPETE (the precursor of leukotrienes), it is improbable that these compounds are important for insulin secretion.

In summary, it is clear that islets contain a 12-lipoxygenase enzyme capable of utilizing arachidonic acid as substrate. Inhibitor studies are consistent with the involvement of this enzyme in nutrient stimulation of insulin secretion, but certain metabolic data do not entirely favour this view. Therefore, the extent to which a 12-lipoxygenase product of arachidonic acid metabolism is involved in stimulus–secretion coupling of the B-cell and the identity of the coupling factor, remain uncertain.

Free arachidonic acid as a potential signalling molecule in the B-cell

One possibility that should not be overlooked when considering the fate of released arachidonic acid in nutrient-stimulated islets, is that the molecule itself may have a signal function. The data supporting this concept are not straightforward and conflicting reports abound in the literature. Nevertheless, there is evidence that high glucose concentrations promote the accumulation of free arachidonic acid in islet cells (Wolf *et al.*, 1986).

Exogenous arachidonic acid has been reported to stimulate insulin secretion (Morgan & Pek, 1984; Phair *et al.*, 1984; Wolf *et al.*, 1986), although this appears to require specialized incubation conditions, including depletion of extracellular Ca^{2+} (Metz *et al.*, 1987). This requirement has been attributed to formation of Ca^{2+}–arachidonic acid complexes in Ca^{2+}-containing medium and to consequent depletion of the free arachidonic acid concentration (Metz, 1988*a*). Irrespective of the merits of this idea, stimulation of secretion by arachidonic acid is not sufficient evidence upon which to base a hypothesis concerning the messenger role of this molecule. For this reason, a number of groups have investigated whether arachidonic acid can modulate intracellular events in the B-cell.

Effects of arachidonic acid on Ca^{2+} mobilization

Metz *et al.* (1987) reported that exogenous arachidonic acid increased fura 2 fluorescence in dispersed islet cells incubated in Ca^{2+}-depleted medium. This could have been owing to release of Ca^{2+} from intracellular stores, since treatment of permeabilized islets with exogenous arachidonic acid induced the release of Ca^{2+} from endoplasmic reticulum (Wolf *et al.*, 1986). Wollheim & Biden (1986*b*) also demonstrated arachidonic acid-induced Ca^{2+} mobilization from B-cell endoplasmic reticulum, but they concluded that the effect was due to membrane disruption and unlikely to be of physiological significance.

Incubation of islets under conditions designed to promote activation of phospholipase A_2 (e.g. with melittin) also led to intracellular Ca^{2+} mobilization (Morgan *et al.*, 1987*a,b*), although the dose–response relationship did not correlate well with either arachidonic acid release or insulin secretion. Metz (1988*a*) has criticized these experiments on the basis of failure to achieve isotopic equilibrium during labelling with $^{45}Ca^{2+}$. However, in long-term labelling experiments, he was able to show that 2 μg/ml melittin induced only marginal Ca^{2+} release (Metz, 1988*a*) under conditions when arachidonic acid release was increased 4-fold and secretion was enhanced by up to 10-fold (Metz, 1986*a*).

Thus, there is a limited amount of evidence to support the idea that free arachidonic acid might cause Ca^{2+} release in the B-cell, and, since nutrient-induced insulin secretion is essentially independent of intracellular Ca^{2+} mobilization, it is doubtful whether this is of physiological significance.

Activation of protein kinase C by arachidonic acid

In 1984, McPhail *et al.* reported that arachidonic acid could activate protein kinase C from human neutrophils, raising the possibility of a similar mechanism in islets. To date, there is no direct evidence to support this concept, although the stimulatory effect of arachidonic acid on insulin secretion from permeabilized islets was prevented under conditions when protein kinase C activity was depleted (Metz, 1988*a*). Since protein kinase C is probably not a major signalling factor in stimulation of insulin secretion by glucose (see Chapter 12 by Persuad *et al.* in this book) any effects on the enzyme are likely to be of significance only as modulators of insulin secretion rate.

Lysophospholipids and insulin secretion

Activation of phospholipases of either the A_1 or A_2 types yields a free fatty acid as one product and lysophospholipid as the other. This is significant since the presence of these components may alter the physical properties of biological membranes, and could be important in facilitating the process of exocytosis. Indeed, Metz (1987*b*) has argued that an increase in membrane lyso-PtdCho accumulation of as little as 10–15 % could be sufficient to initiate insulin secretion.

Addition of exogenous lysophospholipids (containing either ester- or ether-linked hydrocarbon chains) resulted in enhanced insulin output from rat islets (Metz, 1986*b*) which exhibited the biphasic time course characteristic of glucose stimulation (Metz, 1987b). This was attributed to translocation of the lipid to the inner leaflet of the plasma membrane, which is the presumed site of production of lysophospholipid in the cell. Stimulation of insulin secretion by lysophospholipids exhibited a degree of substrate specificity with either lyso-PtdIns or lyso-PtdCho being effective, whereas lysophosphatidic acid was not (Metz, 1986c, 1987b; Fujimoto & Metz, 1987).

Incubation of islets under conditions favouring a rise in lysophospholipid production was associated with stimulation of insulin secretion (Fujimoto & Metz, 1987) and with mobilization of cellular Ca^{2+} (Metz, 1988b). However, direct measurement of endogenous lyso-PtdCho levels in glucose-stimulated rat islets revealed that glucose promoted a net decrease rather than an increase (Turk et al., 1986b). This was not a modest effect, since 28 mM-glucose reduced islet lyso-PtdCho levels by as much as 10-fold (Turk et al., 1986b). Since PtdCho is a major substrate for islet phospholipase A_2, this observation raises serious questions about the possibility that lyso-PtdCho could be involved in stimulation of insulin secretion. Further studies seem warranted to resolve this discrepancy.

PC hydrolysis as a signalling mechanism in the B-cell

In addition to the well-characterized phospholipid signalling systems described above, recent studies have revealed the presence of an agonist-stimulated hydrolysis of PtdCho in some cells (Exton, 1990; Loffelholz, 1989). This reflects the rapid activation of a phospholipase D enzyme which hydrolyses PtdCho to yield phosphatidic acid and free choline. The physiological significance of this process is unclear at present, but generation of phosphatidic acid has been associated with alterations of several intracellular messenger systems in cells (Exton, 1989). Indeed, exogenous phosphatidic acid has recently been reported to increase adenylate cyclase activity and phosphoinositide hydrolysis in neonatal islets (Dunlop & Larkins, 1989).

It is not clear whether incubation of islets with glucose promotes phospholipase D activation, but there is evidence to suggest that B-cells contain a phospholipase D activity which can be activated by pharmacological agents (Dunlop & Metz, 1989). It will be of interest to determine whether this enzyme also becomes activated in nutrient-stimulated islets.

Conclusions

The studies reported in this review show quite clearly that there is a dramatic increase in the metabolism of a variety of phospholipids in the pancreatic B-cell during nutrient-stimulated insulin secretion. This increased turnover of membrane phospholipids is thought to play a number of important roles in the secretory process. Thus, evidence has been presented in this review for the involvement of phospholipid metabolism in the stimulus–secretion coupling mechanism of the B-cell and in the exocytotic insulin release process itself. However, it should always be remembered that the turnover of membrane phospholipids may follow as a consequence of the secretory process rather than being instrumental in causing or controlling the process.

References

Allen, D. & Michell, R. H. (1975) Accumulation of 1,2-diacylglycerol in the plasma membrane may lead to echinocyte transformation of erythrocytes. Nature (London) **258**, 343–349

Axen, K. V., Schubart, U. K., Blake, A. D. & Fleisher, N. (1983) Role of Ca^{2+} in secretagogue-stimulated breakdown of phosphatidylinositol in rat pancreatic islets. J. Clin. Invest. **72**, 13–21

Berggren, P.-O., Hallberg, A., Welsh, N., Arkhammar, P., Nilsson, T. & Welsh, M. (1989) Transfection of insulin-producing cells with a transforming c-Ha-ras oncogene stimulates phospholipase C activity. Biochem. J. **259**, 701–707

Best, L. (1986) A role for calcium in the breakdown of inositol phospholipids in intact and digitonin-permeabilized pancreatic islets. Biochem. J. **238**, 773–779

Best, L. & Malaisse, W. J. (1983a) Stimulation of phosphoinositide breakdown in rat pancreatic islets by glucose and carbamylcholine. Biochem. Biophys. Res. Commun. **116**, 9–16

Best, L. & Malaisse, W. J. (1983b) Phosphatidylinositol and phosphatidic acid metabolism in rat pancreatic islets in response to neurotransmitter and hormonal stimuli. Biochim. Biophys. Acta **750**, 157–163

Best, L. & Malaisse, W. J. (1984) Nutrient and hormone-neurotransmitter stimuli induce hydrolysis of polyphosphoinositides in rat pancreatic islets. Endocrinology **115**, 1814–1820

Best, L., Lebrun, P., Saceda, M., Garcia-Morales, P., Malaisse-Lagae, F., Valverde, I. & Malaisse, W. J. (1984a) Impairment of insulin release by methylation inhibitors. Biochem. Pharmacol. **33**, 2033–2039

Best, L., Sener, A. & Malaisse, W. J. (1984b) Does glucose affect phospholipase A_2 activity in pancreatic islets? Biochem. Int. **8**, 803–809

Best, L., Sener, A., Mathias, P. C. F. & Malaisse, W. J. (1984c) Inhibition by mepacrine and p-bromophenacyl-bromide of phosphoinositide hydrolysis, glucose oxidation, calcium uptake and insulin release in rat pancreatic islets. Biochem. Pharmacol. **33**, 2657–2662

Best, L., Tomlinson, S., Hawkins, P. T. & Downes, C. P. (1987) Production of inositol trisphosphates and inositol tetrakisphosphate in stimulated pancreatic islets. Biochim. Biophys. Acta **927**, 112–116

Biden, T. J. & Wollheim, C. B. (1986a) Active transport of *myo*-inositol in rat pancreatic islets. Biochem. J. **236**, 889–893

Biden, T. J. & Wollheim, C. B. (1986b) Ca^{2+} regulates the inositol tris/tetrakis-phosphate pathway in intact and broken preparations of insulin-secreting RINm5F cells. J. Biol. Chem. **261**, 11931–11934

Biden, T. J., Prentki, M., Irvine, R. F., Berridge, M. J. & Wollheim, C. B. (1984) Inositol 1,4,5-trisphosphate mobilizes intracellular Ca^{2+} from permeabilized insulin-secreting cells. Biochem. J. **223**, 467–473

Biden, T. J., Peter-Reisch, B., Schlegel, W. & Wollheim, C. B. (1987a) Ca^{2+}-mediated generation of inositol 1,4,5-trisphosphate and inositol 1,3,4,5-tetrakisphosphate in pancreatic islets: studies with K^+, glucose and carbamylcholine. J. Biol. Chem. **262**, 3567–3571

Biden, T. J., Comte, M., Cox, J. A. & Wollheim, C. B. (1987b) Calcium–calmodulin stimulates inositol 1,4,5-trisphosphate kinase activity from insulin secreting RINm5F cells. J. Biol. Chem. **262**, 9437–9440

Blachier, F. & Malaisse, W. J. (1987) Possible role of a GTP-binding protein in the activation of phospholipase C by carbamylcholine in tumoral insulin-producing cells. Res. Commun. Chem. Path. Pharmacol. **58**, 237–255

Blachier, F. & Malaisse, W. J. (1988) Effect of exogenous ATP upon inositol phosphate production, cationic fluxes and insulin release in pancreatic islet cells. Biochim. Biophys. Acta **970**, 222–229

Chang, J., Musser, J. H. & McGregor, H. (1987) Phospholipase A_2: function and pharmacological regulation. Biochem. Pharmacol. **15**, 2429–2436

Chiba, T., Yamatani, T., Kadowaki, S., Yamaguchi, A., Inui, T., Saito, Y. & Fujita, T. (1987) Glucose stimulates insulin release without altering cyclic AMP production or inositol phospholipid turnover in freshly obtained human insulinoma cells. Biochem. Biophys. Res. Commun. **145**, 263–268

Clements, R. S., Evans, M. H. & Pace, C. S. (1981) Substrate requirements for the phosphoinositide response in rat pancreatic islets. Biochim. Biophys. Acta **674**, 1–9

Cortizo, A. M., Garcia, M. E. & Gagliardiono, J. J. (1987) Effect of glucose upon pancreatic islet fatty acid composition. Med. Sci. Res. **15**, 289–290

Deleers, M., Ruysschaert, J. M. & Malaisse, W. J. (1981) Glucose induces membrane changes detected by fluorescence polarisation in endocrine pancreatic cells. Biochem. Biophys. Res. Commun. **98**, 255–260

Dho, S., Grinstein, S., Corey, E. J., Su, W.-G. & Pace-Asciak, C. R. (1990) Hepoxilin A_3 induces changes in cytosolic calcium, intracellular pH and membrane potential in human neutrophils. Biochem. J. **266**, 63–68

Dunlop, M. E. & Larkins, R. G. (1984) The role of calcium in phospholipid turnover following glucose stimulation in neonatal rat cultured islets. J. Biol. Chem. **259**, 8407–8411

Dunlop, M. E. & Larkins, R. G. (1985) Pancreatic islets synthesize phospholipids de novo from glucose via acyl-dihydroxyacetone phosphate. Biochem. Biophys. Res. Commun. **132**, 467–473

Dunlop, M. E. & Larkins, R. G. (1986) Muscarinic-agonist and guanine nucleotide activation of polyphosphoinositide phosphodiesterase in isolated islet cell membranes. Biochem. J. **240**, 731–737

Dunlop, M. E. & Larkins, R. G. (1988) GTP- and inositol 1,4,5-trisphosphate-induced release of $^{45}Ca^{2+}$ from a membrane store co-localized with pancreatic-islet-cell plasma membrane. Biochem. J. **253**, 67–72

Dunlop, M. E. & Larkins, R. G. (1989) Effects of phosphatidic acid on islet cell phosphoinositide hydrolysis, Ca^{2+} and adenylate cyclase. Diabetes **38**, 1187–1192

Dunlop, M. E. & Malaisse, W. J. (1986) Phosphoinositide phosphorylation and hydrolysis in pancreatic islet cell membranes. Arch. Biochem. Biophys. **244**, 421–429

Dunlop, M. E. & Metz, S. A. (1989) A phospholipase D-like mechanism in pancreatic islet cells: stimulation by calcium, ionophore, phorbol ester and sodium fluoride. Biochem. Biophys. Res. Commun. **163**, 922–928

Dunlop, M. E., Christanthou, A., Fletcher, A., Veroni, M., Woodman, P. & Larkins, R. G. (1984) Effects of inhibitors of eicosanoid synthesis on insulin release by neonatal pancreatic islets. Biochim. Biophys. Acta **801**, 10–15

Evans, M. H., Pace, C. S. & Clements, R. S. (1983) Endogenous prostaglandin synthesis and glucose-induced insulin secretion from the adult rat pancreatic islets. Diabetes **32**, 509–515

Exton, J. H. (1990) Signaling through phosphatidylcholine breakdown. J. Biol. Chem. **265**, 1–4

Fain, J. N., Wallace, N. A. & Wojcikiewicz, R. J. (1988) Evidence for involvement of guanine nucleotide-binding regulatory proteins in the activation of phospholipases by hormones. FASEB J. **2**, 2569–2574

Farese, R. V., DiMarco, P. E., Barnes, D. E., Sabir, M. A., Larson, R. E., Davis, J. S. & Morrison, A. D. (1986) Rapid glucose-dependent increase in phosphatidic acid and phosphoinositides in rat pancreatic islets. Endocrinology **118**, 1498–1503

Fex, G. & Lernmark, A. (1972) Effect of D-glucose on the incorporation of ^{32}P into phospholipids of mouse pancreatic islets. FEBS Lett. **25**, 287–291

Fujimoto, W. Y. & Metz, S. A. (1987) Phasic effects of glucose, phospholipase A_2 and lysophospholipids on insulin secretion. Endocrinology **120**, 1750–1757

Hallberg, A. (1984) Effects of starvation and different culture conditions on the phospholipid content of isolated pancreatic islets. Biochim. Biophys. Acta **796**, 328–335

Hallberg, A. (1986) Dissociation of phosphatidylinositol hydrolysis and insulin secretion of cultured mouse pancreatic islets. Acta Physiol. Scand. **128**, 267–276

Heaney, T. P. & Larkins, R. G. (1981) The effect of prostacyclin and 6-keto-prostaglandin $F_{1\alpha}$ on insulin secretion and cyclic adenosine $3',5'$-monophosphate content in isolated rat islets. Diabetes **30**, 824–828

Hellman, B., Gylfe, E. & Wesslen, N. (1986) Inositol 1,4,5-trisphosphate mobilizes glucose-incorporated calcium from pancreatic islets. Biochem. Int. **13**, 383–389

Hirata, F. & Axelrod, J. (1978) Enzymatic methylation of phosphatidylethanolamine increases erythrocyte membrane fluidity. Nature (London) **275**, 219–220

Hirata, F. & Axelrod, J. (1980) Phospholipid methylation and biological signal transmission. Science **209**, 1082–1090

Irvine, R. F. (1982) How is the level of free arachidonic acid controlled in mammalian cells? Biochem. J. **204**, 3–16

Joseph, S. K., Williams, R. J., Corkey, B. E., Matschinsky, F. M. & Williamson, J. R. (1984) The effect of inositol trisphosphate on Ca^{2+} fluxes in insulin-secreting tumour cells. J.Biol. Chem. **259**, 12952–12955

Kelly, K. L. & Laychock, S. G. (1981) Prostaglandin synthesis and metabolism in isolated islets of the rat. Prostaglandins **21**, 759–769

Kelly, K. L. & Laychock, S. G. (1984) Activity of prostaglandin biosynthetic pathways in rat pancreatic islets. Prostaglandins **27**, 925–938

Kolesnik, R. N., Musacchio, I., Colette, T. & Gershengorn, M. C. (1984) Arachidonic acid mobilizes calcium and stimulates prolactin secretion from GH3 cells. Am. J. Physiol. **246**, E458–E462

Kowluru, A., Rana, R. S. & MacDonald, M. J. (1984) Stimulation of phospholipid methylation by glucose in pancreatic islets. Biochem. Biophys. Res. Commun. **122**, 706–711

Lacy, P. E. (1961) Electron microscopy of beta cells of the pancreas. Am. J. Med. **31**, 851–859

Laychock, S. G. (1982) Phospholipase A_2 activity in pancreatic islets is calcium-dependent and stimulated by glucose. Cell Calcium **3**, 43–54

Laychock, S. G. (1983a) Identification and metabolism of polyphosphoinositides in isolated islets of Langerhans. Biochem. J. **216**, 101–106

Laychock, S. G. (1983b) Fatty acid incorporation into phospholipids of isolated pancreatic islets of the rat. Relationship to insulin release. Diabetes **32**, 6–13

Laychock, S. G. (1985) Phosphatidylethanolamine N-methylation and insulin release in isolated pancreatic islets of the rat. Mol. Pharmacol. **27**, 66–73

Laychock, S. G. (1989a) Prostaglandin E_2 inhibits phosphoinositide metabolism in isolated pancreatic islets. Biochem. J. **260**, 291–294

Laychock, S. G. (1989b) Prostaglandin E_2 and alpha 2 adrenoceptor agonists inhibit the pentose phosphate shunt in pancreatic islets. Arch. Biochem. Biophys. **269**, 354–358

Laychock, S. G., Hoffman, J. M., Meisel, E. & Bilgin, S. (1986) Pancreatic islet arachidonic acid turnover and metabolism and insulin release in response to delta-9-tetrahydrocannabinol. Biochem. Pharmacol. **35**, 2003–2008

Loffelholz, K. (1989) Receptor regulation of choline phospholipid hydrolysis. A novel source of diacylglycerol and phosphatidic acid. Biochem. Pharmacol. **38**, 1543–1549

MacAdams, M. R., Pek, S. B. & Lands, W. E. M. (1984) The effect of flurbiprofen, a potent inhibitor of prostaglandin synthesis on insulin and glucagon release from isolated rat pancreas. Endocrinology **114**, 1364–1370

MacDonald, M. J., Fahien, L. A., Mertz, R. J. & Rana, R. S. (1989a) Effect of esters of succinic acid and other citric acid cycle intermediate on insulin release and inositol phosphate formation by pancreatic islets. Arch. Biochem. Biophys. **269**, 400–406

MacDonald, M. J., Mertz, R. J. & Rana, R. S. (1989b) Glyceraldehyde phosphate: an insulin secretagogue with possible effects on inositol phosphate formation in pancreatic islets. Arch. Biochem. Biophys. **269**, 194–200

McPhail, L. C., Clayton, C. C. & Snyderman, R. (1984) A potential second messenger role for unsaturated fatty acids, activation of Ca^{2+}-dependent protein kinase. Science **224**, 622–624

Malaisse, W. J., Dunlop, M. E., Mathias, P. C. F., Malaisse-Lagae, F. & Sener, A. (1985) Stimulation of protein kinase C and insulin release by 1-oleoyl-2-acetyl-glycerol. Eur. J. Biochem. **149**, 23–27

Mathias, P. C. F., Best, L. & Malaisse, W. J. (1985a) Stimulation by glucose and carbamyl choline of phospholipase C in pancreatic islets. Diabetes Res. **2**, 267–270

Mathias, P. C. F., Best, L. & Malaisse, W. J. (1985b) Stimulation by glucose and carbamylcholine of phospholipase C in pancreatic islets. Cell Biochem. Func. **3**, 173–177

Metz, S. A. (1985) Glucose increases the synthesis of lipoxygenase-mediated metabolites of arachidonic acid in intact rat islets. Proc. Natl. Acad. Sci. U.S.A. **82**, 198–202

Metz, S. A. (1986a) Lack of specificity of melittin as a probe for insulin release mediated by endogenous phospholipase A_2 or lipoxygenase. Biochem. Pharmacol. **35**, 3371–3383

Metz, S. A. (1986b) Ether-linked lysophospholipids initiate insulin secretion. Lysophospholipids may mediate effects of phospholipase A_2 activation on hormone release. Diabetes **35**, 808–817

Metz, S. A. (1986c) Lysophosphatidylinositol but not lysophosphatidic acid stimulates insulin release. A possible role for phospholipase A_2 but not de novo synthesis of lysophospholipid in pancreatic islet function. Biochem. Biophys. Res. Commun. **138**, 720–727

Metz, S. A. (1987a) Lipoxygenase inhibitors reduce insulin secretion without impairing calcium mobilization. Endocrinology **120**, 2534–2546

Metz, S. A. (1987b) Metabolism of lysophospholipids in intact rat islets. The insulin secretagogue p-hydroxymercuribenzoic acid impairs lysophosphatidyl choline catabolism and permits its accumulation. Biochem. J. **241**, 863–869

Metz, S. A. (1988a) Membrane phospholipid turnover as an intermediary step in insulin secretion. Putative roles of phospholipases in cell signalling. Am. J. Med. **85**, (5A) 9–21

Metz, S. A. (1988b) Mobilization of cellular Ca^{2+} by lysophospholipids in rat islets of Langerhans. Biochim. Biophys. Acta **968**, 239–252

Metz, S. A., Robertson, R. P. & Fujimoto, W. Y. (1981) Inhibition of prostaglandin E synthesis augments glucose-induced insulin secretion in cultured pancreas. Diabetes **30**, 551–557

Metz, S. A., Fujimoto, W. Y. & Robertson, R. P. (1982) Lipoxygenation of arachidonic acid: a pivotal step in stimulus–secretion coupling in the pancreatic beta cell. Endocrinology **111**, 2141–2143

Metz, S. A., VanRollins, M., Strife, R., Fujimoto, W. & Robertson, R. P. (1983) Lipoxygenase pathway in islet endocrine cells. Oxidative metabolism of arachidonic acid promotes insulin release. J. Clin. Invest. **71**, 1191–1205

Metz, S. A., Murphy, R. C. & Fujimoto, W. (1984) Effects on glucose-induced insulin secretion of lipoxygenase-derived metabolites of arachidonic acid. Diabetes **33**, 119–124

Metz, S. A., Draznin, B., Sussman, K. E. & Leitner, J. W. (1987) Unmasking of arachidonate-induced insulin release by removal of extracellular calcium. Biochem. Biophys. Res. Commun. **142**, 251–258

Montague, W. & Parkin, E. N. (1980) Changes in membrane lipids of the B-cell during insulin secretion. Horm. Metab. Res. **12**, 153–157

Montague, W., Morgan, N. G., Rumford, G. M. & Prince, C. A. (1985) Effect of glucose on polyphosphoinositide metabolism in isolated rat islets of Langerhans. Biochem. J. **227**, 483–489

Morgan, N. G. (1989) Cell Signalling, p. 203, Open Univ. Press, Buckingham

Morgan, N. G. & Hurst, R. D. (1988) Dissociation between intracellular calcium mobilization and insulin secretion in isolated rat islets of Langerhans. FEBS Lett. **227**, 153–156

Morgan, N. G. & Montague, W. (1984) Stimulation of insulin secretion from isolated rat islets of Langerhans by melittin. Biosci. Rep. **4**, 665–671

Morgan, N. G., Rumford, G. M. & Montague, W. (1985a) Studies on the role of inositol trisphosphate in the regulation of insulin secretion from isolated rat islets of Langerhans. Biochem. J. **228**, 713–718

Morgan, N. G., Rumford, G. M. & Montague, W. (1985b) Studies on the mechanism by which melittin stimulates insulin secretion from isolated rat islets of Langerhans. Biochim. Biophys. Acta **845**, 526–532

Morgan, N. G., Hurst, R. D., Rumford, G. M. & Montague, W. (1987a) Intracellular Ca^{2+} mobilization in isolated rat islets of Langerhans. Biochem. Soc. Trans. **15**, 939–940

Morgan, N. G., Rumford, G. M. & Montague, W. (1987b) Mechanisms involved in intracellular calcium mobilization in isolated islets of Langerhans. Biochem. J. **244**, 669–674

Morgan, N. G., Hurst, R. D., Berrow, N. S. & Montague, W. (1989) Calcium handling by stimulated islets of Langerhans. Biochem. Soc. Trans. **17**, 64–66

Morgan, R. O. & Pek, S. B. (1984) Role of arachidonate lipoxygenase and cyclooxygenase products in insulin and glucagon secretion from rat pancreatic islets. Metabolism **33**, 928–935

Navarro, J., Toivio-Kinnucan, M. & Racker, E. (1984) Effect of lipid composition on the calcium/adenosine 5'-trisphosphate coupling ratio of the Ca^{2+}-ATPase of sarcoplasmic reticulum. Biochemistry **23**, 130–135

Needleman, P., Turk, J., Jakschik, B. A., Morrison, A. R. & Lefkowith, J. B. (1986) Arachidonic acid metabolism. Annu. Rev. Biochem. **55**, 69–102

Nilsson, T., Arkhammar, P., Hallberg, A., Hellman, B. & Berggren, P.-O. (1987) Characterization of the inositol 1,4,5-trisphosphate-induced Ca^{2+} release in pancreatic beta-cells. Biochem. J. **248**, 329–336

Orci, L. (1974) A portrait of the pancreatic B-cell. Diabetologia **10**, 163–187

Pace, C. S. & Clements, R. S. (1981) Myo-inositol and the maintenance of beta-cell function in cultured rat pancreatic islets. Diabetes **30**, 621–625

Pace-Asciak, C. R. & Martin, J. M. (1984) Hepoxilin, a new family of insulin secretagogues formed by intact rat pancreatic islets. Prost. Leuk. Med. **16**, 173–180

Pace-Asciak, C. R., Martin, J. M., Corey, E. J. & Su, W. G. (1985) Endogenous release of hepoxilin A3 from isolated perifused pancreatic islets of Langerhans. Biochem. Biophys. Res. Commun. **128**, 942–946

Patrono, C., Pugliese, F., Ciabattoni, G., DiBlasi, S., Pierucci, A., Cinotti, G. A., Maseri, A. & Chierchia, S. (1981) Prostacyclin does not affect insulin secretion in humans. Prostaglandins **21**, 379–385

Pek, S. B. & Walsh, M. F. (1984) Leukotrienes stimulate insulin release from the rat pancreas. Proc. Natl. Acad. Sci. U.S.A. **81**, 2199–2202

Pek, S. B., Tai, T.-Y., Elster, A. & Fajans, S. S. (1975) Stimulation by prostaglandin E2 of glucagon and insulin release from isolated rat pancreas. Prostaglandins **10**, 493–502

Pek, S. B., Tai, T.-Y. & Elster, A. (1978) Stimulatory effects of prostaglandins E-1, E-2 and F-2-alpha on glucagon and insulin release in vitro. Diabetes **27**, 801–809

Peter-Reisch, B., Fathi, M., Schlegel, W. & Wollheim, C. B. (1988) Glucose and carbachol generate 1,2-diacylglycerols by different mechanisms in pancreatic islets. J. Clin. Invest **81**, 1154–1161

Phair, R. D., Pek, S. B. & Lands, W. E. M. (1984) Arachidonic acid induced release of insulin and glucagon: role of endogenous prostaglandins in pancreatic hormone secretion. Diabete Metabolisme **10**, 71–77

Pralong, W.-F., Bartley, C. & Wollheim, C. B. (1990) Single islet beta-cell stimulation by nutrients: relationship between pyridine nucleotides, cytosolic Ca^{2+} and secretion. EMBO J. **9**, 53–60

Prentki, M. & Matschinsky, F. M. (1987) Ca^{2+}, cAMP, and phospholipid-derived messengers in coupling mechanisms of insulin secretion. Physiol. Rev. **67**, 1185–1247

Prentki, M., Biden, T. J., Janjic, D., Irvine, R. F., Berridge, M. J. & Wollheim, C. B. (1984) Rapid mobilization of Ca^{2+} from rat insulinoma microsomes by inositol-1,4,5-trisphosphate. Nature (London) **309**, 562–564

Prentki, M., Corkey, B. E. & Matschinsky, F. M. (1985) Inositol 1,4,5-trisphosphate and the endoplasmic reticulum Ca^{2+} cycle of a rat insulinoma cell line. J. Biol. Chem. **260**, 9185–9190

Rana, R. S. & MacDonald, M. J. (1986) Phosphatidylinositol kinase in rat pancreatic islets: subcellular distribution and sensitivity to calcium. Horm. Metab. Res. **18**, 659–662

Rana, R. S., Mertz, R. J., Kowluru, A., Dixon, J. F., Hokin, L. E. & MacDonald, M. J. (1985) Evidence for glucose-responsive and -unresponsive pools of phospholipid in pancreatic islets. J. Biol. Chem. **260**, 7861–7867

Rana, R. S., Kowluru, A. & MacDonald, M. J. (1986a) Enzymes of phospholipid metabolism in rat pancreatic islets: subcellular distribution and the effect of glucose and calcium. J. Cell. Biochem. **32**, 143–150

Rana, R. S., Kowluru, A. & MacDonald, M. J. (1986b) Secretagogue-responsive and -unresponsive pools of phosphatidylinositol in pancreatic islets. Arch. Biochem. Biophys. **245**, 411–416

Rana, R. S., Sekar, M. C., Hokin, L. E. & MacDonald, M. J. (1986c) A possible role for glucose metabolites in the regulation of inositol 1,4,5-trisphosphate 5-phosphomonoesterase activity in pancreatic islets. J. Biol. Chem. **261**, 5237–5240

Rana, R. S., Sekar, M. C., Mertz, R. J., Hokin, L. E. & MacDonald, M. J. (1987)

Potentiation by glucose metabolites of inositol trisphosphate-induced calcium mobilization in permeabilized rat pancreatic islets. J. Biol. Chem. **262**, 13567–13570

Robertson, R. P. (1983) Hypothesis: PGE, carbohydrate homeostasis and insulin secretion. A suggested resolution of the controversy. Diabetes **32**, 231–234

Robertson, R. P. (1986) Arachidonic acid regulation of insulin secretion. Diabetes Metab. Rev. **2**, 261–296

Robertson, R. P. (1988) Eicosanoids as pluripotential modulators of pancreatic islet function. Diabetes **37**, 367–370

Robertson, R. P., Tsai, P., Little, S. A., Zhang, H.-J. & Walseth, T. F. (1987) Receptor-mediated adenylate cyclase coupled mechanism for PGE2 inhibition of insulin secretion in HIT cells. Diabetes **36**, 1047–1053

Saceda, M., Garcia-Morales, P., Malaisse, W. J. & Valverde, I. (1985) Calcium dependency of glucose stimulated phospholipid methylation in rat pancreatic islets. IRCS Med. Sci. **13**, 110–111

Schmitt, J. K., Davis, J. L., Lorenzi, M., Benet, L., Burns, A. & Karam, J. H. (1980) Inhibition by indomethacin of the glycemic response to arginine in man. Proc. Soc. Exp. Biol. Med. **163**, 237–239

Schrey, M. P. & Montague, W. (1983) Phosphatidylinositol hydrolysis in isolated guinea-pig islets of Langerhans. Biochem. J. **216**, 433–441

Tadayyon, M., Bonney, R. C. & Green, I. C. (1990) Starvation decreases insulin secretion, prostaglandin E production and phospholipase A_2 activity in rat pancreatic islet. J. Endocrinol. **124**, 455–461

Tanaka, N., Kagawa, S., Murakoso, K., Shimizu, S. & Matsuoka, A. (1983) Enhancement of insulin release due to inhibition of phospholipase A_2 activity. Horm. Metab. Res. **15**, 255–256

Tooke, N. E., Hales, C. N. & Hutton, J. C. (1984) Ca^{2+}-sensitive phosphatidylinositol-4-phosphate metabolism in a rat B-cell tumour. Biochem. J. **219**, 471–480

Turk, J., Colca, J. R., Kotagal, N. & McDaniel, M. L. (1984a) Arachidonic acid metabolism in isolated pancreatic islets. I. Identification and quantitation of lipoxygenase and cyclooxygenase products. Biochim. Biophys. Acta **794**, 110–124

Turk, J., Colca, J. R., Kotagal, N. & McDaniel, M. L. (1984b) Arachidonic acid metabolism in isolated pancreatic islets. II. The effect of glucose and of inhibitors of arachidonate metabolism on insulin secretion and metabolite synthesis. Biochim. Biophys. Acta **794**, 125–136

Turk, J., Colca, J. R. & McDaniel, M. L. (1985) Arachidonic acid metabolism in isolated pancreatic islets. III. Effects of exogenous lipoxygenase products and inhibitors on insulin secretion. Biochim. Biophys. Acta **834**, 23–36

Turk, J., Wolf, B. A. & McDaniel, M. L. (1986a) Glucose-induced accumulation of inositol-trisphosphates in isolated pancreatic islets. Predominance of the 1,3,4-isomer. Biochem. J. **237**, 259–263

Turk, J., Wolf, B. A., Lefkowith, J. B., Stump, W. T. & McDaniel, M. L. (1986b) Glucose-induced phospholipid hydrolysis in isolated pancreatic islets: quantitative effects on the phospholipid content of arachidonate and other fatty acids. Biochim. Biophys. Acta **879**, 399–409

Turk, J., Wolf, B. A. & McDaniel, M. L. (1987) The role of phospholipid-derived mediators including arachidonic acid, its metabolites and inositol trisphosphate and of intracellular Ca^{2+} in glucose-induced insulin secretion by pancreatic islets. Prog. Lipid Res. **26**, 125–181

Turk, J., Hughes, J. H., Easom, R. A., Wolf, B. A., Scharp, D. W., Lacy, P. E. & McDaniel, M. L. (1988) Arachidonic acid metabolism and insulin secretion by isolated human pancreatic islets. Diabetes **37**, 992–996

Vallar, L., Biden, T. J. & Wollheim, C. B. (1987) Guanine nucleatides induce Ca^{2+}-independent insulin secretion from permeabilized RINm5F cells. J. Biol. Chem. **262**, 5049–5056

Vara, E. & Tamarit-Rodriguez, J. (1986) Glucose stimulation of insulin secretion in islets of fed and starved rats and its dependence on lipid metabolism. Metabolism **35**, 266–271

Walsh, M. F. & Pek, S. B. (1984a) Possible role of endogenous arachidonic acid metabolites in stimulated release of insulin and glucagon from the isolated perfused rat pancreas. Diabetes **33**, 929–936

Walsh, M. F. & Pek, S. B. (1984*b*) Effects of lipoxygenase and cyclooxygenase inhibitors on glucose-stimulated insulin secretion from the isolated perfused pancreas. Life Sci. **34**, 1699–1706

Wolf, B. A., Comens, P. G., Ackerman, K. E., Sherman, W. R. & McDaniel, M. L. (1985) The digitonin-permeabilized pancreatic islet model. Effect of *myo*-inositol 1,4,5-trisphosphate on Ca^{2+} mobilization. Biochem. J. **227**, 965–969

Wolf, B. A., Turk, J., Sherman, W. R. & McDaniel, M. L. (1986) Intracellular Ca^{2+} mobilization by arachidonic acid. Comparison with myo-inositol 1,4,5-trisphosphate in isolated pancreatic islets. J. Biol. Chem. **261**, 3501–3511

Wolf, B. A., Florholmen, J., Colca, J. R. & McDaniel, M. L. (1987) GTP mobilization of Ca^{2+} from the endoplasmic reticulum of islets. Comparison with *myo*-inositol 1,4,5-trisphosphate. Biochem. J. **242**, 137–141

Wolf, B. A., Florholmen, J., Turk, J. & McDaniel, M. L. (1988) Studies of the Ca^{2+} requirement for glucose- and carbachol-induced augmentation of inositol trisphosphate and inositol tetrakisphosphate accumulation in digitonin-permeabilized islets. J. Biol. Chem. **263**, 3565–3575

Wolf, B. A., Easom, R. A., McDaniel, M. L. & Turk, J. (1990) Diacylglycerol synthesis De Novo from glucose by pancreatic islets isolated from rats and humans. J. Clin. Invest. **85**, 482–490

Wollheim, C. B. & Biden, T. J. (1986*a*) Second messenger function of inositol 1,4,5-trisphosphate. J. Biol. Chem. **261**, 8314—8319

Wollheim, C. B. & Biden, T. J. (1986*b*) Signal transduction in insulin secretion: comparison between fuel stimuli and receptor agonists. Ann. N.Y. Acad. Sci. **488**, 317–333

Wollheim, C. B. & Sharp, G. W. G. (1981) Regulation of insulin release by calcium. Physiol. Rev. **61**, 914–973

Wollheim, C. B., Ullrich, S., Meda, P. & Vallar, C. (1987) Regulation of exocytosis in electrically permeabilized insulin-secreting cells. Evidence for Ca^{2+} dependent and independent secretion. Biosci. Rep. **7**, 443–454

Yamamoto, S., Nakadate, T., Uzumaki, H. & Kato, R. (1985) Lipoxygenase inhibitors and cyclicAMP-mediated insulin secretion caused by forskolin, theophylline and dibutyryl cyclic AMP. Pharmacol. Exp. Ther. **233**, 176–180

Yokokawa, N., Komatsu, M., Takeda, T., Aizawa, T. & Yamada, T. (1989) Mastoparan, a wasp venom, stimulates insulin release by pancreatic islets through pertussis toxin sensitive GTP-binding protein. Biochem. Biophys. Res. Commun. **158**, 712–716

Zawalich, W. S., Takuwa, N., Takuwa, Y., Diaz, V. A. & Rasmussen, H. (1987) Interactions of cholecystokinin and glucose in rat pancreatic islets. Diabetes **36**, 426–433

Zawalich, W. S., Zawalich, K. C. & Rasmussen, H. (1989) The conditions under which rat islets are labelled with [^{3}H]inositol alter the subsequent responses of these islets to a high glucose concentration. Biochem. J. **259**, 743–749

8

Intracellular pH and B-cell function

Leonard Best

Department of Medicine, University of Manchester,
Manchester, M13 9WL, U.K.

Introduction

It will be clear from previous chapters that the stimulation of insulin release by a nutrient is related to both the generation of entero-insular stimuli and to the metabolism of that nutrient in the pancreatic B-cell. The processes of nutrient metabolism, whether a hexose such as glucose or a metabolizable keto- or amino-acid, would necessarily be accompanied by the generation of acidic metabolites, principally lactic acid and CO_2. From these basic premises, a number of interesting questions arise. First, is it possible that a change in intracellular pH (pHi) resulting from production of acidic metabolites could be a coupling factor linking nutrient metabolism and the altered ionic fluxes associated with enhanced insulin release? Secondly, what are the mechanisms whereby pHi is regulated in the B-cell? Thirdly, what are the consequences of pH regulation in terms of B-cell function?

The aims of this chapter are to assess the possible role of pHi as a coupling factor in nutrient-stimulated insulin secretion by examining the functional consequences of manipulating pHi and the changes in pHi reported to occur in nutrient-stimulated B-cells. In addition, the mechanisms by which pHi is regulated in B-cells and the possible significance and implications of such regulation will be explored.

Manipulation of B-cell pHi: effects on B-cell function

The initial suggestion that pHi might provide a link between nutrient metabolism and enhanced insulin release arose from experiments designed to pharmacologically manipulate pHi in a predictable fashion and to observe the consequences in terms of altered secretory, electrical or ionic activity. Such manipulations can be achieved in a number of ways (Fig. 1).

The inhibition of Na^+/H^+ exchange by the diuretic amiloride or its derivatives results in an intracellular acidification in B-cells (Pace & Tarvin, 1986; Deleers *et al.*, 1983, 1985; Best *et al.*, 1988*a,b*; Lynch *et al.*, 1989) and prevents recovery from an acid load (Lynch *et al.*, 1989). It

---

Fig. I. Principal antiport systems by which intracellular pH is regulated; manipulation of pHi by treatment with weak acids and bases

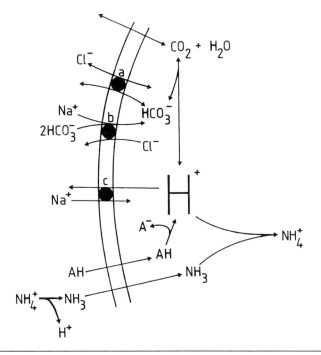

Abbreviations used: a and b, Na^+-independent and Na^+-dependent HCO_3^-/Cl^- exchangers (inhibited by SITS, DIDS and probenecid); c, amiloride-sensitive Na^+/H^+ exchanger; AH, weak acid.

---

should be noted, however, that amiloride has also been shown in other tissues to inhibit several Na^+-dependent processes including Na^+/Ca^{2+} exchange (Siegl *et al.*, 1984), Na^+/K^+-ATPase activity and Na^+-coupled amino acid transport (Renner *et al.*, 1988).

The stilbene disulphonates, 4,4'-di-isothiocyano-2,2'-stilbene disulphonic acid (DIDS) and 4-acetamido-4'-isothiocyanato-2,2'-stilbene disulphonic acid (SITS), have been shown in other tissues to inhibit both the Na^+-dependent and -independent HCO_3^-/Cl^- exchange systems (Frelin *et al.*, 1988) which would be predicted to result in acidification and alkalinization respectively. There have been no reports, to the author's knowledge, of the effects of these disulphonates on islet cell pHi, although they have been assumed to cause intracellular acidification (Pace *et al.*, 1983). Incubation of HIT-T15 insulinoma cells with either DIDS or SITS did not appear to influence either resting or stimulated changes in pHi (Trebilcock *et al.*, 1990). Withdrawal of extracellular bicarbonate has been reported to cause a sustained increase in pHi in rat islets (Lebrun *et al.*, 1982), although prolonged incubation of HIT-T15 cells in the absence of bicarbonate tended to result in lower resting pHi values (Trebilcock *et al.*, 1990). It should be borne in mind that manipulation of bicarbonate in the incubation medium could exert multiple effects on intracellular pH as discussed in a later section.

In the case of weak acid and weak base treatment, the predicted, respective fall and rise in B-cell pHi have been extensively demonstrated in native islet and HIT-T15 cells (Pace & Tarvin, 1986; Best *et al.*, 1988*a*, *b*; Lynch *et al.*, 1989).

pHi manipulation and insulin secretion

In the majority of studies, amiloride has been shown to enhance the basal rate of insulin secretion, although this effect is dependent on the presence of a low, substimulatory concentration of glucose (Pace *et al.*, 1983; Pace, 1984; Lebrun *et al.*, 1986; Best *et al.*, 1988*a*, *b*; Lynch *et al.*, 1989). Paradoxically, secretion evoked by a high concentration of glucose (16.7 mM) appeared to be suppressed by amiloride (Pace *et al.*, 1983; Biden *et al.*, 1986). In an attempt to rationalize this apparent inconsistency, we have recently shown that the potentiation of insulin release by amiloride is dependent on a substimulatory concentration of glucose or other nutrients as a source of acidic metabolites. However, in the presence of a high concentration of glucose, prolonged exposure to amiloride appeared to impair secretory activity (A. P. Yates & L. Best, unpublished work). The latter effect was associated with impaired glucose oxidation rate in the presence of amiloride, probably resulting from the prolonged reduction in pHi and hence inhibition of certain key glycolytic enzymes such as phosphofructokinase. Thus, the primary effect of amiloride on B-cell pHi and the secondary effect of the latter on nutrient oxidation rate could explain the stimulatory and inhibitory effects of the drug on B-cell function. Inhibition of B-cell Na^+/H^+ exchange by omission of Na^+ from the incubation medium produced essentially similar results to amiloride (Biden *et al.*, 1986) while exposure to monensin, an Na^+/H^+ ionophore, inhibited glucose-induced insulin release (Pace *et al.*, 1983; Kanatsuka *et al.*, 1987).

Fewer data exist concerning the secretory effects of the anion exchange inhibitors SITS and DIDS. Pace *et al.* (1983) reported enhanced secretory activity in rat islets in the presence of either DIDS or probenecid, another inhibitor of anion exchange pathways. These results suggest that these compounds caused an intracellular acidification, implying the existence of an Na^+-dependent HCO_3^-/Cl^- antiporter in rat islet cells.

Omission of Cl^- or HCO_3^- from the incubation medium would also be expected to block activity of the HCO_3^-/Cl^- antiporters. Incubation of *ob/ob* mouse islets in Cl^--deficient medium reversibly inhibited glucose-induced insulin release (Sehlin, 1978), although it was suggested that this could have reflected an involvement of Cl^- in membrane depolarization by the sugar. In the case of HCO_3^-, acute omission of this anion has been reported to cause a modest, transient inhibition of glucose-induced insulin secretion concomitant with a rise in islet cell pHi (Lebrun *et al.*, 1982). A considerable number of reports have emerged concerning the effects of weak acids and weak bases on insulin release, again with some inconsistencies arising. The weak acids sulphamerazine, acetate and propionate have been shown to potentiate glucose-induced insulin release in rat islets (Smith & Pace, 1983; Best *et al.*, 1988*b*) and in HIT-T15 cells (Lynch *et al.*, 1989). Similarly, exposure of rat islets to NH_4Cl or imidazole caused a rapid, reversible inhibition of insulin release (Best *et al.*, 1988*b*; Smith & Pace, 1983). In contrast with the above studies, most of which employed rat islets, Lindstrom & Sehlin (1984, 1986) have reported that raising pHi in mouse islets by treatment with NH_4Cl results in a potentiation of insulin secretion. Whether these discrepancies are solely a reflection of species differences remains to be established.

Electrical activity

The changes in secretory rate brought about by manipulating pHi appear to be accompanied by corresponding alterations in B-cell electrical activity, reflecting changes in ion permeability of the plasma membrane (for review of this topic see Chapters 9 and 10 by Henquin *et al.* and Ashcroft *et al.*). Thus, the potentiation of insulin secretion by amiloride or Na^+ omission was accompanied by depolarization and enhanced electrical activity of B-cells (Pace, 1984; Pace *et al.*, 1983; Pace & Tarvin, 1983; Eddlestone & Beigelman, 1983) while monensin inhibited glucose-induced electrical activity (Tarvin *et al.*, 1981; Pace *et al.*, 1983). Glucose-induced electrical activity of islet cells was also potentiated by inhibitors of HCO_3^-/Cl^- exchange, including DIDS, SITS and probenecid, or by omission of Cl^- or HCO_3^- from the medium (Pace *et al.*, 1983; Pace & Tarvin, 1983; Pace, 1984; Eddlestone & Beigelman, 1983). It was assumed that these manipulations would result in intracellular acidification.

Treatment of pancreatic islets with weak acids or bases has also been shown to cause the predicted effects on B-cell electrical activity. Thus, sulphamerazine caused B-cell depolarization and increased spike activity (Pace & Goldsmith, 1986), while NH_4Cl and imidazole resulted in hyperpolarization and inhibition of glucose-induced electrical activity (Tarvin et al., 1981; Pace et al., 1983; Smith & Pace, 1983).

Ionic fluxes

It is likely that the changes in B-cell secretory and electrical activity elicited by manipulating pHi are the result of altered ion permeability of the plasma membrane. The principal candidates which have received attention are K^+ and Ca^{2+}.

The efflux of $^{86}Rb^+$ (a convenient isotopic marker for K^+) from pre-loaded perifused islets has been used extensively as an index of K^+ permeability (see Chapter 9 by Henquin et al.). In general, $^{86}Rb^+$ efflux rate is reduced by manipulations designed to cause intracellular acidification, including amiloride (Lebrun et al., 1986, Best et al., 1988b), omission of Na^+ (Lebrun et al., 1989) and treatment with acetate, propionate (Best et al., 1988b) or CO_2 (Carpinelli & Malaisse, 1980). Conversely, NH_4Cl caused a marked increase in $^{86}Rb^+$ efflux rate (Best et al., 1988b). The effects of intracellular protons on K^+ permeability of the B-cell plasma membrane are likely to be mediated via interactions with one or more K^+ channels. It has been reported that the activity of one such channel, the large Ca^{2+}-activated K^+ conductance, is inhibited by a lowering of pHi (Cook et al., 1984; Rosario & Rojas, 1986), while a more recent study has reported a regulatory effect of protons on the nucleotide-sensitive K^+ channel (Misler et al., 1989).

The inhibition of K^+-channel activity by reduced pHi would tend to result in membrane depolarization, which would be consistent with the observed potentiation of glucose-induced electrical activity (spiking) and insulin release. It would also be predicted that altered Ca^{2+} fluxes would accompany these effects.

Studies of $^{45}Ca^{2+}$ efflux from pre-loaded perifused islets suggest that intracellular acidification and alkalinization are accompanied by reduced and enhanced rates of $^{45}Ca^{2+}$ efflux, respectively (Carpinelli et al., 1980; Lebrun et al., 1982, 1986; Best et al., 1988a,b). The modulation of $^{45}Ca^{2+}$ outflow by pHi is largely dependent upon the presence of Na^+ in the medium (Carpinelli et al., 1980; Lebrun et al., 1982; Best et al., 1988b), suggesting that protons inhibit the activity of the Na^+/Ca^{2+} exchange system (Malaisse et al., 1980). Such an action, in addition to depolarization of the plasma membrane, would be expected to result in an increased cytosolic Ca^{2+} concentration, which would again be consistent with the potentiation of insulin secretion caused by lowering pHi.

Thus, there is little doubt that manipulations of pHi can influence ionic fluxes and hence both the electrical and secretory activities of insulin-secreting cells. However, the marked dependence of these effects on the presence of glucose (or other nutrients) must question whether pHi acts as a coupling factor *per se* in nutrient-stimulated insulin secretion.

Effects of nutrients on B-cell pHi

A considerable number of conflicting reports have appeared in the literature regarding the effects of glucose and other nutrients on B-cell pHi. It is likely that these inconsistencies have resulted, at least in part, from differences in experimental design, particularly regarding the techniques used to assess cytosolic pH. For example, several studies have utilized a method based upon the distribution of a penetrant labelled weak acid, 5,5-dimethyl [2-^{14}C]oxazolidine-2,4-dione (^{14}C]DMO), across the plasma membrane. Using such a technique, there have been reports that a high concentration of glucose increased the equilibrium uptake of ^{14}C]-DMO corresponding to a rise in pHi of approximately 0.15 units in both rat (Lebrun *et al.*, 1982) and *ob/ob* mouse (Lindstrom & Sehlin, 1984) islets. In contrast, Pace & Tarvin (1986) reported that glucose reduced ^{14}C]DMO equilibrium uptake in rat islets with a half-maximally effective concentration of 4 mM. A similar reduction in pHi in rat islets, assessed by ^{14}C]DMO distribution, was observed in response to another nutrient, 4-methyl-2-oxopentanoate (Hutton *et al.*, 1979). These authors also calculated that 4-methyl-2-oxopentanoate caused intracellular acidification in islet cells using an indirect method based upon extracellular pH measurement and buffering capacity of islet homogenates (Hutton *et al.*, 1980). Since the distribution of the labelled weak acid will take a finite length of time to reach equilibrium for any given pHi value, difficulties are likely to arise with this technique in assessing the kinetics of changes in pHi. Such factors could, at least in part, explain the inconsistencies which have arisen from using weak acid distribution to measure pHi.

The use of fluorescent, pH-sensitive dyes has permitted the continuous monitoring of pHi, which, unlike isotope equilibration experiments, readily enables kinetic studies to be made of responses to stimulation. In studies employing one such dye, fluorescein diacetate, Deleers and colleagues (1983, 1985) demonstrated that glucose and the non-sugar nutrient secretagogue 4-methyl-2-oxopentanoate induced a rapid, sustained rise in pHi in rat islets. In contrast, non-nutrient stimuli such as glibenclamide or high depolarizing concentrations of K^+ decreased pHi. While fluorescein diacetate did permit the continuous recording of islet cell pHi, continued incubation of fluorescein diacetate-loaded islets resulted in a progressive shift in fluorescence intensity, probably as a result of leakage of the dye from the cells (Deleers *et al.*, 1983, 1984, 1985).

The subsequent development of a related dye, $2',7'$ biscarboxy-ethyl-$5',(6')$-carboxyfluorescein (BCECF), which can be loaded into cells in an esterified (acetomethoxy) form followed by de-esterification by cellular esterases, permits a continuous and sensitive measurement of pHi without the complication of leakage and shifting baseline fluorescence. Studies using this dye have shown that the rise in islet cell pHi following glucose stimulation is preceded by an immediate, transient intracellular acidification (Best *et al.*, 1988*a,b*). Essentially similar findings have subsequently been obtained with the cultured hamster B-cell line HIT-T15 (Lynch *et al.*, 1989). Somewhat in contrast to glucose, the nutrients 4-methyl-2-oxopentanoate and glyceraldehyde together with several non-nutrient stimuli including high concentrations of K^+ and Ba^{2+}, were found to cause a more pronounced initial acidification in these cells. In contrast with the above reports, a more recent study using fluorescence ratio microscopy in *ob/ob* mouse B-cells found that raising the concentration of glucose from 3 to 20 mM did not influence pHi, although tolbutamide and carbachol caused a fall and rise in pHi respectively (Grappengiesser *et al.*, 1989).

The lack of a clear correlation between observed changes in pHi and secretory activity thus casts further doubt on the role of pHi as a key intracellular signal in nutrient-induced insulin release, although this does not imply that other types of secretagogue may not influence B-cell function via changes in pHi. It is, of course, conceivable that changes in pHi within the first few seconds of exposure to a nutrient may exert subtle modulatory effects. Despite these reservations regarding pHi as an intracellular signal in insulin release, the study of changes in pHi in the B-cell has raised at least two important questions. First, how is pHi regulated in the B-cell? Secondly, what is the significance of such regulation?

Regulation of pHi in the B-cell

The regulation of cytosolic pH in mammalian cells and the importance of this process in cellular function has received a considerable amount of attention in recent years, and has accordingly been extensively reviewed (Roos & Boron, 1981; Boron, 1983; Busa, 1986; Madshus, 1988; Frelin *et al.*, 1988). It is well established that pHi is closely regulated, and does not fluctuate passively under varying cellular conditions. The observed values of pHi are also considerably higher than they would be if protons were distributed across the plasma membrane according to electrochemical gradients and membrane potential. The process of pHi regulation in mammalian cells is accomplished to a large extent by a number of plasma membrane-bound antiport systems (Fig. 1). The most widely studied of these antiporters is the amiloride-sensitive Na^+/H^+ exchanger (Grinstein & Rothstein, 1986), by which H^+ extrusion from the cell is driven by the inwardly directed Na^+ gradient. In addition to this exchange system, a number of anion exchange pathways have been described, including the Na^+-dependent and -independent HCO_3^-/Cl^- antiporters (Boron, 1983; Madshus, 1988; Frelin et al., 1988). The former of these, driven by the Na^+ gradient, would promote recovery from an intracellular acid load, while the latter could theoretically operate in either direction depending upon the intracellular:extracellular H^+ and Cl^- gradients. All of the above antiport systems are electroneutral.

In the case of the pancreatic B-cell, there are clearly a number of mechanisms by which a stimulus could influence pHi. As mentioned earlier, it would be predicted that metabolism of nutrients such as glucose, with the resultant production of acidic metabolites, would cause a fall in pHi. While such an acidification, albeit transient, has been detected in certain studies, the majority of reports suggest that the long-term response to glucose and possibly 4-methyl-2-oxopentanoate is an intracellular alkalinization. Thus, it appears that the B-cell possesses at least one mechanism to mask and overcome the acidification which would be expected to result from nutrient metabolism. The most probable candidates for such a regulation of cytosolic pH are Na^+/H^+ exchange and Na^+-dependent Cl^-/HCO_3^- exchange.

Several studies have provided evidence that regulation of pHi in rat pancreatic islet cells (Deleers et al., 1985; Best et al., 1988a,b) and in hamster insulin-secreting tumour (HIT) cells (Lynch et al., 1989) is highly sensitive to amiloride, an inhibitor of Na^+/H^+ exchange. Furthermore, when islets or HIT cells were incubated in the presence of amiloride, a progressive intracellular acidification, rather than alkalinization, has been observed in response to glucose (Deleers et al., 1985; Lebrun et al., 1986; Lynch et al., 1989; Trebilcock et al., 1990) suggesting that glucose might in some way activate Na^+/H^+ exchange. The mechanism by which glucose might activate this process is unknown, although a number of possibilities exist. First, it has been proposed that activity of the antiporter is enhanced by the binding of protons to an allosteric 'modifier' site on its cytoplasmic face (Aaronson et al., 1982; Grinstein & Rothstein, 1986). Such a mechanism could also explain the 'overshoot' alkalinization following intracellular acidification in HIT-T15 cells (Lynch et al., 1989). An alternative possibility is that Na^+/H^+ exchange can be stimulated by diacylglycerol via an activation of protein kinase C (Grinstein & Rothstein, 1986). It is well established that glucose, in common with several other nutrients, induces inositol lipid hydrolysis in islets (Best & Malaisse, 1983; Prentki & Matschinski, 1987; Chapter 7 by Morgan & Montague), resulting in elevated diacylglycerol levels in nutrient-stimulated islet cells.

A possible involvement of Cl^-/HCO_3^- exchange in islet cell pHi homoeostasis was suggested by the observation that glucose provoked an intracellular acidification in islets incubated in the absence of bicarbonate in contrast with the alkalinization observed in the presence of the anion (Deleers *et al.*, 1985). In addition, an increase in $H^{14}CO_3^-$ uptake has been observed in glucose-stimulated islets (Deleers *et al.*, 1983), suggesting that uptake of bicarbonate, perhaps via the anion antiporter, could at least contribute toward the neutralization of acid equivalents derived from nutrient oxidation. Such an exchanger would presumably be the Na^+-dependent system which acts as a cell alkalinizing mechanism (Frelin *et al.*, 1988; Fig. 1). In contrast, the Na^+-independent Cl^-/HCO_3^- exchange system normally acts as a cell acidifying mechanism, promoting recovery from an alkaline load (Frelin *et al.*, 1988). In recent experiments using BCECF-loaded HIT-T15 cells incubated in the absence of chloride or bicarbonate, or in the presence of DIDS, we failed to observe any modification of pHi responses to nutrients, weak acids or bases, thereby questioning the activity of either type of Cl^-/HCO_3^- exchange system in these cells (Trebilcock *et al.*, 1990).

Whether Na^+/H^+ or Cl^-/HCO_3^- exchange is predominantly responsible for the dissipation of protons from the cytosol, the net effect of nutrient oxidation in islet cells would be the extrusion of H^+ from the cell into the extracellular medium. Malaisse and colleagues (1979) have indeed demonstrated that glucose caused a concentration-related increase in output of H^+ from pancreatic islets, while no change in pHi was detected. This provides evidence for one or more regulatory mechanisms in islet cells responsible for pHi homoeostasis.

It should be emphasized that processes other than nutrient oxidation could influence islet cell pHi. For example, the H^+-coupled transport of nutrients or metabolites across the plasma membrane would be predicted to cause an intracellular acidification. Such a process could at least contribute towards the fall in pHi observed upon stimulating islets or HIT cells with 4-methyl-2-oxopentanoate, pyruvate and lactate (Hutton *et al.*, 1979, 1980; Lynch *et al.*, 1989). Acidification of HIT-T15 cells by pyruvate and lactate is sensitive to cinnamate derivatives (R. Trebilcock & L. Best, unpublished work), suggesting that these metabolites enter the cell principally via a specific H^+-coupled carrier (Halestrap & Poole, 1989). Such a carrier, operating 'in reverse', could itself play an important role in pHi regulation in the B-cell. As mentioned earlier, a large proportion of glucose utilized by the B-cell can be accounted for by lactic acid production, and it is likely that the output of this lactic acid from the cell is mediated in part by the $lactate^-/H^+$ carrier (see Fig. 2). Inhibition of this carrier, for example by cinnamate derivatives might therefore be predicted to result in intracellular acidification, particularly in cells exposed to high concentrations of glucose.

The acidification of islet and HIT cells following exposure to non-nutrient secretagogues such as tolbutamide and glibenclamide, high concentrations of K^+, Ca^{2+} ionophores and Ba^{2+} (Deleers *et al.*, 1984,

1985; Lynch *et al.*, 1989), is unlikely to be the result of H$^+$ transport into the cell, but rather a consequence of an increased cytosolic Ca^{2+} concentration, a response common to the above treatments. It is well established that changes in cytosolic Ca^{2+} concentration can influence pHi

Fig. 2. **Generation of acidic metabolites of glucose (or other nutrient)**

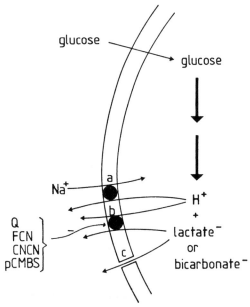

a, Na$^+$/H$^+$ exchanger; b, lactic acid carrier (inhibited by quercetin, cinnamate derivatives and pCMBS); c, putative anionic pathway for lactate$^-$/bicarbonate$^-$. Abbreviations used: Q, quercetin; FCN, α-fluorocinnamate; CNCN, α-cyano-4-hydroxycinnamate; pCMBS, p-chloromercuribenzene sulphonic acid.

(Meech & Thomas, 1977; Ives & Daniel, 1987), presumably owing to protons and calcium ions competing for common intracellular binding sites (Ives & Daniel, 1987; Hellman, 1975).

Thus, the overall effect of a given agonist on islet cell pHi is likely to be determined by a number of factors including H$^+$ co-transport, oxidative metabolism, changes in cytosolic Ca^{2+} concentration and activation of Na$^+$/H$^+$ and possibly Cl$^-$/HCO$_3^-$ exchange.

Bicarbonate and B-cell function

In considering pHi regulation in the B-cell, some attention should be given to the role of bicarbonate ions in cell function, since this anion makes a major contribution to cellular buffering power. It is well established that the secretory response to glucose is progressively impaired in the prolonged absence of bicarbonate (Henquin & Lambert, 1975, 1976; Lebrun et al., 1982). Under such conditions, calcium uptake was reduced although glucose metabolism was unaffected (Henquin & Lambert, 1976) suggesting that the requirement for bicarbonate is at a 'distal' stage of the stimulus–secretion pathway. It is unlikely that this dependence of secretory activity on bicarbonate is related to the role of this anion in pHi regulation. Lebrun and colleagues (1982) have reported that withdrawal of bicarbonate causes a rise in pHi in rat islet cells. Conversely, the addition of bicarbonate to ob/ob mouse B-cells caused an immediate acidification, although this was followed by an increase to higher resting pHi values (Grappengiesser et al., 1989). In an attempt to explain these findings, it may be worth while considering the possible consequences of bicarbonate withdrawal and addition to the incubation medium. The removal of bicarbonate from the medium necessarily involves the simultaneous reduction in pCO_2, to maintain the pH of the medium. This manipulation would thus result initially in the rapid exit of CO_2 from the cell and hence alkalinization (see Fig. 1). Conversely, addition of bicarbonate, together with an increase in pCO_2 would cause CO_2 entry and acidification of the cell. In contrast with the short-term effects of bicarbonate manipulation, the prolonged omission of the anion would be predicted to inhibit the activity of the HCO_3^-/Cl^- exchange systems whereby bicarbonate can enter the cell. This latter effect could explain the higher resting pHi values in cells incubated in the presence of bicarbonate and vice versa. Similarly, the presence or absence of HCO_3^-/Cl^- exchange systems in B-cells from different species could, in part, account for differing responses in pHi to various stimuli.

Consequences of pHi regulation

Given the high capacity of the B-cell for metabolizing nutrients, and consequently generating acidic metabolites, it is not surprising that the cell is equipped with one or more homoeostatic mechanisms for extruding protons from the cell, namely Na^+/H^+ and possibly HCO_3^-/Cl^- exchange. The close regulation of intracellular pH is likely to be important for the activity of numerous enzymes and ion channels. By virtue of the fact that these antiporters not only counteract accumulation of H^+ but can be activated, by intracellular mediators such as Ca^{2+} and diacylglycerol and by H^+, stimulation of the B-cell and/or intracellular acidification is often followed by a period of prolonged alkalinization. It is at present unknown whether raised pHi in the stimulated B-cell plays any active or permissive role in stimulus–secretion coupling. Investigation of this possibility will require techniques which permit buffering of pHi without affecting any of the numerous, closely associated processes in the cell. One can speculate that raised pHi could permit an increased rate of nutrient metabolism which would be compatible with enhanced secretory activity. Alternatively, changes in B-cell pHi might be more relevant to the control of processes such as insulin biosynthesis, DNA replication and cell division, all of which are sensitive to nutrient concentration (Lin & Haist, 1969; Nielsen, 1985; Swenne, 1985). In this context, it has been suggested that mitogen-induced changes in pHi in numerous cell types could play a role in the control of the cell cycle (Busa, 1986; Rosengurt, 1986; Madshus, 1988; Frelin et al., 1988).

One aspect of pHi regulation via the Na^+/H^+ and HCO_3^-/Cl^- exchange systems which may be worth consideration, particularly from the point of view of the B-cell in which nutrients exert profound effects on membrane potential, is the electroneutrality of these exchangers. Clearly, the generation of H^+ by nutrient metabolism in the cell will be accompanied by production of an anion—predominantly lactate or bicarbonate. It might therefore be argued that the electroneutral extrusion of H^+ (in exchange for Na^+ entry or Cl^- exit via the respective antiporters) will be accompanied by the electrogenic exit of a corresponding amount of the anion from the cell (see Fig. 2). The exit of lactate or bicarbonate from the cell by such an electrogenic process, concomitant with electroneutral Na^+/H^+ or HCO_3^-/Cl^- exchange, would represent the net loss of negative charge from the inside of the cell. Such a mechanism could contribute towards depolarization of the cell membrane elicited by glucose and other nutrients (Best et al., 1989). This could explain why certain cell types (Bashford & Pasternak, 1986), including insulin-secreting HIT-T15 cells (Meats et al., 1989), are depolarized in lactate-containing media. Although there is, as yet, no direct evidence for such electrogenic pathways of lactate or bicarbonate efflux in islet cells, it has been pointed out that channels which conduct chloride could also theoretically conduct a number of other anionic species (Wright & Diamond, 1977). In addition, we have recently obtained indirect evidence, based on increased rates of [^{14}C]lactate uptake in depolarized B-cells, for an electrogenic component to lactate movement across the plasma membrane (L. Best, unpublished work). The full physiological significance of the coupled processes of acidic metabolite formation and the trans-membrane movement of H^+ and organic anions in the B-cell clearly awaits a considerable amount of further investigation.

Conclusions

Pancreatic B-cell function can be stimulated and inhibited by manipulations which, respectively, lower and raise intracellular pH. However, measurements of pHi in nutrient-stimulated B-cells do not, on the whole, support the idea that intracellular acidification is a key intracellular signal in triggering insulin secretion. Intracellular pH in the B-cell appears to be regulated by Na^+/H^+ exchange and possibly also by HCO_3^-/Cl^- antiport systems. Activation of these antiporters in stimulated B-cells tends to result in increased pHi, although the importance of this response is at present obscure. The electroneutrality of these H^+-extruding mechanisms raises the possibility that exit from the cell of the corresponding anions, principally lactate and bicarbonate, could occur in part via electrogenic pathways which might contribute towards cell-membrane depolarization.

References

Aaronson, P. S., Nee, J. & Suhm, M. A. (1982) Modifier role of internal H^+ in activating the Na^+/H^+ exchanger in renal microvillus membranes. Nature (London) **299**, 161–163

Bashford, C. L. & Pasternak, C. A. (1986) Plasma membrane potential of some animal cells is generated by ion pumping, not ion gradients. Trends Biochem Sci. **11**, 113–116

Best, L. & Malaisse, W. J. (1983) Phospholipids and islet function. Diabetologia **25**, 299–305

Best, L., Bone, E. A., Meats, J. E. & Tomlinson, S. (1988a) Is intracellular pH a coupling factor in nutrient-stimulated pancreatic islets? J. Mol. Endocrinol. **1**, 33–38

Best, L., Yates, A. P., Gordon, C. & Tomlinson, S. (1988b) Modulation by cytosolic pH of calcium and rubidium fluxes in rat pancreatic islets. Biochem. Pharmacol. **37**, 4611–4615

Best, L., Yates, A. P., Meats, J. E. & Tomlinson, S. (1989) Effects of lactate on pancreatic islets: Lactate efflux as a possible determinant of islet cell depolarization by glucose. Biochem. J. **259**, 507–511

Biden, T. J., Janjic, D. & Wollheim, C. B. (1986) Sodium requirement for insulin release: putative role in the regulation of intracellular pH. Am. J. Physiol. **250**, C207–C213

Boron, W. F. (1983) Transport of H^+ and of ionic weak acids and bases. J. Membr. Biol. **72**, 1–16

Busa, W. B. (1986) Mechanisms and consequences of pH-mediated cell regulation. Annu. Rev. Physiol. **48**, 389–402

Carpinelli, A. R. & Malaisse, W. J. (1980) Regulation of $^{86}Rb^+$ outflow from pancreatic islets. II Effect of changes in extracellular and intracellular pH. Diabete Metab. **6**, 193–198

Carpinelli, A. R., Sener, A., Herchuelz, A. & Malaisse, W. J. (1980) The stimulus-secretion coupling of glucose-induced insulin release. XLI Effect of intracellular acidification upon calcium efflux from islet cells. Metabolism **29**, 540–545

Cook, D. L., Musatoshi, I. & Fujimoto, W. Y. (1984) Lowering of pHi inhibits Ca^{2+}-activated K^+ channels in pancreatic β-cells. Nature (London) **311**, 269–271

Deleers, M., Lebrun, P. & Malaisse, W. J. (1983) Increase in HCO_3^- influx and cellular pH in glucose-stimulated pancreatic islets. FEBS Lett. **154**, 97–100

Deleers, M., Lebrun, P. & Malaisse, W. J. (1984) Effects of cations, ionophores and hypoglycaemic sulphonylureas on the fluorescence of fluorescein-labelled pancreatic islets. Res. Commun. Chem. Path. Pharmacol. **44**, 83–92

Deleers, M., Lebrun, P. & Malaisse, W. J. (1985) Nutrient-induced changes in the pH of pancreatic islet cells. Horm. Metabol. Res. **17**, 391–395

Eddlestone, G. T. & Beigelman, P. M. (1983) Pancreatic β-cell electrical activity: the role of anions and the control of pH. Am. J. Physiol. **244**, C188–C197

Frelin, C., Vigne, P., Ladoux, A. & Lazdunski, M. (1988) The regulation of the intracellular pH in cells from vertebrates. Eur. J. Biochem. **174**, 3–14

Grappengiesser, E., Gylfe, E. & Hellman, B. (1989) The regulation of pH in individual pancreatic B-cells as evaluated by fluorescence ratio microscopy. Biochim. Biophys. Acta **1014**, 219–224

Grinstein, S. & Rothstein, A. (1986) Mechanisms of regulation of the Na^+/H^+ exchanger. J. Membr. Biol. **90**, 1–12

Halestrap, A. P. & Poole, R. C. (1989) The transport of pyruvate and lactate across mitochondrial and plasma membranes. In Anion Transport Protein of the Red Blood Cell Membrane (Hamasaki, N. & Jennings, M. L., eds.), pp. 73–86, Elsevier, Amsterdam

Hellman, B. (1975) The significance of calcium for glucose stimulation of insulin release. Endocrinology **97**, 392–398

Henquin, J. C. & Lambert, A. E. (1975) Extracellular bicarbonate ions and insulin secretion. Biochim. Biophys. Acta **381**, 437–442

Henquin, J. C. & Lambert, A. E. (1976) Bicarbonate modulation of glucose-induced biphasic insulin release by rat islets. Am. J. Physiol. **231**, 713–721

Hutton, J. C., Sener, A. & Malaisse, W. J. (1979) The metabolism of 4-methyl-2-oxopentanoate in rat pancreatic islets. Biochem. J. **184**, 291–301

Hutton, J. C., Sener, A., Herchuelz, A., Valverde, I., Boschero, A. C. & Malaisse, W. J. (1980) The stimulus-secretion coupling of glucose-induced insulin release. XLII Effects of extracellular pH on insulin release: their dependency on nutrient concentration. Horm. Metab. Res. **12**, 294–299

Ives, H. E. & Daniel, T. O. (1987) Interrelationship between growth factor-induced pH changes and intracellular Ca^{++}. Proc. Natl. Acad. Sci. U.S.A. **84**, 1950–1954

Kanatsuka, A., Makino, H., Sakurada, M., Hasimoto, N., Yamaguchi, T. & Yoshida, S. (1987) Biphasic insulin response to high glucose and a role for protons and calcium. Endocrinology **120**, 77–82

Lebrun, P., Malaisse, W. J. & Herchuelz, A. (1982) Effect of the absence of bicarbonate upon intracellular pH and calcium fluxes in pancreatic islet cells. Biochim. Biophys. Acta **721**, 357–365

Lebrun, P., van Ganse, E., Juvent, M., Deleers, M. & Herchuelz, A. (1986) Na^+-H^+ exchange in the process of glucose-induced insulin release from the pancreatic β-cell. Effects of amiloride on $^{86}Rb^+$, $^{45}Ca^{++}$ fluxes and insulin release. Biochim. Biophys. Acta **886**, 448–456

Lebrun, P., Plasman, P. O. & Herchuelz, A. (1989) Effect of extracellular sodium removal upon ^{86}Rb outflow from pancreatic islet cells. Biochim. Biophys. Acta **1011**, 6–11

Lin, B. J. & Haist, R. E. (1969) insulin biosynthesis: effects of carbohydrates and related compounds. Can. J. Physiol. Pharmacol. **47**, 791–801

Lindstrom, P. & Sehlin, J. (1984) Effect of glucose on the intracellular pH of pancreatic islet cells. Biochem. J. **218**, 887–892

Lindstrom, P. & Sehlin, J. (1986) Effect of intracellular alkalinization on pancreatic islet calcium uptake and insulin secretion. Biochem J. **239**: 199–204

Lynch, A. M., Meats, J. E., Best, L. & Tomlinson, S. (1989) Effects of nutrient and non-nutrient stimuli on cytosolic pH in cultured insulinoma (HIT-T15) cells. Biochim. Biophys. Acta. **1012**, 166–170

Madshus, I. H. (1988) Regulation of intracellular pH in eukaryotic cells. Biochem. J. **250**, 1–8

Malaisse, W. J., Hutton, J. C., Kawazu, S., Herchuelz, A., Valverde, I. & Sener, A. (1979) The stimulus-secretion coupling of glucose-induced insulin release. XXXV Links between metabolic and cationic events. Diabetologia **16**, 331–341

Malaisse, W. J., Herchuelz, A. & Sener, A. (1980) The possible significance of intracellular pH in insulin release. Life Sci. **26**, 1367–1371

Meats, J. E., Tuersley, M. D., Best, L., Lynch, A. M. & Tomlinson, S. (1989) Lactate alters plasma membrane potential, increases the concentration of cytosolic Ca^{2+} and stimulates the secretion of insulin by the hamster B-cell line HIT-T15. J. Mol. Endocrinol. **3**, 121–128

Meech, R. W. & Thomas, R. C. (1977) The effect of calcium injection on the intracellular sodium and pH of snail neurones. J. Physiol. (London) **265**, 867–879

Misler, S., Gillis, K. & Tabcharani, J. (1989) Modulation of gating of a metabolically-regulated ATP-dependent potassium channel by intracellular pH in B-cells of pancreatic islets. J. Membr. Biol. **109**, 135–143

Nielsen, J. H. (1985) Growth and function of the pancreatic B-cell *in vitro*: Effects of glucose, hormones and serum factors on mouse, rat and human pancreatic islets in organ culture. Acta Endocrinol. **108**, (Suppl. 266), 1–39

Pace, C. S. (1984) Role of pH as a transduction device in triggering electrical activity and secretory responses in islet B-cells. Fed. Proc. Fed. Am. Soc. Exp. **43**, 2379–2384

Pace, C. S. & Goldsmith, K. T. (1986) Effect of substitution of a permeant weak acid for the permissive role of glucose in amino acid-induced electrical activity in β-cells. Endocrinology **119**, 2433–2438

Pace, C. S. & Tarvin, J. T. (1983) pH modulation of glucose-induced electrical activity in β-cells: involvement of Na/H and HCO_3/Cl antiporters. J. Membr. Biol. **73**, 39–49

Pace, C. S. & Tarvin, J. T. (1986) Amiloride-sensitive regulation of intracellular pH in β-cells: Activation by glucose. Metabolism **35**, 176–181

Pace, C. S., Tarvin, J. T. & Smith, J. S. (1983) Stimulus-secretion coupling in B-cells: modulation by pH. Am. J. Physiol. **244**, E3-E18

Prentki, M. & Matschinski, F. M. (1987) Ca^{2+}, cAMP and phospholipid-derived messengers in coupling mechanisms of insulin secretion. Physiol. Rev. **67**, 1185–1248

Renner, E. L., Lake, J. R., Cragoe, E. J. & Scharschmidt, B. F. (1988) Amiloride and amiloride analogues inhibit Na^+/K^+ transporting ATP-ase and Na^+-coupled alanine transport in rat hepatocytes. Biochim. Biophys. Acta **938**, 386–398

Roos, A. & Boron, W. F. (1981) Intracellular pH. Physiol. Rev. **61**: 296–434

Rosario, L. M. & Rojas, E. (1986) Modulation of K^+ conductance by intracellular pH in pancreatic β-cells. FEBS Lett. **200**, 203–209

Rosengurt, E. (1986) Early signals in the mitogenic response. Science **234**, 161–166

Sehlin, J. (1978) Interrelationship between chloride fluxes in pancreatic islets and insulin release. Am. J. Physiol. **235**, E501–E508

Siegl, P. K. S., Cragoe, E. J., Trumble, M. J. & Kaczorowski, G. J. (1984) Inhibition of Na^+/Ca^{2+} exchange in membrane vesicle and papillary muscle preparations from guinea pig heart by analogues of amiloride. Proc. Natl. Acad. Sci. U.S.A. **81**, 3238–3242

Smith, J. S. & Pace, C. S. (1983) Modification of glucose-induced insulin release by alteration of pH. Diabetes **32**, 61–66

Swenne, I. (1985) Glucose-stimulated DNA replication of the pancreatic islets during the development of the rat foetus: Effects of nutrients, growth hormone and T_3. Diabetes **34**, 803–809

Tarvin, J. T., Sachs, G. & Pace, C. S. (1981) Glucose-induced electrical activity in the pancreatic β-cell: modulation by pH. Am. J. Physiol. **241**, C264–C268

Trebilcock, R., Tomlinson, S. & Best, L. (1990) Na^+/H^+ exchange is responsible for the regulation of pHi in HIT-T15 insulinoma cells. Mol. Cell Endocr. **71**, 21–25

Wright, E. M. & Diamond, J. M. (1977) Anion selectivity in biological systems. Physiol. Rev. **57**, 109–156

9

Regulation of K+ permeability and membrane potential in insulin-secreting cells

Jean-Claude Henquin*†‡, Anne Debuyser*, Gisela Drews† and Tim D. Plant†

Unité de Diabétologie et Nutrition, University of Louvain Faculty of Medicine, B-1200, Brussels, Belgium, and †I. Physiologisches Institut, University of Saarland, D-6650, Homburg/Saar, Germany

Introduction

The pancreatic B-cell is able to adjust the rate of insulin release to the fluctuations of numerous metabolic, hormonal, neural and pharmacological signals. This fine control is mediated by several mechanisms, among which changes in B-cell membrane potential and remodelling of ionic fluxes across the plasma and intracellular membranes play a central role.

A rise in the concentration of free cytoplasmic Ca^{2+} is a pivotal step in the stimulation of insulin secretion by glucose, the major physiological secretagogue. There is now almost general agreement that the sugar triggers this rise by enhancing Ca^{2+} influx from the extracellular medium rather than by mobilizing Ca^{2+} from intracellular stores (Prentki & Matschinsky, 1987; Gylfe, 1988; Pralong et al., 1990). The regulation of Ca^{2+} influx by glucose is achieved through highly controlled oscillations of the B-cell membrane potential illustrated in Fig. 1.

The resting potential of mouse B-cells perifused with a medium containing 0 or 3 mM-glucose is between -60 and -70 mV. It is determined by the high K^+ permeability (P_K) of the membrane (Meissner et al., 1978), but is not at the equilibrium potential of K^+ (E_K) because of the influence of other permeabilities and of the currents produced by electrogenic pumps (e.g. Na^+/K^+) and countertransports (e.g. Na^+/Ca^{2+}) (Henquin & Meissner, 1984a). Raising the concentration of glucose above 3 mM progressively depolarizes the membrane to a threshold potential.

‡ To whom correspondence should be addressed at the Unité de Diabétologie et Nutrition, UCL 54.74, B-1200 Brussels, Belgium.

When this threshold potential is reached (at about 7 mM-glucose), electrical activity appears, that is characterized by slow waves of the membrane potential with spikes superimposed on the plateau (Fig. 1).

Studies with intracellular microelectrodes combined with measurements of ionic fluxes have long established that a decrease in P_K underlies

---

Fig. 1.   Effects of glucose on the membrane potential of mouse B-cells, measured with intracellular microelectrodes

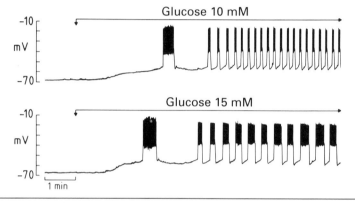

The two recordings were obtained in different mice.

---

the initial depolarization to the threshold potential, and that slow waves and spikes reflect the influx of Ca^{2+} through voltage-dependent Ca^{2+} channels (for a review see Henquin & Meissner, 1984a). However, it is only after the identification of different types of K^+ channels by the patch-clamp technique that elucidation of the exact mode of action of glucose has become possible (see chapter 10 by Ashcroft *et al.*).

In this chapter, we briefly review the role of the changes of P_K of the B-cell membrane for the control of insulin release by glucose and other secretagogues. We focus on certain misunderstood concepts, on controversial issues born from the use of a particular technique or preparation, and on difficulties in the interpretation of some results.

How can a decrease in P_K cause depolarization?

There is general agreement that the initial depolarization from the resting potential, which is brought about by substimulatory concentrations of glucose, is caused by a decrease in P_K of the plasma membrane. However, this decrease in P_K is, alone, not sufficient to account for the membrane depolarization. Another ionic permeability must be present, which provides a current that causes the membrane to depolarize as P_K decreases. Assuming that this depolarizing current is carried by a monovalent cation and considering the Goldman equation:

$$E_m = \frac{R T}{F} \ln \frac{P_K[K^+]_o + P_X[X^+]_o}{P_K[K^+]_i + P_X[X^+]_i}$$

where E_m is the membrane potential, R the gas constant, T the temperature, F the Faraday constant, and P_K and P_X the permeabilities for K^+ and an unknown cation X^+ respectively, it can be seen that E_m will be close to the equilibrium potential for potassium ions (E_K), where

$$E_K = \frac{R T}{F} \ln \frac{[K^+]_o}{[K^+]_i}$$

as long as P_K is much larger than P_X. If, however, P_K decreases, P_X will be increasingly important, and the membrane potential will deviate more from E_K towards E_X. If E_X is positive to E_K, the membrane will depolarize. It is important to underline that P_X must exist, but need not increase for the B-cell membrane to be depolarized by agents that decrease P_K. The identity of the permeability responsible for the initial depolarizing current is, as yet, unclear.

Replacement of extracellular Na$^+$ by an impermeant substitute largely reverses the glucose- or tolbutamide-induced depolarization in RINm5F cells (Dunne *et al.*, 1990*a*). Moreover, tetrodotoxin, a specific blocker of voltage-dependent Na$^+$ channels inhibits depolarization and spike activity. The authors, therefore, concluded that a Na$^+$ permeability is essential for the depolarization and that part of the current may flow through voltage-dependent Na$^+$ channels. These observations contrast markedly with the data obtained from microelectrode recordings of the membrane potential in normal mouse B-cells. Here, removal of external Na$^+$ in the presence of a stimulatory concentration of glucose results in a transient hyperpolarization (Ribalet & Beigelman, 1982; De Miguel *et al.*, 1988). In the steady state very long slow waves and intervals are recorded. Tetrodotoxin also has no inhibitory effect on glucose-induced electrical activity (Meissner & Preissler, 1980). A role for voltage-dependent Na$^+$ channels in the mouse is also unlikely in view of patch-clamp data which show that Na$^+$ channels are completely inactivated at potentials above -80 mV (Plant, 1988*a*). All these experiments of Na$^+$-removal show thus that Na$^+$ ions are involved in, and may modulate electrical activity in normal mouse B-cells, but that activity persists in the absence of Na$^+$.

The role of an inward Ca^{2+} current is not easy to assess with membrane potential measurements because of the difficulties of recording in the absence of Ca^{2+}. However, it has been shown that removal of extracellular Ca^{2+} abolishes most spike and slow-wave activity. The membrane potential initially remains close to the level which is normally attained during the intervals between the slow waves, and then decreases (Meissner & Schmelz, 1974; Ribalet & Beigelman, 1980). Repolarization to the resting potential is never observed. Removal of external Mg^{2+} has little effect on glucose-induced depolarization and electrical activity in mouse B-cells (Atwater & Beigelman, 1976). On removal of extracellular Cl^-, glucose-induced electrical activity is decreased but not abolished, and the membrane does not repolarize to the resting potential (Eddlestone & Beigelman, 1983; Pace & Tarvin, 1983; Sehlin & Meissner, 1988).

The available evidence suggests that a specific permeability for Na^+, Cl^-, Ca^{2+} or Mg^{2+} is not involved in the initial depolarization, since the cells remain depolarized at the threshold potential or display electrical activity in the absence of these ions. As suggested by Cook *et al.* (1988), a more likely possibility is a non-specific leakage current which would tend to move the membrane potential towards 0 mV.

Which K^+ channels are the targets of glucose?

The patch-clamp technique has identified several types of K^+ channels in the B-cell membrane (Petersen & Findlay, 1987). The major ones are (Fig. 2): (1) The ATP-sensitive K^+ (K^+-ATP) channels which are voltage-independent and are closed by application of ATP at the inner face of the membrane (Cook & Hales, 1984). They are also closed by tolbutamide or other hypoglycaemic sulphonylureas, and opened by diazoxide (Trube *et al.*, 1986; Gillis *et al.*, 1989; Panten *et al.*, 1989). (2) The voltage-dependent K^+ (K^+-V) channels which are also called 'delayed rectifiers'. They are not sensitive to ATP or sulphonylureas and are closed by low concentrations of tetraethylammonium ions (TEA^+) (Bokvist *et al.*, 1990). (3) The voltage- and Ca^{2+}-dependent K^+ (K^+-VCa) channels which are activated on depolarization and by a rise in cytosolic Ca^{2+}. They are also inhibited by low concentrations of TEA^+ (Petersen & Findlay, 1987).

Depolarization from the resting to the threshold potential

Using the cell-attached configuration of the patch-clamp technique, it could be shown that glucose inhibits the activity of K^+-ATP channels in the B-cell membrane (Ashcroft *et al.*, 1984; Rorsman & Trube, 1985; Misler *et al.*, 1986). This inhibition was most pronounced with glucose concentrations (< 7–8 mM) which cause the depolarization to the threshold potential. Blockade of K^+-ATP channels by tolbutamide (in a glucose-free medium) depolarized the B-cell membrane in a similar way to glucose (Fig. 3). In contrast, 2 mM-TEA^+ did not affect the resting potential of B-cells perifused with a medium containing 0 or 3 mM-glucose (Henquin, 1990*a*).

Fig. 2.   Schematic representation of the mechanisms by which glucose and other agents control the membrane potential of normal mouse B-cells

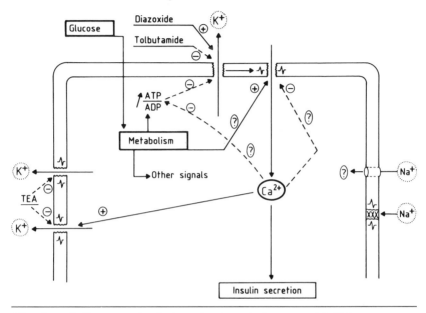

The sign + indicates a stimulation; the sign − indicates an inhibition.

Fig. 3.   Effects of tolbutamide on the membrane potential of a mouse B-cell

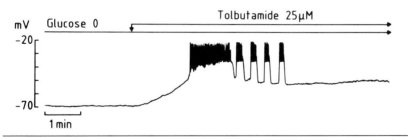

The preparation was perifused with a glucose-free medium.

There remains thus no doubt that the contribution of K^+-V and K^+-VCa channels to P_K is very low in resting (not depolarized) B-cells, and that the closure of K^+-ATP channels underlies the decrease in P_K that causes the initial depolarization to the threshold potential.

Slow-wave modulation

The most important effect of glucose concentrations which stimulate insulin release (> 7 mM in mouse B-cells) is to control the duration of the phases of electrical activity (slow waves) during which Ca^{2+} influx takes

Fig. 4. **Effects of glucose (G), tolbutamide (Tolb) and diazoxide (DZ) on the membrane potential of mouse B-cells**

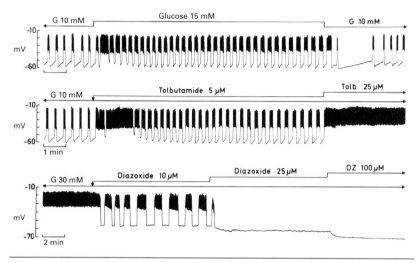

The composition of the perifusion medium was changed as indicated on top of each recording. The upper two recordings are from the same cell. Reproduced from Henquin (1988) with permission.

place. This is illustrated in the upper panel of Fig. 4. The possible role of K^+-ATP channels in the control of slow waves was not supported by patch-clamp experiments which showed that most of these channels are closed at the stimulatory concentrations of glucose (Misler *et al.*, 1986; Ashcroft *et al.*, 1988).

However, addition of a low concentration of tolbutamide (5 μM) to a medium containing 10 mM-glucose reproduces the increase in electrical activity induced by raising the glucose concentration to 15 mM. A higher concentration of tolbutamide (25 μM) persistently depolarizes the membrane to the plateau potential and triggers continuous spike activity (Fig. 4, middle panel) as does a maximally effective concentration of glucose (30 mM) (Fig. 4, lower panel). The observation that tolbutamide still has effects on the spike activity in the presence of 30 or 40 mM-glucose (Henquin, 1988) indicates that not all K^+-ATP channels are closed by these very high concentrations of the sugar.

Increasing concentrations of diazoxide cause a graded inhibition of the depolarizing effect of 30 mM-glucose, first restoring slow waves and then repolarizing the membrane to the threshold and the resting potentials (Fig. 4, lower panel).

These observations that tolbutamide and diazoxide mimic the changes in electrical activity produced by an increase and a decrease in glucose concentration strongly suggest that closure and opening of K^+-ATP channels also underlie the effects of the sugar within this range of stimulatory concentrations (Henquin, 1988; Cook & Ikeuchi, 1989). There is thus an apparent disagreement between this conclusion and that of patch-clamp studies. It is possible that the very few K^+-ATP channels that remain open under these conditions are sufficient to subserve the subtle control of electrical activity exerted by small variations in the glucose concentration within a stimulatory range. Alternatively, patch-clamp measurements made at room temperature may have underestimated the actual K^+-ATP channel activity at 37 °C.

It should, however, be noted that the slow waves of membrane potential induced by tolbutamide in the absence of glucose rapidly stop (Fig. 3), whereas they persist when the sulphonylurea is added to a medium containing a non-stimulatory concentration of glucose (3 mM) (Henquin *et al.*, 1987). This may suggest that K^+-ATP channels are not the sole target on which glucose acts to influence electrical activity (Cook & Ikeuchi, 1989), or that some metabolic factor is necessary for optimal functioning of these channels.

In contrast to tolbutamide, TEA (0.5–2 mM) does not increase slow wave duration, but consistently causes a large increase in spike amplitude (Fig. 5), an effect not produced by an increase in the concentration of glucose. These findings, therefore, indicate that K^+-V and K^+-VCa channels may be involved in the repolarization of the spikes but not in that of the slow waves, and that these channels do not subserve the modulation of electrical activity by glucose (Henquin, 1990a). This conclusion, drawn from experiments with normal cells, is at variance with the suggestion that high concentrations of glucose and potentiators of insulin release reduce the activity of K^+-VCa channels in tumoral insulin-secreting RINm5F cells (Ribalet *et al.*, 1988).

A model of glucose-induced electrical activity

The metabolism of glucose and other nutrients within B-cells closes K^+-ATP channels in the plasma membrane (Fig. 2). The molecular mechanisms of this closure are discussed elsewhere (Rorsman & Trube, 1990; see also Chapter 10 in this book by Ashcroft *et al.*). It will be sufficient to emphasize here the critical role of the rise in the ATP/ADP ratio in the cytoplasm.

Numerous other putative signals are produced by glucose metabolism, including diacylglycerol (Peter-Riesch *et al.*, 1988; Wolf *et al.*, 1989). The observation that phorbol esters close K^+-ATP channels and cause depolarization of the membrane in RINm5F cells, has prompted the suggestion that protein kinase C could link glucose metabolism and K^+-ATP channels (Wollheim *et al.*, 1988). This hypothesis is not supported by

---

Fig. 5.   Effects of increasing concentrations of tetraethylammonium (TEA) on the electrical activity induced by 10 mM-glucose (G) in a mouse B-cell

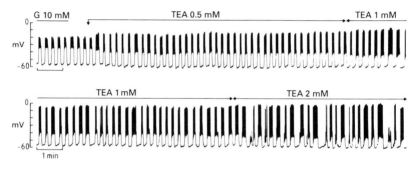

The lower recording is the direct continuation of the upper one. Reproduced from Henquin (1990a) with permission.

---

our studies in normal mouse B-cells, in which activators of protein kinase C have no or very little effect on the membrane potential and on K^+-ATP channels (Bozem *et al.*, 1987; Henquin *et al.*, 1987, 1989), although they markedly increase insulin secretion.

The decrease in P_K causes depolarization of the membrane which leads to opening of voltage-dependent Ca^{2+} channels. In mouse B-cells, only L-type Ca^{2+} channels have been identified (Plant, 1988*b*). T-type Ca^{2+} channels may be present in other species (Hiriart & Matteson, 1988), but no functional role of these channels has yet been identified (Plasman *et al.*, 1990). The properties of L-type Ca^{2+} channels may be influenced by the changes in cellular metabolism (Smith *et al.*, 1989). The molecular mechanisms of this influence have not been established, but the intervention of both the cyclic AMP–protein kinase A pathway (Henquin & Meissner, 1984*b*) and the diacylglycerol–protein kinase C pathway (Pace & Goldsmith, 1985; Velasco & Petersen, 1989) have been proposed.

We have seen above that repolarization of the slow waves and, hence, termination of Ca^{2+} influx in B-cells, cannot be ascribed to activation of K^+-VCa channels by the rise in cytosolic Ca^{2+} as originally thought (Henquin, 1979; Atwater *et al.*, 1979). Two other non-exclusive explanations have recently been proposed. Patch-clamp experiments under conditions where slow waves of the membrane potential were preserved have suggested that repolarization of the slow waves is caused by Ca^{2+}-channel inactivation (Smith *et al.*, 1990). It is indeed known that Ca^{2+} channels may undergo voltage- and Ca^{2+}-dependent inactivation (Plant, 1988*b*; Satin & Cook, 1989). However, Ca^{2+}-induced inactivation is too rapid to be involved in the control of slow waves. On the other hand, a slow, voltage-dependent inactivation could contribute to the termination of slow waves if it occurs in normal B-cells as in the hamster insulinoma HIT cell line (Satin & Cook, 1989). Alternatively, the rise in the free cytosolic Ca^{2+} could indirectly reactivate a few K^+-ATP channels by lowering the ATP/ADP ratio beneath the membrane (Henquin, 1990*b*). This could result from a localized use of ATP (e.g. by a Ca^{2+} pump). Through this mechanism, Ca^{2+} would exert a negative feed-back control on its own entry in B-cells.

Usefulness of K+ flux measurements

The concept that glucose depolarizes the B-cell membrane by decreasing its P_K was first established by measuring ^{42}K or ^{86}Rb efflux from islet cells (Sehlin & Täljedal, 1975; Henquin, 1978). The technique has since become very useful to determine the mode of action of numerous agents which affect B-cell function. It is, however, pertinent to ask whether ^{86}Rb efflux measurements have not become outdated with the advent of the patch-clamp technique, and whether data obtained with this technique can still be reliably interpreted.

In our view, measurements of ^{86}Rb efflux from islets perifused with a medium containing no or a low concentration of glucose remain the simplest and probably the most sensitive test to determine whether a substance closes K^+-ATP channels in B-cells. We are not aware of an agent that closes K^+-ATP channels in intact B-cells and does not inhibit ^{86}Rb efflux. Moreover, only rare conditions decrease ^{86}Rb efflux in the absence of glucose while not inhibiting K^+-ATP channels. They are those which reduce a permeability (P_X) contributing to the resting potential (see above). For instance, omission of extracellular Na^+ decreases ^{86}Rb efflux but hyperpolarizes the membrane (De Miguel *et al.*, 1988). In this case the change in efflux is the consequence of the move of the membrane potential towards E_K.

Less straightforward is the interpretation of the results obtained in the presence of stimulatory concentrations of glucose, because more than one type of K^+ channel is implicated. Thus, K^+-ATP channels are largely closed, but K^+-V and K^+-VCa channels start to open. An example of the paradoxical results that can be obtained is shown in Fig. 6. Although glucose is known to inhibit K^+-ATP channels, raising the concentration of glucose from 10 to 15 mM increases ^{86}Rb efflux, whereas the reverse change decreases it. However, the 'expected' changes in ^{86}Rb efflux are observed

---

Fig. 6.   **^{86}Rb efflux from perifused mouse islets**

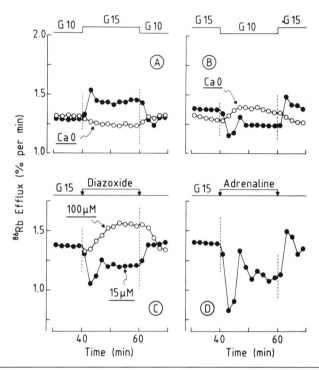

A and B: Effects of an increase and a decrease in glucose concentration (G in mM). The medium contained 2.5 mM-CaCl$_2$ (●) or no CaCl$_2$ (○). C. Effects of 15 μM (●) or 100 μM (○) diazoxide in the presence of 15 mM-glucose (G) and 2.5 mM-CaCl$_2$. D. Effects of 100 nM-adrenaline in the presence of 15 mM-glucose (G) and 2.5 mM-CaCl$_2$. Panels C and D are reproduced from Drews et al. (1990) with permission.

---

when the concentration of glucose is increased or decreased in a Ca^{2+}-free medium. These results can be interpreted as follows. Although the increase in glucose concentration and the ensuing stimulation of glucose metabolism may close a few more K^+-ATP channels, the more sustained depolarization of the membrane (Fig. 4, upper panel) and larger influx of Ca^{2+} activate K^+-V and K^+-VCa channels. The acceleration of ^{86}Rb efflux through the latter channels masks the small decrease expected to result from the closure of K$^+$-ATP channels. No such masking occurs if Ca^{2+} is not present in the medium, since Ca^{2+} influx and Ca^{2+}-dependent depolarization do not occur.

Paradoxical changes in ^{86}Rb efflux can also be produced by diazoxide which is considered to open K$^+$-ATP channels selectively

Fig. 7. Effects of adrenaline and diazoxide on the electrical activity induced by 15 mM-glucose (G) in mouse B-cells

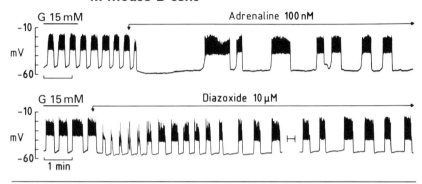

Reproduced from Drews et al. (1990) with permission.

(Trube *et al.*, 1986; Gillis *et al.*, 1989). In the presence of 15 mM-glucose, a 'high' concentration of diazoxide (100 μM) accelerates ^{86}Rb efflux as expected, whereas a 'low' concentration of the drug (10–15 μM) surprisingly decreases it (Fig. 6). The differences in the changes in membrane potential produced by the two concentrations of diazoxide provide an explanation. The low concentration of the drug only partially inhibits glucose-induced electrical activity in B-cells (Fig. 7), whereas the high concentration abolishes it and repolarizes the membrane to the resting potential (not shown, but see Fig. 4 and Garrino *et al.*, 1989). The opening of a few K$^+$-ATP channels by 10–15 μM-diazoxide is not reflected by an increase in ^{86}Rb efflux because the partial repolarization of the membrane and decreased electrical activity reduce the efflux of the tracer through K$^+$-V and K$^+$-VCa channels. The net effect is a paradoxical decrease in ^{86}Rb efflux like that seen when the concentration of glucose is lowered from 15 to 10 mM. On the other hand, the efflux of ^{86}Rb through the greater number of K$^+$-ATP channels opened by the high concentration of diazoxide is sufficient to be detected as a net increase in spite of the abolition of tracer efflux through K$^+$-V and K$^+$-VCa channels, which close when the membrane repolarizes completely.

As previously pointed out (Dawson *et al.*, 1983), changes in the rate of ^{42}K or ^{86}Rb efflux do not directly reflect changes in P$_K$ of the membrane. The latter also depend on the membrane potential. It should thus be emphasized that adequate interpretation of ^{86}Rb efflux under conditions where B-cells are stimulated is only possible if membrane potential measurements are available. From a practical standpoint, is it possible to establish whether a drug inhibits glucose-induced insulin release through a direct activation of K^+-ATP channels without having recourse to patch-clamp or membrane-potential measurements? If the drug is very potent, an increase in ^{86}Rb efflux will be observed regardless of the glucose concentration. Otherwise, an acceleration of ^{86}Rb efflux should be sought in the presence of 5–7 mM-glucose, when many K^+-ATP channels are closed and few K^+-V and K^+-VCa channels are open. In addition, it should be verified that the drug does not inhibit K^+-induced insulin secretion (Henquin *et al.*, 1982), and does not impair glucose metabolism. If these conditions are fulfilled, there is a good probability that the drug inhibits insulin release by directly opening K^+-ATP channels.

Neurohormonal control of P_K in B-cells

The amount of insulin that is released in response to a given nutrient stimulus can be modulated by various hormones and neurotransmitters. The underlying mechanisms of amplification or attenuation are usually multifactorial. Recent evidence indicates that changes in P_K of the B-cell membrane might sometimes be implicated. We will focus on this aspect since the other mechanisms are extensively discussed in Chapter 14 by Berggren *et al.*

Catecholamines

It is well established that catecholamines inhibit insulin release by activating α_2-adrenoceptors (Nakaki *et al.*, 1980). However, the relative contribution of the adenylate cyclase inhibition (Howell & Montague, 1973), of the decrease in cytosolic Ca^{2+} (Nilsson *et al.*, 1988), and of the interference with the exocytosis, at a stage distal to the generation of second messengers (Tamagawa *et al.*, 1985), is still unclear.

The decrease in free cytoplasmic Ca^{2+} may result from the partial repolarization of the B-cell membrane and inhibition of glucose-induced electrical activity that catecholamines produce (Fig. 7) (Cook & Perara, 1982; Santana de Sa *et al.*, 1983; Drews *et al.*, 1990; Joffre & Debuyser, 1990). Several mechanisms could cause this change in membrane potential. An inhibition of Ca^{2+} channels has been described in insulin-secreting HIT cells (Keahey *et al.*, 1989) but not in normal mouse B-cells. An increase in P_K was first excluded (Tamagawa & Henquin, 1983) because adrenaline decreases ^{86}Rb efflux from islets perifused with a medium containing calcium and a stimulatory concentration of glucose (Fig. 6). However, we have seen above that this 'paradoxical' change can also be produced by a decrease in glucose concentration or by diazoxide, and, therefore, is not incompatible with the opening of some K$^+$ channels. Such an opening is suggested by two other observations: adrenaline slightly accelerates ^{86}Rb efflux from islets perifused with 6 mM-glucose, and does not affect ^{86}Rb efflux and B-cell membrane potential in the presence of high K$^+$ and diazoxide, i.e. when most K$^+$ channels are already opened (Drews et al., 1990). In contrast to diazoxide, however, adrenaline does not persistently repolarize the membrane to the resting potential, even when used at high concentrations (Cook & Perara, 1982; Joffre & Debuyser, 1990). This suggests that only a subset of K$^+$ channels might be under control of α_2-adrenoceptors. Another difference to diazoxide is that adrenaline causes a marked and delayed decrease in ^{86}Rb efflux from islets perifused with a Ca^{2+}-free medium (Drews et al., 1990). Finally, it was recently observed that omission of extracellular Na$^+$ decreases the inhibitory potency of clonidine on insulin secretion (Bertrand & Henquin, 1990). This could mean that interference with Na$^+$ influx in B-cells (Na$^+$/H$^+$ exchange or resting Na$^+$ permeability) participates in the effects of catecholamines or that consequences of Na$^+$ removal (e.g. a decrease in cytosolic pH) counteracts one of the effects of α-adrenoceptor activation (perhaps on K$^+$ channels).

Galanin

Several studies have shown that the neuropeptide galanin affects B-cell function in a manner very similar to catecholamines (see Chapter 14 by Berggren et al.), although its effects are mediated by specific receptors (Amiranoff et al., 1987) distinct from α_2-adrenoceptors (Drews et al., 1990). With patch-clamp experiments using tumoral insulin-secreting cells it could be established that galanin repolarizes the membrane by activating K$^+$-ATP channels (De Weille et al., 1988; Dunne et al., 1989). A similar, though weak and not easily detectable effect of galanin has been observed in normal B-cells (Ahren et al., 1989). Although the evidence that galanin hyperpolarizes the membrane of normal B-cells by activating K$^+$-ATP channels seems to be stronger than for catecholamines, it is not yet entirely conclusive. The significance of this change in membrane potential for the inhibition of insulin release has yet to be established (Drews et al., 1990).

Somatostatin

It has long been suggested that somatostatin inhibits insulin release by increasing a Ca^{2+}-independent P_K of the B-cell membrane (Pace, 1980). This hypothesis was recently supported by the demonstration that somatostatin opens K$^+$-ATP channels in RINm5F cells (De Weille et al.,

1989). This effect has, however, not yet been described in normal B-cells. It is also evident that the inhibitory action of somatostatin on insulin secretion involves more than one pathway (see Chapter 14 by Berggren *et al.*).

Vasopressin

Vasopressin was recently detected in relatively high concentrations in the human or rat pancreas (Amico *et al.*, 1988), which suggests that it may play a role in the modulation of islet function. It was indeed found to increase insulin release by the perfused rat pancreas (Dunning *et al.*, 1984), by mouse islets (Gao *et al.*, 1990) and by tumoral insulin-secreting cells (Richardson *et al.*, 1990). Martin *et al.* (1989) have shown that vasopressin depolarizes the membrane of RINm5F cells by closing K^+-ATP channels. However, our measurements of ^{86}Rb efflux from whole islets, of the B-cell membrane potential with intracellular microelectrodes, and of K^+-ATP-channel activity by different configurations of the patch-clamp technique, have excluded the hypothesis that vasopressin closes K^+-ATP channels in normal mouse B-cells (Gao *et al.*, 1990). The potentiation of insulin secretion could be attributed to a stimulation of phosphoinositide metabolism. This is a further example of differences between the control of P_K in tumoral insulin-secreting cells and in normal B-cells.

Pharmacological control of P_K in B-cells

The ability of many drugs to affect insulin secretion can now be ascribed to their action on K^+-ATP channels in B-cells. The most 'classical' ones are the sulphonylureas and their derivatives, which all act by a similar mechanism, a closure of K^+-ATP channels, and diazoxide, which opens these channels (see Chapter 15 by Nelson *et al.* for consideration of sulphonylureas). It is not our purpose to detail the increasingly long list of agents affecting K^+ channels in B-cells. We shall simply summarize the effects of two groups of recently studied substances.

A new class of potential antihypertensive agents including pinacidil and cromakalim are thought to relax smooth muscles by opening K^+ channels. Pinacidil inhibits insulin secretion and accelerates ^{86}Rb efflux in mouse and rat islets (Garrino *et al.*, 1989; Lebrun *et al.*, 1989). It increases K^+-ATP currents and hyperpolarizes the membrane of mouse B-cells (Garrino *et al.*, 1989). The effects of pinacidil are thus similar to those of diazoxide, but much less potent. Cromakalim also causes a small inhibition of glucose-induced insulin secretion, but does not increase K^+-ATP currents in normal B-cells (Garrino *et al.*, 1989). This is in contrast with the apparent ability of cromakalim to open K^+-ATP channels in tumoral insulin-secreting cells (Dunne *et al.*, 1990b).

Phentolamine was known to counteract the effects of diazoxide on ^{86}Rb efflux and insulin secretion in rat islets (Henquin *et al.*, 1982). We recently observed that it directly inhibits K$^+$-ATP channels in B-cells (Plant & Henquin, 1990). A similar, though weaker, effect was produced by yohimbine. As the inhibition of K$^+$-ATP channels requires relatively high concentrations of phentolamine and yohimbine, it is unlikely to result from a blockade of α-adrenoceptors. These findings of a sulphonylurea-like action of blockers of α-adrenoceptors call for re-interpretation of numerous *in vivo* and *in vitro* studies.

Conclusions

The control of the membrane potential is an essential event of stimulus–secretion coupling in B-cells. Initiators of insulin secretion depolarize the membrane, activate voltage-dependent Ca^{2+} channels, stimulate Ca^{2+} influx and eventually increase the concentration of cytoplasmic Ca^{2+}. The depolarization brought about by glucose and other fuel secretagogues is owing to a decrease in K$^+$ permeability of the plasma membrane. This decrease results from the closure of K$^+$-ATP channels, which thus couple B-cell metabolism to membrane potential and ionic fluxes. Modulation of the activity of ATP-sensitive K$^+$ channels also explains, to a variable extent, the changes in insulin secretion produced by certain drugs, hormones and neurotransmitters. Much progress has been made recently in the elucidation of the role and of the control mechanisms of the various types of K$^+$ channels present in the membrane of normal B-cells. It will now be important to evaluate whether these channels are directly or indirectly implicated in states of defective insulin secretion (see Chapter 16 by Flatt *et al.*).

The authors' work referred to in this article was supported by grants of the Fonds National de la Recherche Scientifique Médicale, Brussels, from the Ministry of Scientific Policy, Brussels, and from the Deutsche Forschungsgemeinschaft, Bonn-Bad-Godesberg. J.C.H. is 'Directeur de Recherches' of the Fonds National de la Recherche Scientifique, Brussels. We are grateful to M. Nenquin for editorial assistance.

References

Ahren, B., Berggren, P. O., Bokvist, K. & Rorsman, P. (1989) Does galanin inhibit insulin secretion by opening of the ATP-regulated K$^+$ channels in the β-cell? Peptides **10**, 453–457

Amico, J. A., Finn, F. M. & Haldar, J. (1988) Oxytocin and vasopressin are present in human and rat pancreas. Am. J. Med. Sci. **296**, 303–307

Amiranoff, B., Servin, A. L., Rouyer-Fessard, C., Couvineau, A., Tatemoto, K. & Laburthe, M. (1987) Galanin receptors in a hamster pancreatic β-cell tumour: identification and molecular characterization. Endocrinology **121**, 284–289

Ashcroft, F. M., Harrison, D. E. & Ashcroft, S. J. H. (1984) Glucose induces closure of single potassium channels in isolated rat pancreatic β-cells. Nature (London) **312**, 446–448

Ashcroft, F. M., Ashcroft, S. J. H. & Harrison, D. E. (1988) Properties of single potassium channels modulated by glucose in rat pancreatic β-cells. J. Physiol. **400**, 501–527

Atwater, I. & Beigelman, P. M. (1976) Dynamic characteristics of electrical activity in pancreatic β-cells. I. Effects of calcium and magnesium removal. J. Physiol. (Paris) **72**, 769–786

Atwater, I., Dawson, C. M., Ribalet, B. & Rojas, E. (1979) Potassium permeability activated by intracellular ion concentration in the pancreatic B-cell. J. Physiol. **288**, 575–588

Bertrand, G. & Henquin, J. C. (1990) The influence of sodium omission on α_2-adrenergic inhibition of insulin release by mouse islets. Life Sci. **47**, 299–305

Bokvist, K., Rorsman, P. & Smith, P. A. (1990) Effects of external tetraethylammonium ions and quinine on delayed rectifying K^+ channels in mouse pancreatic β-cells. J. Physiol. **423**, 311–325

Bozem, M., Nenquin, M. & Henquin, J. C. (1987) The ionic, electrical, and secretory effects of protein kinase C activation in mouse pancreatic B-cells: studies with a phorbol ester. Endocrinology **121**, 1025–1033

Cook, D. L. & Hales, C. N. (1984) Intracellular ATP directly blocks K^+ channels in pancreatic B-cells. Nature (London) **311**, 271–273

Cook, D. L. & Ikeuchi, M. (1989) Tolbutamide as mimic of glucose on β-cell electrical activity. Diabetes **38**, 416–421

Cook, D. L. & Perara, E. (1982) Islet electrical pacemaker response to alpha-adrenergic stimulation. Diabetes **31**, 985–990

Cook, D. L., Satin, L. S., Ashford, M. L. J. & Hales, C. N. (1988) ATP-sensitive K^+ channels in pancreatic β-cells: spare-channel hypothesis. Diabetes **37**, 495–498

Dawson, C. M., Croghan, P. C., Atwater, I. & Rojas, E. (1983) Estimation of potassium permeability in mouse islets of Langerhans. Biomed. Res. **4**, 389–392

De Miguel, R., Tamagawa, T., Schmeer, W., Nenquin, M. & Henquin, J. C. (1988) Effects of acute sodium omission on insulin release, ionic fluxes and membrane potential in mouse pancreatic B-cells. Biochim. Biophys. Acta **969**, 198–207

De Weille, J., Schmid-Antomarchi, H., Fosset, M. & Lazdunski, M. (1988) ATP-sensitive K^+ channels that are blocked by hypoglycaemia-inducing sulphonylureas in insulin-secreting cells are activated by galanin, a hyperglycaemia-inducing hormone. Proc. Natl. Acad. Sci. U.S.A. **85**, 1312–1316

De Weille, J., Schmid-Antomarchi, H., Fosset, M. & Lazdunski, M. (1989) Regulation of ATP-sensitive K^+ channels in insulinoma cells: activation by somatostatin and protein kinase C, and the role of cAMP. Proc. Natl. Acad. Sci. U.S.A. **86**, 2971–2975

Drews, G., Debuyser, A., Nenquin, M. & Henquin, J. C. (1990) Galanin and epinephrine act on distinct receptors to inhibit insulin release by the same mechanisms including an increase in K^+ permeability of the B-cell membrane. Endocrinology **126**, 1646–1653

Dunne, M. J., Bullett, M. J., Guodong, L., Wollheim, C. B. & Petersen, O. H. (1989) Galanin activates nucleotide-dependent K^+ channels in insulin secreting cells via a pertussis toxin-sensitive G-protein. EMBO J. **8**, 413–420

Dunne, M. J., Yule, D. I., Gallacher, D. V. & Petersen, O. H. (1990*a*) Stimulant-evoked depolarization and increase in $[Ca^{2+}]_i$ in insulin-secreting cells is dependent on external Na^+. J. Membr. Biol. **113**, 131–138

Dunne, M. J., Aspinall, R. J. & Petersen, O. H. (1990*b*) The effects of cromakalim on ATP-sensitive potassium channels in insulin-secreting cells. Br. J. Pharmacol. **99**, 169–175

Dunning, B. E., Moltz, J. H. & Fawcett, C. P. (1984) Modulation of insulin and glucagon secretion from the perfused rat pancreas by the neurohypophysial hormones and by desamino-D-arginine vasopressin (DDAVP). Peptides **5**, 871–875

Eddlestone, G. T. & Beigelman, P. M. (1983) Pancreatic β-cell electrical activity: the role of anions and the control of pH. Am. J. Physiol. **244**, C188–C197

Gao, Z. Y., Drews, G., Nenquin, M., Plant, T. D. & Henquin, J. C. (1990) Mechanisms of the stimulation of insulin release by arginine-vasopressin in normal mouse islets. J. Biol. Chem. **265**, 15724–15730

Garrino, M. G., Plant, T. D. & Henquin, J. C. (1989) Effects of putative activators of K^+ channels in mouse pancreatic β-cells. Br. J. Pharmacol. **98**, 957–965

Gillis, K. D., Gee, W. M., Hammoud, A., McDaniel, M. L., Falke, L. C. & Misler, S. (1989) Effects of sulphonamides on a metabolite-regulated ATP_i-sensitive K^+ channel in rat pancreatic B-cells. Am. J. Physiol. **257**, C1119–C1127

Gylfe, E. (1988) Glucose-induced early changes in cytoplasmic calcium of pancreatic B-cells studied with time-sharing dual-wavelength fluorometry. J. Biol. Chem. 263, 5044–5048

Henquin, J. C. (1978) D-glucose inhibits potassium efflux from pancreatic islet cells. Nature (London) 271, 271–273

Henquin, J. C. (1979) Opposite effects of intracellular Ca^{2+} and glucose on K$^+$ permeability of pancreatic islet cells. Nature (London) 280, 66–68

Henquin, J. C. (1988) ATP-sensitive K$^+$ channels may control glucose-induced electrical activity in pancreatic B-cells. Biochem. Biophys. Res. Commun. 156, 769–775

Henquin, J. C. (1990a) Role of voltage- and Ca^{2+}-dependent K$^+$ channels in the control of glucose-induced electrical activity in pancreatic B-cells. Pflüegers Arch. 416, 568–572

Henquin, J. C. (1990b) Glucose-induced electrical activity in B-cells: feedback control of ATP-sensitive K$^+$ channels by calcium? Diabetes 39, 1457–1460

Henquin, J. C. & Meissner, H. P. (1984a) Significance of ionic fluxes and changes in membrane potential for stimulus-secretion coupling in pancreatic B-cells. Experientia 40, 1043–1052

Henquin, J. C. & Meissner, H. P. (1984b) The ionic, electrical, and secretory effects of endogenous cyclic adenosine monophosphate in mouse pancreatic B cells: studies with forskolin. Endocrinology 115, 1125–1134

Henquin, J. C., Charles, S., Nenquin, M., Mathot, F. & Tamagawa, T. (1982) Diazoxide and D600 inhibition of insulin release: distinct mechanisms explain the specificity for different stimuli. Diabetes 31, 776–783

Henquin, J. C., Bozem, M., Schmeer, W. & Nenquin, M. (1987) Distinct mechanisms of two amplification systems of insulin release. Biochem. J. 246, 393–399

Henquin, J. C., Schmeer, W., Nenquin, M. & Plant, T. D. (1989) Does protein kinase C link glucose metabolism to B-cell membrane depolarization? Diabetologia 32, 496 (Abstract)

Hiriart, M. & Matteson, D. R. (1988) Na channels and two types of Ca channels in rat pancreatic B cells identified with the reverse hemolytic plaque assay. J. Gen. Physiol. 91, 617–639

Howell, S. L. & Montague, W. (1973) Adenylate cyclase activity in isolated rat islets of Langerhans: effects of agents which alter rates of insulin secretion. Biochim. Biophys. Acta 320, 44–52

Joffre, M. & Debuyser, A. (1990) Glucose- and concentration-dependence of noradrenalin effects on electrical activity in mouse pancreatic β-cells. Biochim. Biophys. Acta 1052, 285–292

Keahey, H. H., Boyd, A. E. & Kunze, D. L. (1989) Catecholamine modulation of calcium currents in clonal pancreatic β-cells. Am. J. Physiol. 257, C1171–C1176

Lebrun, P., Devreux, V., Hermann, M. & Herchuelz, A. (1989) Similarities between the effects of pinacidil and diazoxide on ionic and secretory events in rat pancreatic islets. J. Pharmacol. Exp. Ther. 250, 1011–1018

Martin, S. C., Yule, D. I., Dunne, M. J., Gallacher, D. V. & Petersen, O. H. (1989) Vasopressin directly closes ATP-sensitive potassium channels evoking membrane depolarization and an increase in the free intracellular Ca^{2+} concentration in insulin-secreting cells. EMBO J. 8, 3595–3599

Meissner, H. P. & Preissler, M. (1980) Ionic mechanisms of the glucose-induced membrane potential changes in B-cells. Horm. Metab. Res. (Suppl.) 10, 91–99

Meissner, H. P. & Schmelz, H. (1974) Membrane potential of beta-cells in pancreatic islets. Pflüegers Arch. 351, 195–206

Meissner, H. P., Henquin, J. C. & Preissler, M. (1978) Potassium dependence of the membrane potential of pancreatic B cells. FEBS Lett. 94, 87–89

Misler, S., Falke, L. C., Gillis, K. & McDaniel, M. L. (1986) A metabolite-regulated potassium channel in rat pancreatic B cells. Proc. Natl. Acad. Sci. U.S.A. 83, 7119–7123

Nakaki, T.,Nakadate, T. & Kato, R. (1980) α$_2$-Adrenoceptors modulating insulin release from isolated pancreatic islets. Naunyn-Schmiedeberg's Arch. Pharmacol. 313, 151–153

Nilsson, T., Arkhammar, P., Rorsman, P. & Berggren, P. O. (1988) Inhibition of glucose-stimulated insulin release by α$_2$-adrenoceptor activation is paralleled by both a repolarization and a reduction in cytoplasmic free Ca^{2+} concentration. J. Biol. Chem. 263, 1855–1860

Pace, C. S. (1980) Somatostatin: control of stimulus-secretion coupling in pancreatic islet cells. In Peptides: Integrators of Cell and Tissue Function (F. E. Bloom, ed.), pp. 163–195, Raven Press, New York

Pace, C. S. & Goldsmith, K. T. (1985) Action of a phorbol ester on B-cells: Potentiation of stimulant-induced electrical activity. Am. J. Physiol. **248**, C527–C534

Pace, C. S. & Tarvin, J. T. (1983) pH Modulation of glucose-induced electrical activity in B-cells: involvement of Na/H and HCO_3/Cl antiporters. J. Membr. Biol. **73**, 39–49

Panten, U., Burgfeld, J., Goerke, F., Rennicke, M., Schwanstecher, M., Wallasch, A., Zünkler, B. J. & Lenzen, S. (1989) Control of insulin secretion of sulphonylureas, meglitinide and diazoxide in relation to their binding to the sulphonylurea receptor in pancreatic islets. Biochem. Pharmacol. **38**, 1217–1229

Peter-Riesch, B., Fahti, M., Schlegel, W. & Wollheim, C. B. (1988) Glucose and carbachol generate 1,2-diacylglycerol by different mechanisms in pancreatic islets. J. Clin. Invest. **81**, 1154–1161

Petersen, O. H. & Findlay, I. (1987) Electrophysiology of the pancreas. Physiol. Rev. **67**, 1054–1116

Plant, T. D. (1988*a*) Na^+ currents in cultured mouse pancreatic B-cells. Pflüegers Arch. **411**, 429–435

Plant, T. D. (1988*b*) Properties and calcium-dependent inactivation of calcium currents in cultured mouse pancreatic B-cells. J. Physiol. **404**, 731–747

Plant, T. D. & Henquin, J. C. (1990) Phentolamine and yohimbine inhibit ATP-sensitive K^+ channels in mouse pancreatic β-cells. Br. J. Pharmacol. **101**, 115–120

Plasman, P. O., Hermann, M., Herchuelz, A. & Lebrun, P. (1990) Sensitivity to Cd^{2+} but resistance to Ni^{2+} of Ca^{2+} inflow into rat pancreatic islets. Am. J. Physiol. **258**, E529–E533

Pralong, W.-F., Bartley, C. & Wollheim, C. B. (1990) Single islet B-cell stimulation by nutrients: relationship between pyridine nucleotides, cytosoloic Ca^{2+} and secretion. EMBO J. **9**, 53–60

Prentki, M. & Matschinsky, F. M. (1987) Ca^{2+}, cAMP, and phospholipid-derived messengers in coupling mechanisms of insulin secretion. Physiol. Rev. **67**, 1185–1248

Ribalet, B. & Beigelman, P. M. (1980) Calcium action potentials and potassium permeability activation in pancreatic β-cells. Am. J. Physiol. **239**, C124–C133

Ribalet, B. & Beigelman, P. M. (1982) Effects of sodium on β-cell electrical activity. Am. J. Physiol. **242**, C296–C303

Ribalet, B., Eddlestone, G. T. & Ciani, S. (1988) Metabolic regulation of the K(ATP) and a Maxi-K(V) channel in the insulin-secreting RINm5F cell. J. Gen. Physiol. **92**, 219–237

Richardson, S. B., Eyler, N., Twente, S., Monaco, M., Altszuler, N. & Gibson, M. (1990) Effects of vasopressin on insulin secretion and inositol phosphate production in a hamster beta cell line (HIT). Endocrinology **126**, 1047–1052

Rorsman, P. & Trube, G. (1985) Glucose-dependent K^+-channels in pancreatic β-cells are regulated by intracellular ATP. Pflüegers Arch. **405**, 305–309

Rorsman, P. & Trube, G. (1990) Biophysics and physiology of ATP-regulated K^+ channels. In Potassium Channels (Cook, N., ed.), pp. 96–116, Ellis Horwood, Hemel Hempstead

Santana de Sa, S., Ferrer, R., Rojas, E. & Atwater, I. (1983) Effects of adrenaline and noradrenaline on glucose-induced electrical activity of mouse pancreatic β-cell. Q. J. Physiol. **68**, 247–258

Satin, L. S. & Cook, D. L. (1989) Calcium current inactivation in insulin-secreting cells is mediated by calcium influx and membrane depolarization. Pflüegers Arch. **414**, 1–10

Sehlin, J. & Meissner, H. P. (1988) Effects of Cl^- deficiency on the membrane potential in mouse pancreatic β-cells. Biochim. Biophys. Acta **937**, 309–318

Sehlin, J. & Täljedal, I. B. (1975) Glucose-induced decrease in Rb^+ permeability in pancreatic β-cells. Nature (London) **253**, 635–636

Smith, P. A., Rorsman, P. & Ashcroft, F. M. (1989) Modulation of dihydropyridine-sensitive Ca^{2+} channels by glucose metabolism in mouse pancreatic β-cells. Nature (London) **342**, 550–553

Smith, P. A., Ashcroft, F. M. & Rorsman, P. (1990) Simultaneous recordings of glucose-dependent electrical activity and ATP-regulated K^+-currents in isolated mouse pancreatic β-cells. FEBS Lett. **261**, 187–190

Tamagawa, T. & Henquin, J. C. (1983) Epinephrine modifications of insulin release and of $^{86}Rb^+$ or $^{45}Ca^{2+}$ fluxes in rat islets. Am. J. Physiol. **244**, E245–E252

Tamagawa, T., Niki, I., Niki, H. & Niki, A. (1985) Catecholamines inhibit insulin release independently of changes in cytosolic free Ca^{2+}. Biomed. Res. **6**, 429–432

Trube, G., Rorsman, P. & Ohno-Shosaku, T. (1986) Opposite effects of tolbutamide and diazoxide on the ATP-dependent K^+ channel in mouse pancreatic β-cells. Pflüegers Arch. **407**, 493–499

Velasco, J. M. & Petersen, O. H. (1989) The effect of a cell-permeable diacylglycerol analogue on single Ca^{2+} (Ba^{2+}) channel currents in the insulin-secreting cell line RINm5F. Q. J. Exp. Physiol. **74**, 367–370

Wolf, B. A., Easom, R. A., Hughes, J. H., McDaniel, M. L. & Turk, J. (1989) Secretagogue-induced diacylglycerol accumulation in isolated pancreatic islets. Mass spectrometric characterization of the fatty acyl content indicates multiple mechanisms of generation. Biochemistry **28**, 4291–4301

Wollheim, C. B., Dunne, M. J., Peter-Riesch, B., Bruzzone, R., Pozzan, T. & Petersen, O. H. (1988) Activators of protein kinase C depolarize insulin-secreting cells by closing K^+ channels. EMBO J. **7**, 2443–2449

10

Ion channels involved in the regulation of nutrient-stimulated insulin secretion

Frances M. Ashcroft*, Beatrice Williams, Paul A. Smith and Clare M. S. Fewtrell†

University Laboratory of Physiology, Oxford, OX1 3PT, U.K.

Introduction

Insulin secretion from the pancreatic B-cell is controlled by a plethora of nutrients, hormones, neurotransmitters and pharmacological agents. There is considerable evidence that electrical activity of the B-cell membrane plays a central role in coupling activation by these stimuli to insulin release. In this chapter, we focus on the properties of the ion channels that underlie B-cell electrical activity.

Much of the evidence that electrical activity of the B-cell membrane plays an important role in stimulus-secretion coupling has been obtained from microelectrode recordings from B-cells within intact islets of Langerhans (for review see Henquin & Meissner, 1984). Such studies have shown that glucose depolarizes the B-cell and induces a characteristic pattern of electrical activity which consists of slow oscillations in membrane potential (known as slow waves), with accompanying Ca^{2+}-dependent action potentials, separated by electrically silent intervals. B-cell electrical activity is discussed in more detail by Henquin *et al.* in Chapter 9.

Application of the patch-clamp technique (Hamill *et al.*, 1981) to single B-cells has clarified our understanding of the way in which secretagogues modulate B-cell electrical activity. This technique, which is outlined below, allows either (i) the current flowing through a single ion channel to be measured in cell-attached or excised membranes patches; or (ii) the summed current which flows through all of the ion channels in the cell to be recorded (the whole-cell current). It is also possible to use the whole-cell recording configurations to measure the B-cell membrane potential. Electrical activity recorded from single B-cells using the

* To whom correspondence should be addressed: University Laboratory of Physiology, Parks Rd, Oxford, OX1 3PT, U.K.

† Present address: Department of Pharmacology, Cornell University, Ithaca, NY 14853, U.S.A.

Fig. I. Electrical activity recorded from a dissociated B-cell using the perforated patch technique

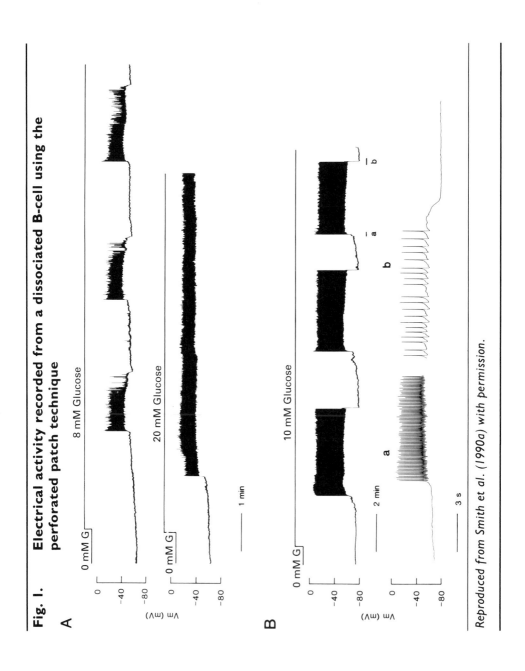

Reproduced from Smith et al. (1990a) with permission.

perforated patch configuration (Smith *et al.*, 1990*a* and Fig. 1), which preserves cellular metabolism, is broadly similar to that found in microelectrode recordings (compare Fig. 1 with Fig. 1 in Chapter 9). This indicates that a single B-cell possesses the necessary machinery for producing the characteristic electrical activity and that electrical coupling to adjacent islet cells is not essential for the generation of this activity.

Patch-clamp studies have enabled the different ion channels which underlie B-cell electrical activity to be identified and characterized, and the effects of nutrient secretagogues on the properties of these channels to be determined. Such studies have shown that the activity of the ATP-regulated K^+ channel determines the resting potential of the B-cell. Closure of these channels, either by glucose metabolism (Ashcroft *et al.*, 1984; Rorsman & Trube, 1985; Misler *et al.*, 1986) or by sulphonylureas (Sturgess *et al.*, 1985) reduces the membrane K^+-permeability and leads to membrane depolarization. This opens voltage-dependent Ca^{2+} channels (Rorsman & Trube, 1986; Rorsman *et al.*, 1988) and so elicits electrical activity. The increased Ca^{2+} influx that takes place through open Ca^{2+} channels produces a rise in intracellular calcium which stimulates insulin secretion (Prentki & Matchinsky, 1987).

Patch-clamp configurations

Various patch-clamp configurations have been used for recording single-channel currents and whole-cell currents in B-cells. These are illustrated in Fig. 2. The stippled area indicates the cytoplasm. All configurations are obtained by first forming a high-resistance seal between the cell membrane and a glass micropipette pressed against the surface of the cell. The high electrical resistance of the seal permits current flowing through single ion channels in the patch of membrane beneath the pipette to be recorded with a low level of background noise, and also allows the potential across the patch membrane to be altered in a controlled fashion (voltage-clamped). When the pipette is sealed to the surface of an intact cell it is referred to as cell-attached (Fig. 2A). Cell-attached recording has the advantage that the cell is intact and the channel may be studied under physiological conditions. It can also be used to determine whether nutrient secretagogues (such as glucose) or hormones mediate their effects by metabolism or intracellular second messengers. This is because the glass–membrane seal is too tight to permit the diffusion of substances between the pipette and bath solutions: thus any effect of a substance added to the bath solution on the activity of ion channels in the patch of membrane beneath the pipette tip must be mediated via an intracellular route. The open-cell-attached patch (Fig. 2A) is a variant of the cell-attached patch in which the rest of the cell membrane is permeabilized by substances such as saponin (Dunne *et al.*, 1986). This allows the intracellular solution to be modified and putative channel modulators introduced. It has the advantage that cytosolic second messengers which may be required for channel function are lost less rapidly than in the excised patch configurations (see below).

Fig. 2.   **Patch–clamp configurations applied to single pancreatic B-cells (Hamill *et al.*, 1981; Horn & Marty, 1988; Kakei *et al.*, 1985)**

A: Single-channel-recording configurations

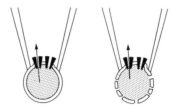

Cell-attached patch   Open-cell-attatched patch

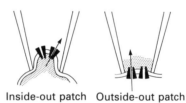

Inside-out patch   Outside-out patch

B: Whole-cell-recording configurations

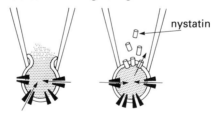

Standard whole-cell   Perforated patch

Reproduced from Ashcroft & Rorsmann (1990) with permission

Two other single-channel recording configurations are possible (Fig. 2A) because the high mechanical stability of the seal results in the membrane breaking before the seal. Thus if the pipette is withdrawn from the cell surface, an isolated membrane patch is produced, spanning the pipette tip, which has its intracellular surface exposed to the bath solution (inside-out patch). An outside-out patch is produced when the pipette is withdrawn from the whole-cell configuration. With these two configurations channel properties can be measured under controlled ionic conditions and measurements made in different solutions without detachment of the patch pipette. In addition, inside-out patches can be used to test the effects of putative intracellular modulators on channel activity. The two whole-cell configurations (Fig. 2B) allow the summed activity of many ion channels (the whole-cell current) to be investigated under controlled voltage conditions. The standard whole-cell method (Fig. 2B, left) is obtained by forming a cell-attached patch and then destroying the patch membrane with strong suction. It has the advantage that the intracellular solution can be manipulated but the concomitant disadvantage that soluble cytosolic constituents are lost from the cell. By contrast, the perforated-patch method (Fig. 2B, right) preserves cellular metabolism and intracellular second messenger systems (Falke *et al.*, 1989; Smith *et al.*, 1990*a*). In this configuration, the patch membrane is permeabilized by the pore-forming antibiotic nystatin. Nystatin is included in the pipette solution and incorporates into the patch membrane, thus providing a low-resistance electrical pathway to the cell interior. The nystatin pores allow the permeation of the monovalent cations but not molecules with a molecular mass larger than about 200 Da—which includes most metabolic constituents and second messengers. Anions are very poorly permeable through these pores.

Ion channels present in the B-cell membrane

The different types of ion channels that have been identified in B-cells and the various cell lines derived from them are illustrated in Fig. 3. A number of earlier reviews have considered the properties of B-cell ion channels and their importance for insulin secretion (Petersen & Findlay, 1987; Atwater *et al.*, 1989; Findlay *et al.*, 1989; Ashford, 1990, Rajan *et al.*, 1990). A recent, fully comprehensive account may be found in the review by Ashcroft & Rorsman (1990); here, we briefly summarize the main features.

K$^+$-DR channel

The delayed rectifier (the K$^+$-DR channel) has a single-channel conductance of ~ 15 pS in symmetrical 150 mM-K$^+$-solutions and of ~ 9 pS under quasi-physiological ionic conditions (Zunkler *et al.*, 1988; Smith *et al.*, 1990*b*). Channel activity is voltage-dependent, increasing with depolarization. The functional role of the K$^+$-DR channel is to repolarize the action potential (Bokvist *et al.*, 1990*a*; Smith *et al.*, 1990*b*).

K⁺-Ca²⁺ channel

Ca^{2+}-activated K^+ channels (K^+-Ca^{2+} channels) are activated both by an increase in the cytoplasmic Ca^{2+} and by depolarization (Cook *et al.*, 1984; Findlay *et al.*, 1985; Tabcharini & Misler, 1989; Satin *et al.*, 1989). The

Fig. 3.   Types of ion channels found in the B-cell membrane

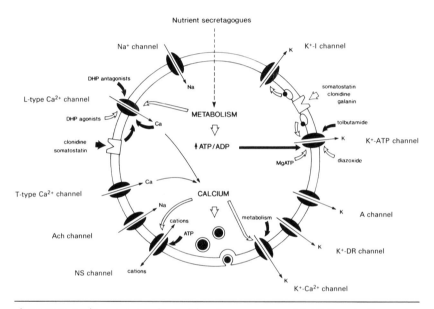

Activatory pathways are indicated by open arrows and inhibitory pathways by filled arrows. Channels are indicated by closed symbols and receptors by open symbols. Abbreviations: K^+-I channel, K^+ channel activated by inhibitors such as clonidine; K^+-ATP channel, ATP-regulated K^+ channel; A channel, transient outward K^+ channel; K^+-DR channel, delayed rectifying K^+ channel; K^+-Ca^{2+} channel, Ca^{2+}-activated K^+ channel; NS channel, non-selective cation channel; ACh channel, acetylcholine-activated channel. Modified from Ashcroft & Rorsman (1990) with permission.

single-channel conductance is 200–250 pS (Cook *et al.*, 1984) in symmetrical 150 mM-KCl solutions and 110–155 pS when exposed to physiological ion concentration gradients (Bokvist *et al.*, 1990b; Mancilla & Rojas, 1990). The sensitivity to external tetraethylammonium ions (TEA) is higher than that of other B-cell K^+ channels ($K_i \sim 0.2$ mM; Tabcharini & Misler, 1989; Bokvist *et al.*, 1990b) so that it is possible to block this channel relatively selectively with low concentrations of TEA. Such studies suggest that K^+-Ca^{2+} channels contribute to action potential repolarization but not to the slow waves (Bokvist *et al.*, 1990*b*; Bangham & Smith, 1987; Henquin, 1990; Velasco & Petersen, 1987); see below, and Chapter 9 in this book by Henquin *et al.* for further discussion of this point.

K$^+$-ATP channel

Unlike the K$^+$-DR and K$^+$-Ca^{2+} channels, the ATP-sensitive K$^+$ channel (K$^+$-ATP channel) is voltage-independent. The single-channel conductance is about 20 pS with 5 mM external K$^+$ and increases to 50 pS when $[K^+]_0$ is raised to 140 mM (Ashcroft, 1988; Ashcroft & Ashcroft, 1990). K$^+$-ATP-channel activity is inhibited by a rise in the intracellular ATP concentration (Cook & Hales, 1984; Rorsman & Trube, 1985) and is modulated by a considerable number of other cytosolic constituents. Of particular clinical importance is the fact that K$^+$-ATP channels are selectively blocked by sulphonylureas, such as tolbutamide and glibenclamide (Sturgess *et al.*, 1985; Trube *et al.*, 1986; Gillis *et al.*, 1989). These drugs have been used for many years in the treatment of non-insulin-dependent diabetes mellitus (NIDDM) but it is only recently that it has been recognized that their therapeutic site of action is the K$^+$-ATP channel (for review see Ashcroft & Ashcroft, 1990; Ashford, 1990 and Chapter 15 by Nelson *et al.*).

K$^+$-I channel

Recently, a K$^+$ channel activated by the inhibitors of insulin secretion, clonidine, somatostatin and galanin, has been found in mouse B-cells, which may account for the hyperpolarization produced by these agents (Chapter 14 by Berggren *et al.*). The conductance of this channel (the K$^+$-I channel) is very low; estimates from analyses of membrane-current noise yield a value of around 1 pS under physiological ionic gradients and single-channel currents cannot be resolved. A pertussis-toxin-sensitive G-protein appears to mediate the effect of receptor activation on channel activity.

A channel

One brief report has described the presence of an A-current in mouse B-cells (Smith *et al.*, 1989*a*). This is a transient outward K$^+$-current that rapidly inactivates. It is about 50 % inactivated at the resting potential of the B-cell and largely inactivated at potentials which occur during glucose-stimulated electrical activity: furthermore, it is not observed in all B-cells. Whether this channel has a role in B-cell electrical activity is therefore unclear.

NS channel

A non-selective cation channel that is permeable to both Na$^+$ and K$^+$ has been seen in inside-out patches excised from human B-cells (Sturgess *et al.*,

1987*a*) and GRI-G1 insulinoma cells (Sturgess *et al.*, 1986, 1987*b*). This channel is activated by intracellular Ca^{2+} ($> 100 \,\mu\text{M}$) and blocked by adenine nucleotides, with AMP being more effective than ATP. Its functional significance is uncertain as these properties would suggest the channel is closed in the intact cell.

ACh channel

Acetylcholine is known to stimulate insulin secretion and electrical activity through activation of muscarinic receptors (Henquin *et al.*, 1988). Although the latter effect is believed to be mediated by Na^+ influx, ACh-activated Na^+ currents have not yet been described.

Na^+ channel

In most species investigated, Na^+ channels do not contribute significantly to the action potential depolarization in the B-cell since tetrodotoxin has no effect on B-cell electrical activity (Meissner & Schmelz, 1974; Ribalet & Beigelman 1982). This is because the Na^+ channels are largely inactivated at the plateau potential (Plant, 1988*a*; Satin & Cook, 1988; Hirriat & Matteson, 1988). The exception is the dog (Pressel & Misler, 1990) where Na^+ channels are found to contribute to action potential depolarization.

L-type and T-type Ca^{2+} channels

Two types of voltage-dependent single-Ca^{2+}-channel currents have been described in rat B-cells (Ashcroft *et al.*, 1990*a*; Sala & Matteson, 1990). The properties of these channels roughly conform to those of the L-type and the T-type Ca^{2+} channels described by Nowycky *et al.*, (1985). That is, with 100 mm-Ba^{2+} in the external solution the L-type channels have a single-channel conductance of ~ 25 pS, a high threshold for activation (-30 mV) and show little inactivation. The dihydropyridine Ca^{2+}-channel agonist BAYK 8644 promotes long-channel openings and dihydropyridine antagonists, e.g. nifedipine, inhibit channel activity. T-type channels are characterized by activation at very negative potentials (-50 mV), rapid voltage-dependent inactivation and a single-channel conductance of ~ 8 pS with 100 mm external Ba^{2+}. Interestingly, mouse B-cells possess only L-type Ca^{2+} channels (Plant 1988*b*; Rorsman *et al.*, 1988).

The properties of the L-type Ca^{2+} current suggest that it underlies the action potentials and the plateau potential. It seems unlikely that the T-type channel plays a substantial role in B-cell electrical activity for at least two reasons. First, this channel is not present in mouse B-cells and secondly, even in rat B-cells the rapid inactivation of the current indicates it cannot be involved in its maintenance of the plateau potential. Furthermore, pharmacological experiments suggest most of the Ca^{2+}

current required for insulin secretion flows through L-type Ca^{2+} channels, as 1 μM-nifedipine, a specific blocker of this channel type, completely inhibits glucose-stimulated insulin secretion in the rat (Malaisse-Lagae *et al.*, 1984).

Regulation of B-cell ion channel by cellular metabolism

Metabolic regulation of K^+-ATP channels, K^+-Ca^{2+} channels and L-type Ca^{2+} channels has so far been reported. We now discuss this regulation and its role in B-cell electrical activity (and thus insulin secretion).

K^+-ATP channels

Cell-attached and perforated-patch recordings have been used to study the regulation of K^+-ATP-channel activity in the intact B-cell since metabolism remains undisturbed in these configurations. The results of such experiments are summarized here.

In the absence of glucose, the resting potential of the B-cell is dominated by the activity of the K^+-ATP channel and many single-channel openings can be recorded from B-cells lacking an exogenous fuel supply (Ashcroft *et al.*, 1984, 1988). Perforated-patch recordings suggest that about 10–25 % of the total K^+-ATP conductance is activated at rest in the mouse B-cell (Ashcroft & Rorsman, 1990) and rather less, about 4%, in rat B-cells (Cohen *et al.*, 1990).

Substrates for B-cell metabolism produce a rapid, reversible and dose-dependent decrease of K^+-ATP-channel activity. Cell-attached patch recordings have established that 50 % of the channels active in the absence of glucose are inhibited by around 2 mM-glucose and more than 90 % at the physiological glucose concentration of 5 mM (Ashcroft *et al.*, 1988; Misler *et al.*, 1986; Rosman & Trube, 1990). At a concentration of 5 mM, glyceraldehyde also almost completely blocks single K^+-ATP-channel activity in rat B-cells but mannose is only about half as effective (Misler *et al.*, 1986).

One problem in measuring the glucose-dependence of channel activity in cell-attached patches is that very long periods of recording are required to obtain sufficient data at higher glucose concentrations. Over this time interval, it is unlikely that channel activity will be stable; furthermore, the success rate of such long-term recordings is lower. The problem can be overcome by measuring the glucose-dependence of the whole-cell K^+-ATP currents, using the perforated-patch configuration to retain cellular metabolism (Horn & Marty, 1988; Smith *et al.*, 1990*a*; Falke *et al.*, 1989). Our recent studies using this method have shown that there is considerable variability in the glucose sensitivity of different B-cells

(Ashcroft *et al.*, 1990*b,c*). Whereas some B-cells show a sensitivity similar to that reported for single-channel recordings (half-maximal inhibition at ~ 2 mM), other B-cells are markedly less sensitive with more than 8 mM-glucose being needed to produce 50% inhibition. In almost all cells, however, inhibition is complete in 15–20 mM-glucose. Thus, as first suggested by Henquin (1988), glucose concentrations between 5 and 20 mM are indeed able to modulate K^+-ATP-channel activity. Differences in B-cell metabolism probably underlie the observed heterogeneity in the glucose sensitivity of the K^+-ATP current since a similar variability has been reported for glucose-induced changes in NAD(P)H fluorescence in single B-cells, which provides an index of cellular metabolism (Pralong *et al.*, 1990). Variation in the glucose dose–response curve for the K^+-ATP currents may account for the heterogeneity in the glucose sensitivity of insulin secretion found for single B-cells (Salomon & Meda, 1986; Hiriart & Matteson, 1988).

As is the case for insulin secretion (Ashcroft, 1980), nutrient secretagogues must be metabolized to close K^+-ATP channels since metabolic inhibitors reverse the effects of secretagogues. These results are consistent with the known metabolic pathways in the B-cell (see Chapters 5 by Malaisse and 6 by Lenzen). Thus, mannoheptulose (which blocks glucokinase, and thus glycolysis) reverses glucose- (Ashcroft *et al.*, 1984) but not glyceraldehyde-inhibition of channel activity (Misler *et al.*, 1986); iodoacetate reverses inhibition by both glucose and glyceraldehyde but not that produced by 4-methyl-2-oxo-pentanoate (ketoisocaproate) (Misler *et al.*, 1986), and rotenone blocks the effects of all these secretagogues (Ashcroft *et al.*, 1985; Ashcroft, F. M., unpublished work). Furthermore, K^+-ATP-channel activity is not influenced by the non-metabolized sugars galactose and 3-O-methylglucose (Misler *et al.*, 1986).

Leucine and its de-amination product, 4-methyl-2-oxo-pentanoate, are primarily metabolized by the mitochondria. Both these secretagogues close K^+-ATP channels, indicating that oxidative phosphorylation also generates an intracellular mediator of channel inhibition, one that is also common to glucose and glyceraldehyde metabolism (Ashcroft *et al.*, 1987; Ribalet *et al.*, 1988; Eddlestone *et al.*, 1989). There is even some indication that oxidative metabolism may be a more important regulator of K^+-ATP-channel activity than glycolysis since inhibitors of mito-chondrial metabolism (such as rotenone, azide and oligomycin) are very effective at rapidly increasing channel activity blocked by glucose (Ashcroft *et al.*, 1985; Misler *et al.*, 1986; Ribalet & Ciani, 1987). Indeed, these agents are able to promote channel activity in the absence of exogenous fuels (Ashcroft *et al.*, 1985).

It should be emphasized that the effects of these metabolites are probably mediated via a common mechanism. This is believed to be the ATP/ADP ratio inside the cell (see below).

K$^+$-Ca^{2+} channels

Nutrient secretagogues have also been reported to inhibit the activity of the K$^+$-Ca^{2+} channel in the insulin-secreting cell lines HIT-T15 and RINm5F (Ribalet *et al.*, 1988; Eddlestone *et al.*, 1989). For glucose, inhibition is half maximal at 7·5 mM and complete at 25 mM. The slow time course of the effect and the fact that it is reversed by metabolic inhibitors suggest that a metabolic intermediate is involved.

L-type Ca^{2+} channels

Theoretically, there are at least two ways in which nutrient secretagogues may influence Ca^{2+} influx through voltage-dependent Ca^{2+} channels: by regulating the B-cell membrane potential or by biochemical modulation of the Ca^{2+} channel itself. As discussed above, closure of K$^+$-ATP channels depolarizes the B-cell and thereby activates voltage-dependent Ca^{2+} channels. Glucose metabolism also modulates L-type Ca^{2+} channels directly, although it is without effect on T-type Ca^{2+} channels.

Increasing glucose from zero to 20 mM produces an approximate doubling of the mouse B-cell Ca^{2+} current measured under approximately physiological ionic conditions using the perforated-patch configuration (Smith *et al.*, 1989*b*). Single-channel studies in cell-attached patches have shown that this results principally from a decrease in the duration of the long closures between bursts of channel openings and an increase in the channel availability (the number of sweeps which fail to elicit channel openings is reduced).

In RINm5F cells glyceraldehyde stimulates insulin release and, like glucose, increases the activity of L-type Ca^{2+} channels (Velasco *et al.*, 1988). It does this by increasing the frequency of channel openings and prolonging their duration; there is also a shift in the activation curve to more negative potentials.

Several pieces of evidence support the idea that the effect of glucose is mediated by an intracellular second messenger (Smith *et al.*, 1989*b*). First, the effect is slow, requiring several minutes to develop. Secondly, in cell-attached patches glucose is effective when added to the bath solution only and not directly to the membrane patch. Since the diffusion of substances between the bath and pipette solution does not occur (see Fig. 1), the effect of glucose must be mediated by an intracellular route. Thirdly, a specific inhibitor of glucose metabolism, mannoheptulose, was capable of reversing the effect of glucose on Ca^{2+}-channel activity suggesting that the intracellular messenger is generated by metabolism of the sugar. Furthermore, oligomycin, an inhibitor of oxidative metabolism, reduced channel activity below that found in the absence of glucose, consistent with its ability to inhibit metabolism of endogenous substrates and indicating that channel modulation is present in resting B-cells.

What substances link metabolism to channel activity?

K⁺-ATP channel

A considerable body of evidence supports the hypothesis that changes in the cytosolic ATP/ADP ratio constitute the mechanism by which glucose metabolism is linked to K⁺-ATP-channel inhibition (for reviews see Ashcroft 1988; Rorsman & Trube, 1990; Ashcroft & Ashcroft 1990; Ashcroft & Rorsman 1990). This may be summarized as follows: Intracellular ATP blocks channel activity in inside-out patches (Cook & Hales, 1984) and in whole-cell recordings (Rorsman & Trube, 1985), an effect which is modulated by ADP (Kakei *et al.*, 1986; Dunne *et al.*, 1988). Channel activity in cell-attached patches is reduced by agents that increase the intracellular ATP/ADP ratio (such as glucose) and is increased by metabolic inhibitors that lower this ratio. Changes in K⁺-ATP-channel activity (Ashcroft *et al.*, 1988; Kakei *et al.*, 1986; Dunne *et al.*, 1988) and in the cellular ATP/ADP ratio (Malaisse *et al.*, 1979; Meglasson *et al.*, 1989) occur over the same range of glucose concentrations and with a similar time course. The major change in channel activity and ATP content both occur between zero and 8 mM-glucose. The effect of glucose on channel kinetics in cell-attached patches on intact B-cells resembles that found for ATP in inside-out patches (Rorsman & Trube, 1985).

Estimates of the ATP sensitivity of the channel in intact cells suggest that cytsolic ATP concentrations of ~ 1 mM produce half-maximal inhibition of channel activity (Niki *et al.*, 1989*b*; Schmid-Antomarchi *et al.*, 1987). At ATP concentrations (3–5 mM) found in B-cells exposed to glucose-free solution less than 10 % of the channels are active. This is not inconsistent with the level of channel activity seen in resting B-cells in perforated-patch recordings. By contrast, when measured in inside-out patches, the K⁺-ATP channel is 50 % blocked by 10 μM-ATP applied to the intracellular membrane surface (Cook & Hales, 1984). The possible reasons for this discrepancy have been documented previously and include: alteration of the ATP sensitivity in the isolated patch owing to the loss of additional modulators of channel activity, such as ADP (Kakei *et al.*, 1986; Dunne *et al.*, 1988); alteration of the channel properties in the isolated patch as a consequence of disruption of cytoskeletal elements (Noma & Shibasaki, 1985); and a difference in the submembrane and the total cytosolic ATP concentration, which is measured in biochemical experiments (Niki *et al.*, 1989*a*); the possibility that free ATP may be more important than Mg²⁺-ATP in regulating channel activity (Ashcroft & Kakei, 1989). All these mechanisms may contribute to the regulation of channel activity in the intact cell.

ATP has a dual effect on channel activity: in addition to inhibiting the channel, as described above, the nucleotide can also maintain channel activity. That is, it prevents the loss of K^+-ATP-channel activity which occurs following patch excision (Findlay & Dunne, 1986; Ohno-Shosaku *et al.*, 1987). There is evidence that phosphorylation is involved in this process but the identity of the kinase has not been established. The modulation of K^+-ATP-channel activity by cytosolic constituents is in fact extremely complex and still not fully understood: a more detailed account can be found elsewhere (Petersen & Findlay, 1987; Ashcroft, 1988; Ashcroft & Ashcroft, 1990; Rorsman & Trube, 1990; Ashford, 1990).

L-type Ca^{2+} channels

The identity of the intracellular second messenger that directly links glucose metabolism to Ca^{2+}-channel activation remains to be established. Two putative candidates are cyclic AMP, leading to activation of the cyclic AMP-dependent protein kinase pathway, and diacylglycerol, which activates protein kinase C. The former possibility, also considered by Hughes & Ashcroft in Chapter 13, is suggested by the fact that phosphorylation by cyclic AMP-dependent protein kinase (protein kinase A) increases L-type Ca^{2+}-channel activity in cardiac muscle and other endocrine cells (Armstrong, 1988). The fact that Ca^{2+}-channel activity declines in excised patches from B-cells in the absence of MgATP (Ashcroft & Rorsman, 1990), as it does in these tissues, supports this hypothesis. However, the effect of cyclic AMP on L-type Ca^{2+}-channel activity in the B-cell is currently unclear. On the one hand, a membrane permeant analogue of cyclic AMP (dibutyryl cyclic AMP, 1 mM) appears to increase channel activity reversibly in cell-attached patches on mouse B-cells (Smith *et al.*, 1990c). Whereas, on the other hand, in perforated-patch studies no effect of dibutyryl cyclic AMP or the adenylate cyclase activator forskolin was found on whole-cell Ca^{2+} currents (P. A. Smith, C. M. S. Fewtrell & F. M. Ashcroft, unpublished work). The reason for this discrepancy is not clear but it may reflect differences in the recording conditions.

The possible involvement of the protein kinase C pathway is also unclear. In RINm5F cells, Ca^{2+}-channel activity is stimulated by didecanoylglycerol (DiC_{10}) a membrane-permeable diacylglycerol analogue which activates protein kinase C (Velasco & Petersen, 1989). The phorbol ester phorbol-12-myristate 13-acetate (PMA), however, was without effect. It is therefore possible that several different C kinases exist in RINm5F cells and that activation of only one type is involved in mediating the effects of glyceraldehyde. It should not be forgotten, however, that diacylglycerol analogues may exert their effects by mechanisms independent of activation of protein kinase C (Hockberger *et al.*, 1989). That Ca^{2+}-channel activity in normal B-cells is modulated by the protein kinase C pathway seems unlikely, in view of the observation that PMA has no effect on B-cell electrical activity (Bozem *et al.*, 1987). Furthermore, in preliminary studies on mouse B-cells, we found that DiC_{10} (10 µM) actually decreased channel activity in four out of five patches and only increased channel activity in one patch. However, the possibility that diacylglycerol itself (unlike DiC_{10}) stimulates Ca^{2+} channels either directly or by activation of a protein kinase C isoenzyme that is insensitive to PMA cannot be excluded.

A number of other possible candidates linking metabolism to Ca^{2+}-channel activity can also be suggested. For example, ATP itself may serve as a second messenger with changes in submembrane ATP levels influencing Ca^{2+}-channel opening, either directly or through the activity of protein kinases.

The contribution of the different ion channels to B-cell electrical activity

In the absence of glucose, the resting potential of the B-cell is principally determined by the activity of the K^+-ATP channel. Interestingly, substantial channel inhibition is present under these conditions and less than 25 % of the channels are open. Closure of K^+-ATP channels by metabolism produces a slow depolarization, which for glucose concentrations that elicit insulin release (> 7 mM) is sufficient to initiate electrical activity. It is now recognized that the K^+-Ca^{2+} channel is not active at the resting potential and is not involved in the initiation of electrical activity (for review Ashcroft & Rorsman, 1990).

Like insulin secretion, B-cell electrical activity increases with glucose concentration, the duration of the slow waves becoming longer as the sugar concentration is increased until at around 20 mM-glucose continuous electrical activity occurs. In most B-cells, glucose concentrations that initiate electrical activity (7 mM) reduce K^+-ATP-channel activity substantially: to less than 30 % of that found in glucose-free solution, or to less than 10 % of the total number of channels. The remaining K^+-ATP-channel activity is further inhibited as the glucose concentration is increased, with inhibition being almost complete when the glucose concentration reaches ~ 20 mM (Ashcroft et al., 1990b,c). This suggests that glucose may also regulate the duration of the slow waves by modulating K^+-ATP channels. Further evidence in favour of this idea comes from the finding that tolbutamide, a specific inhibitor of K^+-ATP channels in B-cells, is able to regulate the duration of the slow waves in a manner similar to glucose; likewise, diazoxide, which activates K^+-ATP channels, converts continuous electrical activity into slow waves (Henquin, 1988). We have also found a good correlation between the pattern of B-cell electrical activity and the magnitude of the whole-cell K^+-ATP current in perforated-patch recordings. That is, the duration of the slow waves varies inversely with the magnitude of the K^+-ATP current. Taken together, these results indicate that in addition to depolarizing the B-cell and initiating electrical activity, closure of K^+-ATP channels contributes to the change in electrical activity that occurs as the glucose concentration is increased. The high resistance of the B-cell membrane in the presence of glucose means that only very small changes in K^+-ATP current are needed to produce profound effects on electrical activity.

Oscillations in glycolysis and in the ATP/ADP ratio have been described in a number of systems (Corkey *et al.*, 1988; Tornheim, 1988). It has therefore been proposed that a similar phenomenon, if present in the B-cell, might lead to oscillations in K^+-ATP-channel activity and so produce the slow waves (Corkey *et al.*, 1990). This hypothesis seems unlikely to be correct, however, since no difference in K^+-ATP-current amplitude was found between the plateau phase of the slow wave and the interburst interval (Smith *et al.*, 1990*a*). Instead, the K^+-ATP current appears to constitute a time-invariant, outward K^+ current.

There is now good evidence that the K^+-Ca^{2+} channel does not play a role in the generation of the slow waves, since it is unaffected by concentrations of TEA that specifically inhibit this channel (Henquin, 1990; Bokvist *et al.*, 1990*a*, *b*; Smith *et al.*, 1990*b*; see also Chapter 9 by Henquin *et al.* in this book). The functional role of the K^+-Ca^{2+} channel is to assist in the repolarization of the action potential (Bangham & Smith, 1987), which is thought mainly to occur by the delayed rectifier (Smith *et al.*, 1990*b*). Although glucose modulates K^+-Ca^{2+}-channel activity in insulinoma cells (Ribalet *et al.*, 1988; Eddlestone *et al.*, 1989), its physiological significance has yet to be determined.

The available evidence favours the idea that both the depolarizing phase of the action potentials and the slow waves themselves result from activation of L-type Ca^{2+} channels (for references, see Ashcroft & Rorsman, 1990 and Chapter 9 by Henquin *et al.*). The physiological importance of glucose modulation of these channels is difficult to assess because no data concerning the concentration-dependence of the effect is yet available. The effect of glucose is to increase the Ca^{2+} current at a given membrane potential and consequently lower the threshold potential for activation of both the action potential and the slow wave. If this effect is graded with glucose concentration, it might be expected to reduce the interburst interval (by reducing the threshold for initiation of the burst) and to prolong the duration of the slow wave.

It seems probable that the slow waves are principally determined by a balance between the L-type Ca^{2+} current, the K^+-DR and K^+-Ca^{2+} currents and the K^+-ATP current. Thus the slow wave begins with activation of voltage-dependent Ca^{2+} channels. Subsequent activation of K^+-DR and K^+-Ca^{2+} channels repolarizes the membrane to the plateau potential, where these channels slowly de-activate. Since Ca^{2+} channels are still open at this potential, the decrease in the K^+-Ca^{2+} and K^+-DR currents produces a net inward current which depolarizes the membrane and initiates another action potential. The repolarization of the burst may be a consequence of a slow inactivation of the Ca^{2+} current, which finally becomes too small to balance the hyperpolarizing effect of the K^+-ATP current, and the interburst interval may therefore reflect the rate at which the Ca^{2+} channels recover from inactivation. Thus in this model, the K^+-ATP current is roughly constant throughout the slow wave.

Glucose prolongs the burst, at least partly, by reducing the K^+-ATP current and thus maintaining the net inward (depolarizing) current for longer. Modulation of the Ca^{2+} current produced by glucose may also contribute to both the increase in slow-wave duration and the reduction of the interburst interval.

Conclusions

The application of the patch-clamp technique to single B-cells has allowed identification of the various kinds of ionic channels in the B-cell membrane. The characterization of their gating properties, modulation and pharmacology has contributed greatly to our understanding of B-cell electrical activity and its role in insulin release. In particular, inhibition of the K^+-ATP channel has been shown to be the common mechanism by which both glucose and sulphonylureas stimulate electrical activity and insulin release. Both the L-type Ca^{2+} channel and the K^+-Ca^{2+} channels are also modulated by nutrient metabolism but the details of these mechanisms and their physiological importance remain to be resolved. Likewise the mode of action of many hormones and neurotransmitters on electrical activity have yet to be determined at the single channel level. It seems probable that significant advances will be made in this area in the next few years.

The authors' work referred to in this chapter was supported by grants from the British Diabetic Association, the Medical Research Council, the Wellcome Trust, and the Royal Society. FMA was a Royal Society 1983 University Research Fellow. CF was an NIH Senior Fellow. BW was a Commonwealth Scholar.

References

Armstrong, D. L. (1988) Calcium channel regulation by protein phosphorylation in a mammalian tumour cell line. Biomed. Res. **9**, 11–15

Ashcroft, S. J. H. (1980) Glucoreceptor mechanisms and the control of insulin release and biosynthesis. Diabetologia **18**, 5–15

Ashcroft, F. M. (1988) Adenosine tri-phosphate sensitive K^+-channels. Ann. Rev. Neurosci. **11**, 97–118

Ashcroft, F. M. & Ashcroft, S. J. H. (1990) Properties and functions of ATP-sensitive K-channels. Cellular Signalling **2**, 197–214

Ashcroft, F. M. & Kakei, M. (1989) ATP-sensitive K^+ channels in rat pancreatic β-cells: Modulation by ATP and Mg^{2+} ions. J. Physiol. **416**, 349–367

Ashcroft, F. M. & Rorsman, P. (1989) Electrophysiology of the pancreatic β-cell. Prog. Biophys. Molec. Biol., **54**, 87–143

Ashcroft, F. M., Harrison, D. E. & Ashcroft, S. J. H. (1984) Glucose induces closure of single potassium channels in isolated rat pancreatic β-cells. Nature (London) **312**, 446–448

Ashcroft, F. M., Ashcroft, S. J. H. & Harrison, D. E. (1985) The glucose-sensitive potassium channel in rat pancreatic β-cells is inhibited by intracellular ATP. J. Physiol. **369**, 101P

Ashcroft, F. M., Ashcroft, S. J. H. & Harrison, D. E. (1987) Effects of 2-keto-isocaproic acid on insulin release and single potassium channel activity in dispersed rat pancreatic B-cells. J. Physiol. **385**, 517–529

Ashcroft, F. M., Ashcroft, S. J. H. & Harrison, D. E. (1988) Properties of single potassium channels modulated by glucose in rat pancreatic B-cells. J. Physiol. **400**, 501–527

Ashcroft, F. M., Kelly, R. & Smith, P. A. (1990*a*) Two types of Ca channel in rat pancreatic β-cells. Pfluegers Arch. **415**, 504–506

Ashcroft, F. M., Fewtrell, C., Oosawa, Y., Rorsman, P. & Smith, P. A. (1990*b*). ATP-regulated K channels regulate electrical activity in mouse isolated pancreatic β-cells J. Physiol. **424**, 27P

Ashcroft, F. M., Faehling, M., Fewtrell, C. M. S., Rorsman, P. & Smith, P. A. (1990*c*) Perforated patch recordings of ATP-regulated K-currents and electrical activity in murine pancreatic β-cells. Diabetologica **33**, A78

Ashford, M. L. J. (1990) Potassium channels and the modulation of insulin secretion. In Potassum Channels: Structure, Function and Therapeutic Potential, (Cook, N. S., ed.), pp. 300–326, Ellis Horwood, Chichester, U.K.

Atwater, I., Carroll, P. & Li, M. X. (1989) Electrophysiology of the pancreatic β-cell. In Molecular and Cellular Biology of Diabetes Mellitus. 1. Insulin Secretion (Draznin, B., Melmed, S. & Le Roith, D., eds.), pp. 49–68, Alan R. Liss, New York

Bangham, J. A. & Smith, P. A. (1987) Non-conforming action potentials from isolated mouse islets of Langherans. J. Physiol. **392**, 15P

Bokvist, K., Rorsman, P. & Smith, P. A. (1990*a*) Effects of external tetraethylammonium ions and quinine on delayed K^+-channels in mouse pancreatic β-cells. J. Physiol. **423**, 311–325

Bokvist, K., Rorsman, P. & Smith, P. A. (1990*b*) Block of ATP-regulated and Ca^{2+}-activated K^+-channels in mouse pancreatic β-cells by external tetraethylammonium and quinine. J. Physiol. **423**, 327–342

Bozem, M., Nenquin M. & Henquin J. C. (1987) The ionic, electrical and secretory effects of protein kinase C activation in mouse pancreatic B-cells: Studies with a phorbol ester. Endocrinology **121**, 1025–1033

Cohen, D. R., Matteson, R., Parsey, V. & Sala, S. (1990) Ionic currents in rat pancreatic β-cells recorded with the perforated patch technique. Biophys. J. **57**, 509A

Cook, D. L. & Hales, C. N. (1984) Intracellular ATP directly blocks K^+ channels in pancreatic β-cells. Nature (London) **311**, 271–273

Cook, D. L., Ikeuchi, M. & Fujimoto, W. Y. (1984) Lowering of pH_i inhibits Ca^{2+}-activated K^+ channels in pancreatic β-cells. Nature (London) **311**, 269–271

Corkey, B. E., Tornheim, K., Deeney, J. T., Glennon, M. C., Parker, J. C., Matschinsky, F. M., Ruderman, N. B. & Prentki, M. (1988) Linked oscillations of free Ca^{2+} and the ATP/ADP ratio in permeabilized RINm5F insulinoma cells supplemented with a glycolysing cell-free muscle extract. J. Biol. Chem. **263**, 4254–4258

Corkey, B. E., Deeney, J. T., Longo, E. A., Varnum, B. A. & Tornheim, K. (1990) Calcium oscillations in isolated rat pancreatic islets. Diabetologia **33**, A63

Dunne, M. J., Findlay, I., Petersen, O. H. & Wollheim, C. B. (1986) ATP-sensitive K^+ channels in an insulin-secreting cell line are inhibited by D-glyceraldehyde and activated by membrane permeabilization. J. Membr. Biol. **93**, 271–273

Dunne, M. J., West-Jordan, J. A., Abraham, R. J., Edwards, R. H. T. & Petersen, O. H. (1988) The gating of nucleotide-sensitive K^+ channels in insulin-secreting cells can be modulated by changes in the ratio ATP^{4-}/ADP^{3-} and by non-hydrolysable derivatives of both ATP and ADP. J. Membr. Biol. **104**, 165–177

Eddlestone, G. T., Riabalet, B. & Ciani, S. (1989) Comparative study of K channel behaviour in beta cell lines with different secretory responses to glucose. J. Membr. Biol. **109**, 123–134

Falke, L. C., Gillis, K. D., Pressel D. M. & Misler, S. (1989) Perforated patch recording allows long-term monitoring of metabolite induced electrical activity and Ca-currents in pancreatic β-cells. FEBS Lett. **251**, 167–172

Findlay, I. & Dunne, M. (1986) ATP maintains ATP-inhibited K$^+$-channels in an operational state. Pfluegers Arch. **407**, 238–240

Findlay, I., Dunne M. J. & Petersen, O. H. (1985) High conductance K$^+$ channel in pancreatic islet cells can be activated and inactivated by internal calcium. J. Membr. Biol. **83**, 169–175

Findlay, I., Ashcroft, F. M., Kelly, R. P., Rorsman, P., Petersen, O. H. & Trube, G. (1989) Calcium currents in insulin-secreting β-cells. Ann. N.Y. Acad. Sci. **560**, 387–390

Gillis, K. D., Gee, W. M., Hammoud, A., McDaniel, M. L., Flake, L. C. & Misler, M. (1989) Effects of sulfonamides on a metabolite-regulated ATPi-sensitive K$^+$-channel in rat pancreatic β-cell. Am. J. Physiol. **257**, C1119–C1127

Hamill, O. P., Marty, A., Neher, E., Sakmann, B. & Sigworth, F. J. (1981) Improved patch clamp techniques for high resolution current recording from cells and cell-free membrane patches. Pfluegers Arch. **391**, 85–100

Henquin, J. C. (1988) ATP-sensitive K-channels may control glucose-induced electrical activity in pancreatic β-cells. Biochem. Biophys. Res. Comm. **156**, 769–775

Henquin, J. C. (1990) Role of voltages and Ca-dependent K-channels in the control of glucose-induced electrical activity in pancreatic β-cells. Pfluegers Arch. **416**, 568–572

Henquin, J. C. & Meissner H. P. (1984) Significance of ionic fluxes and changes in membrane potential for stimulus-secretion coupling in pancreatic β-cells. Experientia **40**, 1043–1052

Henquin, J. C., Garcia, M. C., Bozem, M., Hermans, M. P. & Nenquin, M. (1988) Muscarinic control of pancreatic β-cell function involves sodium-dependent depolarization and calcium-influx. Endocrinology **122**, 2134–2142

Hirriat, M. & Matteson, D. R. (1988) Na channels and two types of Ca channels in rat pancreatic β-cells identified with the reverse hemolytic plaque assay. J. Gen Physiol. **91**, 617–639

Hockberger, P., Toselli, M., Swandulla, D. & Lux, H. D. (1989) A diacyglycerol analogue reduces neuronal calcium currents independently of protein kinase C activation. Nature (London) **338**, 340–342

Horn, R. & Marty, A. (1988) Muscarinic activation of ionic currents measured by a new whole-cell recording method. J. Gen. Physiol. **92**, 145–159

Kakei, M., Noma, A. & Shibasaki, T. (1985) Properties of adenosine-triphosphate-regulated potassium channels in guinea-pig ventricular cells. J. Physiol. **363**, 441–462

Kakei, M., Kelly, R. P., Ashcroft, S. J. H. & Ashcroft, F. M. (1986) The ATP-sensitivity of K$^+$ channels in rat pancreatic β-cells is modulated by ADP. FEBS Lett, **208**, 63–66

Malaisse, W. J., Hutton, J. C., Kawazu, S., Herchulz, A., Valverde, I. & Sener, A. (1979) The stimulus secretion coupling of glucose induced insulin release: the links between metabolism and cationic events. Diabetologia **16**, 321–341

Malaisse-Lagae, F., Mathias, P. C. F. & Malaisse, W. J. (1984) Gating and blocking of calcium channels by dihydropyridines in the pancreatic β-cell. Biochem. Biophys. Res. Comm. **124**, 1062–1068

Mancilla, E. & Rojas, E. (1990) Quinine blocks the high conductance, calcium-activated potassium channel in the rat pancreatic β-cell. FEBS Lett. **260**, 105–108

Meglasson, M. D., Nelson, J., Nelson, D. & Erecinska, M. (1989) Bioenergetic response of pancreatic islets to stimulation by fuel molecules. Metabolism **38**, 1188–1195

Meissner, H. P. & Schmelz, H. (1974) Membrane potential of β-cells in pancreatic islets. Pfluegers Arch. **351**, 195–206

Misler, D. S., Falke, L. C., Gillis, K. & McDaniel, M. L. (1986) A metabolite regulated potassium channel in rat pancreatic β cells. Proc. Natl. Acad. Sci. U.S.A. **83**, 7119–7123

Niki, I., Kelly, R. P., Ashcroft, S. J. H. & Ashcroft, F. M. (1989a) ATP-sensitive K$^+$-channels in HIT T15 β-cells studied by patch-clamp methods, [86]Rb$^+$ efflux and glibenclamide binding. Pfluegers Arch. **415**, 47–55

Niki, I., Ashcroft, S. J. H. & Ashcroft, F. M. (1989b) The dependence on intracellular ATP concentration of ATP-sensitive K-channels and of the Na, K-ATPase in intact HIT T15 β-cells. FEBS Lett. **257**, 361–364

Noma, A. & Shibasaki, T. (1985) Membrane current through adenosine-triphosphate-regulated potassium channels in guinea-pig ventricular cells. J. Physiol. **363**, 463–480

Nowycky, M. C., Fox, A. P. & Tsien, R. W. (1985) Three types of neuronal calcium channel with different calcium agonist sensitivity. Nature (London) **316**, 440–443

Ohno-Shosaku, T., Zunkler, B. J. & Trube, G. (1987). Dual effects of ATP on K$^+$-currents in mouse pancreatic β-cells. Pfluegers Arch. **408**, 133–138

Petersen, O. H. & Findlay, I. (1987) Electrophysiology of the pancreas. Physiol. Rev. **67**, 1054–1116

Plant, T. D. (1988*a*) Na$^+$ currents in cultured mouse pancretic β-cell. Pfluegers Arch. **411**, 429–435

Plant, T. D. (1988*b*) Properties and calcium-dependent inactivation of calcium currents in cultured mouse pancreatic β-cells. J. Physiol. **404**, 731–747

Pralong W. F., Bartley, C. & Wollheim C. B. (1990) Single islet β-cell stimulation by nutrients: Relationship between pyridine nucleotides, cytosolic Ca^{2+} and secretion. EMBO J. **9**, 53–60

Prenki, M. & Matchinsky, F. M. (1987) Ca^{2+}, cAMP, and phospholipid-derived messengers in coupling mechanisms of insulin secretion. Physiol. Rev. **67**, 1185–1249

Pressel, D. & Misler, S. (1990) Sodium currents in pancreatic islet β-cells. Biophys. J. **57**, 104A

Rajan, A. S., Aguilar-Bryan, L., Nelson, D. A., Yaney, G. C., Hsu, W. H., Kunze, D. L. & Boyd, A. E. III (1990) Ion channels and insulin secretion. Diabetes **13**, 340–363

Ribalet, B. & Beigelman P. M. (1982) Effects of sodium on β-cell electrical activity. Am. J. Physiol. **242**, C296–303

Ribalet, B. & Ciani, S. (1987) Regulation by cell metabolism and adenine nucleotides of a K channel in insulin-secreting β-cells (RINm5F). Proc. Natl. Acad. Sci. U.S.A. **84**, 1721–1725

Ribalet, B., Eddlestone, G. T. & Ciani, S. (1988) Metabolic regulation of the K(ATP) and a maxi-K(V) channel in the insulin-secreting RINm5F cell. J. Gen. Physiol. **92**, 219–237

Rorsman, P. & Trube, G. (1985) Glucose dependent K$^+$-channels in mouse pancreatic β-cells are regulated by intracellular ATP. Pfluegers Arch. **405**, 305–309

Rorsman, P. & Trube, G. (1986) Calcium and delayed potassium currents in mouse pancreatic β-cells under voltage-clamp conditions. J. Physiol. **374**, 531–550

Rorsman, P. & Trube, G. (1990) Biophysics and physiology of ATP-regulated K$^+$ channels. In Potassium Channels: Structure Function and Therapeutic Potential (Cook, N. S., ed.), pp. 300–326, Ellis Horwood, Chichester

Rorsman, P., Ashcroft, F. M. & Trube, G. (1988) Single Ca channel currents in mouse pancreatic B-cells. Pfluegers Arch. **412**, 597–603

Sala, S. & Matteson, D. R. (1990) Single channel recordings of two types of calcium channels in rat pancreatic β-cells. Biophys. J. **58**, 567–571

Saloman, D. & Meda, P. (1986) Heterogeneity and contact-dependent regulation of hormone secretion by individual β-cells. Exp. Cell. Res. **162**, 507–520

Satin, L. S. & Cook, D. L. (1988) Evidence for two calcium currents in insulin-secreting cells. Pfluegers Arch. **411**, 401–409

Satin, L. S., Hopkins, W., Fatherazi, S. & Cook, D. L. (1989) Expression of a rapid low-voltage activated K$^+$ current in insulin-secreting cells is dependent on intracellular calcium buffering. J. Membr. Biol. **112**, 213–222

Schmid-Antomarchi, S., De Weille, J., Fosset, M. & Lazdunski, M. (1987) The receptor for antidiabetic sulphonylureas controls the activity of the ATP-modulated K$^+$-channel in insulin-secreting cells. J. Biol. Chem. **262**, 15840–15844

Smith, P. A., Bokvist, K. & Rorsman, P. (1989*a*) Demonstration of A-currents in pancreatic islet cells. Pfluegers Arch. **413**, 441–443

Smith, P. A., Rorsman, P. & Ashcroft, F. M. (1989*b*) Modulation of dihydropyridine-sensitive Ca^{2+} channels by glucose metabolism in pancreatic β-cells. Nature (London) **342**, 550–553

Smith, P. A., Rorsman, P. & Ashcroft, F. M. (1990*a*) Simultaneous recording of β-cell electrical activity and ATP-sensitive K-currents in mouse pancreatic β-cells. FEBS Lett. **261**, 187–190

Smith, P. A., Bokvist, K., Arkhammar, P., Berggren, P. O. & Rorsman, P. (1990*b*) Delayed rectifying and calcium-activated K⁺-channels and their significance for action potential repolarization in mouse pancreatic β-cells. J. Gen. Physiol. **95**, 1041–1059

Smith, P. A., Fewtrell, C. M. S. & Ashcroft, F. M. (1990*c*) Cyclic AMP potentiates L-type Ca-channel activity in murine pancreatic β-cells. Diabetologia **33**, A104

Sturgess, N. C., Ashford, M. L. J., Cook D. L. & Hales, C. N. (1985) The sulphonylurea receptor may be an ATP-sensitive potassium channel. Lancet **ii**, 474–475

Sturgess, N. C., Hales, C. N. & Ashford, M. L. J. (1986) Inhibition of a calcium-activated, non-selective cation channel, in a rat insulinoma cell line, by adenine derivatives. FEBS Lett. **208**, 397–400

Sturgess, N. C., Carrington, C. A., Hales, C. N. & Ashford, M. L. J. (1987*a*) Nucleotide-sensitive ion-channels in human insulin producing tumour cells. Pfluegers Arch. **410**, 169–172

Sturgess, N. C., Hales, C. N. & Ashford, M. L. J. (1987*b*) Calcium and ATP regulate the activity of a non-selective cation channel in a rat insulinoma cell line. Pfluegers Arch. **409**, 607–615

Tabcharini, J. A. & Misler, S. (1989) Ca^{2+}-activated K⁺-channel in rat pancreatic islet B-cells: permeation gating and block by cations. Biochim. Biophys. Acta **982**, 67–72

Tornheim, K. (1988) Fructose 2,6-bisphosphate and glycolytic oscillations in skeletal muscle extracts. J. Biol. Chem. **263**, 2619–2624

Trube, G., Rorsman, P. & Ohno-Shosaku, T. (1986) Opposite effects of tolbutamide and diazoxide on the ATP-dependent K⁺-channel in mouse pancreatic β-cells. Pfluegers Arch. **407**, 493–499

Velasco, J. M. & Petersen, O. H. (1987) Voltage-activation of high conductance K⁺ channel in the insulin-secreting cell line RINm5F is dependent on local extracellular Ca^{2+} concentration. Biochim. Biophys. Acta **896**, 305–321

Velasco, J. M. & Petersen, O. H. (1989) The effects of a cell-permeable diacylglycerol analogue on Ca^{2+} (Ba^{2+}) channel currents in insulin-secreting cell line RINm5F. Q. Exp. Physiol. **74**, 367–370

Velasco, J. M., Petersen, J. U. H. & Petersen, O. H. (1988) Single channel Ba^{2+} currents in insulin secreting cells are activated by glyceraldehyde stimulation. FEBS Lett. **213**, 366–370

Zunkler, B. J., Trube, G. & Ohno-Shosaku, T. (1988) Forskolin-induced block of delayed rectifying K⁺ channels in pancreatic β-cells is not mediated by cyclic AMP. Pfluegers Arch. **411**, 613–619

Cytoplasmic calcium and insulin secretion

Bo Hellman, Erik Gylfe, Eva Grapengiesser, Per-Eric Lund and Arne Marcström

Department of Medical Cell Biology, University of Uppsala, Biomedicum, S-751 23 Uppsala, Sweden

Introduction

Insulin is stored in secretory granules which are released from the pancreatic B-cells by exocytosis. With the introduction of the concept of stimulus-secretion coupling (Douglas, 1968), it was natural to predict a decisive role for Ca^{2+} in the insulin secretory process. Early evidence in support of this idea was that omission of extracellular Ca^{2+} resulted in inhibition of insulin release evoked by glucose and other secretagogues (Grodsky & Bennett, 1966; Milner & Hales, 1967). Moreover, it was independently demonstrated by Malaisse-Lagae & Malaisse (1971) and Hellman et al. (1971) that glucose promotes the net uptake of ^{45}Ca by isolated islets.

During the last two decades there has been a considerable expansion in our knowledge as to how cytoplasmic Ca^{2+} ($[Ca^{2+}]_i$) participates in the insulin secretory process. The pancreatic B-cell is actually one of the most extensively studied with regard to the significance of Ca^{2+} for exocytosis of granule-bound material, as indicated by a number of previous reviews of the topic (Hellman, 1976a, 1985, 1986, 1988; Hellman et al., 1979, 1980a, 1988; Hellman & Gylfe, 1985, 1986a; Malaisse et al., 1978; Wollheim & Sharp, 1981; Herchuelz & Malaisse, 1981; Rubin, 1982; Prentki & Wollheim, 1984; Prentki & Matschinsky, 1987; Atwater et al., 1989; Boyd et al., 1989; Zawalich & Rasmussen, 1990). The development of suitable indicators and the use of dual-wavelength fluorometry has recently enabled direct measurements of how glucose and other secretagogues alter the $[Ca^{2+}]_i$ in individual pancreatic B-cells (Grapengiesser et al., 1988a,b, 1989a–c, 1990a,b; Yada et al., 1989; Wang & McDaniel, 1990; Hellman et al., 1990a–c). This review will examine the results of these studies as well as data obtained with different techniques from populations of cells present in intact islets or suspensions.

The cytoplasmic Ca²⁺ signal and insulin release

Measurements with the fluorescent indicators quin-2 and fura-2 have provided support for the idea that stimulation of insulin release by different agents, including glucose, is associated with a rise of $[Ca^{2+}]_i$ (Rorsman *et al.*, 1983, 1984; Deleers *et al.*, 1985; Rorsman & Abrahamsson, 1985; Boyd *et al.*, 1986; Hoenig & Sharp, 1986; Sussman *et al.*, 1987; Nelson *et al.*, 1987; Nilsson *et al.*, 1987; Hughes & Ashcroft, 1988; Gylfe 1988*a,b*, 1989*a*; Grapengiesser *et al.*, 1988*a,b*, 1989*a–c*, 1990*a,b*; Lund *et al.*, 1989; Komatsu *et al.*, 1989; Gobbe & Herchuelz, 1989; Yada *et al.*, 1989; Wang & McDaniel, 1990; Hellman *et al.*, 1990*a,b*). Since the data reflect the average temporal and spatial changes of $[Ca^{2+}]_i$, nothing definite can be said about the magnitude of the increase at the site of the exocytosis. Moreover, no attempts have been made to study the relationship between $[Ca^{2+}]_i$ and insulin release using individual B-cells. It is, for example, unclear whether an oscillatory Ca²⁺ signal gives rise to more secretion than a sustained one.

The direct effect of Ca²⁺ concentration on exocytosis has been studied, either in cells made permeable to small solutes or in cells internally dialysed using the patch-clamp technique in its whole-cell configuration. With the latter approach Penner & Neher (1988) demonstrated that injection of Ca²⁺ into B-cells increased the cell membrane capacitance in a way supposed to reflect stimulated exocytosis. In other studies these authors observed that a non-hydrolysable GTP analogue, GTP-γ-S, both increased the membrane capacitance and evoked Ca²⁺ transients under hyperpolarizing voltage-clamp conditions (Fig. 1). In support of a role for ATP in a cyclic uptake and release of intracellular Ca²⁺, a rise of ATP from 0.2 (panel A) to 3 mM (panel B) resulted in repetitive Ca²⁺ transients in response to GTP-γ-S. It is important to note that a capacitance increase is seen even when $[Ca^{2+}]_i$ has returned to its pre-stimulatory level. The interpretation of the above-mentioned patch-clamp data is complicated by the fact that the analyses were performed at room temperature, at which the secretory response to $[Ca^{2+}]_i$ has been reported to be absent (Atwater *et al.*, 1984; Hellman *et al.*, 1990*a*). In addition to suggesting that G-proteins are involved in the signal transduction in the pancreatic B-cells, the data may be taken to indicate a dual control of insulin release mediated by Ca²⁺ and G-proteins. Ample support for the idea that a guanine-nucleotide site is involved in the regulation of insulin release has been obtained in studies of the clonal insulin-releasing RINm5F cells permeabilized by high-voltage discharges (Vallar *et al.*, 1987; Wollheim *et al.*, 1987). In the latter preparation GTP-γ-S was found to stimulate the release of insulin even at vanishingly low (< 10 pM) concentrations of Ca²⁺.

Electropermeabilization of islets (Pace *et al.*, 1980; Yaseen *et al.*,

1982) or of insulin-secreting cells in suspensions (Nilsson *et al.*, 1987; Vallar *et al.*, 1987; Wollheim *et al.*, 1987) have provided useful information about the effects of Ca^{2+} on the secretory machinery. With suspended cells, raising Ca^{2+} concentration above 0.1 μM initiated secretion and optimal

Fig. 1.   **Effects on cell-membrane capacitance and cytoplasmic Ca^{2+} of injecting 100 μM-GTP-γ-S together with 0.2 (A) or 3 (B) mM-ATP in a pancreatic B-cell**

(A)   0.2 mM-ATP

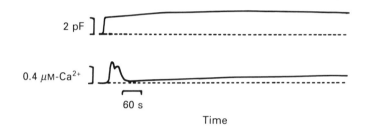

Time

(B)   3 mM-ATP

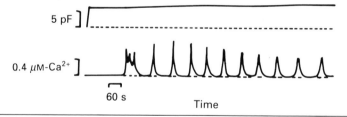

Time

The experiments were performed at room temperature using the whole-cell configuration of the patch-clamp technique. $[Ca^{2+}]_i$ was monitored with 0.5 μM-fura-2 included in a salt-balanced pipette medium containing Ca^{2+}-EGTA/EGTA in a ratio of 6:1. Reproduced from Penner & Neher (1988) with permission.

effects were obtained at about 10 μM. The corresponding optimum for the permeabilized islets was considerably lower. Whereas addition of GTP-γ-S did not increase insulin release beyond that seen during maximal stimulation with Ca^{2+}, activation of protein kinases appeared to sensitize the secretory machinery to the ion. The latter phenomenon will be further discussed in the sections on cyclic AMP and phospholipase C.

Although glucose stimulation of insulin release requires extra-cellular Ca^{2+}, a rise of the cation concentration above a critical level results in a decrease of the effect of the sugar (Hellman, 1975). In the light of these and other observations it has been suggested that there is an optimal concentration of Ca^{2+} above which insulin release will be suppressed (Hellman, 1986). In support of this idea Yaseen *et al.* (1982) demonstrated

Fig. 2.   Diagram illustrating the regulation of the exocytosis of insulin-containing secretory granules by Ca^{2+} and GTP

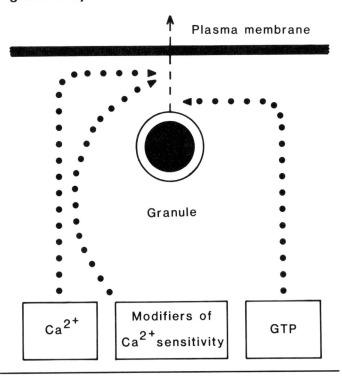

that a rise of Ca^{2+} from 1 to 10 μM resulted in inhibition of insulin release from permeabilized rat islets. In cells where the basal $[Ca^{2+}]_i$ exceeds that maximally stimulating exocytosis, a rise of $[Ca^{2+}]_i$ can normally be expected to suppress the secretory activity. Recent studies indicate that this is the case for the parathyroid cells (Nygren *et al.*, 1987).

The mechanisms by which Ca^{2+} triggers the extrusion of the insulin secretory granules remain obscure. In Fig. 2 an attempt has been made to summarize current ideas of how exocytosis is regulated in the pancreatic B-cell. Whereas $[Ca^{2+}]_i$ can be regarded as a major determinant for the extrusion of the granules, the process may also be directly stimulated by the binding of GTP to sites other than those controlling cyclic AMP generation or phospholipid hydrolysis. Further studies should decide whether the Ca^{2+}-binding site is more distal than the GTP-sensitive one as suggested in this scheme. The effect of $[Ca^{2+}]_i$ on the insulin secretory process is not only a function of the concentration of the ion but also of the sensitivity of the secretory machinery to the Ca^{2+} signal. This sensitivity will be increased after activation of protein kinases (see also Chapter 13 by Hughes & Ashcroft).

Glucose effect on calcium turnover

The pancreatic B-cells are rich in calcium. When expressed in terms of intracellular water the average concentration of calcium in the mouse B-cells ranges from 16–25 mM (Hellman, 1986). This represents a more than 10-fold accumulation compared with the extracellular concentration. An important aspect of the B-cell content of calcium is its regulation by glucose. Although glucose is a potent stimulator of the net uptake of ^{45}Ca in isolated islets (Malaisse-Lagae & Malaisse, 1971; Hellman et al., 1971), it was established from later studies that most of this accumulation was owing to increased calcium turnover, the effect being relatively small when maintaining isotopic equilibrium (Bergsten & Hellman, 1984). Direct measurements have actually failed to demonstrate a glucose-induced increase of the total amount of intracellular calcium both in mouse (Andersson et al., 1982) and rat (Wolters et al., 1982) islets.

It is well established that glucose promotes entry of Ca^{2+} by altering the B-cell membrane potential in a way which results in the opening of the L-type Ca^{2+} channels (Hellman, 1988). However, the metabolism of glucose may also favour the influx of Ca^{2+} by directly affecting these channels (Smith et al., 1989) and others relatively insensitive to the membrane potential (Rojas et al., 1990). Current ideas about the effect of glucose on the rate of Ca^{2+} influx into the B-cells are based both on the radioactive isotope approach and on electrophysiological studies. Using the former technique it is imperative to correct for the proportionately large amounts of radioactivity bound to the exterior of the cells. Taking advantage of the ability of the La^{3+} ion to displace superficially bound ^{45}Ca and prevent its disappearance from the interior of the B-cells, it was possible to measure the initial (15 s) uptake of the isotope by aggregates of cells subsequently centrifuged across an oil layer (Wesslén & Hellman, 1986). Fig. 3 illustrates the effect of glucose on the influx of Ca^{2+} employing this technique. It is evident that the presence of 20 mM-glucose results in a doubling of the influx, increasing the rate of Ca^{2+} entry by about 1 mmol kg^{-1} min^{-1}. Exposure to 20 mM-glucose is known to induce a continuous spike activity in the B-cells with a frequency of 5–10 Hz (for detailed consideration of B-cell electrical activity and ion channels see Chapters 9 and 10 by Henquin et al. and Ashcroft et al., respectively). Using the whole-cell configuration of the patch-clamp technique the amount of Ca^{2+} entering the B-cells during a single action potential can be calculated as 10^{-18} mol (Rorsman & Trube, 1986). When recalculated in terms of dry weight, this figure gives a value for the

Fig. 3.   Effect of glucose on the uptake of ^{45}Ca by pancreatic B-cells

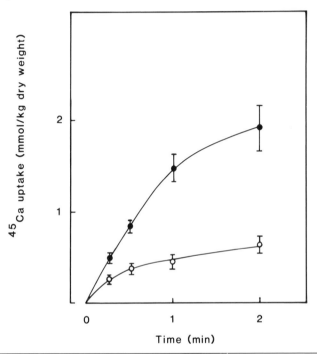

After preincubation with 1.28 mM-Ca^{2+} in the absence (○) or presence (●) of 20 mM-glucose, aggregates of mouse B-cells were exposed for different periods of time to ^{45}Ca in media of the same composition. The curves illustrate intracellular uptake after the radioactivity bound to the cell surface had been displaced by La^{3+}.

glucose-stimulated influx of Ca^{2+} similar to that obtained with the ^{45}Ca technique.

The extrusion of Ca^{2+} is mediated both by Na^+–Ca^{2+} exchanges (Hellman *et al.*, 1980*b*; Herchuelz & Malaisse, 1980) and a calmodulin-activated transport system based on a high-affinity ATPase (Pershadsingh *et al.*, 1980). So far, it has not been possible to measure directly the outward transport of Ca^{2+} under conditions of stimulated entry of the ion. However, it can be estimated how different agents affect the extrusion of

Ca^{2+} by comparing the rates of entry with the observed alterations of the calcium content of the B-cells. As mentioned above exposure to glucose resulted in a pronounced stimulation of the influx of Ca^{2+} but only in a modest increase in the intracellular content of this element. Contrary to previous arguments for a direct inhibitory action of glucose on the outward transport of Ca^{2+} (Herchuelz & Malaisse, 1981; Wollheim & Sharp, 1981), it is therefore clear that this process is, in fact, stimulated by the sugar. Indeed, the most impressive effect of the sugar on the B-cell handling of Ca^{2+} is to increase the turnover of the element. In mouse B-cells the turnover rate has been calculated to exceed 5% per min after glucose stimulation (Hellman, 1986).

Dual effect of glucose on cytoplasmic Ca^{2+}

Studies with the quin-2 indicator by Rorsman et al. (1984) represent the first direct demonstration that glucose stimulation of insulin release is associated with a rise of $[Ca^{2+}]_i$ in the B-cells. These investigations also revealed that glucose decreased $[Ca^{2+}]_i$ when the entry of Ca^{2+} was suppressed either by lowering its extracellular concentration or by blocking the voltage-dependent Ca^{2+} channels. With the introduction of the fura-2 indicator it became possible to make more detailed observations. Using time-sharing dual-wavelength fluorometry for measurements in suspensions of cells obtained from the B-cell-rich pancreatic islets of ob/ob-mice, Gylfe (1988a,b, 1989a) reported that the glucose effects on $[Ca^{2+}]_i$ mimic those on ^{45}Ca efflux in that an initial lowering was followed by a rise owing to stimulated entry of Ca^{2+} (Fig. 4, left panel). In insulin-release studies the temporal resolution can be improved by perifusing isolated B-cells in a column of polyacrylamide beads (Lund et al., 1989). Using the latter approach it was found that the initial action of glucose in lowering $[Ca^{2+}]_i$ had its counterpart in a transient inhibition of the secretory activity (Fig. 4, right panel). The demonstration that glucose exposure resulted in initial lowering of $[Ca^{2+}]_i$ deserves particular attention in the light of the proposal that the first phase of the glucose-stimulated insulin release depends on mobilization of Ca^{2+} from intracellular stores (Wollheim & Sharp, 1981; Wollheim & Biden, 1986). So far, there is no evidence that the following stimulatory phase is accounted for by factors other than an increased entry of Ca^{2+}. The time needed for glucose to promote stimulation of insulin release coincides with that observed for inducing stimulation of influx of ^{45}Ca into aggregates of cells subsequently centrifuged across oil (Wesslén & Hellman, 1986). Moreover, the early increase of $[Ca^{2+}]_i$ induced by glucose was also found to depend on Ca^{2+} influx under conditions of filled intracellular calcium pools (Gylfe, 1988a).

X-ray microanalysis of sections of unfixed islets or pieces of pancreas (Howell et al., 1975; Norlund et al., 1987) indicate that the B-cell cytoplasm contains substantial amounts of calcium. However, under resting conditions $[Ca^{2+}]_i$ is only 60–100 nM, a value which increased 5–10 times after maximal stimulation of insulin release. Accordingly, the

---

Fig. 4.   Effects on cytoplasmic Ca^{2+} (left panel) and insulin release (right panel) of raising glucose from 3 to 20 mM

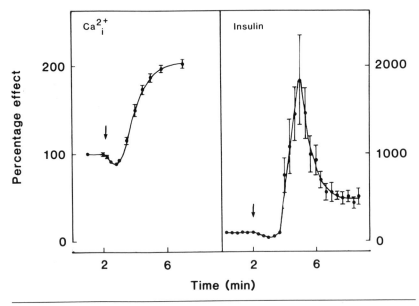

The studies were performed with mouse B-cells kept in suspension ($[Ca^{2+}]_i$) or perifused in a microcolumn (insulin release). Mean values ± s.e.m. for 7–10 experiments.

---

pancreatic B-cells have a considerable capacity for binding Ca^{2+} to anions and macromolecules. This binding together with the presence of Ca^{2+}-buffering organelles can be expected to retard severely the intracellular diffusion of the ion. There may consequently be considerable concentration gradients within the cytoplasm, implying that the $[Ca^{2+}]_i$ below the plasma membrane, which triggers insulin release, could be much higher than in the rest of the cytoplasm. The existence of such a gradient can be visualized by digital image analysis both during resting conditions and after glucose stimulation of the Ca^{2+} influx (Fig. 5). Further technical development based on the use of the confocal microscope will probably result in the demonstration of even more pronounced concentration gradients for $[Ca^{2+}]_i$ than so far observed.

As mentioned above, glucose will induce a sustained lowering of $[Ca^{2+}]_i$ in the absence of stimulated entry of the ion. The effect of raising glucose concentration has also been tested when already stimulating the influx of Ca^{2+} by other depolarizing agents. Under the latter condition an

Fig. 5.   Three-dimensional analyses of cytoplasmic Ca^{2+} in an individual mouse B-cell exposed to 3 (A) and 20 (B) mM-glucose

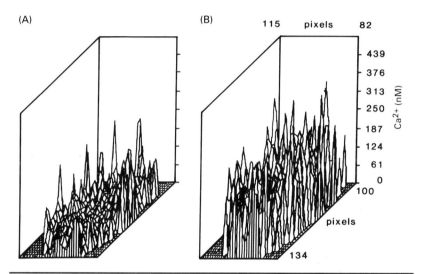

increase of the glucose concentration from 3, 5 or 10 mM to 20 mM resulted in a pronounced temporary decrease of $[Ca^{2+}]_i$ (Gylfe, 1989a; Lund et al., 1989; Hellman et al., 1990c). This lowering of $[Ca^{2+}]_i$ was associated with a concomitant inhibition of insulin release (Fig. 6). The opposing actions of glucose on the $[Ca^{2+}]_i$ regulating insulin release differed not only with respect to the latency of onset but also with regard to the sensitivity to the glucose stimulus. Whereas the dependence of the increase of $[Ca^{2+}]_i$ on glucose was a sigmoidal function similar to that of insulin release, the lowering of $[Ca^{2+}]_i$ was hyperbolically related to the sugar concentration (Fig. 7). Accordingly, at the threshold concentration for the glucose-induced rise of $[Ca^{2+}]_i$ (about 5 mM) the sugar evokes almost half-maximal lowering.

It has been argued that the glucose-induced lowering of $[Ca^{2+}]_i$ is an experimental artifact caused by refilling of depleted intracellular Ca^{2+} pools when raising ATP after previous substrate depletion (Wollheim & Biden, 1986; Prentki & Matschinsky, 1987; Nilsson et al., 1988). This idea can be refuted in the light of the observations that an increase of glucose from concentrations known to maintain a high content of ATP results in a lowering of $[Ca^{2+}]_i$ (cf. Figs. 4 and 6). The time required for initiating an increase of $[Ca^{2+}]_i$ will be shortened with increasing concentrations of glucose during the pre-stimulatory phase. Accordingly, the initial lowering may sometimes be masked after pre-exposure to a high glucose

Fig. 6.   Effects on cytoplasmic Ca²⁺ (left panel) and insulin release (right panel) of raising glucose from 3 to 20 mM in the presence of 100 μM-tolbutamide

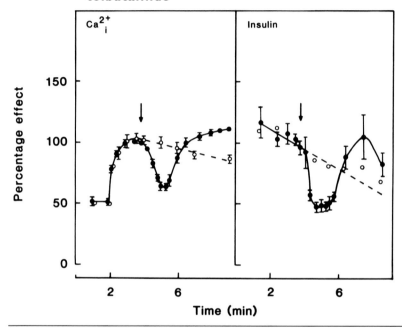

The studies were performed with mouse B-cells kept in suspension ($[Ca^{2+}]_i$) or perifused in a microcolumn (insulin release). Arrows indicate the time when the glucose concentration was increased. Whereas tolbutamide was present throughout the experiments in the right panel, it was added 2 min before raising glucose in the left panel. The open symbols refer to control experiments keeping the glucose concentration at 3 mM. Mean values ± s.e.m. for 4–5 experiments.

concentration (Gylfe, 1988a), or when raising the concentration of the sugar from values exceeding 5 mM (Gylfe, 1989a). Glucose has been found to lower $[Ca^{2+}]_i$ also in pancreatic A-cells (Johansson *et al.*, 1987). The observations of opposite effects of glucose on $[Ca^{2+}]_i$ in suspensions of islet cells might therefore be taken to reflect the different reactions of the B- and A-cells. However, it was also found that glucose had dual effects on $[Ca^{2+}]_i$ in individual pancreatic B-cells (Grapengiesser *et al.*, 1988a).

Fig. 7.   **Effects of glucose concentration on the magnitude of the increase (upper panel) and lowering (lower panel) of cytoplasmic Ca²⁺ in pancreatic B-cells**

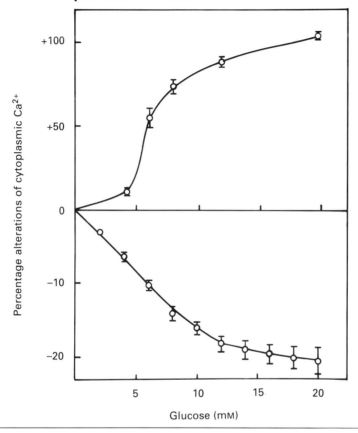

The increase was investigated by measuring the maximal elevation above basal [Ca²⁺]ᵢ at the indicated concentrations in per cent of the value obtained after a subsequent increase of glucose to 20 mM. Characterization of the dose–response relationships for lowering of [Ca²⁺]ᵢ was performed in a Ca²⁺-deficient medium. The studies were performed with suspensions of mouse B-cells loaded with the fluorescent indicator fura-2. Mean values ± s.e.m. for 5–10 experiments. Reproduced from Gylfe (1989b) with permission.

In Fig. 8 an attempt has been made to summarize the present knowledge of how glucose affects the $[Ca^{2+}]_i$ regulating insulin release. It is obvious that the available data call for a reconsideration of previous views that Ca^{2+} mobilization from intracellular stores contributes to glucose-induced stimulation of insulin release (Wollheim & Sharp, 1981; Prentki & Wollheim, 1984), and that the sugar increases $[Ca^{2+}]_i$ by inhibiting outward transport of the ion (Herchuelz & Malaisse, 1981; Wollheim & Sharp, 1981). Since glucose apparently has the opposite

Fig. 8.   **Diagram illustrating glucose-induced modifications of the cytoplasmic Ca^{2+}-regulating insulin release**

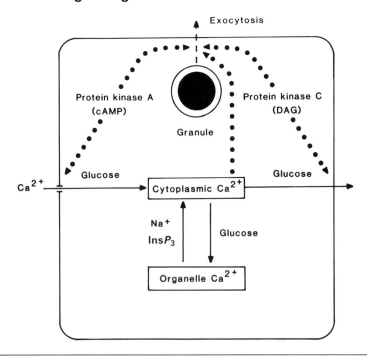

Glucose has a dual action on $[Ca^{2+}]_i$ in B-cells in promoting both the influx of the ion and its removal by organelle uptake and outward transport. Calcium incorporated into organelles in response to glucose can be mobilized either by increase of intracellular Na^+ or by the inositol 1,4,5-trisphosphate [$Ins(1,4,5)P_3$] generated by polyphosphoinositide breakdown. Activation of protein kinases promotes insulin release by making the secretory machinery more sensitive to the Ca^{2+} ion. Protein kinases also affect Ca^{2+} fluxes by stimulating the entry (kinase A) and outward transport (kinase C) of the ion.

actions, the effect of the sugar on the cytoplasmic Ca^{2+} activity will instead reflect the balance between the increased entry of Ca^{2+} and enhanced removal of the ion from the cytoplasm by organelle uptake and outward transport.

The discovery of the opposing actions of glucose on the cytoplasmic Ca^{2+} activity contributes to the understanding of several unresolved questions related to the function of the B-cells. Since Ca^{2+} is involved in the regulation of the K^+ permeability of the B-cells (Hellman, 1988; Atwater *et al.*, 1989), the glucose-induced lowering of $[Ca^{2+}]_i$ may be part of the mechanism causing depolarization (see Chapters 9 and 10 by Henquin *et al.* and Ashcroft *et al.* for further discussion). Glucose promotion of the intracellular Ca^{2+} buffering can be expected to become less pronounced with time owing to saturation. This may help to explain the existence of a slowly increasing second phase in glucose-stimulated insulin release, and why the secretory response is improved after priming with the sugar. With the observation of a glucose-induced decrease of $[Ca^{2+}]_i$ it was natural to predict that the sugar could have inhibitory effects on insulin release. Indeed, it has been possible to demonstrate that this paradoxical effect may be even more long-lasting than indicated in Figs. 4 and 6 (Hellman, 1988; Hellman *et al.*, 1988).

It is evident that the glucose-induced removal of Ca^{2+} from the cytoplasm can be more easily observed when the metabolism of the sugar fails to depolarize the B-cells or when the Ca^{2+} channels are defective. Glucose inhibition of insulin release is therefore, in itself, an indicator of a lesion in the B-cells, significant for their ability to counteract diabetes. It has been repeatedly observed that B-cells from experimental animals made slightly diabetic with alloxan and streptozotocin respond abnormally to glucose with inhibition of insulin release (Hellman, 1986, 1988; Hellman *et al.*, 1990*c*). More importantly, however, intravenous injections of glucose are often associated with a prompt reduction of circulating insulin in animal models with spontaneous diabetes and patients with non-insulin-dependent diabetes mellitus (NIDDM) or early insulin-dependent diabetes mellitus (IDDM) (Metz *et al.*, 1979; Hellman *et al.*, 1985, 1990*c*; Bailey & Flatt, 1986; Hellman, 1988). In causing an unexpected and usually temporary depression of only 10–15 %, it is not surprising that this phenomenon has been overlooked in conventional glucose tolerance tests. Defective insulin secretion in diabetes is considered further in Chapter 16 by Flatt *et al.* in this book.

Effects of cyclic AMP

Although cyclic AMP does not fulfil the criteria for a second messenger in the pancreatic B-cells, it is certainly important for potentiating the response to glucose and other initiators of insulin release (Hellman *et al.*, 1979; Malaisse & Malaisse-Lagae, 1984; Hellman, 1986; Hellman & Gylfe, 1986*a*; Prentki & Matschinsky, 1987; Chapter 13 by Hughes & Ashcroft). The cyclic AMP content increases when isolated islets are exposed to glucose and other fuel secretagogues (Charles *et al.*, 1975; Grill & Cerasi,

1976). In requiring extracellular Ca^{2+}, the nutrient-induced accumulation of cyclic AMP has been attributed to the elevation of $[Ca^{2+}]_i$ (Valverde *et al.*, 1979; Sharp *et al.*, 1980). Studies of purified B-cells obtained by fluorescence-activated cell sorting have emphasized the importance of cyclic AMP, suggesting that the nucleotide has a permissive role for the glucose-stimulated insulin release (Pipeleers *et al.*, 1985). In the purified B-cells a marked impairment of the secretory response was correlated with a reduction of the cyclic AMP content to 40 % of that found in intact islets. Moreover, it was possible to obtain a normal secretory response to glucose by addition of dibutyryl cyclic AMP, glucagon or glucagon-secreting A-cells. The studies of the purified B-cells have also resulted in a re-evaluation of the mechanisms for the glucose-induced rise of cyclic AMP, suggesting that this is accounted for by potentiation of the glucagon-induced stimulation of its formation (Schuit & Pipeleers, 1985).

It was observed early that the insulin secretory response to an increase of extracellular Ca^{2+} was considerably improved if the islet content of cyclic AMP was raised (Hellman, 1976*a,b*). Moreover, the maximal stimulatory action of glucose was reached at lower concentrations of extracellular Ca^{2+} when isolated islets were exposed to agents known to increase cyclic AMP. On the basis of these observations it was suggested that a major effect of cyclic AMP is to sensitize the secretory machinery to the Ca^{2+} signal (Hellman *et al.*, 1979). This idea was supported by Ca^{2+}-clamp experiments with permeabilized islet cells indicating that activation of adenylate cyclase results in stimulation of insulin release (Tamagawa *et al.*, 1985).

The effect of cyclic AMP on insulin release is not restricted to sensitization of the secretory apparatus. It has been repeatedly demonstrated that a higher cyclic AMP concentration results in an increased efflux of radioactivity from islets preloaded with ^{45}Ca (Hellman & Gylfe, 1986*a*). From this and other types of radioactive approaches, it was concluded that cyclic AMP mobilizes intracellular calcium in the B-cells (Brisson *et al.*, 1972) or prevents the sequestration of the ion in the organelles (Hahn *et al.*, 1980; Gylfe & Hellman, 1981). Measurements of $[Ca^{2+}]_i$ have given contradictory results regarding the effects of cyclic AMP. Whereas Rorsman & Abrahamsson (1985) did not observe a forskolin-induced increase of $[Ca^{2+}]_i$ in the B-cell-rich suspensions obtained from *ob/ob*-mice, glucose-stimulated individual B-cells from the same source reacted with irregular $[Ca^{2+}]_i$ transients after exposure to forskolin or glucagon, and with a steady rise of $[Ca^{2+}]_i$ after addition of theophylline (Grapengiesser *et al.*, 1989*b*). The failure to detect effects on $[Ca^{2+}]_i$ in suspensions is probably owing to the use of quin-2 instead of the more sensitive indicator fura-2. Indeed, using the latter indicator Sussman *et al.* (1987) reported that forskolin and dibutyryl cyclic AMP increased $[Ca^{2+}]_i$ in suspensions of rat-islet cells. Since this effect was observed even after removal of extracellular Ca^{2+}, they concluded that it was owing to intracellular mobilization of calcium. However, studies of individual B-cells (Grapengiesser *et al.*, 1989*b*) and of glucagon-releasing A-cells (Johansson *et al.*, 1989) indicated that it is only in the latter type of cells in which the cyclic AMP-induced rise of $[Ca^{2+}]_i$ is owing to an intracellular mobilization of Ca^{2+}. In the light of these observations it seems likely that cyclic AMP mobilization of intracellular Ca^{2+} from pancreatic islets or islet-cell suspensions essentially reflects the response of the glucagon-producing A-cells.

Different views have been expressed also regarding the cyclic AMP effects on $[Ca^{2+}]_i$ on clonal insulin-releasing cells. Whereas experiments with quin-2 did not reveal any increase of $[Ca^{2+}]_i$ when raising cyclic AMP in glucose-exposed RINm5F cells (Wollheim *et al.*, 1984) or hamster insulin-secreting tumour (HIT) cells (Hill *et al.*, 1987; Hughes & Ashcroft, 1988), this was found to be the case in fura-2-loaded HIT cells (Prentki *et al.*, 1987; Rajan *et al.*, 1989).

Studies of the electrical activity of the B-cells have indicated that increase of cyclic AMP favours influx of Ca^{2+} in the pancreatic B-cells (Henquin & Meissner, 1984; Eddlestone *et al.*, 1985). This conclusion is supported by some of the results obtained when measuring $[Ca^{2+}]_i$ in cell suspensions (Prentki *et al.*, 1987; Rajan *et al.*, 1989) as well as by recent observations in individual B-cells (Grapengiesser *et al.*, 1989*b*). The idea that cyclic AMP promotes the entry of Ca^{2+} received ample support with the demonstration that the nucleotide is an important determinant of the balance between the stimulatory and inhibitory effects of glucose on insulin release (Bergsten *et al.*, 1989). Fig. 9 illustrates the critical role of cyclic AMP for the type of $[Ca^{2+}]_i$ response obtained when raising the glucose concentration from 3 to 20 mM. In the presence of the α_2-adrenergic agonist clonidine, the glucose-induced decrease and subsequent rise of $[Ca^{2+}]_i$ was altered into a sustained lowering. The addition of dibutyryl cyclic AMP together with clonidine resulted in a secondary rise of $[Ca^{2+}]_i$ but did not completely restore the normal glucose response.

The present uncertainties about the role of cyclic AMP for the B-cell handling of Ca^{2+} may depend on the fact that most studies have been performed under experimental situations where other types of islet cells can be expected to influence the cyclic AMP content via their secretory products. Moreover, attention should be paid to the possibility that the agents used to manipulate the cyclic AMP levels may also have other effects. The responses of individual B-cells have, for example, been found to vary depending on the type of agent used to raise cyclic AMP levels (Grapengiesser *et al.*, 1989*b*). With these reservations in mind, it seems appropriate to restrict the discussion of the effects of cyclic AMP on insulin release to the stimulated entry of Ca^{2+} and the sensitization of the secretory machinery to the action of the ion (Fig. 8).

Fig. 9.   **Effects of raising glucose from 3 to 20 mм on [Ca²⁺]ᵢ in the presence or absence of clonidine and dibutyryl cyclic AMP (dbcAMP)**

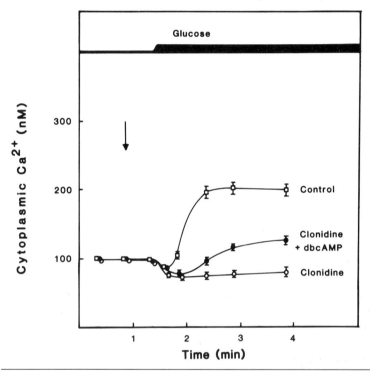

Suspended mouse B-cells were loaded with fura-2 and incubated in a medium containing 1.28 mм-Ca²⁺. The arrow indicates the addition of 1 μм-clonidine and/or 1 mм-dbcAMP and the horizontal bar the change of the glucose concentration from 3 to 20 mм. Mean values ± s.e.m. for 5–8 experiments. Reproduced from Bergsten et al. (1989) with permission.

Activation of phospholipase C

As with other cells the pancreatic B-cells contain membrane-bound phospholipase C (Turk *et al.*, 1987; Prentki & Matschinsky, 1987), the activation of which results in hydrolysis of phosphatidylinositol 4,5-bisphosphate into inositol 1,4,5-trisphosphate [Ins(1,4,5)P_3] and diacylglycerol (see Chapter 7 by Morgan & Montague for a detailed account of phospholipid metabolism and insulin secretion). Whereas Ins(1,4,5)P_3 is known to mobilize calcium from intracellular stores, diacylglycerol has an important role as an activator of protein kinase C (PKC). The potential significance of phospholipase C for the secretory activity of the B-cells is emphasized by the fact that not only binding of receptor agonists, (e.g. carbachol, cholecystokinin, ATP) but also exposure to metabolic stimuli (Montague et al., 1985; Prentki & Matschinsky, 1987; Turk et al., 1987; Wolf et al., 1988) and hypoglycaemic sulphonylureas (Zawalich & Zawalich, 1988) favour polyphosphoinositide breakdown in isolated pancreatic islets.

In the original concept, a rather simple biochemical pathway was envisaged for the formation and breakdown of the Ca^{2+}-mobilizing $Ins(1,4,5)P_3$ (Berridge, 1983). However, with the discovery of cyclic inositol phosphates as well as the inositol tris/tetrakis phosphate pathway (Irvine et al., 1988) it became evident that phospholipase C activation may also affect the Ca^{2+} handling by other inositol phosphates. Actually the predominant inositol phosphate accumulating in the islets in response to glucose is not $Ins(1,4,5)P_3$, but its 1,3,4 isomer (Turk et al. 1986). So far, $Ins(1,4,5)P_3$ is the only inositol phosphate found to affect the Ca^{2+} handling of insulin-secreting cells. Comparing the $Ins(1,4,5)P_3$ effect on different subcellular fractions of rat insulinoma cells, Prentki et al. (1984) observed selective mobilization of Ca^{2+} from the microsomes. Islets from *ob/ob* mice permeabilized by high-voltage discharges proved to be particularly useful for studying the intracellular effects of $Ins(1,4,5)P_3$. In exhibiting a large ATP-dependent buffering of Ca^{2+}, these islets could maintain an ambient Ca^{2+} concentration of about 0.15 μM (Nilsson et al., 1987). $Ins(1,4,5)P_3$ promoted a rapid but transient increase of the ambient Ca^{2+} concentration (Fig. 10), the maximal effect being obtained at 6 μM. Since attempts to compensate for possible degradation by repeated pulses of $Ins(1,4,5)P_3$ failed to maintain elevated levels of Ca^{2+}, it seems likely that the disappearance of the $Ins(1,4,5)P_3$ effect reflects a desensitization of its receptor and/or re-uptake of released Ca^{2+} into a pool insensitive to $Ins(1,4,5)P_3$. In support of the latter alternative, the addition of Ca^{2+} was found to shorten the period of insensitivity. Using $Ins(1,4,5)P_3$ as a probe for the calcium present in the endoplasmic reticulum it was possible to demonstrate that glucose, indeed, stimulates the uptake of Ca^{2+} into this organelle (Hellman et al., 1986). Present ideas of how $Ins(1,4,5)P_3$ affects the B-cell handling of Ca^{2+} are summarized in Fig. 11. $Ins(1,4,5)P_3$ generated by activation of phospholipase C is supposed to release Ca^{2+} from the endoplasmic reticulum (pool 1) into the cytoplasm, from which it is then taken up by an $Ins(1,4,5)P_3$-insensitive compartment (pool 2). The stored calcium is then recycled to pool 1, a process completed within 20 min at a basal $[Ca^{2+}]_i$ value.

In apparent contradiction to the effect of glucose in raising the islet content of $Ins(1,4,5)P_3$ (Montague et al., 1985; Turk et al., 1986), the sugar was found to lack a mobilizing action on intracellular calcium both when measuring ^{45}Ca efflux and $[Ca^{2+}]_i$. Actually these methodological approaches, as well as measurements of net fluxes of Ca^{2+}, have made it possible to demonstrate that glucose instead promotes the sequestration of Ca^{2+} into the $Ins(1,4,5)P_3$-sensitive pool (Hellman *et al.*, 1986, 1988; Hellman, 1988). In analogy to what has been proposed for a glucose-

Fig. 10. **Effects of repetitive pulses of inositol 1,4,5-trisphosphate (InsP$_3$; 6 μM) and a pulse of Ca^{2+} (0.125 nmol) on the ambient Ca^{2+} concentration maintained by permeabilized mouse B-cells**

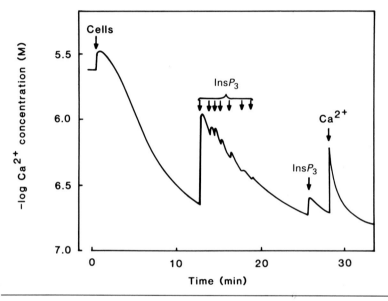

The experiment was initiated by the addition of 1.6 × 10^5 cells. Reproduced from Nilsson et al. (1987) with permission.

induced regulation of various processes in the plasma membrane, it seems likely that the ATP generated by the metabolism of the sugar is critical for the ATPase activity associated with the Ca^{2+} uptake into the endoplasmic reticulum. It has also been proposed that glucose-6-phosphate acts as a connecting link between the metabolism of glucose and the intracellular Ca^{2+} handling, both by augmenting Ca^{2+} sequestration in the endoplasmic reticulum as well as attenuating $Ins(1,4,5)P_3$-induced Ca^{2+} release (Wolf *et al.*, 1986).

Many cells display cyclic changes of $[Ca^{2+}]_i$ resulting from periodic release of Ca^{2+} from intracellular reservoirs (Berridge *et al.*, 1988). The ability of $Ins(1,4,5)P_3$ to mobilize calcium from the endoplasmic reticulum is a significant feature of several of the models used for explaining these oscillations. So far, it has not been demonstrated by direct intracellular application that $Ins(1,4,5)P_3$ induces oscillations of $[Ca^{2+}]_i$ in pancreatic B-cells. However, after initiating polyphosphoinositide break-down by receptor agonists it was possible to demonstrate rapid oscillations

---

Fig. II.   Diagram illustrating phosphatidylinositol 4,5-bisphosphate [PtdIns(4,5)P_2] hydrolysis by receptor activation of phospholipase C

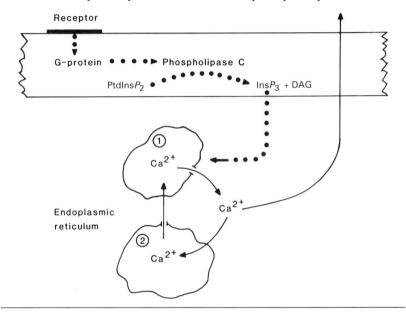

Whereas the resulting diacylglycerol (DAG) activates protein kinase C, inositol 1,4,5-trisphosphate (InsP$_3$) releases Ca^{2+} from the endoplasmic reticulum (pool 1) into the cytoplasm. Ca^{2+} is then taken up by an InsP$_3$-insensitive compartment (pool 2) and gradually recycled to pool 1.

---

of $[Ca^{2+}]_i$ in insulin-releasing insulinoma cells (Prentki *et al.*, 1988) as well as in normal B-cells (Grapengiesser *et al.*, 1989*b*). In the latter cells the activation of purinergic P_2 receptors with ATP mimicked the effect of the muscarinic agonist carbachol in transforming glucose-induced oscillations of $[Ca^{2+}]_i$ (see below) into a steady-state increase, which was initiated by repetitive 6–11 s spikes of decreasing amplitude. After removal of extracellular Ca^{2+}, or addition of a blocker of the potential-dependent Ca^{2+} channels, the effect on $[Ca^{2+}]_i$ was only transient with the generation of a couple of spikes.

Diacylglycerol formed during phospholipid hydrolysis is an endogenous activator of PKC. By extrapolation from other types of cells it seems likely that the activation of PKC leads to its translocation from the cytoplasm to the plasma membrane (Metz, 1988). Diacylglycerol is, however, rapidly metabolized. In the attempts to elucidate how PKC participates in the insulin-release process it has therefore been considered advantageous to use phorbol myristate acetate (PMA) as an activator of the enzyme. Increases of the islet diacylglycerol concentration (Best & Malaisse, 1983; Dunlop & Larkins, 1986; Peter-Riesch *et al.*, 1988) as well as of the PKC activity (Dunlop & Larkins, 1986; Arkhammar *et al.*, 1989) have been reported not only in response to PMA and carbachol but also to glucose.

Although several studies have demonstrated stimulation of insulin release in the presence of PMA, doubts have been expressed regarding the physiological role of PKC as a regulator of the secretory activity of the B-cells (Metz, 1988; see Chapter 12 by Persaud *et al.* for a full account of this topic). With the demonstration that PMA increases the amounts of insulin released from permeabilized cells in response to a given Ca^{2+} concentration (Tamagawa *et al.*, 1985; Jones *et al.*, 1985), it seems likely that a major effect of PKC is to sensitize the secretory machinery to the Ca^{2+} signal. The fact that cyclic AMP also makes Ca^{2+} more efficient as a stimulator (see above) suggests that the phosphorylation of key proteins on the secretory granules or in the cytoskeleton is important for the secretory process. When analysing how PKC affects Ca^{2+} handling it has been informative to measure net fluxes of the ion in clonal insulin-releasing RINm5F cells suspended in a medium containing $10–20 \, \mu M$-Ca^{2+}. In this way it was demonstrated that glucose promotes a high-affinity uptake of Ca^{2+} independent of depolarization (Gylfe *et al.*, 1983; Gylfe & Hellman, 1986). As shown in Fig. 12, PMA exhibited effects opposite to glucose. Moreover, PMA suppressed the mobilization of calcium otherwise obtained after addition of carbachol. After detailed analyses of the net fluxes of Ca^{2+} it was postulated that the PMA-induced mobilization of calcium is caused by stimulation of the ATPase mediating extrusion of Ca^{2+} across the plasma membrane (Gylfe 1989*b*). In support of this idea, PMA has been found to lower $[Ca^{2+}]_i$ in intact B-cells exposed to glucose and to lack effects on the buffering of Ca^{2+} in permeabilized cells (Arkhammar *et al.*, 1989). Although it has been proposed that PMA closes ATP-regulated K^+ channels in clonal insulin-releasing RINm5F cells (Wollheim *et al.*, 1988), there is no indication of a PMA-induced depolarization mediating entry of Ca^{2+} in normal B-cells (Henquin *et al.*, 1987; see also Chapter 10 by Ashcroft *et al.*).

Provided that the PMA-induced lowering of $[Ca^{2+}]_i$ reflects a physiological activation of PKC, it can be expected from the scheme in Fig. 11 that the receptor-mediated stimulation of polyphosphoinositide breakdown after an initial $Ins(1,4,5)P_3$-mediated $[Ca^{2+}]_i$ transient results in a decrease below the starting level. This is actually the case (Hellman *et al.*,

1989). The phenomenon is illustrated in Fig. 13, which shows the effects of activating the P_2-purinergic receptors in mouse B-cells exposed to 20 mM-glucose. In a medium deficient in Ca^{2+} (panel A) addition of ATP resulted only in transient increase of $[Ca^{2+}]_i$. However, when $[Ca^{2+}]_i$ was

---

Fig. 12.   Release of glucose-incorporated calcium from clonal insulin-releasing RINm5F cells by carbachol, PMA, antimycin A and A-23187

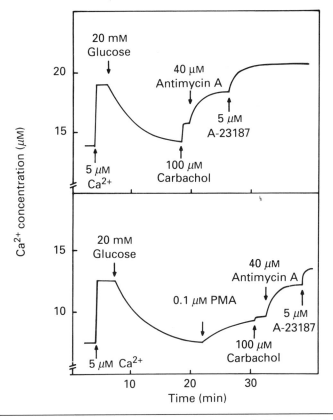

The experiments were performed with cells (4–5 mg of protein/ml) suspended in a medium containing indicators enabling recording of external Ca^{2+} (Arsenazo III) and pH (Phenol Red). Automated additions of NaOH kept pH at 7.4. Reproduced from Gylfe (1989b) with permission.

---

raised in response to glucose-stimulated entry of the ion (panel B) the effect of ATP became biphasic and the transient was followed by lowering of $[Ca^{2+}]_i$.

Glucose favours the accumulation of Ca^{2+} into the pool released by muscarinic and purinergic receptor activation in intact B-cells (Hellman & Gylfe, 1986*b*; Hellman *et al.*, 1987; Gylfe & Hellman, 1987; Grapengiesser *et al.*, 1989*b*) and by Ins(1,4,5)P_3 in permeabilized B-cells (Hellman *et al.*, 1986). Moreover, it has been established from direct

---

Fig. 13.   Effects of ATP on the cytoplasmic Ca^{2+} activity in mouse B-cells suspended in media deficient or not in Ca^{2+}

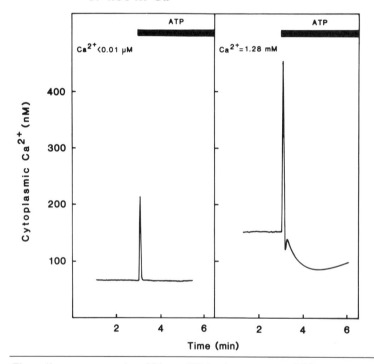

The cells were exposed to 200 μM-ATP in the presence of 20 mM-glucose during the periods indicated by the horizontal bars. The figure shows [Ca^{2+}]$_i$ calculated from the 340/380 nm fluorescence excitation ratio using the indicator fura-2. Reproduced from Hellman et al. (1989) with permission.

---

measurements in mouse B-cells that even the earliest rise of [Ca^{2+}]$_i$ after exposure to the sugar is dependent on the influx of Ca^{2+} (Gylfe, 1988*a,b*). These observations urge for a reconsideration of previous views (Wollheim & Biden, 1986) that the first phase of glucose-stimulated insulin release is owing to mobilization of calcium by Ins(1,4,5)P_3 (see also Chapter 7 by Morgan & Montague).

It has been suggested that the ATP and ADP released during exocytosis of the secretory granules represents a physiological mechanism for amplifying a secretory response by initiating polyphosphoinositide hydrolysis (Hellman *et al.*, 1987; Gylfe & Hellman, 1987). The observation that activation of phospholipase C even lowers $[Ca^{2+}]_i$ below the starting level should not be taken to imply that insulin release will be inhibited. As mentioned above, an important effect of the diacylglycerol activation of PKC is to make the secretory machinery more sensitive to the Ca^{2+} signal.

Nutrient-induced oscillations of cytoplasmic Ca^{2+}

When monitoring Ca^{2+} continuously in single pancreatic B-cells by dual-wavelength microfluorometry we have not only been able to confirm the existence of an initial lowering after exposure to glucose (Grapengiesser *et al.*, 1988*a*), but also to demonstrate that this event is often followed by large amplitude oscillations from the basal level up to 5–10-fold higher values (Grapengiesser *et al.*, 1988*b*, 1989*a,b*). The ability of glucose to induce large amplitude $[Ca^{2+}]_i$ oscillations in individual pancreatic B-cells has now been confirmed in studies from Japan (Yada *et al.*, 1989) and U.S.A. (Wang & McDaniel, 1990). Fig. 14 shows such oscillations in a mouse B-cell.

So far, glucose-induced oscillations of $[Ca^{2+}]_i$ have been observed both in B-cells from mice (Grapengiesser *et al.*, 1988*b*, 1989*a,b*) and rats (Grapengiesser *et al.*, 1989*b*; Yada *et al.*, 1989; Wang & McDaniel, 1990). Arguments in favour of the idea that these oscillations reflect cyclic variations in the Ca^{2+} permeability of the plasma membrane are: (1) the oscillations become more pronounced with a rise of extracellular Ca^{2+} and they disappear when blocking of the voltage-dependent Ca^{2+} channels occurs (Grapengiesser *et al.*, 1989*b*); (2) in mouse B-cells the frequency of the oscillations corresponds to 0.2–0.5 min^{-1}, which is similar to the slow cyclic variations of the burst activity recorded with intracellular microelectrodes in intact islets (Henquin *et al.*, 1982; Cook, 1983), and (3) patch-clamp analyses of single B-cells at 37 °C have indicated that the large amplitude oscillations have their counterpart in slow bursts of action potentials (Hellman *et al.*, 1990*a*).

Digital image analyses have provided further insight into the large amplitude oscillations (Gylfe *et al.*, 1990). The oscillations were synchronized in clusters of cells, rapidly propagating from one cell to another (Fig. 15). The cycles originated from different cells, implying that there were no special pacemaker cells. Although coupling accelerated the pace of slowly oscillating cells, the frequency did not usually exceed 1.0 min^{-1}. It is important to note that the large amplitude oscillations remain largely unaffected with coupling of the cells. Indeed, it has been possible to identify cyclic variations of cytoplasmic Ca^{2+} in intact mouse islets with a frequency similar to the large amplitude oscillations in the individual B-cells (Valdeolmillos *et al.*, 1989).

The induction of large amplitude Ca²⁺ oscillations is not unique for glucose but can also be obtained with nutrients such as leucine (Grapengiesser *et al.*, 1989*c*), as well as with hypoglycaemic sulphonylureas (Grapengiesser *et al.*, 1990*a*). Actually, the large amplitude oscillations are

---

Fig. 14.   The cytoplasmic Ca²⁺ concentration of a single mouse B-cell after raising glucose from 3 to 11 mM

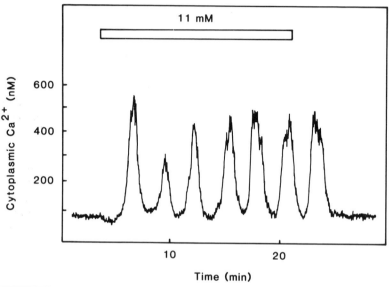

The figure shows [Ca²⁺]ᵢ calculated from the 340/380 nm fluorescence excitation ratio using the indicator fura-2.

---

seen under the same conditions as those initiating the electrical activity in B-cells within islets. In the search for mechanisms responsible for the induction of the large amplitude oscillations of [Ca²⁺]ᵢ different alternatives should be considered. Inhibition of Ca²⁺ influx through the voltage-dependent channels by raised [Ca²⁺]ᵢ may be important. Another feed-back loop involving hyperpolarization by Ca²⁺-activated K⁺ channels can also be envisaged. Since glycolysis represents a prototype of an oscillatory metabolic pathway (Hess, 1979), it is also possible that the ATP/ADP ratio determining depolarization is a major component.

Hitherto it has not been possible to demonstrate that single B-cells release insulin in a pulsatile manner. Nevertheless, we have reasons to believe that the large amplitude oscillations of [Ca²⁺]ᵢ initiate phasic insulin release. Since coupling of the B-cells is associated with synchronization of their Ca²⁺ cycles, it is not surprising that isolated islets from mice (Opara

Fig. 15. Image analysis of glucose-induced oscillations of cytoplasmic Ca²⁺ in a cluster of six mouse B-cells

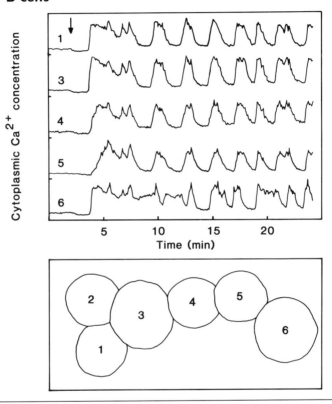

Freshly isolated cells were attached to a cover-glass and loaded with fura-2. Analysis of $[Ca^{2+}]_i$ was based on 340/380 nm fluorescence excitation ratio images every 4.6 s using the Tardis program and a Joyce-Loebl (Gateshead, U.K.) Magiscan equipment. When the glucose concentration was raised from 3 to 11 mM (arrow), all cells responded with a small initial lowering of $[Ca^{2+}]_i$. This was followed by an increase, which appeared first in cells 1, 2 (trace not shown), 3 and 6. After a small delay of the first increase of $[Ca^{2+}]_i$ in cell 4 and a slightly longer delay in cell 5, the oscillations in cells 1–5 became tightly coupled throughout the experiment. Cell 6 reacted essentially independently, although the data do not exclude brief periods of coupling of this cell also. Each mark on the ordinate indicates the 0 nM level of $[Ca^{2+}]_i$ for the trace above and/or the 400 nM level of the trace below.

et al., 1988) and rats (Bergstrom *et al.*, 1989) have been reported to have oscillatory insulin release. Indeed, the periodicity of insulin release from mouse islets was similar to that observed for $[Ca^{2+}]_i$ in the isolated B-cells. The synchronization of the rhythmic activity of the B-cells includes not

Fig. 16.   Effect of streptozotocin on glucose-induced oscillations of cytoplasmic Ca^{2+} in an individual mouse B-cell

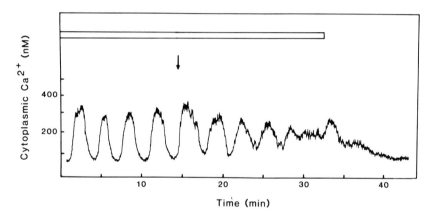

The figure shows $[Ca^{2+}]_i$ calculated from the 340/380 nm fluorescence excitation ratio using the indicator fura-2. The arrow indicates the time for the addition of 2.2 mм-streptozotocin and the horizontal bar when glucose was present at 20 mм instead of 3 mм.

only those occurring within an islet but apparently also those in the other islets of the pancreas. Otherwise, it is difficult to understand why pronounced cyclic variations of serum insulin have been found in various species including man (Lefebvre *et al.*, 1987).

    The oscillatory pattern of serum insulin may be of physiological importance in preventing down-regulation of the peripheral insulin receptors. It is therefore of interest that loss of these oscillations is an early event during the development of diabetes and is seen even in subjects with minimal glucose intolerance (O'Rahilly *et al.*, 1988). In support of the notion that disappearance of the oscillations is accounted for by a primary lesion of the B-cells, it has been possible to demonstrate that exposure to toxic agents *in vitro* may result in a selective loss of the oscillations with maintenance of a glucose-induced rise of $[Ca^{2+}]_i$ (Hellman *et al.*, 1990c; Grapengiesser *et al.*, 1990b). Fig. 16 illustrates such a disappearance of the large amplitude oscillations when exposing a B-cell to the diabetogenic agent streptozotocin.

An important question is whether glucose also evokes rapid oscillations of $[Ca^{2+}]_i$ in the individual B-cell corresponding to the bursts

Fig. 17.   Effect of glucagon on glucose-induced oscillations of cytoplasmic Ca^{2+} in an individual mouse B-cell

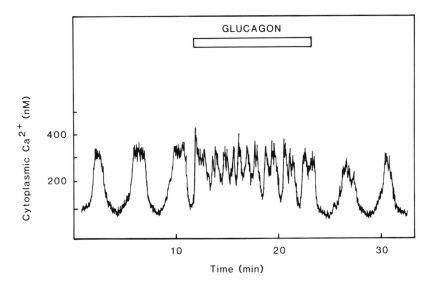

The figure shows $[Ca^{2+}]_i$ calculated from the 340/380 nm fluorescence excitation ratio using the indicator fura-2. The bar indicates the period of exposure to 1 nM-glucagon in a medium containing 11 mM-glucose.

of action potentials observed with intracellular microelectrodes in intact pancreatic islets. This is evidently the case, as indicated from the occasional appearance of Ca^{2+} transients with a frequency of 2–5/min (Hellman *et al.*, 1990*b*). The fact that these oscillations were less abundant than those reported to occur in intact islets (Valdeolmillos *et al.*, 1989) may well reflect a deficient formation of cyclic AMP in the isolated B-cells caused by their separation from the glucagon-secreting A-cells (Schuit & Pipeleers, 1985). Recent studies in our laboratory (Hellman *et al.*, 1990*b*) provide evidence in support of this idea, in demonstrating that the presence of glucagon results in unmasking of an ability of glucose to induce rapid oscillations of $[Ca^{2+}]_i$ (Fig. 17). These transients were either superimposed on a sustained elevated level of $[Ca^{2+}]_i$ or on the large amplitude oscillations evoked by glucose.

Conclusions

Stimulation of insulin release by glucose and other nutrients has been attributed to a rise of cytoplasmic Ca^{2+} mediated by increased entry of the ion into the pancreatic B-cells. In addition to providing final evidence for this view recent studies have revealed that the regulation of $[Ca^{2+}]_i$ by nutrient secretagogues involves other effects significant for our understanding of the insulin secretory process. In accordance with predictions made from measurements of ^{45}Ca fluxes, glucose was found to have a dual action on $[Ca^{2+}]_i$, implying that the sugar could also inhibit insulin release. A second major discovery was that glucose induced cyclic variations of $[Ca^{2+}]_i$ in the single B-cell with a periodicity equivalent to that characteristic for pulsatile insulin release. Both the glucose-stimulated entry of Ca^{2+} and the $[Ca^{2+}]_i$ oscillations are vulnerable processes affected by mild damage of the B-cells. This fact might explain why paradoxical glucose suppression of circulating insulin and loss of its cyclic variations are early indicators of the development of diabetes.

The generous support of the Swedish Medical Research Council (12x-562, 12x-6240), the Swedish Diabetes Association, the Nordic Insulin Foundation, the Swedish Hoechst and Novo-Nordisk Companies and the Family Ernfors Foundation is gratefully acknowledged. The establishment of the technique for digital image analysis was made possible by the Swedish Council for Planning and Co-ordination of Research.

References

Andersson, T., Berggren, P. O., Gylfe, E. & Hellman, B. (1982) Amounts and distribution of intracellular magnesium and calcium in pancreatic β-cells. Acta Physiol. Scand. **114**, 235–241

Arkhammar, P., Nilsson, T., Welsh, M., Welsh, N. & Berggren, P. O. (1989) Effects of protein kinase C activation on the regulation of the stimulus-secretion coupling in pancreatic β-cells. Biochem. J. **264**, 207–215

Atwater, I., Goncalves, A., Herchuelz, A., Lebrun, P., Malaisse, W. J., Rojas, E. & Scott, A. (1984) Cooling dissociates glucose-induced insulin release from electrical activity and cation fluxes in rodent pancreatic islets. J. Physiol. **348**, 615–627

Atwater, I., Carrol, P. & Li, M. X. (1989) Electrophysiology of the pancreatic β-cell. In Molecular and Cellular Biology of Diabetes Mellitus. 1. Insulin Secretion, (Draznin, B., Melmed, S. & Le Roith, D., eds.), pp. 49–68, Alan R. Liss, New York

Bailey, C. J. & Flatt, P. R. (1986) Animal models of diabetes. In Recent Advances in Diabetes (Nattrass, M., ed.), vol. 2, pp. 71–89, Churchill Livingstone, Edinburgh

Bergsten, P. & Hellman, B. (1984) Differentiation between the short and long term effects of glucose on the intracellular calcium content of the pancreatic β-cell. Endocrinology **114**, 1854–1859

Bergsten, P., Löfberg, C. & Hellman, B. (1989) Reversal of glucose-induced inhibition of insulin release by dibutyryl cyclic-AMP. Exp. Clin. Endocrinol. **93**, 307–312

Bergstrom, R. W., Fujimoto, W. Y., Teller, D. C. & de Haen, C. (1989) Oscillatory insulin secretion in perifused isolated rat islets. Am. J. Physiol. **257**, E479–E485

Berridge, M. J. (1983) Rapid accumulation of inositol trisphosphate reveals that agonists hydrolyse polyphosphoinositides instead of phosphatidylinositol. Biochem. J. **212**, 849–858

Berridge, M. J., Cobbold, P. H. & Cuthbertson, K. S. R. (1988) Spatial and temporal aspects of cell signalling. Philos. Trans. Soc. R. Lond. (Biol) **320**, 325–343

Best, L. & Malaisse, W. J. (1983) Phospholipids and islet function. Diabetologia **25**, 299–305

Boyd III, A. E., Hill, R. S., Oberwetter, J. M. & Berg, M. (1986) Calcium dependency and free calcium concentrations during insulin secretion in a hamster beta cell line. J. Clin. Invest. **77**, 774–781

Boyd III, A. E., Rajan, A. S. & Gaines, K. L. (1989) Regulation of insulin release by calcium. In Insulin Secretion (Draznin, B., Melmed, S. & Le Roith, D., eds.), pp. 93–105, Alan R. Liss, New York

Brisson, G. R., Malaisse-Lagae, F. & Malaisse, W. J. (1972) The stimulus-secretion coupling of glucose-induced insulin release. VII. A proposed site of action for adenosine-3′,5′-cyclic monophosphate. J. Clin. Invest. **51**, 232–241

Charles, M. A., Lawecki, J., Pictet, R. & Grodsky, G. M. (1975) Insulin secretion. Interrelationships of glucose, cyclic adenosine 3′,5′-monophosphate, and calcium. J. Biol. Chem. **250**, 6134–6140

Cook, D. L. (1983) Isolated islets of Langerhans have slow oscillations of electrical activity. Metabolism **32**, 681–685

Deleers, M., Mahy, M. & Malaisse, W. J. (1985) Glucose increases cytosolic Ca^{2+} activity in pancreatic islet cells. Biochem. Int. **10**, 97–103

Douglas, W. W. (1968) Stimulus-secretion coupling: the concept and clues from chromaffin and other cells. Br. J. Pharmacol. **34**, 451–474

Dunlop, M. E. & Larkins, R. G. (1986) Glucose-induced phospholipid-dependent protein phosphorylation in neonatal rat islets. Arch. Biochem. Biophys. **248**, 562–569

Eddlestone, G. T., Oldham, S. B., Lipson, L. G., Premdas, F. H. & Beigelman, P. M. (1985) Electrical activity, cAMP concentration, and insulin release in mouse islets of Langerhans. Am. J. Physiol. **248**, C145–C153

Gobbe, P. & Herchuelz, A. (1989) Does glucose reduce cytosolic free Ca^{2+} in normal pancreatic islet cells? Res. Commun. Chem. Pathol. Pharmacol. **63**, 231–247

Grapengiesser, E., Gylfe, E. & Hellman, B. (1988a) Dual effect of glucose on cytoplasmic Ca^{2+} in single pancreatic β-cells. Biochem. Biophys. Res. Commun. **150**, 419–425

Grapengiesser, E., Gylfe, E. & Hellman, B. (1988b) Glucose-induced oscillations of cytoplasmic Ca^{2+} in the pancreatic β-cell. Biochem. Biophys. Res. Commun. **151**, 1299–1304

Grapengiesser, E., Gylfe, E. & Hellman, B. (1989a) Glucose effects on cytoplasmic Ca^{2+} of individual pancreatic β-cells recorded by two procedures for dual-wavelength fluorometry. Exp. Clin. Endocrinol. **93**, 321–327

Grapengiesser, E., Gylfe, E. & Hellman, B. (1989b) Three types of cytoplasmic Ca^{2+} oscillations in stimulated pancreatic β-cells. Arch. Biochem. Biophys. **268**, 404–407

Grapengiesser, E., Gylfe, E. & Hellman, B. (1989c) Ca^{2+} oscillations in pancreatic β-cells exposed to leucine and arginine. Acta Physiol. Scand. **136**, 113–119

Grapengiesser, E., Gylfe, E. & Hellman, B. (1990a) Sulfonylurea mimics the effect of glucose in inducing large amplitude oscillations of cytoplasmic Ca^{2+} in pancreatic β-cells. Mol. Pharmacol. **37**, 461–467

Grapengiesser, E., Gylfe, E. & Hellman, B. (1990b) Disappearance of glucose-induced oscillations of cytoplasmic Ca^{2+} in pancreatic β-cells exposed to streptozotocin or alloxan. Toxicology **63**, 263–271

Grill, V. & Cerasi, E. (1976) Effects of hexoses and mannoheptulose on cyclic AMP accumulation and insulin secretion in rat pancreatic islets. Biochim. Biophys. Acta **437**, 36–50

Grodsky, G. M. & Bennett, L. L. (1966) Cation requirements for insulin secretion in the isolated perfused pancreas. Diabetes **15**, 910–912

Gylfe, E. (1988a) Glucose-induced early changes in cytoplasmic calcium of pancreatic β-cells studied with time-sharing dual wavelength fluorometry. J. Biol. Chem. **263**, 5044–5048

Gylfe, E. (1988b) Nutrient secretagogues induce bimodal early changes in cytoplasmic calcium of insulin-releasing ob/ob mouse β-cells. J. Biol. Chem. **263**, 13750–13754

Gylfe, E. (1989a) Glucose-induced buffering of cytoplasmic Ca^{2+} in the pancreatic β-cell — an artifact or a physiological phenomenon. Biochem. Biophys. Res. Commun. **159**, 907–912

Gylfe, E. (1989*b*) Phorbol ester desensitization of clonal insulin-releasing cell response to carbachol involves depletion of an intracellular calcium pool. Acta Physiol. Scand. **135**, 107–111

Gylfe, E. & Hellman, B. (1981) Calcium and pancreatic β-cell function: Modification of ^{45}Ca fluxes by methylxanthines and dibutyryl cyclic-AMP. Biochem. Med. **26**, 365–376

Gylfe, E. & Hellman, B. (1986) Glucose-stimulated sequestration of Ca^{2+} in clonal insulin-releasing cells. Evidence for opposing effect of muscarinic receptor activation. Biochem. J. **233**, 865–870

Gylfe, E. & Hellman, B. (1987) External ATP mimics carbachol in initiating calcium mobilization from pancreatic β-cells conditioned by previous exposure to glucose. Br. J. Pharmacol. **92**, 281–289

Gylfe, E., Andersson, T., Rorsman, P., Abrahamsson, H., Arkhammar, P., Hellman, P., Hellman, B., Oie, H. K. & Gazdar, A. F. (1983) Depolarization-independent net uptake of calcium into clonal insulin-releasing cells exposed to glucose. Biosci. Rep. **3**, 927–937

Gylfe, E., Grapengiesser, E. & Hellman, B. (1990) Propagation of Ca^{2+} oscillations in clusters of β-cells studied with a digital imaging technique. Diabetologia **33**, A64

Hahn, H. J., Gylfe, E. & Hellman, B. (1980) Calcium and pancreatic β-cell function. 7. Evidence for cyclic AMP-induced translocation of intracellular calcium. Biochim. Biophys. Acta **630**, 425–432

Hellman, B. (1975) The significance of calcium for glucose stimulation of insulin release. Endocrinology **97**, 392–398

Hellman, B. (1976*a*) Calcium and the control of insulin secretion. In Diabetes Research Today. Meeting of the Minkowski Prize-Winners (Lindenlaub, E., ed.), pp. 207–222, F. K. Schattauer Verlag, Stuttgart

Hellman, B. (1976*b*) Stimulation of insulin release after raising extracellular calcium. FEBS Lett. **63**, 125–128

Hellman, B. (1985) β-cell cytoplasmic Ca^{2+} balance as a determinant for glucose-stimulated insulin release. Diabetologia **28**, 494–501

Hellman, B. (1986) Calcium transport in pancreatic β-cells. Implications for glucose regulation of insulin release. Diab./Metab. Rev. **2**, 215–241

Hellman, B. (1988) Calcium transport and deficient insulin release. In Pathology of the Endocrine Pancreas (Lefebvre, P. J. & Pipeleers, D. G., eds.), pp. 249–268, Springer Verlag, Heidelberg

Hellman, B. & Gylfe, E. (1985) Glucose regulation of insulin release involves intracellular sequestration of calcium. In Calcium in Biological Systems (Rubin, R. P., Weiss, G. B. & Putney Jr., J. W., eds.), pp. 93–99, Plenum Publ. Corp., New York

Hellman, B. & Gylfe, E. (1986*a*) Calcium and the control of insulin secretion. In Calcium and Cell Function (Cheung, W. E., ed.), vol. VI, pp. 253–326, Academic Press, Orlando

Hellman, B. & Gylfe, E. (1986*b*) Mobilization of different intracellular calcium pools after activation of muscarinic receptors in pancreatic beta-cells. Pharmacology **32**, 257–267

Hellman, B., Sehlin, J. & Täljedal, I. B. (1971) Calcium uptake by pancreatic β-cells as measured with the aid of ^{45}Ca and mannitol-^{3}H. Am. J. Physiol. **221**, 1795–1801

Hellman, B., Andersson, T., Berggren, P. O., Flatt, P., Gylfe, E. & Kohnert, K. D. (1979) The role of calcium in insulin secretion. In Hormones and Cell Regulation (Dumont, J. & Nunez, J., eds.), vol 3, pp. 69–96, Elsevier/North Holland Biomed. Press, Amsterdam

Hellman, B., Abrahamsson, H., Andersson, T., Berggren, P. O., Flatt, P., Gylfe, E. & Hahn, H. J. (1980*a*) Calcium movements in relation to glucose-stimulated insulin secretion. Horm. Metab. Res. (Suppl. Ser.) **10**, 122–130

Hellman, B., Andersson, T., Berggren, P. O. & Rorsman, P. (1980*b*) Calcium and pancreatic β-cell function. XI. Modification of ^{45}Ca fluxes by Na^+ removal. Biochem. Med. **24**, 143–152

Hellman, B., Hällgren, R., Abrahamsson, H., Bergsten, P., Berne, C., Gylfe, E., Rorsman, P. & Wide, L. (1985) The dual action of glucose on cytosolic Ca^{2+} activity in pancreatic β-cells. Demonstration of an inhibitory effect of glucose on insulin release in the mouse and man. Biomed. Biochim. Acta **44**, 63–70

Hellman, B., Gylfe, E. & Wesslén, N. (1986) Inositol 1,4,5-trisphosphate mobilizes glucose-incorporated calcium from pancreatic islets. Biochem. Int. **13**, 383–389

Hellman, B., Gylfe, E. & Bergsten, P. (1987) Mobilization of different pools of glucose-incorporated calcium in pancreatic β-cells after muscarinic receptor activation. In Biophysics of the Pancreatic β-cell (Atwater, I., Rojas, E. & Soria, B., eds.), pp. 325–341, Plenum Press, New York

Hellman, B., Gylfe, E., Bergsten, P., Johansson, H. & Wesslén, N. (1988) Glucose-induced modifications of the calcium movements regulating insulin and glucagon release. In Pathogenesis of Non-Insulin Dependent Diabetes Mellitus, (Grill, V. & Efendic, S., eds.), pp. 39–60, Raven Press, New York

Hellman, B., Gylfe, E., Wesslén, N., Hallberg, A., Grapengiesser, E. & Marcström, A. (1989) Plasma membrane associated ATP as a regulator of the secretory activity of the pancreatic β-cell. Exp. Clin. Endocrinol. **93**, 125–135

Hellman, B., Gylfe, E., Grapengiesser, E., Panten, U., Schwanstecher, C. & Heipel, C. (1990a) Glucose induces temperature-dependent oscillations of cytoplasmic Ca^{2+} in single pancreatic β-cells related to their electrical activity. Cell Calcium **11**, 413–418

Hellman, B., Gylfe, E. & Grapengiesser, E. (1990b) Glucose induces fast oscillations of cytoplasmic Ca^{2+} in single pancreatic β-cells. Diabetologia **33**, A63

Hellman, B., Berne, C., Grapengiesser, E., Grill, V., Gylfe, E. & Lund, P. E. (1990c) The cytoplasmic Ca^{2+} response to glucose as an indicator of impairment of the pancreatic β-cell function. Eur. J. Clin. Invest. **20** (Suppl. 1), S10–S17

Henquin, J. C. & Meissner, H. P. (1984) Effects of theophylline and dibutyryl cyclic adenosine monophosphate on the membrane potential of mouse pancreatic β-cells. J. Physiol. (London) **351**, 595–612

Henquin, J. C., Meissner, H. P. & Schmeer, W. (1982) Cyclic variations of glucose-induced electrical activity in pancreatic β-cells. Pflüegers Arch. **393**, 322–327

Henquin, J. C., Bosem, M., Schmeer, W. & Nenquin, M. (1987) Distinct mechanisms for two amplification systems of insulin release. Biochem. J. **246**, 393–399

Herchuelz, A. & Malaisse, W. J. (1980) Regulation of calcium fluxes in rat pancreatic islets. Dissimilar effects of glucose and of sodium ion accumulation. J. Physiol. **302**, 263–280

Herchuelz, A. & Malaisse, W. J. (1981) Calcium movements and insulin release in pancreatic islet cells. Diabete Metabolisme (Paris) **7**, 283–288

Hess, B. (1979) The glycolytic oscillator. J. Exp. Biol. **81**, 7–14

Hill, R. S., Oberwetter, J. M. & Boyd III, A. E.(1987) Increase in cAMP levels in β-cell line potentiates insulin secretion without altering cytosolic free-calcium concentration. Diabetes **36**, 440–446

Hoenig, M. & Sharp, G. W. G. (1986) Glucose induces insulin release and a rise in cytosolic calcium concentration in a transplantable rat insulinoma. Endocrinology **119**, 2502–2507

Howell, S. L., Montague, W. & Tyhurst, M. (1975) Calcium distribution in islets of Langerhans: A study of calcium concentrations and of calcium accumulation in β-cell organelles. J. Cell Sci. **19**, 395–409

Hughes, S. J. & Ashcroft, S. J. H. (1988) Effect of secretagogues on cytosolic free Ca^{2+} and insulin release in the hamster clonal β-cell line HIT-T15. J. Mol. Endocrinol. **1**, 13–17

Irvine, R. F., Moor, R. M., Pollock, W. K., Smith, P. M. & Wreggett, K. A. (1988) Inositol phosphate: proliferation, metabolism and function. Philos. Trans. R. Soc. Lond. (Biol) **320**, 281–298

Johansson, H., Gylfe, E. & Hellman, B. (1987) The actions of arginine and glucose on glucagon secretion are mediated by opposite effects on cytoplasmic Ca^{2+}. Biochem. Biophys. Res. Commun. **147**, 309–314

Johansson, H., Gylfe, E. & Hellman, B. (1989) Cyclic AMP raises cytoplasmic calcium in pancreatic α_2-cells by mobilizing calcium incorporated in response to glucose. Cell Calcium **10**, 205–211

Jones, P. M., Stutchfield, J. & Howell, S. L. (1985) Effects of Ca^{2+} and a phorbol ester on insulin secretion from islets of Langerhans permeabilized by high voltage discharge. FEBS Lett. **191**, 102–106

Komatsu, M., Aizawa, T., Takasu, N. & Yamada, T. (1989) Glucose raises cytosolic free calcium in the rat pancreatic islets. Horm. Metab. Res. **21**, 405–409

Lefebvre, P. J., Paolisso, G., Scheen, A. J. & Henquin, J. C. (1987) Pulsatility of insulin and glucagon release: physiological significance and pharmacological implications. Diabetologia **30**, 433–452

Lund, P. E., Gylfe, E. & Hellman, B. (1989) Leucine induces initial lowering of cytoplasmic Ca^{2+} in pancreatic β-cells without concomitant inhibition of insulin release. Biochem. Int. **19**, 83–88

Malaisse, W. J. & Malaisse-Lagae, F. (1984) The role of cyclic AMP in insulin release. Experientia **40**, 1068–1075

Malaisse, W. J., Herchuelz, A., Devis, G., Somers, G., Boschero, A. C., Hutton, J. C., Kawazu, S., Sener, A., Atwater, I. J., Duncan, G., Ribalet, B. & Rojas, E. (1978) Regulation of calcium fluxes and their regulatory roles in pancreatic islets. Ann. N.Y. Acad. Sci. **307**, 562–582

Malaisse-Lagae, F. & Malaisse, W. J. (1971) Stimulus-secretion coupling of glucose-induced insulin release. III. Uptake of ^{45}calcium by isolated islets of Langerhans. Endocrinology **88**, 72–80

Metz, S. A. (1988) Is protein kinase C required for physiologic insulin release. Diabetes **37**, 3–7

Metz, G. A., Halter, J. B. & Robertson, R. P. (1979) Paradoxical inhibition of insulin secretion by glucose in human diabetes mellitus. J. Clin. Endocrinol. Metab. **48**, 827–835

Milner, R. D. G. & Hales, C. N. (1967) The role of calcium and magnesium in insulin secretion from rabbit pancreas studied *in vitro*. Diabetologia **3**, 47–49

Montague, W., Morgan, N. G., Rumford, G. M. & Prince, C. A. (1985) Effect of glucose on polyphosphoinositide metabolism in isolated rat islets of Langerhans. Biochem. J. **227**, 483–489

Nelson, T. Y., Gaines, K. L., Rajan, A. S., Berg, M. & Boyd, A. E. (1987) Increased cytosolic calcium a signal for sulfonylurea-stimulated insulin release from beta cells. J. Biol. Chem. **262**, 2608–2612

Nilsson, T., Arkhammar, P., Hallberg, A., Hellman, B. & Berggren, P. O. (1987) Characterization of the inositol 1,4,5-trisphosphate-induced Ca^{2+} release in pancreatic β-cells. Biochem. J. **248**, 329–336

Nilsson, T., Arkhammar, P. & Berggren, P. O. (1988) Dual effect of glucose on cytoplasmic free Ca^{2+} concentration and insulin release reflects the β-cell being deprived of fuel. Biochem. Biophys. Res. Commun. **153**, 984–991

Norlund, R., Roos, N. & Täljedal, I.-B. (1987) Quantitative energy dispersive X-ray microanalysis of eight elements in pancreatic endocrine and exocrine cells after cryo-fixation. Biosci. Rep. **7**, 859–869

Nygren, P., Larsson, R., Lindh, E., Ljunghall, S., Rastad, J., Åkerström, G. & Gylfe, E. (1987) Bimodal regulation of secretion by cytoplasmic Ca^{2+} as demonstrated by the parathyroid. FEBS Lett. **213**, 195–198

Opara, E. C., Atwater, I. & Go., V. L. W. (1988) Characterization and control of pulsatile secretion of insulin and glucagon. Pancreas **3**, 484–487

O'Rahilly, S., Turner, R. C. & Matthews, D. R. (1988) Impaired pulsatile secretion of insulin in relatives of patients with non-insulin-dependent diabetes. N. Engl. J. Med. **318**, 1225–1230

Pace, C. S., Tarvin, J. T., Neighbors, A. S., Pirkle, J. A. & Greider, M. H. (1980) Use of a high voltage technique to determine the molecular requirements for exocytosis in islet cells. Diabetes **29**, 911–918

Penner, R. & Neher, E. (1988) The role of calcium in stimulus-secretion coupling in excitable and non-excitable cells. J. Exp. Biol. **139**, 329–345

Pershadsingh, H. A., McDaniel, M. L., Landt, M., Bry, C. G., Lacy, P. E. & McDonald, J. M. (1980) Ca^{2+}-activated ATPase and ATP-dependent calmodulin-stimulated Ca^{2+}-transport in islet cell plasma membrane. Nature (London) **288**, 492–495

Peter-Reisch, B., Fathi, M., Schlegel, W. & Wollheim, C. B. (1988) Glucose and carbachol generate 1,2-diacylglycerols by different mechanisms in pancreatic islets. J. Clin. Invest. **81**, 1154–1161

Pipeleers, D. G., Schuit, F. C., In't Veld, P. A., Maes, D. E., Hooghe-Peters, E. L., Van de Winkel, M. & Gepts, W. (1985) Interplay of nutrients and hormones in the regulation of insulin release. Endocrinology **117**, 824–833

Prentki, M. & Matschinsky, F. M. (1987) Ca^{2+}, cAMP and phospholipid-derived messengers in coupling mechanisms of insulin secretion. Physiol. Rev. **67**, 1185–1248

Prentki, M. & Wollheim, C. B. (1984) Cytosolic free Ca^{2+} in insulin secretory cells and its regulation by isolated organelles. Experientia **40**, 1052–1060

Prentki, M., Janjic, D., Biden, T. J., Blondel, B. & Wollheim, C. B. (1984) Regulation of Ca^{2+} transport by isolated organelles of a rat insulinoma. Studies with endoplasmic reticulum and secretory granules. J. Biol. Chem. **259**, 10118–10123

Prentki, M., Glennon, M. C., Geschwind, J. F., Matschinsky, F. M. & Corkey, B. E. (1987) Cyclic AMP raises cytosolic Ca^{2+} and promotes Ca^{2+} influx in a clonal pancreatic β-cell line (HIT T-15). FEBS Lett. **220**, 103–107

Prentki, M., Glennon, M. C., Thomas, A. P., Morris, R. L., Matschinsky, F. M. & Corkey, B. E. (1988) Cell-specific patterns of oscillating free Ca^{2+} in carbamylcholine-stimulated insulinoma cells. J. Biol. Chem. **263**, 11044–11047

Rajan, A. S., Hill, R. S. & Boyd III, A. E. (1989) Effect of rise in cAMP levels on Ca^{2+} influx through voltage-dependent Ca^{2+} channels in HIT cells. Second messenger synarchy in β-cells. Diabetes **38**, 874–880

Rojas, E., Hidalgo, J., Carrol, P. B., Li, M. X. & Atwater, I. (1990) A new class of calcium channels activated by glucose in human pancreatic β-cells. FEBS Lett. **261**, 265–270

Rorsman, P. & Abrahamsson, H. (1985) Cyclic AMP potentiates glucose-induced insulin release from mouse pancreatic islets without increasing cytosolic free Ca^{2+}. Acta Physiol. Scand. **125**, 639–647

Rorsman, P. & Trube, G. (1986) Calcium and delayed potassium currents in mouse pancreatic β-cells under voltage-clamp conditions. J. Physiol. (London) **374**, 531–550

Rorsman, P., Berggren, P. O., Gylfe, E. & Hellman, B. (1983) Reduction of the cytosolic Ca^{2+} activity in clonal insulin-releasing cells exposed to glucose. Biosci. Rep. **3**, 939–946

Rorsman, P., Abrahamsson, H., Gylfe, E. & Hellman, B. (1984) Dual effects of glucose on the cytosolic Ca^{2+} activity of mouse pancreatic β-cells. FEBS Lett. **170**, 196–200

Rubin, R. P. (1982) Calcium and Cellular Secretion, pp. 1–276, Plenum Press, New York

Schuit, F. C. & Pipeleers, D. G. (1985) Regulation of adenosine 3′,5′-monophosphate levels in the pancreatic β-cell. Endocrinology **117**, 834–840

Sharp, G. W. G., Wiedenkeller, D. E., Kaelin, D., Siegel, E. G. & Wollheim, C. B. (1980) Stimulation of adenylate cyclase by Ca^{2+} and calmodulin in rat islets of Langerhans. Explanation for the glucose-induced increase in cyclic AMP levels. Diabetes **29**, 74–77

Smith, P. A., Rorsman, P. & Ashcroft, F. M. (1989) Modulation of dihydropyridine-sensitive Ca^{2+} channels by glucose metabolism in mouse pancreatic β-cells. Nature (London) **342**, 550–553

Sussman, K. E., Leitner, J. W. & Draznin, B. (1987) Cytosolic free-calcium concentrations in normal pancreatic islet cells. Diabetes **36**, 571–577

Tamagawa, T., Niki, H. & Niki, A. (1985) Insulin release independent of a rise in cytosolic free Ca^{2+} by forskolin and phorbol ester. FEBS Lett. **183**, 430–432

Turk, J., Wolf, B. A. & McDaniel, M. L. (1986) Glucose-induced accumulation of inositol trisphosphates in isolated pancreatic islets. Predominance of the 1,3,4-isomer. Biochem. J. **237**, 259–263

Turk, J., Wolf, B. A. & McDaniel, M. L. (1987) The role of phospholipid-derived mediators including arachidonic acid, its metabolites, and inositol trisphosphate and of intracellular Ca^{2+} in glucose-induced insulin secretion by pancreatic islets. Prog. Lipid Res. **26**, 125–181

Valdeolmillos, M., Santos, R. M., Contreras, D., Soria, B. & Rosario, L. M. (1989) Glucose-induced oscillations of intracellular Ca^{2+} concentration resembling bursting electrical activity in single mouse islets of Langerhans. FEBS Lett. **259**, 19–23

Vallar, L., Biden, T. J. & Wollheim, C. B. (1987) Guanine nucleotides induce Ca^{2+}-independent insulin secretion from permeabilized RINm5F cells. J. Biol. Chem. **262**, 5049–5056

Valverde, I., Vandermeers, A., Anjaneyulu, R. & Malaisse, W. J. (1979) Calmodulin activation of adenylate cyclase in pancreatic islets. Science **206**, 225–227

Wang, J. L. & McDaniel, M. L. (1990) Secretagogue-induced oscillations of cytoplasmic Ca^{2+} in single β- and α_2-cells obtained from pancreatic islets by fluorescence-activated cell sorting. Biochem. Biophys. Res. Commun. **166**, 813–818

Wesslén, N. & Hellman, B. (1986) The influx of Ca^{2+} into pancreatic β-cells and its regulation by glucose. Biomed. Res. **7**, 339–344

Wolf, B. A., Colca, J. R., Comens, P. G., Turk, J. & McDaniel, M. L. (1986) Glucose 6-phosphate regulates Ca^{2+} steady state in endoplasmic reticulum of islets. J. Biol. Chem. **261**, 16284–16287

Wolf, B. A., Florholmen, J., Turk, J. & McDaniel, M. L. (1988) Studies of the Ca^{2+} requirements for glucose- and carbachol-induced augmentation of inositol trisphosphate and inositol tetrakisphosphate accumulation in digitonin-permeabilized islets. J. Biol. Chem. **263**, 3565–3575

Wollheim, C. B. & Biden, T. J. (1986) Signal transduction in insulin secretion: comparison between fuel stimuli and receptor agonists. Ann. N.Y. Acad. Sci. **488**, 317–333

Wollheim, C. B. & Sharp, G. W. G. (1981) Regulation of insulin release by calcium. Physiol. Rev. **61**, 914–973

Wollheim, C. B., Ullrich, S. & Pozzan, T. (1984) Glyceraldehyde but not cyclic AMP-induced insulin release is preceded by a rise in cytosolic free Ca^{2+}. FEBS Lett. **177**, 17–22

Wollheim, C. B., Ullrich, S., Meda, P. & Vallar, L. (1987) Regulation of exocytosis in electrically permeabilized insulin-secreting cells. Evidence for Ca^{2+} dependent and independent secretion. Biosci. Rep. **7**, 443–454

Wollheim, C. B., Dunne, M. J., Peter-Riesch, B., Bruzzone, R., Pozzan, T. & Petersen, O. H. (1988) Activators of protein kinase C depolarize insulin-secreting cells by closing K^+ channels. EMBO J. **7**, 2443–2449

Wolters, G. H. J., Wiegman, J. B. & Konijnendijk, W. (1982) The effect of glucose stimulation on ^{45}calcium uptake of rat pancreatic islets and their total calcium content as measured by a fluorometric micromethod. Diabetologia **22**, 122–127

Yada, T., Kakei, M., Sorimacha, M. & Tanaka, H. (1989) Biphasic change of cytoplasmic Ca^{2+} in response to glucose in single β-cells from rats. Proc. XXXI Int. Congr. Physiol. Sci. p. 1400

Yaseen, M. A., Pedley, K. C. & Howell, S. L. (1982) Regulation of insulin secretion from islets of Langerhans rendered permeable by electric discharge. Biochem. J. **206**, 81–87

Zawalich, W. S. & Rasmussen, H. (1990) Control of insulin secretion: a model involving Ca^{2+}, cAMP and diacylglycerol. Mol. Cell. Endocrinol. **70**, 119–137

Zawalich, W. S. & Zawalich, K. C. (1988) Induction of memory in rat pancreatic islets by tolbutamide. Dependence on ambient glucose level, calcium and phosphoinositide hydrolysis. Diabetes **37**, 816–823

12

The role of protein kinase C in insulin secretion

Shanta J. Persaud, Peter M. Jones and Simon L. Howell

Biomedical Sciences Division, Kings College London, Kensington,
London, W8 7AH, U.K.

Introduction

In recent years evidence has accumulated implicating the involvement of
novel second messengers in stimulus–response coupling in many cell
types. The molecules generated by the enzymic actions of specific
phospholipases on membrane phospholipids have received considerable
attention, particularly the products of the hydrolysis of inositol phospholipids (see Chapter 7 by Morgan & Montague). Phosphatidylinositol
(PtdIns) is a minor (5–10%) phospholipid component of mammalian cell
membranes. PtdIns can be phosphorylated to phosphatidylinositol 4-
phosphate (PtdIns4P) which, in turn, can be further phosphorylated to
phosphatidylinositol 4,5-bisphosphate [PtdIns(4,5)P_2]. This form is the
major inositol phospholipid hydrolysed as a result of phospholipase C
(PLC) activation, and the products formed by this reaction, inositol 1,4,5-
trisphosphate, [Ins(1,4,5)P_3] and diacylglycerol, act as intracellular second
messengers in diverse signalling systems in eukaryotic cells (reviewed by
Berridge, 1985).

 The hydrophobic product of the phosphodiesteratic cleavage of
inositol phospholipids, diacylglycerol, is thought to have a second
messenger function through the activation of the Ca^{2+}/phospholipid-
dependent protein kinase known as protein kinase C (PKC; Nishizuka,
1984). It has become apparent that PKC is a closely-related family of
isoenzymes. To date, at least seven isoforms of PKC (designated α, βI, βII,
γ, δ, ε, ζ) have been identified by chromatographic separation or by nucleic
acid sequencing (Nishizuka, 1988; Schaap et al., 1989; Parker et al., 1989).
It is not yet certain that all of these isoforms are normally expressed in
mammalian tissues, but there is convincing evidence that different tissues
express different PKC isoenzymes (Nishizuka, 1988).

 At physiological Ca^{2+} concentrations, PKC is activated by
diacylglycerol or by tumour-promoting phorbol esters, such as phorbol

myristate acetate (PMA), which can substitute for diacylglycerol (Nishi-zuka, 1984). PKC (in particular the γ subtype) may also be activated by arachidonic acid, an unsaturated fatty acid produced by phospholipase A_2-mediated cleavage of membrane phospholipids (Nishizuka, 1988), and there have been reports that other unsaturated fatty acids can activate PKC *in vitro* (Seifert *et al.*, 1988; Holian *et al.*, 1989). PKC has been identified in isolated islets of Langerhans (Tanigawa *et al.*, 1982), in individual B-cells (Ito *et al.*, 1989; Onoda *et al.*, 1990) and in insulin-secreting cell lines (Ito *et al.*, 1989; Onoda *et al.*, 1990). The biochemical characteristics of PKC activity in insulin-secreting tissues appear to be the same as those of PKC in other tissues, as regards sensitivity to Ca^{2+}, diacylglycerol and phosphatidylserine (Tanigawa *et al.*, 1982; Lord & Ashcroft, 1984; Persaud *et al.*, 1989a). The expression of PKC isozymes in B-cells has not yet been extensively studied, although two recent reports (Ito *et al.*, 1989; Onoda *et al.*, 1990) suggest that pancreatic B-cells contain both α and βII isoforms, but not the βI isoform, nor the γ isoform which appears to be confined to neuronal tissues (Nishizuka, 1988). In the same studies, rat insulinoma cells (RINr) were shown to contain the α isoform but, in contrast to normal B-cells, β-isoforms of PKC were undetectable in these tumour cells.

There is already a vast body of literature on PKC and its many putative functions in signal transduction (reviewed by Nishizuka, 1988). This chapter will concentrate solely on the role of PKC in stimulus–secretion coupling in pancreatic B-cells by evaluating the evidence for and against PKC activation as a mediator of B-cell secretory responses to physiological secretagogues.

Activators of PKC in B-cells

One fundamental approach towards identifying an involvement of PKC in the regulation of insulin secretion is to measure the generation of activators of the enzyme, and a subsequent increase in enzyme activity, in response to insulin secretagogues. As is evident from earlier chapters, physiological regulators of insulin secretion can be classified into two main types: nutrient secretagogues, such as glucose, which can initiate a secretory response; and non-nutrient secretagogues, such as hormones and neurotransmitters, which act to modulate (but cannot initiate) the secretory response (reviewed by Wollheim & Sharp, 1981). B-cells appear to use very different mechanisms to recognize these different secretagogues. For example, glucose, the major nutrient insulin secretagogue, is thought to stimulate insulin secretion as a consequence of its metabolism within the B-cell (Hedeskov, 1980) whereas carbachol, a cholinergic agonist, enhances insulin secretion through interaction with B-cell muscarinic receptors

(Henquin & Nenquin, 1988; also see Chapters 5 and 14 by Malaisse and Berggren *et al.*). Despite these differences in signal recognition, both classes of secretagogue appear to be capable of generating potential activators of PKC.

Generation of PKC activators in B-cells

Diacylglycerol is a product of PLC activation, and there have been numerous studies of the effects of insulin secretagogues on PLC activation in intact tissues (Best & Malaisse, 1983; Yamaguchi *et al.*, 1989), permeabilized tissues (Yamaguchi *et al.*, 1989; Wollheim *et al.*, 1987) and membrane preparations (Dunlop & Malaisse, 1986; Dunlop & Larkins, 1986*a*). Glucose and other nutrient secretagogues, such as leucine and mannose, activate PLC as assessed by increases in radiolabelled $Ins(1,4,5)P_3$ production in cells pre-equilibrated with [^{3}H]inositol (reviewed by Best *et al.*, 1984; Morgan & Montague in Chapter 7). These effects are dependent upon metabolism of the secretagogues, since non-metabolizable sugars, such as galactose, do not stimulate PLC activity. PLC is known to be a Ca^{2+}-sensitive enzyme (Eberhard & Holz, 1988), and detailed studies in intact rat islets suggest that glucose-stimulated $PtdIns(4,5)P_2$ hydrolysis is largely a Ca^{2+}-dependent event, mediated by Ca^{2+} influx through voltage-dependent Ca^{2+} channels (Biden *et al.*, 1987). In contrast, it has been reported that, independently of its metabolism, glucose can activate PLC in Ca^{2+}-clamped digitonin-permeabilized islets (Wolf *et al.*, 1988), although the functional relevance of this observation remains to be established.

Receptor-mediated secretagogues can also activate PLC in B-cells (reviewed by Best *et al.*, 1984; Morgan & Montague in Chapter 7). Thus, for example, carbachol (Best & Malaisse, 1983; Wollheim *et al.*, 1987; Dunlop & Malaisse, 1986; Dunlop & Larkins, 1986*a*; Best *et al.*, 1984; Biden *et al.*, 1987; Wolf *et al.*, 1988), ATP (Blachier & Malaisse, 1988; Arkhammar *et al.*, 1990) and the peptide hormones cholecystokinin (Zawalich *et al.*, 1987*a*; Yamaguchi *et al.*, 1989) and vasopressin (Monaco *et al.*, 1988) cause a rapid stimulation of $Ins(1,4,5)P_3$ in islets or insulin-secreting tumour cells. Studies with rat islet cell membranes revealed that cholinergic stimulation of inositol phospholipid turnover is mediated by a plasma membrane-associated PLC (Dunlop & Malaisse, 1986), which is coupled to a pertussis toxin- and cholera toxin-insensitive GTP binding protein (Dunlop & Larkins, 1986*a*; Wollheim & Biden, 1986; Blachier *et al.*, 1987).

Measurements of diacylglycerol formation are much more technically demanding than measurements of $Ins(1,4,5)P_3$ production, and this is reflected in the relative paucity of information about the effects of insulin secretagogues on the accumulation of diacylglycerol in B-cells. In studies using neonatal rat islets pre-radiolabelled with [^{3}H]arachidonic acid, glucose stimulated a rapid fall in radiolabelled PtdIns concomitant with a transient rise in diacylglycerol, and a mepacrine-sensitive generation of arachidonic acid from phosphatidylcholine (Dunlop & Larkins, 1984). Although arachidonic acid preferentially activates the γ isoform of PKC (Nishizuka, 1988), which is not expressed in B-cells (Ito *et al.*, 1989;

Fig. I.   Time-dependent changes of diacylglycerol (DAG) in rat islets labelled to steady state with [³H]glycerol after stimulation with carbachol (0·5 mm) and glucose (16·7 mm)

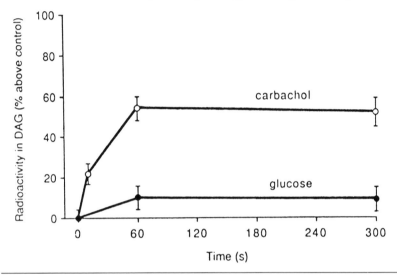

Control islets incubated under identical conditions in the absence of stimulators maintained stable levels of ³H-labelled DAG which averaged 119±6 c.p.m. (n = 53). Data are means±s.ε.м. (n = 20–30). Reproduced from Peter-Riesch et al., 1988.

Onoda *et al.*, 1990), there has been a preliminary report that arachidonic acid can stimulate PKC activity in islet cytosol (Landt *et al.*, 1988). It remains to be determined whether this observation has any physiological significance with respect to effects of endogenous arachidonic acid on PKC activation in intact cells.

Rapid changes in diacylglycerol formation in response to both glucose and carbachol have been detected in rat islets by measuring changes in the rate of turnover of diacylglycerol and its total mass and fatty acid composition (Peter-Riesch *et al.*, 1988; Wolf *et al.*, 1989). The increase in diacylglycerol mass in response to both secretagogues was maximal by 60 s and maintained for at least 5 min (Peter-Riesch *et al.*, 1988; Fig. 1). However, the diacylglycerol generated in response to carbachol was predominantly of a stearoyl-arachidonoyl configuration, consistent with it being a product of inositol phospholipid hydrolysis, while the diacylglycerol within glucose-stimulated islets contained mainly palmitic acid, suggesting that it had been produced *de novo*.

Thus, both nutrient and non-nutrient secretagogues increase B-cell diacylglycerol, but of different compositions and by different routes. The different fatty acid species of the diacylglycerols produced by muscarinic agonists and glucose could offer a means of differential control of PKC activity by these stimuli. On the other hand, there are several potential metabolic pathways for diacylglycerol production, and it is unlikely that diacylglycerol is present in B-cells for the sole purpose of activating PKC. It is also reasonable to assume that the cellular location of diacylglycerol generation (perhaps in addition to its fatty acid composition) will determine whether it acts as a regulator of PKC activity. In this case, measurements of diacylglycerol generation in response to insulin secretagogues will provide only circumstantial evidence for a subsequent activation of PKC, and more direct evidence of PKC activation is required.

PKC activation in B-cells

Activation of protein kinases within cells is often assessed by measuring changes in the phosphorylation state of specific endogenous substrates of the kinase being studied, usually by measuring changes in the incorporation of ^{32}P into the proteins. Furthermore, activation of PKC is thought to be accompanied by its translocation, involving a redistribution of enzyme activity from a predominantly cytosolic form to a membrane-associated form (Kraft & Anderson, 1983). Measurements of the translocation of PKC and the subsequent phosphorylation of its target proteins may, therefore, offer an indication of the activation of PKC in response to specific stimuli.

Translocation of PKC

Several methods have been reported for quantifying the (re)-distribution of PKC activity between membrane-bound and soluble fractions. These include measurements of Ca^{2+}/phospholipid-dependent phosphorylating activity; measurements of binding sites for radiolabelled phorbol esters; and cytochemical localization of PKC within cells using specific antibodies or fluorescence-labelled probes.

To date, there have been few reported studies of PKC translocation in insulin-secreting tissues. Measurements of PKC activity in membrane and cytosolic fractions prepared from unstimulated rat islets have demonstrated that PKC activity was mainly associated with the cytosolic fraction with little (approx. 5%) activity in the membrane fraction (Persaud *et al.*, 1989*a*; Easom *et al.*, 1989). As in other tissues,

Fig. 2.   **PMA-dependent translocation of protein kinase C in intact and electrically permeabilized rat islets**

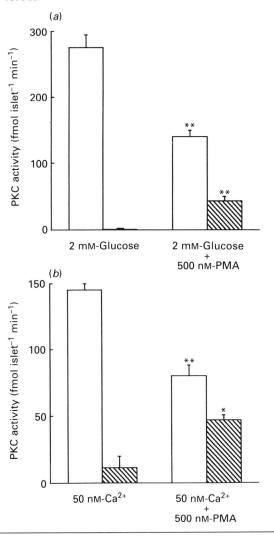

Groups of 500 rat islets were incubated in the presence of either 2 mM-glucose (intact islets; upper panel) or 50 nM-Ca²⁺ (permeabilized islets; lower panel) ±500 nM-PMA for 5 min, after which cytosol and membrane fractions were prepared by sonication and centrifugation (40 min, 30000 **g**, 4 °C). DE-52-purified PKC activity of membrane (open columns) and cytosolic (hatched columns) fractions was assayed by measuring the increased incorporation of ³²P from [γ³²P]ATP (final specific activity 0·3 Ci/mmol) into histone III-S. The phorbol esters or diacylglycerol analogues stimulated translocation of PKC in rat islets (Persaud *et al.*, 1989*a*; Easom *et al.*, 1989; Fig. 2), and in insulin-secreting tumour cells (Yamatani *et al.*, 1988; Thomas *et al.*, 1989).

There is some evidence that receptor-mediated insulin secreta-gogues which activate PLC induce PKC translocation. Thus, carbachol stimulated rapid redistribution of PKC activity in rat islets (Persaud *et al.*, 1989*a*) and RINr cells (Yamatani *et al.*, 1988) consistent with its reported effects on inositol phospholipid hydrolysis (Best *et al.*, 1984). Interestingly, carbachol could stimulate translocation of PKC activity in rat islets at both substimulatory (2 mM) and stimulatory (20 mM) glucose concentrations, although it has no effect on insulin release in the absence of a stimulatory concentration of glucose (Persaud *et al.*, 1989*b*). These observations suggest that activation and translocation of PKC may not be a sufficient stimulus for the initiation of insulin secretion.

The effects of nutrient secretagogues on PKC translocation are much less clear. Studies using normal islet tissue have been unable to demonstrate any effect of glucose on PKC distribution, although effects of phorbol esters and/or carbachol were detected in the same experiments (Persaud *et al.*, 1989*a*; Easom *et al.*, 1989). The observed lack of effect of glucose is unlikely to be owing to it having a different time-course of effect to those of carbachol or phorbol esters since further experiments failed to show an effect of glucose on PKC translocation after up to 10 min of stimulation (Fig. 3), by which time the second phase of the secretory response to glucose is well under way. Studies of nutrient-induced PKC translocation in insulin-secreting cell lines have produced conflicting results. The tumour cell line RINm5F is not sensitive to glucose, but responds to the glycolytic intermediate glyceraldehyde with an increased generation of diacylglycerol and enhanced insulin secretion (Wollheim *et al.*, 1988). It has been reported that, contrary to the effects of glucose in normal islets, glyceraldehyde produced a rapid redistribution of PKC activity in RINm5F cells (Thomas *et al.*, 1989). In contrast, there has been a preliminary report (Regazzi & Wollheim, 1988) that glucose did not cause translocation of PKC enzymic activity in a glucose-sensitive hamster insulinoma cell line (HIT). However, in another preliminary study using HIT cells, a combination of glucose and forskolin stimulated redistribution of cellular PKC as assessed by the distribution of the fluorescent phorbol ester, bodipy (Pershadsingh *et al.*, 1988). There are clearly differences

*increase in ^{32}P incorporation in the presence of phosphatidylserine (96 µg/ml) and diolein (6·4 µg/ml) was taken to reflect PKC activity in the sample. Bars show mean ± S.E.M., n = 4. *P < 0·005; **P < 0·01 versus activity in absence of PMA.*

between the responses of normal islets and insulin-secreting cell lines, perhaps as a consequence of the expression of different PKC subtypes in islets and the cell lines (Ito *et al.*, 1989; Onoda *et al.*, 1990).

Thus, the limited information available about PKC translocation in normal B-cells provides some evidence for an involvement of this

Fig. 3.   Effect of 20 mM-glucose on protein kinase C translocation in rat islets

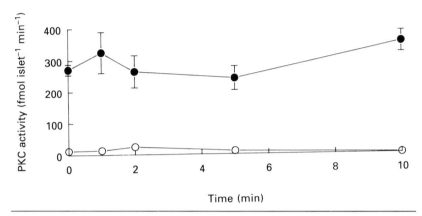

PKC activity was measured in cytosolic and membrane fractions prepared from rat islets (as described in legend to Fig. 2). Exposure to 20 mM-glucose for 1–10 min caused no significant translocation of PKC activity when compared with PKC distribution at 2 mM-glucose (t = 0). (○) shows membrane activity, (●) shows cytosolic activity. Data are means ± s.e.m., n = 3–6.

enzyme in cholinergic signalling mechanisms. Similarly, the effects of glyceraldehyde on PKC translocation in RINm5F cells suggests a role for PKC in nutrient-induced insulin secretion from these tumour cells. In contrast, the lack of effect of glucose on PKC translocation in normal B-cells might imply that PKC is not involved in glucose-stimulated insulin secretion. However, it is possible that glucose activates a minority isoform of PKC which does not translocate to membranes upon activation, or whose translocation is not detectable in present assays. For example, treatment of the human promyelocytic leukaemia cell line, U937, with PMA resulted in time-dependent translocation and down-regulation of PKCα, but under the same conditions, PKCβ remained cytosolic (Strulovici *et al.*, 1989). In addition, the ζ isoform of PKC, when expressed in COS-7 cells, was reported to be fully active in the absence of Ca^{2+} and diolein (or PMA) and did not bind [³H]phorbol 12,13-dibutyrate (Ono *et al.*, 1989). Application of methods which distinguish between the different isoforms of PKC within B-cells, either biochemically or by immunocytochemical means, will be required to resolve conclusively the effect of glucose on PKC redistribution. A further level of regulation of PKC function in B-cells may depend upon the membrane compartment to which translocation of enzyme occurs upon activation. At present, there is little information about the site of translocation of activated PKC in B-cells. It has been reported that PKC present in a cytosolic fraction of a rat insulinoma binds reversibly to insulin secretory granules in the presence of Ca^{2+}, and phosphorylates a granule membrane protein (Brocklehurst & Hutton, 1984; Hutton et al., 1984). In a more recent preliminary report using fluorescent probes for PKC in HIT cells, the enzyme was reported to translocate from cytoplasmic regions to the plasma membrane and nuclear regions (Pershadsingh et al., 1988). This movement of PKC to the nucleus may underlie the reported effects of PKC activators on the levels of proinsulin mRNA (Hammonds et al., 1987) and (pro)insulin synthesis in islets (Slee et al., 1989). Further studies of this kind, particularly those in which individual isoforms of PKC can be identified, should aid our understanding of the roles of PKC in cellular regulation.

Little is known about the fate of activated PKC in B-cells. In other tissues, activated PKC is a substrate for the Ca^{2+}-activated protease, calpain I (Melloni & Pontremoli, 1989), offering a mechanism for the termination of PKC actions within the cell. The extent and duration of PKC activation in B-cells may not, therefore, be entirely determined by the availability of activators of the enzyme, but also by the activity of termination mechanisms. In accordance with this, it has been reported that there is some loss of membrane-associated PKC activity in rat islets after the stimulation of PKC translocation by PMA (Persaud et al., 1989a). This loss of activity was reduced by using electrically permeabilized islets (Fig. 2, lower panel) in which the Ca^{2+} concentration was fixed at 50 nM and protease inhibitors were introduced into the intracellular space (Persaud et al., 1989a), suggesting the action of a Ca^{2+}-activated protease. If proteolysis of PKC proves to be an important terminator of its function(s) in B-cells, it is interesting to note that different isozymes of PKC are differentially susceptible to calpain-mediated proteolysis (Melloni & Pontremoli, 1989), suggesting that subtle means may exist for regulating the activity of PKC isoforms. The proteolytic degradation of activated PKC offers a potentially useful model for studies of the role of PKC in cellular function, as will be discussed in detail later in this review.

PKC-dependent protein phosphorylation

The molecular mechanism through which PKC modifies cellular function is assumed to be by phosphorylating, and thus modifying the function of, specific proteins (Nishizuka, 1984). Studies using intact islets (Dunlop & Larkins, 1986b), permeabilized cells (Colca et al., 1985; Jones et al., 1988), homogenates (Thams et al., 1984) and subcellular fractions (Hutton et al.,

Fig. 4.   **Effects of PMA and clomiphene on protein phosphorylation in intact rat islets**

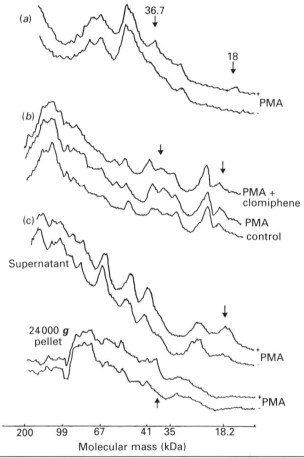

Islets were preincubated for 1 h with 100 μCi of [^{32}P]Pi (carrier free), 10 mM-glucose and BSA (2 mg/ml). Incubations were continued for a further 30 min in (a) the absence or presence of PMA (100 nM), or (b) in the presence of PMA, PMA and clomiphene (50 μM) or no additions. After incubation, islets were washed in Hepes-buffered Krebs medium. For the experiments in (a) and (b), the islets were then sonicated in 50 mM-sodium phosphate (pH 7)/50 mM-NaF/2 mM-EDTA/0·2 mM-EGTA/0·5 mM-PMSF/2 mM-benzamidine. For the experiment in (c), islets were homogenized in 0·3 M-sucrose/50 mM-sodium phosphate (pH 7)/1 mM-PMSF/2 mM-benzamidine and fractionated by differential centrifugation to yield 600 **g** and 24 000 **g** particulate fractions and a supernatant fraction. Samples were subjected to electrophoresis on SDS/16% acrylamide/0·5% AcrylAide gels.

1984; Hughes & Ashcroft, 1988) have indicated the presence of many protein substrates for PKC in insulin-secreting cells. To date, identification of these substrates has been almost exclusively by molecular mass determinations on polyacrylamide gel electrophoresis and it is quite possible that substrates which apparently differ slightly in molecular mass are in fact the same proteins.

In the absence of information about molecular identity or cellular function, it is difficult to determine which, if any, of the PKC-dependent phosphorylation events are important in the control of insulin secretion. However, there is circumstantial evidence that some PKC substrates may be involved in secretion, based on their cellular location or on combined measurements of protein phosphorylation and insulin secretion. For example, a protein of molecular mass 29 kDa was phosphorylated in response to PMA, and to glucose, in neonatal rat islets (Dunlop & Larkins, 1986b). This may be the protein which, in insulinoma cells, is associated with insulin secretory granules and phosphorylated by PKC activity, and which binds reversibly to secretory granules in the presence of Ca^{2+} (Brocklehurst & Hutton, 1984). The location of this substrate might indicate its involvement in the exocytotic process. A similar protein (28 kDa) has been reported to be a Ca^{2+}/phospholipid-dependent kinase substrate in mouse islets (Thams et $al.$, 1984). This protein was reportedly cytosolic in location (Thams et $al.$, 1984), but this might reflect a dissociation of membrane-bound PKC activity to the cytosol under the conditions used in this study (Hughes & Ashcroft, 1988). Another PKC substrate which has been studied in some detail is a 37 kDa protein located in the particulate fraction ($24\,000\,g$) of rat islets (Hughes & Ashcroft, 1988). PMA-induced ^{32}P incorporation into this substrate was reduced by clomiphene, a PKC inhibitor (Hughes & Ashcroft, 1988; Fig. 4). In parallel experiments, clomiphene totally inhibited PMA-induced insulin secretion, with little effect on glucose-stimulated secretion, suggesting that phosphorylation of the 37 kDa protein is required for PMA-induced, but not glucose-induced, secretory responses. Comparable results have recently been obtained in preliminary studies using PKC-depleted islets in which PMA-induced phosphorylation and secretory events were abolished without inhibition of glucose-stimulated insulin secretion (Jones et $al.$, 1989a).

It is clear that there are a number of different substrates for PKC within B-cells. Measuring phosphorylation of these particular substrates is

Dried gels were autoradiographed and the figure shows the densitometric traces of the autoradiograms (530 nm). The arrows indicate the position of the 36·7 kDa phosphopeptide. Reproduced from Hughes & Ashcroft, 1988 with permission.

a useful indication of the activation of PKC *in situ*, but until more positive identification of these substrates is available their importance in the secretory response to nutrient and non-nutrient secretagogues is uncertain. This is therefore an area which merits further investigation.

PKC-mediated insulin secretion

As might be expected, one of the most common approaches to studying the involvement of PKC in the secretory process has been the measurement of effects of PKC activators and inhibitors, or down-regulation of PKC, on insulin secretion. Each of these experimental approaches has certain disadvantages, but the information obtained from a combination of these methods may provide a consensus view about the role of this enzyme in B-cell signalling processes.

Exogenous PKC activators and insulin secretion

There have been numerous reports that agents which directly activate PKC, such as phorbol esters and diacylglycerol analogues, stimulate insulin secretion from both islets (Virji *et al.*, 1978; Malaisse *et al.*, 1980; Hubinont *et al.*, 1984; Jones *et al.*, 1985; Malaisse *et al.*, 1985) and insulin-secreting tumour cells (Hutton *et al.*, 1984; Yamatani *et al.*, 1988; Thomas *et al.*, 1989; Yada *et al.*, 1989; Hughes *et al.*, 1990). The mechanisms by which PKC activation stimulate insulin secretion have not been elucidated. Phorbol esters have been reported to have effects on ATP-sensitive K^+ channels in RINm5F cells (Wollheim *et al.*, 1988), and the influx (Malaisse *et al.*, 1985; Yada *et al.*, 1989) and extrusion (Berggren *et al.*, 1989) of Ca^{2+} in islets and in insulin-secreting tumour cells (see also Chapters 10 and 11 by Ashcroft *et al.* and Hellman *et al.*). Elevation of cytosolic Ca^{2+} concentrations by PKC activators can not entirely explain their effects on secretion since PMA can stimulate insulin release independently of increases in intracellular Ca^{2+} (Hughes *et al.*, 1989), and activation of PKC-stimulated secretion from Ca^{2+}-clamped permeabilized islets (Jones *et al.*, 1985; Tamagawa *et al.*, 1985). Studies using intact (Hughes *et al.*, 1987), digitonin-permeabilized (Tamagawa *et al.*, 1985) or electrically perme-abilized islets (Jones *et al.*, 1985), or RINm5F cells (Vallar *et al.*, 1987) indicate that one possible mode of action of PMA-activated PKC is to sensitize the secretory mechanism to Ca^{2+} (see Chapter 11 by Hellman *et al.*). However, other modes of action of PKC must exist since, in permeabilized cells, activation of PKC stimulated insulin secretion above the maximal Ca^{2+}-induced response (Jones *et al.*, 1985; Vallar *et al.*, 1987), and PMA stimulated secretion from Ca^{2+}-insensitive permeabilized islets, perhaps suggesting a Ca^{2+}-independent action (Jones *et al.*, 1989*b*).

Since pharmacological activation of PKC stimulates insulin secretion, it has been proposed that this activation is important in normal responses to physiological secretagogues. For example, the observation that PMA induced a slowly rising secretory response, rather like the second phase of glucose-induced insulin secretion, led to the suggestion that the activation of PKC is responsible for the second, maintained phase of insulin release (Zawalich *et al.*, 1983). However, similar profiles of secretion in response to a PKC activator, and to glucose, provide no causal evidence that activation of the enzyme is required for glucose-stimulated secretion. Determination of such a relationship requires measurement of secretory responses to physiological secretagogues under conditions in which PKC activity can be experimentally manipulated.

PKC inhibitors and insulin secretion

There have been a number of reports on the effects of PKC inhibitors on insulin secretion in response to nutrient and non-nutrient secretagogues, but the results of these studies are confusing and often conflicting. There have been several reports in which PKC inhibitors were shown to block glucose-induced insulin secretion, suggesting that activation of PKC is essential for secretory responses to glucose. For example, vitamin A and trifluoperazine inhibited both PKC activity and the insulin secretory response to glucose in rat islets (Harrison *et al.*, 1984). Furthermore, polyamines which are known to inhibit PKC activity *in vitro* (Kuo *et al.*, 1983), inhibited both phorbol ester- and glucose-induced secretion (Stutchfield *et al.*, 1986; Thams *et al.*, 1986; Maki *et al.*, 1989). However, these inhibitors are known to inhibit activity of kinases other than PKC (Garland *et al.*, 1987) and studies employing such agents should be interpreted with caution.

Other studies, using more selective PKC inhibitors, do not support an obligatory role for PKC activation in nutrient-induced secretion. Thus, H-7, clomiphene or staurosporine had little effect on glucose-induced secretion when used at concentrations which blocked secretion in response to phorbol esters (Malaisse & Sener, 1985; Hughes & Ashcroft, 1988; Niki *et al.*, 1988; Wolf *et al.*, 1990; Fig. 5), although there may be differences between species (Easom *et al.*, 1989; Wolf *et al.*, 1990). However, it is worth noting that H-7 inhibited carbachol-stimulated insulin release (Malaisse & Sener, 1985).

The variability of the effects of PKC inhibitors on glucose-induced secretion, probably owing to a lack of specificity of some of the inhibitors used (Garland *et al.*, 1987), makes it difficult to reach any firm conclusions from these studies alone about the involvement of PKC in nutrient-induced secretion. However, the observed reduction in carbachol-induced secretion in response to PKC inhibitors is consistent with the effects of carbachol on PKC translocation and further suggests a role for PKC in cholinergic signalling in B-cells.

Fig. 5.   Effects of staurosporine on PMA- and glucose-induced insulin secretion

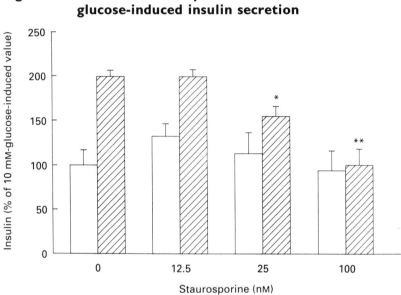

Rat islets were incubated (30 min, 37 °C) at (10 mM) glucose (open columns) or 10 mM-glucose plus 250 nM-PMA (hatched columns) and increasing concentrations of staurosporine. Staurosporine (25 nM and 100 nM) significantly inhibited PMA-induced insulin secretion but was without effect on glucose-stimulated secretion at any of the concentrations used. Bars show means ± s.e.m., n = 5–7. *P < 0·05; **P < 0·01 versus secretion in the absence of staurosporine.

Insulin secretion from PKC-depleted B-cells

An alternative experimental approach to using PKC inhibitors is to down-regulate cellular PKC by prolonged exposure to tumour-promoting phorbol esters (Rodriguez-Pena & Rozengurt, 1984; Gainer & Murray, 1985; Katakami *et al.*, 1986). This appears to be a relatively specific way of down-regulating PKC since loss of mouse fibroblast cellular functions after such treatment was restored by micro-injection of purified PKC into the cells (Pasti *et al.*, 1986). The first report using PKC-depleted rat islets showed that down-regulation of PKC activity did not inhibit glucose-induced insulin release (Hii *et al.*, 1987). These results have since been corroborated by other groups using rat (Metz, 1988) and *ob/ob* mouse

(Arkhammar *et al.*, 1989) islets. In contrast, down-regulation of PKC has been reported to cause a marked inhibition of the second phase of glucose-induced insulin release from perifused mouse islets, which was interpreted as supporting a role for PKC in the maintenance of the secretory response

Fig. 6.   Cholinergic stimulation of insulin secretion from perifused normal and PKC-depleted rat islets

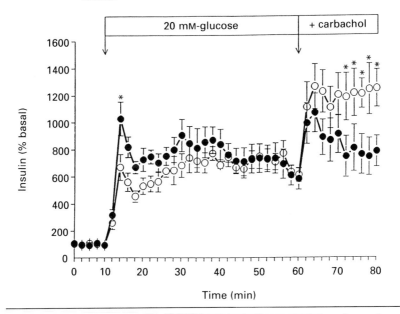

Groups of 50 islets were perifused with buffer containing 2 mM-glucose (0–10 min) and 20 mM-glucose thereafter. After 60 min the buffer (20 mM-glucose) was supplemented with 500 μM-carbachol as shown. Points (● = PMA-treated, ○ = 4αPMA-treated controls) show means ± s.e.m., n = 4. *P < 0·05 comparing PMA-treated versus 4αPMA-treated islets. Reproduced from Persaud et al., 1991 with permission.

to glucose (Thams *et al.*, 1990). However, comparable results were not obtained in similar studies on rat (Persaud *et al.*, 1990; Fig. 6) or *ob/ob* mouse (Arkhammar *et al.*, 1989) islets in which no inhibitory effects of PKC depletion were detected. The reasons for conflicting results from essentially similar studies are not immediately apparent, but the balance of evidence obtained from PKC-depleted islets suggests that the activation of PKC is not essential for either phase of nutrient-induced insulin secretion from normal B-cells. On the other hand, glyceraldehyde-induced insulin secretion from RINm5F cells was inhibited by PKC depletion (Thomas *et* al., 1989), in accordance with the effects of glyceraldehyde on diacylglycerol generation (Wollheim et al., 1988) and PKC translocation (Thomas et al., 1989) in these tumour cells. These observations suggest that there are real differences in the role of PKC in nutrient-stimulated insulin release from normal B-cells and tumour cells.

PKC-depleted B-cells have also been used to investigate the involvement of PKC in secretory responses to non-nutrient stimuli. Insulin secretion from rat islets in response to carbachol was significantly reduced following PKC down-regulation (Persaud et al., 1989b). Perifusion studies subsequently showed that the initial secretory response of PKC-depleted islets to carbachol was unaffected, but that secretion was not maintained (Persaud et al., 1990; Fig. 6). These results suggest that activation of PKC is not the only mechanism by which carbachol modulates insulin release (see also Chapter 14 by Berggren et al.). However, they are consistent with a model in which cholinergic agonists potentiate insulin secretion by a two-stage process (Persaud et al., 1989b). Initiation of cholinergic-induced secretion is mediated by enhancement of both glucose-stimulated B-cell membrane depolarization and consequent Ca^{2+} influx (Hermans et al., 1987; Henquin et al., 1988). Thereafter, maintenance of the insulin secretory response to carbachol is secondary to diacylglycerol-stimulated PKC activation. Different effects of PKC-depletion on cholinergic stimulation of insulin secretion from tumour B-cell lines have been reported. In HIT cells, as in islets, PKC down-regulation inhibited acetylcholine-stimulated insulin release (Hughes et al., 1990) whereas enhancement of carbachol (and vasopressin) secretory responses were reported in PKC-deficient RINm5F cells (Li et al., 1989).

PKC down-regulation appears to specifically block PKC-mediated pathways, without affecting responses to other protein kinases, providing a distinct advantage over the use of PKC inhibitors. Thus, both Ca^{2+}- and cyclic AMP-induced insulin release from electrically permeabilized islets were not reduced by PKC depletion (Hii et al., 1987). The normal responses of PKC-depleted islets to Ca^{2+} implies that Ca^{2+}-induced insulin secretion is not mediated by changes in PKC activity. This in turn suggests that the reported inhibition of Ca^{2+}-stimulated secretion by a polyamine PKC inhibitor (Stutchfield et al., 1986) can not be accounted for by inhibition of PKC, and probably reflects a lack of specificity of the PKC inhibitor (Jones & Howell, 1988).

The major disadvantage of using PKC-down-regulated cells is that prolonged phorbol ester treatment does not totally deplete cellular PKC (Persaud et al., 1989b; Hughes et al., 1990), which is to be expected as PKC synthesis is unaffected although its degradation is promoted (Young et al., 1987). Studies in which partial responsiveness to PKC activators is retained, as has been reported in HIT cells (Hughes et al., 1990) require careful interpretation. However, in most studies, phosphorylating (Jones *et al.*, 1989*a*) and secretory (Hii *et al.*, 1987; Metz, 1988; Persaud *et al.*, 1989*b*; Arkhammar *et al.*, 1989) responses to PMA are abolished in PKC-depleted islets and, as the B-cell PKC isoforms so far identified are PMA-sensitive (Ito *et al.*, 1989; Onoda *et al.*, 1990), it is reasonable to conclude that the residual PKC can not be activated.

PKC-depleted B-cells will undoubtedly be of use in further studies on the physiological functions of PKC. Presently available data using this experimental model provide convincing evidence that PKC is involved in the secretory response to cholinergic neurotransmitters.

PKC-dependent priming of insulin secretion

Previous exposure of B-cells to a stimulatory concentration of glucose potentiates subsequent secretory responses to glucose and other secretagogues (Grodsky *et al.*, 1969; Grill *et al.*, 1978; Nesher *et al.*, 1988; Chalmers & Sharp, 1989). Although the mechanisms underlying this priming effect are not well understood, there is some evidence that PKC may be involved in this complex response. For example, the insulin secretory response to glucose could be primed by prior exposure to PMA (Virji *et al.*, 1978; Niki *et al.*, 1988), although it is uncertain if this was merely a consequence of the inability to completely wash out the lipophilic phorbol ester. However, time-dependent potentiation of insulin secretion by glucose was reduced by the presence of the PKC inhibitor H-7 during the initial (priming) exposure to glucose, but not by the weaker PKC inhibitor HA-1004 (Niki *et al.*, 1988). It is worth noting that the presence of H-7 did not inhibit the secretory response to glucose during the priming period, consistent with an involvement of PKC in the priming mechanism rather than in the glucose-induced secretory response. Agents which stimulate inositol phospholipid hydrolysis are also reported to induce time-dependent potentiations of insulin secretion (Zawalich *et al.*, 1987*b*; Zawalich, 1988) but at present there is little direct evidence supporting a role of PKC in this process. It is obvious that further studies are required to establish the mechanism of, and the involvement of PKC in, priming events in B-cells.

Conclusions

There is a growing body of evidence to support a role for PKC in stimulus–secretion coupling in pancreatic B-cells. Evidence obtained from the application of diverse experimental approaches, which intervene at different parts of the stimulus–secretion pathway, allows us to draw some cautious conclusions about the involvement of PKC in insulin secretory responses to nutrient secretagogues, exemplified by glucose, and to non-nutrient secretagogues, exemplified by cholinergic agonists.

PKC and nutrient-induced insulin secretion

Nutrient secretagogues can elevate cellular production of the PKC activator diacylglycerol, albeit predominantly by *de novo* synthesis rather than by activation of PLC. It is, however, uncertain whether this diacylglycerol activates PKC since measurements of PKC translocation, thought to reflect activation of the enzyme, provide no firm evidence that glucose stimulates PKC redistribution. Studies using PKC inhibitors have produced conflicting results, which may be owing to the questionable specificity of some of the inhibitors used, and which are therefore difficult to interpret in isolation. Perhaps more convincing are the results of studies using PKC-depleted B-cells, most of which have not reported a diminution of secretory responses to glucose. On balance, the available experimental evidence suggests that the activation of PKC is not essential for the initiation and maintenance of nutrient-induced secretion from normal B-cells. This conclusion is not valid for the RIN insulinoma cell line, in which the available evidence suggests that the activation of PKC plays a pivotal role in the secretory response to the nutrient secretagogue, glyceraldehyde.

PKC and non-nutrient-induced insulin secretion

Cholinergic agonists, and some other receptor-mediated secretagogues, enhance cellular generation of diacylglycerol in B-cells through a G-protein-mediated activation of PLC. Cholinergic agonists also promote the translocation of PKC, suggesting that the diacylglycerol produced does activate the enzyme. Inhibitors of PKC have been shown to inhibit the cholinergic potentiation of insulin secretion, and secretory responses of PKC-depleted B-cells to cholinergic agonists are reduced, supporting an involvement of PKC in the secretory process. Thus, the available experimental evidence consistently suggests that PKC activation is required for the expression of a normal secretory response to cholinergic neurotransmitters.

Future studies

Our current understanding of PKC function in B-cells is based mainly on measurements of total PKC activity, and on the use of pharmacological activators, or of often-unsatisfactory inhibitors of PKC. At present we known little about the expression of PKC isozymes in B-cells, and nothing about whether different isozymes subserve separate functions within the cell. Further work is required to characterize the expression of PKC isoforms in B-cells, and their activation in response to physiological secretagogues. It will be important to determine whether different isoforms translocate to different membrane compartments upon activation, the location of these membrane compartments, and the routes and kinetics of PKC inactivation in these compartments. We still know little about the mechanisms through which PKC influences the secretory process. Further studies are required on the location, the identity and, most importantly, the function of the protein substrates for PKC isoforms within B-cells.

Finally, although not within the scope of the present article, PKC is likely to have important functions in the control of (pro)insulin synthesis and in B-cell differentiation and growth. These are potentially exciting areas for future research, since they may have important implications for the development of new strategies for the treatment of diabetes mellitus.

Financial support from the British Diabetic Association and the Medical Research Council (M.R.C.) is gratefully acknowledged. S. J. P. is a Wolfson Foundation Research Fellow, P. M. J. is a M.R.C. Senior Research Fellow (Non-Clinical).

References

Arkhammar, P., Nilsson, T., Welsh, M., Welsh, N. & Berggren, P.-O. (1989) Effects of protein kinase C activation on the regulation of the stimulus-secretion coupling in pancreatic β-cells. Biochem. J. **264**, 207–215

Arkhammar, P., Hallberg, A., Kindmark, H., Nilsson, T., Rorsman, P. & Berggren, P.-O. (1990) Extracellular ATP increases cytoplasmic free Ca^{2+} concentration in clonal insulin-producing RINm5F cells. A mechanism involving direct interaction with both release and refilling of the inositol 1,4,5-trisphosphate-sensitive Ca^{2+} pool. Biochem. J. **265**, 203–211

Berggren, P.-O., Arkhammar, P. & Nilsson, T. (1989) Activation of protein kinase C assists insulin producing cells in recovery from raised cytoplasmic Ca^{2+} by stimulating Ca^{2+} efflux. Biochem. Biophys. Res. Commun. **165**, 416–421

Berridge, M. J. (1985) The molecular basis of communication within the cell. Sci. Am. **253**, 124–134

Best, L. & Malaisse, W. J. (1983) Stimulation of phosphoinositide breakdown in rat pancreatic islets by glucose and carbamylcholine. Biochem. Biophys. Res. Commun. **116**, 9–16

Best, L., Dunlop, M. & Malaisse, W. J. (1984) Phospholipid metabolism in pancreatic islets. Experientia **40**, 1085–1091

Biden, T. J., Peter-Riesch, B., Schlegel, W. & Wollheim, C. B. (1987) Ca^{2+}-mediated generation of inositol 1,4,5-trisphosphate and inositol 1,3,4,5-tetrakisphosphate in pancreatic islets. Studies with K^+, glucose, and carbamylcholine. J. Biol. Chem. **262**, 3567–3571

Blachier, F. & Malaisse, W. J. (1988) Effect of exogenous ATP upon inositol phosphate production, cationic fluxes and insulin release in pancreatic islet cells. Biochim. Biophys. Acta **970**, 222–229

Blachier, F., Segura, M. C. & Malaisse, W. J. (1987) Unresponsiveness of phospholipase C to the regulatory proteins Ns and Ni in pancreatic islets. Res. Commun. Chem. Pathol. Pharmacol. **55**, 335–355

Brocklehurst, K. W. & Hutton, J. C. (1984) Involvement of protein kinase C in the phosphorylation of an insulin-granule membrane protein. Biochem. J. **220**, 283–290

Chalmers, J. A. & Sharp, G. W. G. (1989) The importance of Ca^{2+} for glucose-induced priming in pancreatic islets. Biochim. Biophys. Acta **1011**, 46–51

Colca, J. R., Wolf, B. A., Comens, P. G. & McDaniel, M. L. (1985) Protein phosphorylation in permeabilized pancreatic islet cells. Biochem. J. **228**, 529–536

Dunlop, M. E. & Larkins, R. G. (1984) Activity of endogenous phospholipase C and phospholipase A_2 in glucose stimulated pancreatic islets. Biochem. Biophys. Res. Commun. **120**, 820–827

Dunlop, M. E. & Larkins, R. G. (1986a) Muscarinic-agonist and guanine nucleotide activation of polyphosphoinositide phosphodiesterase in isolated islet-cell membranes. Biochem. J. **240**, 731–737

Dunlop, M. E. & Larkins, R. G. (1986*b*) Glucose-induced phospholipid-dependent protein phosphorylation in neonatal rat islets. Arch. Biochem. Biophys. **248**, 562–569

Dunlop, M. E. & Malaisse, W. J. (1986) Phosphoinositide phosphorylation and hydrolysis in pancreatic islet cell membrane. Arch. Biochem. Biophys. **244**, 421–429

Easom, R. A., Hughes, J. H., Landt, M., Wolf, B. A., Turk, J. & McDaniel, M. L. (1989) Comparison of effects of phorbol esters and glucose on protein kinase C activation and insulin secretion in pancreatic islets. Biochem. J. **264**, 27–33

Eberhard, D. A. & Holz, R. W. (1988) Intracellular Ca^{2+} activates phospholipase C. Trends Neurosci. **11**, 517–520

Gainer, H. St. C. & Murray, A. W. (1985) Diacylglycerol inhibits gap junctional communication in cultured epidermal cells: evidence for a role of protein kinase C. Biochem. Biophys. Res. Commun. **126**, 1109–1113

Garland, L. G., Bonser, R. W. & Thompson, N. T. (1987) Protein kinase C inhibitors are not selective. Trends Pharmacol. Sci. **8**, 334

Grill, V., Adamson, U. & Cerasi, E. (1978) Immediate and time-dependent effects of glucose on insulin release from rat pancreatic tissue. Evidence for different mechanism of action. J. Clin. Invest. **61**, 1034–1043

Grodsky, G. M., Curry, D., Landahl, H. & Bennett, L. L. (1969) Further studies on the dynamic aspects of insulin release *in vitro* with evidence for a two compartmental storage system. Acta Diabetol. Lat. **6**, 554–579

Hammonds, P., Schofield, P. N., Ashcroft, S. J. H., Sutton, R. & Gray, D. W. R. (1987) Regulation and specificity of glucose-stimulated insulin gene expression in human islets of Langerhans. FEBS Lett. **223**, 131–137

Harrison, D. E., Ashcroft, S. J. H., Christie, M. R. & Lord, J. M. (1984) Protein phosphorylation in the pancreatic B-cell. Experientia **40**, 1075–1084

Hedeskov, C. J. (1980) Mechanism of glucose-induced insulin secretion. Physiol. Rev. **60**, 442–509

Henquin, J. C. & Nenquin, M. (1988) The muscarinic receptor subtype in mouse pancreatic B-cells. FEBS Lett. **236**, 89–92

Henquin, J. C., Garcia, M. C., Bozem, M., Hermans, M. P. & Nenquin, M. (1988) Muscarinic control of pancreatic B-cell function involves sodium-dependent depolarization and calcium influx. Endocrinology **122**, 2134–2142

Hermans, M. P., Schmeer, W. & Henquin, J. C. (1987) Modulation of the effect of acetylcholine on insulin release by the membrane potential of B-cells. Endocrinology **120**, 1765–1773

Hii, C. S. T., Jones, P. M., Persaud, S. J. & Howell, S. L. (1987) A re-assessment of the role of protein kinase C in glucose-stimulated insulin secretion. Biochem. J. **246**, 489–493

Holian, O., Kumar, R. & Nyhus, L. M. (1989) Fatty acyl esters potentiate fatty acid induced activation of protein kinase C. Biochem. Biophys. Res. Commun. **160**, 1110–1116

Hubinont, C. J., Best, L. & Malaisse, W. J. (1984) Activation of protein kinase C by a tumor-promoting phorbol ester in pancreatic islets. FEBS Lett. **170**, 247–253

Hughes, S. J. & Ashcroft, S. J. H. (1988) Effects of a phorbol ester and clomiphene on protein phosphorylation and insulin secretion in rat pancreatic islets. Biochem. J. **249**, 825–830

Hughes, S. J., Christie, M. R. & Ashcroft, S. J. H. (1987) Potentiators of insulin secretion modulate Ca^{2+} sensitivity in rat pancreatic islets. Mol. Cell Endocrinol. **50**, 231–236

Hughes, S. J., Chalk, J. G. & Ashcroft, S. J. H. (1989) Effect of secretagogues on cytosolic free Ca^{2+} and insulin release at different extracellular Ca^{2+} concentrations in the hamster clonal β-cell line HIT-T15. Mol. Cell Endocrinol. **65**, 35–41

Hughes, S. J., Chalk, J. G. & Ashcroft, S. J. H. (1990) The role of cytosolic free Ca^{2+} and protein kinase C in acetylcholine-induced insulin release in the clonal β-cell line, HIT-T15. Biochem. J. **267**, 227–232

Hutton, J. C., Peshavaria, M. & Brocklehurst, K. W. (1984) Phorbol ester stimulation of insulin release and secretory-granule protein phosphorylation in a transplantable rat insulinoma. Biochem. J. **224**, 483–490

Ito, A., Saito, N., Taniguchi, H., Chiba, T., Kikkawa, U., Saitoh, Y. & Tanaka, C. (1989) Localization of βII subspecies of protein kinase C in β-cells. Diabetes **38**, 1005–1011

Jones, P. M. & Howell, S. L. (1988) Role of protein kinase C in the regulation of insulin secretion. Biochem. Soc. Trans. **17**, 61–63

Jones, P. M., Stutchfield, J. & Howell, S. L. (1985) Effects of Ca^{2+} and a phorbol ester on insulin secretion from islets of Langerhans permeabilised by high-voltage discharge. FEBS Lett. **191**, 102–106

Jones, P. M., Salmon, D. M. W. & Howell, S. L. (1988) Protein phosphorylation in electrically permeabilized islets of Langerhans. Effects of Ca^{2+}, cyclic AMP, a phorbol ester and noradrenaline. Biochem. J. **254**, 397–403

Jones, P. M., Persaud, S. J. & Howell, S. L. (1989a) Protein kinase C-mediated protein phosphorylation in electrically permeabilised islets of Langerhans. Diabetologia **32**, 500A (Abstract)

Jones, P. M., Persaud, S. J. & Howell, S. L. (1989b) Effects of cAMP and a phorbol ester on insulin secretion from Ca^{2+}-insensitive, electrically permeabilised islets of Langerhans. Diabetic Med. **6**, (Suppl. 1), A20–A21 (Abstract)

Katakami, Y., Nakao, Y., Matsui, T., Koizumi, T., Kaibuchi, K., Takai, Y. & Fujita, T. (1986) Possible involvement of protein kinase C in interleukin-1 production by mouse peritoneal macrophages. Biochem. Biophys. Res. Commun. **135**, 355–362

Kraft, A. S. & Anderson, W. B. (1983) Phorbol esters increase the amount of Ca^{2+}, phospholipid-dependent protein kinase associated with plasma membrane. Nature (London) **301**, 621–623

Kuo, J. F., Raynor, R. L., Mazzei, G. J., Schatzman, R. C., Turner, R. S. & Kem, W. R. (1983) Cobra polypeptide cytotoxin I and marine worm polypeptide cytotoxin A-IV are potent and selective inhibitors of phospholipid-sensitive Ca^{2+}-dependent protein kinase. FEBS Lett. **153**, 183–186

Landt, M., Wolf, B. A., Turk, J., Easom, R. A. & McDaniel, M. L. (1988) Arachidonic acid stimulates protein kinase C from pancreatic islet cytosol. Diabetes **37**, 41A (Abstract)

Li, G. D., Pralong, W., Regazzi, R., Ullrich, S. & Wollheim, C. B. (1989) Potentiation of neurohormone-stimulated insulin secretion in protein kinase C-deficient cells. Diabetologia **32**, 510A (Abstract)

Lord, J. M. & Ashcroft, S. J. H. (1984) Identification and characterization of Ca^{2+}-phospholipid-dependent protein kinase in rat islets and hamster β-cells. Biochem. J. **219**, 547–551

Maki, Y., Nunoi, K., Kikuchi, M. & Fukishima, Y. (1989) Effects of low-concentration polymyxin B on insulin secretion induced by 12-O-tetradecanoyl-phorbol-13-acetate (TPA), glucose, or tolbutamide from the isolated perfused rat pancreas. Metabolism **38**, 334–337

Malaisse, W. J. & Sener, A. (1985) Inhibition by 1-(5-isoquinoline-sulfonyl)-2-methylpiperazine (H-7) of protein kinase C activity and insulin release in pancreatic islets. IRCS Med. Sci. **13**, 1239–1240

Malaisse, W. J., Sener, A., Herchuelz, A., Carpinelli, A. R., Poloczek, P., Winand, J. & Castagna, M. (1980) Insulinotropic effect of the tumor promoter 12-O-tetradecanoylphorbol-13-acetate in rat pancreatic islets. Cancer Res. **40**, 3827–3831

Malaisse, W. J., Dunlop, M. E., Mathias, P. C. F., Malaisse-Lagae, F. & Sener, A. (1985) Stimulation of protein kinase C and insulin release by 1-oleoyl-2-acetyl-glycerol. Eur. J. Biochem. **149**, 23–27

Melloni, E. & Pontremoli, S. (1989) The calpains. Trends Neurosci. **12**, 438–444

Metz, S. A. (1988) Is protein kinase C required for physiologic insulin release? Diabetes **37**, 3–7

Monaco, M. E., Levy, B. L. & Richardson, S. B. (1988) Synergism between vasopressin and phorbol esters in stimulation of insulin secretion and phosphatidylcholine metabolism in RIN insulinoma cells. Biochem. Biophys. Res. Commun. **151**, 717–724

Nesher, R., Praiss, M. & Cerasi, E. (1988) Immediate and time-dependent effects of glucose on insulin release: differential calcium requirements. Acta Endocrinol. **117**, 409–416

Niki, I., Tamagawa, T., Niki, H., Niki, A., Koide, T. & Sakamoto, N. (1988) Possible involvement of diacylglycerol-activated, Ca^{2+}-dependent protein kinase in glucose memory of the rat pancreatic B-cell. Acta Endocrinol. **118**, 204–208

Nishizuka, Y. (1984) The role of protein kinase C in cell surface signal transduction and tumour promotion. Nature (London) **308**, 693–698

Nishizuka, Y. (1988) The molecular heterogeneity of protein kinase C and its implications for cellular regulation. Nature (London) **334**, 661–665

Ono, Y., Fujii, T., Ogita, K., Kikkawa, U., Igarashi, K. & Nishizuka, Y. (1989) Protein kinase C ζ subspecies from rat brain: its structure, expression, and properties. Proc. Natl. Acad. Sci. U.S.A. **86**, 3099–3103

Onoda, K., Hagiwara, M., Hachiya, T., Usuda, N., Nagata, T. & Hidaka, H. (1990) Different expression of protein kinase C isozymes in pancreatic islet cells. Endocrinology **126**, 1235–1240

Parker, P. J., Kour, G., Marais, R. M., Mitchell, F., Pears, C., Schaap, D., Stabel, S. & Webster, C. (1989) Protein kinase C—a family affair. Mol. Cell Endocrinol. **65**, 1–11

Pasti, G., Lacal, J. C., Warren, B. S., Aaronson, S. A. & Blumberg, P. H. (1986) Loss of mouse fibroblast cell response to phorbol esters restored by microinjected protein kinase C. Nature (London) **324**, 375–377

Persaud, S. J., Jones, P. M., Sugden, D. & Howell, S. L. (1989*a*) Translocation of protein kinase C in rat islets of Langerhans: effects of a phorbol ester, carbachol and glucose. FEBS Lett. **245**, 80–84

Persaud, S. J., Jones, P. M., Sugden, D. & Howell, S. L. (1989*b*) The role of protein kinase C in cholinergic stimulation of insulin secretion from rat islets of Langerhans. Biochem. J. **264**, 753–758

Persaud, S. J., Jones, P. M. & Howell, S. L. (1991) Activation of protein kinase C is essential for sustained insulin secretion in response to cholinergic stimulation. Biochim. Biophys. Acta **1091**, 120–122

Pershadsingh, H. A., Gold, G., Haugland, R. P., McOuiston, S. A. & Fulwyler, M. J. (1988) Probing the subcellular distribution of protein kinase C in insulin-secreting cells using a novel fluorescent phorbol ester. J. Cell Biol. **107**, 52A (Abstract)

Peter-Riesch, B., Fathi, M., Schlegel, W. & Wollheim, C. B. (1988) Glucose and carbachol generate 1,2-diacylglycerols by different mechanisms in pancreatic islets. J. Clin. Invest. **81**, 1154–1161

Regazzi, R. & Wollheim, C. B. (1988) Subcellular distribution of protein kinase C during stimulation of insulin secretion. Diabetologia **31**, 534A (Abstract)

Rodriguez-Pena, A. & Rozengurt, E. (1984) Disappearance of Ca^{2+}-sensitive, phospholipid-dependent protein kinase activity in phorbol ester-treated 3T3 cells. Biochem. Biophys. Res. Commun. **120**, 1053–1059

Schaap, D., Parker, P. J., Bristol, A., Kriz, R. & Knopf, J. (1989) Unique substrate specificity and regulatory properties of PKC-ε: a rationale for diversity. FEBS Lett. **243**, 351–357

Seifert, R., Schächtele, C., Rosenthal, W. & Schultz, G. (1988) Activation of protein kinase C by *cis*- and *trans*-fatty acids and its potentiation by diacylglycerol. Biochem. Biophys. Res. Commun. **154**, 20–26

Slee, D. J., Jones, P. M. & Howell, S. L. (1989) The role of protein kinase C in proinsulin biosynthesis. Diabetologia **32**, 542A (Abstract)

Strulovici, B., Daniel-Issakani, S., Oto, E., Nestor, J., Jr, Chan, H. & Tsou, A. P. (1989) Activation of distinct protein kinase C isozymes by phorbol esters: correlation with induction of interleukin 1β gene expression. Biochemistry **28**, 3569–3576

Stutchfield, J., Jones, P. M. & Howell, S. L. (1986) The effects of polymyxin B, a protein kinase C inhibitor, on insulin secretion from intact and permeabilized islets of Langerhans. Biochem. Biophys. Res. Commun. **136**, 1001–1006

Tamagawa, T., Niki, H. & Niki, A. (1985) Insulin release independent of a rise in cytosolic free Ca^{2+} by forskolin and phorbol ester. FEBS Lett. **183**, 430–432

Tanigawa, K., Kuzuya, H., Imura, H., Taniguchi, H., Baba, S., Takai, Y. & Nishizuka, Y. (1982) Calcium-activated, phospholipid-dependent protein kinase in rat pancreas islets of Langerhans. FEBS Lett. **138**, 183–186

Thams, P., Capito, K. & Hedeskov, C. J. (1984) Endogenous substrate proteins for Ca^{2+}-calmodulin-dependent, Ca^{2+}-phospholipid-dependent and cyclic AMP-dependent protein kinases in mouse pancreatic islets. Biochem. J. **221**, 247–253

Thams, P., Capito, K. & Hedeskov, C. J. (1986) An inhibitory role for polyamines in protein kinase C activation and insulin secretion in mouse pancreatic islets. Biochem. J. **237**, 131–138

Thams, P., Capito, K., Hedeskov, C. J. & Kofod, H. (1990) Phorbol-ester-induced down-regulation of protein kinase C in mouse pancreatic islets. Potentiation of phase 1 and inhibition of phase 2 of glucose-induced insulin secretion. Biochem. J. **265**, 777–787

Thomas, T. P., Ellis, T. R. & Pek, S. B. (1989) Insulin release in RINm5F cells and glyceraldehyde activation of protein kinase C. Diabetes **38**, 1371–1376

Vallar, L., Biden, T. J. & Wollheim, C. B. (1987) Guanine nucleotides induce Ca^{2+}-independent insulin secretion from permeabilized RINm5F cells. J. Biol. Chem. **262**, 5049–5056

Virji, M. A. G., Steffes, M. W. & Estensen, R. D. (1978) Phorbol myristate acetate: effect of a tumour promoter on insulin release from isolated rat islets of Langerhans. Endocrinology **102**, 706–711

Wolf, B. A., Florholmen, J., Turk, J. & McDaniel, M. L. (1988) Studies of the Ca^{2+} requirements for glucose- and carbachol-induced augmentation of inositol trisphosphate and inositol tetrakisphosphate accumulation in digitonin-permeabilized islets. Evidence for a glucose recognition site in insulin secretion. J. Biol. Chem. **263**, 3565–3575

Wolf, B. A., Easom, R. A., Hughes, J. H., McDaniel, M. L. & Turk, J. (1989) Secretagogue-induced diacylglycerol accumulation in isolated pancreatic islets. Mass spectrometric characterization of the fatty acyl content indicates multiple mechanisms of generation. Biochemistry **28**, 4291–4301

Wolf, B. A., Easom, R. A., McDaniel, M. L. & Turk, J. (1990) Diacylglycerol synthesis *de novo* from glucose by pancreatic islets isolated from rats and humans. J. Clin. Invest. **85**, 482–490

Wollheim, C. B. & Biden, T. J. (1986) Signal transduction in insulin secretion: comparison between fuel stimuli and receptor agonists. Ann. N.Y. Acad. Sci. **488**, 317–333

Wollheim, C. B. & Sharp, G. W. G. (1981) Regulation of insulin release by calcium. Physiol. Rev. **61**, 914–973

Wollheim, C. B., Ullrich, S., Meda, P. & Vallar, L. (1987) Regulation of exocytosis in electrically permeabilized insulin-secreting cells. Evidence for Ca^{2+} dependent and independent secretion. Biosci. Rep. **7**, 443–454

Wollheim, C. B., Dunne, M. J., Peter-Riesch, B., Bruzzone, R., Pozzan, T. & Petersen, O. H. (1988) Activators of protein kinase C depolarize insulin-secreting cells by closing K^+ channels. EMBO J. **7**, 2443–2449

Yada, T., Russo, L. L. & Sharp, G. W. G. (1989) Phorbol ester-stimulated insulin secretion by RINm5F insulinoma cells is linked with membrane depolarization and an increase in cytosolic free Ca^{2+} concentration. J. Biol. Chem. **264**, 2455–2462

Yamaguchi, T., Kanatsuka, A., Makino, H., Ohsawa, H. & Yoshida, S. (1989) Dual mechanism involved in the hydrolysis of polyphosphoinositides in rat pancreatic islets. Endocrinology **124**, 1870–1874

Yamatani, T., Chiba, T., Kadowaki, S., Hishikawa, R., Yamaguchi, A., Inui, T., Fujita, T. & Kawazu, S. (1988) Dual action of protein kinase C activation in the regulation of insulin release by muscarinic agonist from rat insulinoma cell line (RINr). Endocrinology **122**, 2826–2832

Young, S., Parker, P. J., Ullrich, A. & Stabel, S. (1987) Down-regulation of protein kinase C is due to an increased rate of degradation. Biochem. J. **244**, 775–779

Zawalich, W. S. (1988) Time-dependent potentiation of insulin release induced by alpha-ketoisocaproate and leucine in rats: possible involvement of phosphoinositide hydrolysis. Diabetologia **31**, 435–442

Zawalich, W. S., Brown, C. & Rasmussen, H. (1983) Insulin secretion: combined effects of phorbol ester and A23187. Biochem. Biophys. Res. Commun. **117**, 448–455

Zawalich, W., Takuwa, N., Takuwa, Y., Diaz, V. A. & Rasmussen, H. (1987a) Interactions of cholecystokinin and glucose in rat pancreatic islets. Diabetes **36**, 426–433

Zawalich, W. S., Diaz, V. A. & Zawalich, K. C. (1987b) Cholecystokinin-induced alterations in beta cell sensitivity: duration, specificity and involvement of phosphoinositide metabolism. Diabetes **36**, 1420–1424

13

Cyclic AMP, protein phosphorylation and insulin secretion

Stephen J. Hughes* and Stephen J. H. Ashcroft

Nuffield Department of Clinical Biochemistry, John Radcliffe Hospital, Headington, Oxford, OX3 9DU, U.K.

Introduction

It now seems clear that the role of cyclic AMP in stimulus-secretion coupling is not a primary one and most authors agree that protein kinase A activation potentiates but does not initiate insulin secretion (Sharp, 1979; Malaisse & Malaisse-Lagae, 1984; Henquin & Meissner, 1984a; Hughes et al., 1987; Prentki & Matschinsky, 1987). It is also well established that glucose evokes a modest increase in B-cell cyclic AMP although the contribution of this increase to nutrient-induced secretion has not been quantified.

The development of techniques to monitor intracellular events, particularly the use of Ca^{2+}-sensitive dyes and the patch-clamp technique have increased our understanding of the mechanism(s) by which protein kinases amplify insulin secretion. Increasingly, it has become apparent that the cyclic AMP-mediated system interacts with other signal-transduction pathways in the B-cell (Prentki & Matschinsky, 1987; see also Chapters 10 and 11 by Ashcroft et al. and Hellman et al.). The requirement to monitor intracellular events in intact cell systems has increased our reliance on cell permeable agents which specifically elevate or depress cyclic AMP levels. The use of isobutylmethylxanthine (IBMX) to elevate cyclic AMP has largely been replaced by the adenylate cyclase activator, forskolin because of the non-specific actions of the phosphodiesterase inhibitor (Henquin & Meissner, 1984b). However, it has recently become apparent that the diterpene may also exert cyclic AMP-independent actions on cellular metabolism (Laurenza et al., 1989) and on ionic events in the B-cell (Zunkler et al., 1988). This emphasizes the need for caution when interpreting data from intact-cell studies.

Despite these considerations, it is clear that considerable progress has been made in our understanding of the mechanism(s) by which protein

* Present address: Department of Physiology and Biophysics, St Mary's Hospital Medical School, Norfolk Place, London, W2 1PG, U.K.

kinase A activation potentiates nutrient-stimulated insulin release. In the present review we shall concentrate on three main areas of research: (1) the mechanism by which glucose promotes an increase in cyclic AMP in the B-cell; (2) the role of protein kinase A activation on ionic fluxes and changes in cytosolic free Ca^{2+} ($[Ca^{2+}]_i$) in the B-cell, and (3) the nature and role of protein kinase A substrates in insulin secretion and biosynthesis.

Nutrient-induced cyclic AMP accumulation

It has long been established (Grill & Cerasi, 1973) and confirmed by many laboratories (Charles *et al.*, 1975; Sharp, 1979; Christie & Ashcroft, 1984; Thams *et al.*, 1988) that glucose causes a modest but significant increase in islet cyclic AMP which in turn may contribute to or amplify glucose-induced insulin release. Thus basal cyclic AMP formation may be a requirement for maintenance of the normal secretory response to glucose (Malaisse & Malaisse-Lagae, 1984). Evidence which supports such a concept has been provided from studies in which purified B-cells have been isolated from rat islets by autofluorescence-activated cell sorting (Schuit & Pipeleers, 1985; Pipeleers *et al.*, 1985). In these studies, the poor secretory responses of purified B-cells or purified aggregated B-cells could only be improved by elevation of the depressed cyclic AMP concentrations found in the cell preparations. This concept has recently been contested in a preliminary report by Persaud *et al.* (1990) who reported that both basal and glucose-stimulated insulin release were not significantly altered in rat islets pre-incubated with [R-isomer]-cyclic 3′,5′-monophosphorothioate (Rp-cyclic AMPS), a competitive antagonist of cyclic AMP which binds to and prevents activation of protein kinase A. The mechanism by which glucose promotes the modest increase in cyclic AMP in islet B-cells remains unclear although several possible mechanisms have been postulated.

Ca^{2+}–calmodulin activation of adenylcyclase and phosphodiesterase

Both activation of adenylate cyclase and phosphodiesterase by Ca^{2+}–calmodulin have been shown in homogenates and subcellular fractions of islets. The properties and Ca^{2+} dependencies of the islet enzymes have been reviewed in detail elsewhere (Sharp, 1979; Malaisse & Malaisse-Lagae, 1984) and will not be dealt with here. The observation that glucose did not promote an increase in B-cell cyclic AMP in the absence of extracellular Ca^{2+} (Charles *et al.*, 1975; Sharp, 1979) led to the suggestion that the increase in $[Ca^{2+}]_i$ induced by glucose, in conjunction with calmodulin, activated adenylate cylase and elevated cyclic AMP levels. The possibility arises that changes in $[Ca^{2+}]_i$ regulate cyclic AMP levels by co-ordinate control of adenylate cyclase and phosphodiesterase (Prentki & Matschinsky, 1987). However, Christie & Ashcroft (1984) reported that the calmodulin inhibitor trifluoperazine had no effect on cyclic AMP levels in intact islets incubated for 60 min with stimulatory concentrations of glucose or IBMX. At variance with this, Krausz et al. (1987) have shown that trifluoperazine does inhibit the glucose-stimulated increase of cyclic AMP in rat islets, an effect which was associated primarily with an initial increase in cyclic AMP after 5 min. The different time courses of these studies may thus account for this discrepancy.

Evidence has also been provided that the Ca^{2+}-dependent breakdown of cyclic AMP is of importance in the B-cell. In the clonal B-cell line, HIT-T15, verapamil significantly augmented the increase in cyclic AMP induced by forskolin. It was argued that verapamil blocked Ca^{2+} entry and thus prevented the activation of the Ca^{2+}-dependent phosphodiesterase (Rajan et al., 1989). In RINm5F cells, permeabilized by high-voltage electric discharge, the increase in cyclic AMP concentration evoked by forskolin was inhibited by Ca^{2+} in a dose-dependent manner (Ullrich & Wollheim, 1988). This inhibition was overcome by IBMX which supported the hypothesis that Ca^{2+} activated the phosphodiesterase (Ullrich & Wollheim, 1988).

Role of protein kinase C and endogenous islet glucagon

As mentioned above, Pipeleers & colleagues reported that islet B-cells purified by cell-sorting techniques exhibited poor secretory responses which they argued resulted from reduced levels of cyclic AMP (Schuit & Pipeleers, 1985; Pipeleers et al., 1985). These authors further suggested that endogenously released glucagon and/or other hormones within the intact islet were necessary to facilitate glucose-induced increases in cyclic AMP (see also Chapter 3 by Marks et al.). The evidence to support such a concept was as follows: (1) in purified B-cells, or aggregates of purified B-cells, glucose failed to produce any increase in cyclic AMP in contrast to the action of the hexose in intact islets; (2) nutrient-induced cyclic AMP responses were recovered in aggregates of B-cells plus A-cells or in aggregates of B-cells supplemented with glucagon, and (3) the ability of purified and re-aggregated B-cell preparations to secrete insulin in response to glucose paralleled their ability to produce cyclic AMP. Additional support for involvement of endogenously released glucagon comes from studies using pure B-cell populations such as clonal B-cell lines. Thus, glucose or glyceraldehyde failed to stimulate any increase in cyclic AMP formation in hamster insulin-secretory tumour (HIT-T15) cells (Hill et al., 1987) or radiation-induced transplantable insulinoma (RINm5F) cells (Wollheim et al., 1984) respectively. At variance with this, Ashcroft *et al.* (1986) and Hammonds *et al.* (1987*a*) reported that glucose promoted modest but significant increases in cyclic AMP levels in HIT-T15 cells similar in magnitude to those observed in glucose-stimulated islets.

More recently Thams *et al.* (1988) have proposed that glucose potentiates cyclic AMP formation in the presence of endogenous glucagon in mouse islets, by a mechanism which involves activation of protein kinase C. They reported that both glucose and phorbol 12-myristate 13-acetate (PMA) stimulated cyclic AMP formation (in the presence of IBMX) to a similar extent and that the actions of both secretagogues were inhibited by removing extracellular Ca^{2+}, or by incubation with anti-glucagon antibody, or by depletion of protein kinase C activity following 24 h culture of the islets with phorbol ester. In addition, the neuro-transmitter analogue carbachol which is thought to activate protein kinase C in the B-cell was also shown to stimulate cyclic AMP formation. Furthermore, pretreatment of islets with phorbol ester for 10 min significantly increased glucagon-stimulated adenylate cyclase activity in islet particulate fractions albeit by a modest 15%. This interesting paper raises the possibility that protein kinase C activation by phorbol esters stimulates adenylate cyclase activity, possibly by phosphorylation of the α-subunit of the regulatory GTP-binding protein Ni in pancreatic B-cells as in lymphoma cells (Katada *et al.*, 1985). In support of this hypothesis a modest increase in cyclic AMP formation in response to stimulation by phorbol esters has previously been observed in mouse islets (Henquin *et al.*, 1987; Bozem *et al.*, 1987). However, it could be argued that this results from phorbol-ester-induced glucagon secretion from pancreatic A-cells which in turn stimulates B-cell adenylate cyclase. The phorbol ester PMA has been shown to be a potent stimulator of glucagon secretion in pancreatic islets (Hii *et al.*, 1986). A second debatable point in this proposal concerns the apparent neurotransmitter-induced formation of cyclic AMP in islets. Previous studies have failed to show any significant increase in cyclic AMP formation by cholinergic agents in rat islets (Wollheim *et al.*, 1980), mouse islets (Gagerman *et al.*, 1978) or human insulinoma cells (Chiba *et al.*, 1987). Finally, it has not been conclusively demonstrated that glucose activates protein kinase C in pancreatic islets. Indeed, recent evidence does not favour a role for protein kinase C in glucose-stimulated insulin release (Hii *et al.*, 1987; Persaud *et al.*, 1989; Easom *et al.*, 1989; Hughes *et al.*, 1990; Wolf *et al.*, 1990). This topic is discussed in detail in Chapter 12 by Persaud *et al.*

Despite the comprehensive nature of the evidence produced by Pipeleers and coworkers (Schuit & Pipeleers, 1985; Pipeleers *et al.*, 1985) and by Thams *et al.* (1988), it is difficult to envisage how an increase in the extracellular glucose concentration, which reduces glucagon secretion from pancreatic A-cells (Gerich *et al.*, 1976), would then allow the hormone to facilitate glucose-induced formation of cyclic AMP in pancreatic B-cells, *in vivo*. These authors discuss the role of endogenously released glucagon in such a process and suggest that *in vivo* some other endogenously released or circulating hormone may be important, although to date no specific factor has been identified. Further details of the actions of islet peptides and entero-insular hormones are given in Chapter 14 by Berggren *et al*.

Cyclic AMP, ion fluxes and cytosolic free Ca^{2+}, $[Ca^{2+}]_i$

The mechanism by which increasing the cellular cyclic AMP concentration potentiates insulin release appears to be complex. This may involve an increase in $[Ca^{2+}]_i$ and/or a modification to the secretory machinery which allows it to operate more efficiently (i.e. in general terms, a sensitization process). Since the development of techniques to study changes in intracellular Ca^{2+} in intact cells the debate as to whether increasing cyclic AMP promotes an increase in $[Ca^{2+}]_i$ or not has been resolved. Agents which elevate cyclic AMP levels do increase $[Ca^{2+}]_i$, however, the contribution of this increase to the secretory process is not clear and other mechanisms may be primarily important.

Early studies by Henquin & Meissner (1984a) and Eddlestone *et al.* (1985) showed that both forskolin and IBMX stimulated electrical activity and ion fluxes in mouse pancreatic islets. Forskolin potentiated glucose-stimulated electrical activity and insulin release in the former study but was without effect on the B-cell membrane potential at sub-stimulatory glucose concentrations. The increases in $^{45}Ca^{2+}$ and $^{86}Rb^+$ efflux induced by forskolin in the presence of glucose were prevented by verapamil or by reducing the medium Ca^{2+} concentration. In addition forskolin potentiated glucose-stimulated $^{45}Ca^{2+}$ accumulation into mouse islets in static incubations. Henquin and coworkers confirmed that the secretory nature of forskolin was that of a potentiator using the sulphonylurea, tolbutamide, as a primary stimulus and further suggested that the B-cell must already be depolarized in order that protein kinase A activation may stimulate ionic and secretory events (Henquin *et al.*, 1987). In contrast, Eddlestone *et al.* (1985) showed that forskolin stimulated biphasic electrical activity in mouse pancreatic islets even at sub-stimulatory glucose concentrations, which they suggested indicated that elevation of cellular cyclic AMP primarily reduced K^+ permeability by phosphorylation of a Ca^{2+}-sensitive K^+ channel. Alternatively, Henquin & Meissner (1984a) argued that activation of cyclic AMP-dependent protein kinases altered the gating of Ca^{2+} channels in the B-cell plasma membrane.

Henquin and colleagues (Henquin & Meissner, 1984a; Henquin *et al.*, 1987) did not discount the possibility that elevation of cellular cyclic

AMP triggered other secretory mechanisms in addition to stimulating electrical activity, since the changes in ion fluxes and electrical activity induced by forskolin did not appear to be of sufficient magnitude to account for the potentiation of insulin release produced. Indeed, these authors also showed that agents which elevate B-cell cyclic AMP could modulate insulin secretion without affecting ion fluxes (Henquin & Meissner, 1986). The role of other secretory mechanisms which operate independently from changes in ion fluxes has been examined in studies in which pancreatic islets or RINm5F cells have been permeabilized by treatment with either digitonin or high voltage discharge (Jones et al., 1986; Tamagawa et al., 1985; Vallar et al., 1987). In these B-cell preparations, in which intracellular Ca^{2+} concentrations were held constant by inclusion of EGTA, the addition of cyclic AMP, IBMX or forskolin augmented Ca^{2+}-induced insulin release. In addition, these agents promoted a shift in the dose–response curve of the Ca^{2+}-induced insulin release to lower Ca^{2+} concentrations. These studies suggested that protein kinase A stimulates insulin release, at least in part, by sensitizing the secretory mechanism to Ca^{2+}. Studies in which forskolin modestly stimulated insulin release in the presence of glucose but absence of extracellular Ca^{2+} also support this concept (Malaisse et al., 1984). Indeed, such a hypothesis has been proposed by workers in many laboratories (Hellman et al., 1979; Wollheim et al., 1984; Malaisse et al., 1984; Phang et al., 1984; Rorsman & Abrahamsson, 1985; Hughes et al., 1987; Hill et al., 1987; see also Chapter 11 by Hellman et al. in this book).

Additional evidence for such a hypothesis was provided by early studies in which changes in $[Ca^{2+}]_i$ were measured in B-cells preloaded with the Ca^{2+}-binding fluorescent indicator quin 2 and stimulated by agents which promote insulin secretion via the cyclic AMP-dependent pathway. Thus forskolin, theophylline and dibutyryl cyclic AMP in dispersed pancreatic islet cells from genetically obese (ob/ob) mice (Rorsman & Abrahamsson, 1985), forskolin in RINm5F cells (Wollheim et al., 1984) and forskolin and IBMX in the clonal B-cell line HIT-T15 (Hill et al., 1987) all failed to produce any change in $[Ca^{2+}]_i$ in the presence or absence of glucose (glyceraldehyde in the case of RINm5F cells). However, subsequent studies using the more sensitive Ca^{2+} probe fura 2 produced data which contradicted these observations. In dispersed rat islet B-cells preloaded with fura 2, Sussman et al. (1987) showed that both forskolin and dibutyryl cyclic AMP promoted an increase in $[Ca^{2+}]_i$ which was comparable in magnitude with that produced by stimulatory concentrations of glucose. This is a finding that is not entirely consistent with the role of forskolin as a potentiator of insulin release. Unfortunately, no secretory data concerning this point was presented in this study. Interestingly, data from experiments in which the extracellular medium was depleted of Ca^{2+} indicated that the source of the cyclic AMP-induced

$[Ca^{2+}]_i$ signal was largely intracellular in origin. Studies using fura 2-loaded HIT cells revealed that a spectrum of agents (forskolin, glucagon, IBMX and isoproterenol) which increase cellular cyclic AMP levels all produced modest incremental increases (30–40 nM) in $[Ca^{2+}]_i$ which could be prevented by verapamil or by reducing the Ca^{2+} concentration of the medium (Prentki *et al.*, 1987; Rajan *et al.*, 1989). These authors concluded that protein kinase A activation potentiates insulin release at least in part by increasing $[Ca^{2+}]_i$ via Ca^{2+} influx through voltage-sensitive Ca^{2+} channels. However, an observation that was difficult to understand in these studies was the apparent dependence of the effects of forskolin and IBMX on glucose, particularly since glucose itself failed to produce any increase in $[Ca^{2+}]_i$ in these HIT cells. In our laboratory, glucose stimulates an increase in $[Ca^{2+}]_i$ in parallel with insulin release in HIT cells (Hughes & Ashcroft, 1988), a finding confirmed elsewhere (Meats *et al.*, 1989).

In studies in our laboratory we have attempted to resolve the controversy concerning the role of ion fluxes, $[Ca^{2+}]_i$ and Ca^{2+} sensitivity in cyclic AMP-mediated insulin secretion. We had previously shown that forskolin lowered the dependence of glucose-stimulated insulin release on extracellular Ca^{2+} in intact rat islets (Hughes *et al.*, 1987). To test whether this effect reflected an altered dose response of insulin release to intracellular Ca^{2+}, we compared the changes in insulin release and $[Ca^{2+}]_i$ in HIT cells in the presence and absence of glucose and forskolin at different extracellular Ca^{2+} concentrations (Hughes *et al.*, 1989). In HIT cells, forskolin evoked the same reduction in the dependence of glucose-stimulated insulin release on extracellular Ca^{2+} as observed in rat islets (Hughes *et al.*, 1987). Using an approach in which we increased the extracellular Ca^{2+} concentration in quin 2-loaded HIT cell suspensions in a stepwise manner, we examined the effect of secretagogues on $[Ca^{2+}]_i$. Although inclusion of forskolin produced modest increases in $[Ca^{2+}]_i$ (40–50 nM) only in the presence of glucose, two observations lead us to conclude that this was not the primary mechanism by which forskolin potentiated glucose-induced insulin release. First, forskolin potentiated glucose-induced insulin release at low (0·1 mM) extracellular Ca^{2+} concentrations where no apparent change in $[Ca^{2+}]_i$ was observed. Secondly, the magnitude of the increase in insulin release induced by forskolin was far greater than the modest changes produced in steady-state levels of $[Ca^{2+}]_i$ by the secretagogue. We concluded that stimulation of cyclic AMP-dependent protein kinase to potentiate insulin release involved primarily sensitization of the secretory mechanism to Ca^{2+} or operation of the secretory mechanism more efficiently (Hughes *et al.*, 1989). It is possible that the apparently modest increases in $[Ca^{2+}]_i$ in cell suspensions induced by protein kinase A activators do not represent, or rather oversimplify, the true changes that occur within the B-cell. Protein kinase A activation may elevate $[Ca^{2+}]_i$ only at a specific location in the B-cell (such as adjacent to the plasma membrane) which results in a pronounced effect on the secretory machinery. In such a situation, the fluorescence signal so produced would mask the true significance of the change in $[Ca^{2+}]_i$.

Nevertheless, the operation of a sensitizing effect may underlie the mechanism by which, in general, all potentiators stimulate insulin secretion. Indeed, insulin secretion need not necessarily by preceded by an increase in $[Ca^{2+}]_i$ (Prentki & Matschinsky, 1987) and considerable evidence exists to support the view that potentiation of insulin release by activation of protein kinase C involves sensitization of the secretory mechanism to Ca^{2+} (Hughes et al., 1989). The mechanism by which protein kinases interact with and sensitize the secretory machinery to Ca^{2+} at the molecular level remains unclear.

Cyclic AMP-dependent protein phosphorylation in the B-cell

It is not unreasonable to assume that stimulation of insulin release by agents which elevate cyclic AMP in the B-cell results from phosphorylation by protein kinase A of specific protein substrate(s) involved in the secretory process. Attempts to clearly identify such protein substrates, however, have to date been unsuccessful. The criteria suggested by Harrison et al. (1984) that must be satisfied to implicate protein phosphorylation in the regulation of insulin release are: (1) the particular protein kinase must be present in the B-cell; (2) endogenous substrate(s) and phosphatase(s) for the substrate(s) must also be present; (3) changes in insulin secretion should be paralleled by changes in the phosphorylation state of the endogenous substrate(s) in the intact B-cell, and (4) the role of the endogenous substrate(s) in the secretory machinery and the consequences of the phosphorylation must be established.

In the case of protein kinase A activation, these criteria are far from being satisfied not least because the precise nature of the primary secretory machinery is at present unresolved. Although the presence of protein kinase A has been clearly demonstrated in the B-cell (Montague & Howell, 1972; Sugden et al., 1979), the diverse nature and modifications to experimental protocols adopted by investigators to study the role of cyclic AMP-mediated protein phosphorylation in insulin secretion has hampered identification and confirmation of the key substrate(s) involved.

The protocols adopted by investigators fall into three main categories. Protein phosphorylation in subcellular fractions or homogenates is carried out by following the incorporation of ^{32}P from $[\gamma^{-32}P]$-ATP into endogenous protein substrates in the presence of cyclic AMP or protein kinase A activators (experimental protocol A in Table 1). This

Table I. Substrates for protein kinase A in the B-cell

Stimulus	Phospho-peptide (kDa)	Experimental protocol; [Ref.]	Subcellular location	Possible identity
Gluc, dBcAMP, cAMP	138	A[4]; C[4]	Homogenate	—
Gluc, dBcAMP, cAMP	90–93	B[9]; C[4]	Homogenate	—
IBMX, cAMP	70–80	A[3,6]; B[9]	Cytosol	—
cAMP, C-sub	60	A[6,8]	Cytosol	R-subunit
IBMX, cAMP, C-sub	54–57	A[3,7,8]; C[4]	Cytosol	—
Gluc, dBcAMP, cAMP, IBMX, C-sub	53–54	A[3,4,8]; C[4]	Particulate	—
cAMP, C-sub	43–45	A[4,8]	Particulate, nuclear	—
Gluc, dBcAMP, cAMP, IBMX	35	A[4]; C[4,5]	Cytosol	—
Forsk, C-sub	32	A[8]; C[8]	Particulate	Ribosomal protein
Forsk, cAMP, C-sub	30	A[8]; B[9]; C[8]	Cytosol	—
Gluc, BrcAMP, cAMP, dBcAMP, C-sub	27–28	A[4,6]; C[1,4]	Particulate, cytosol	Ribosomal S6
Gluc, dBcAMP, BrcAMP, IBMX, Forsk	25	A[8]; B[9]; C[5,8]	Cytosol	—
Forsk, cAMP, C-sub	23–24	A[4,6,8]; C[8]	Particulate, cytosol	Secretory granule protein
Gluc, IBMX, dBcAMP, C-sub	18	A[8]; C[5]	Cytosol	—
Gluc	16	C[2]	Cytosol	—
Forsk, Gluc, IBMX, dBcAMP, C-sub	15	A[8]; C[5,8]	Nuclear	Histone H_3

Experimental protocols used (see text): A, [^{32}P]ATP to phosphorylate homogenates or subcellular fractions; B, [^{32}P]ATP to phosphorylate permeabilized islets; C, [^{32}P]P$_i$ preincubated with intact islets. References: [1] Schubart et al. (1977); [2] Schubart, (1982); [3] Harrison & Ashcroft, (1982); [4] Suzuki et al. (1983); [5] Christie & Ashcroft, (1984); [6] Thams et al. (1984); [7] Kowluru & MacDonald (1984); [8] Christie & Ashcroft, (1985); [9] Jones et al. (1988). Abbreviations used: Gluc, glucagon; Forsk, forskolin; dBcAMP, dibutyryl cyclic AMP; C-sub, catalytic subunit; BrcAMP, 8-bromo cyclic AMP.

partially satisfies the second criteria listed above. Protein phosphorylation in intact islets is carried out by pre-incubating islets with ^{32}P$_i$ to label the intracellular ATP pool followed by stimulation to elevate intracellular cyclic AMP. Phosphoproteins may then be analysed in subcellular fractions after various times of incubation (experimental protocol C in Table 1). This protocol satisfies the third criteria listed above. Care must be taken with this protocol to avoid alteration to the specific activity of the $[\gamma\text{-}^{32}\text{P}]$-ATP within the islets which could produce artefactual results (Harrison *et al.*, 1984). Finally, development of techniques to permeabilize cells allowing uptake of low molecular mass molecules (such as $[\gamma\text{-}^{32}\text{P}]$-ATP) also makes it possible to study phosphorylation in intact islets (experimental protocol B in Table 1). One advantage with this protocol is that the short incubation period with radio-isotope may reduce non-specific background labelling of proteins.

Substrates for protein kinase A in the B-cell

Studies with subcellular fractions or intact islets have identified a range of peptides which are phosphorylated by protein kinase A. Several of the phosphopeptides have been identified by more than one laboratory using different stimuli and the various protocols outlined above. These phosphopeptides are listed in Table 1. We assume that for each peptide listed, the different studies have identified the same phosphopeptide rather than distinct phosphopeptides of similar molecular masses. We have previously reviewed this literature in detail (Harrison *et al.*, 1984) and so in the present review we will only highlight key findings and attempt to bring this subject up to date.

Christie & Ashcroft (1985) prelabelled intact islets for 1 h with $^{32}\text{P}_i$ and stimulated with forskolin to elevate intracellular cyclic AMP. Subcellular fractionation revealed the presence of four major phosphorylated peptides; cytosolic phosphopeptides of molecular masses 30 kDa and 25 kDa and particulate phosphopeptides of molecular masses 32 kDa and 23 kDa. A 25 kDa cytosolic phosphopeptide and a 32 kDa particulate phosphopeptide had been reported previously in other studies (see Table 1). Christie & Ashcroft (1985) confirmed this peptide labelling pattern by incubating subcellular fractions with $[\gamma\text{-}^{32}\text{P}]$ATP and purified catalytic subunit from protein kinase A, followed by fractionation using Percoll-density-gradient centrifugation.

The 23 kDa particulate phosphopeptide was located in the secretory granule fraction whereas the 32 kDa particulate phosphopeptide appeared to be ribosomal in origin. These authors also confirmed the slow cyclic AMP-dependent phosphorylation of a histone H3-like protein seen previously (Christie & Ashcroft, 1984). More recently, Jones *et al.* (1988) confirmed the cyclic AMP-dependent phosphorylation of several proteins previously reported (molecular masses 25, 30, 57, 76 and 90 kDa, see Table 1) using $[\gamma\text{-}^{32}\text{P}]$ATP to label rat islets permeabilized by high-voltage discharge. The nature and subcellular locations of these protein kinase A substrates were not further characterized in this study. Indeed, no study to date has attempted to correlate the phosphorylation status of protein kinase A substrates with insulin release so that key peptide substrates involved in the secretory process can be identified. It seems unlikely, however, that the cyclic AMP-dependent phosphorylations of the histone H_3-like protein and the 32 kDa ribosomal protein identified by Christie & Ashcroft (1984, 1985) in the rat islets, or the 28 kDa ribosomal S6 protein previously identified by Schubart *et al.* (1977) in hamster islet tumours are involved in the insulin secretory process. Finally, Pek *et al.* (1990) have recently shown that protein kinase A does not mediate the phosphorylation of a 65 kDa peptide induced by 3-phosphoglycerate in cytosolic extracts of rat pancreatic islets.

Possible identities of protein kinase A substrates in the B-cell

The mechanism by which protein kinase A activation augments glucose-stimulated insulin release may involve potentiation of glucose-induced Ca^{2+} influx (see above). Early studies on the effects of protein kinase A activators on ion fluxes in mouse pancreatic islets indicated that either the Ca^{2+}-sensitive K^+ channel (Eddlestone *et al.*, 1985) or voltage-sensitive Ca^{2+} channels (Henquin & Meissner, 1984*a*) were potential targets for cyclic AMP-dependent protein phosphorylation. Evidence from recent patch-clamp studies on RINm5F cells (De Weille *et al.*, 1989) suggest that protein kinase A does not directly modulate ATP-sensitive K^+-channel activity in the B-cell although the dihydropyridine-sensitive L-type Ca^{2+} channel remains a likely candidate for regulation (see also Chapter 10 by Ashcroft *et al.*). In the heart, β-adrenergic stimulation enhances Ca^{2+} entry by a mechanism involving reversible cyclic AMP-dependent phosphorylation of such channels (Osterrieder *et al.*, 1982; Tsien *et al.*, 1986). A preliminary report suggests that protein kinase A may also regulate L-type Ca^{2+}-channel activity in the pancreatic B-cell (Smith *et al.* 1990). This Ca^{2+} channel has been extensively characterized in skeletal muscle (for review see Campbell *et al.*, 1988) and is thought to be comprised of four subunits (α_1 α_2 β γ) of molecular masses 175, 170, 52 and 32 kDa. The 52 kDa β-subunit is thought to be a regulatory unit and to undergo cyclic AMP-dependent phosphorylation within the Ca^{2+}-channel complex. It is of interest to note that a peptide of similar molecular mass which undergoes cyclic AMP-dependent phosphorylation has been identified in the post-nuclear particulate fraction of pancreatic islets (molecular mass = 53–54 kDa, see Table 1). Further characterization is necessary, however, to clearly establish the identity of this phosphopeptide.

An additional mechanism that has been postulated to explain the potentiation of insulin release by protein kinase A activation (see above) and by protein kinase C activation, involves sensitization of the secretory mechanism to Ca^{2+} (see Chapters 11 and 14 by Hellman *et al.* and Berggren *et al.*). This presumably would involve increasing the efficiency of operation of a particular Ca^{2+}-sensitive stage in the secretory machinery by reversible phosphorylation. Attempts to identify a common substrate for protein kinase A and protein kinase C that interact with the main secretory pathway have not proved successful. Using $[\gamma-^{32}P]ATP$ to label islet subcellular fractions, Thams $et\ al.$ (1984) showed that two phosphopeptides (molecular mass = 72 kDa and 28 kDa) were potentially common substrates for protein kinase A and protein kinase C in the cytosolic fraction of mouse islets. The relationship of these phosphopeptides to the main secretory pathway was not clear and these authors did not examine cyclic AMP-dependent phosphorylation or protein kinase C-mediated phosphorylation in islet particulate fractions. Using a different approach, Jones $et\ al.$ (1988) examined the additive effects of protein kinase activators (cyclic AMP or phorbol ester) and Ca^{2+} on protein phosphorylation in permeabilized rat islets. Although at least one phosphopeptide was apparently a common substrate for the protein kinases (molecular mass = 76 kDa) these authors found that the protein kinase activators did not significantly augment Ca^{2+}-dependent protein phosphorylation at stimulatory Ca^{2+} concentrations (Jones $et\ al.$, 1988).

Cyclic AMP, protein phosphorylation and the regulation of insulin biosynthesis

Considerable progress has been made in our understanding of the mechanism by which insulin biosynthesis is regulated (see Chapter 4 by Guest & Hutton). It has long been established that glucose stimulates $[^3H]$leucine incorporation into insulin in isolated islets (Howell & Taylor, 1966) and it appears that nutrient regulation occurs at both transcriptional and translational levels (Welsh, 1989). Early studies indicated that glucose did not significantly increase pre-proinsulin mRNA levels but rather stimulated the translocation of mRNA from the cytosol to membrane-bound polysomes in rat islets (Itoh & Okamoto, 1980). More recently, glucose has been shown to increase pre-proinsulin mRNA levels in rat and human islets and in HIT-T15 cells (Nielsen $et\ al.$, 1985; Welsh $et\ al.$, 1985; Hammonds $et\ al.$, 1987a,b).

There is also evidence for a role for cyclic AMP in transcriptional regulation of the insulin gene since forskolin significantly potentiated the stimulation, by glucose, on pre-proinsulin mRNA levels in human islets and HIT cells (Hammonds $et\ al.$, 1987a,b). Philippe & Missotten (1990) have analysed the promoter region of the rat insulin I gene and have identified a cyclic AMP-responsive element (CRE) through which cyclic AMP may regulate gene transcription. The CRE was located between positions -177 and -184 in the promoter region of the insulin I gene and was found to have the sequence TGACGTCC, a sequence which closely matched CRE's previously defined in rat and human genes (Roesler $et\ al.$, 1988). Philippe & Missotten (1990) further identified a 43 kDa nuclear protein in HIT cells which bound specifically to the CRE. In rat brain, a similar CRE binding protein (CREB) has been shown to regulate somatostatin gene expression. Phosphorylation of the CREB in response to cyclic AMP elevation was necessary to induce transcription in PC 12 cells (Montminy & Bilezikjian 1987; Yamamoto *et al.*, 1988). The phosphorylation of a 45 kDa peptide in the nuclear fraction of rat islets by exogenous catalytic subunit of protein kinase A (Christie & Ashcroft, 1985; see Table 1) may correspond to a similar regulatory process.

Conclusions

It has become clear that the role of cyclic AMP and protein kinase A activation in insulin secretion is complex involving the interaction of

Fig. I.   Functions of protein kinase A in the B-cell

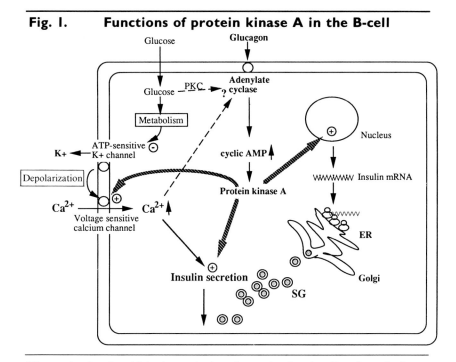

The mechanism by which glucose is thought to stimulate insulin release is shown on the left of the diagram. Glucose metabolism causes membrane depolarization via closure of ATP-dependent K⁺ channels which in turn opens voltage-sensitive calcium channels. Activation of protein kinase A augments insulin release by interaction at two postulated stages of the secretory pathway and stimulates insulin biosynthesis by phosphorylation of nuclear proteins as indicated by the shaded arrows. Abbreviations: ER, endoplasmic reticulum; SG, secretory granules; PKC, protein kinase C.

several signal transduction pathways. In Fig. 1, we summarize the postulated primary sites of action of protein kinase A in the B-cell. Protein kinase A may stimulate insulin release by acting at two distinct locations on the secretory pathway; by phosphorylation of the voltage-sensitive Ca^{2+} channel gating Ca^{2+} entry into the B-cell, and by phosphorylation of some as yet unspecified component of the secretory machinery which allows it to function more efficiently. Clearly, the nature of the protein kinase A substrates involved in these regulatory steps need to be characterized in future studies.

Evidence has also been provided that glucose may increase cyclic AMP in the B-cell by a mechanism involving protein kinase C activation (Thams *et al.*, 1988). In addition, elevation of cyclic AMP and protein kinase A activation may exert an inhibitory effect on inositol phospholipid turnover and the protein kinase C pathway (Zawalich *et al.*, 1988; Zawalich & Zawalich, 1990).

Considerable evidence has also been produced to implicate protein kinase A in the regulation of transcription of the insulin gene. It will be interesting to determine whether glucose promotes insulin gene expression in the B-cell by activation of the cyclic AMP–protein kinase A pathway.

Studies from our own laboratory have been supported by grants from the M.R.C., the British Diabetic Association and the Medical Research Fund. We thank Geraldine Bates for typing the manuscript.

References

Ashcroft, S. J. H., Hammonds, P. & Harrison, D. E. (1986) Insulin secretory responses of a clonal cell line of simian virus 40-transformed B cells. Diabetologia **29**, 727–733

Bozem, M., Nenquin, M. & Henquin, J. C. (1987) The ionic, electrical and secretory effects of protein kinase C activation in mouse pancreatic B-cells: Studies with a phorbol ester. Endocrinology **121**, 1025–1033

Campbell, K. P., Leung, A. T. & Sharp, A. H. (1988) The biochemistry and molecular biology of the dihydropyridine-sensitive calcium channel. Trends Neurosci. **11**, 425–430

Charles, M. A., Lawecki, J., Picett, R. & Grodsky, G. M. (1975) Insulin secretion. Interrelationships of glucose, cAMP and calcium. J. Biol. Chem. **250**, 6134–6140

Chiba, T., Yamatani, T., Kadowaki, S., Yamaguchi, A., Inui, T., Saito, Y. & Fujita, T. (1987) Glucose stimulates insulin release without altering cyclic AMP production or inositolphospholipid turnover in freshly obtained human insulinoma cells. Biochem. Biophys. Res. Commun. **145**, 263–268

Christie, M. C. & Ashcroft, S. J. H. (1984) Cyclic AMP-dependent protein phosphorylation and insulin secretion in intact islets of Langerhans. Biochem. J. **218**, 87–99

Christie, M. C. & Ashcroft, S. J. H. (1985) Substrates for cyclic AMP-dependent protein kinase in islets of Langerhans. Biochem. J. **227**, 727–736

De Weille, J. R., Schmid-Antomarchi, H., Fosset, M. & Lazdunski, M. (1989) Regulation of ATP-sensitive K^+ channels in insulinoma cells: Activation by somatostatin and protein kinase C and the role of cAMP. Proc. Natl. Acad. Sci. U.S.A. **86**, 2971–2975

Easom, R. A., Hughes, J. H., Landt, M., Wolf, B. A., Turk, J. & McDaniel, M. L. (1989) Comparison of effects of phorbol esters and glucose on protein kinase C activation and insulin secretion in pancreatic islets. Biochem. J. **264**, 27–33

Eddlestone, G. T., Oldham, S. B., Lipson, L. G., Premdas, F. H. & Beigelman, P. M. (1985)

Electrical activity, cAMP concentration and insulin release in mouse islets of Langerhans. Am. J. Physiol. **248**, C145–153

Gagerman, E., Idahl, L.-A., Meissner, H. P. & Taljedal, I.-B. (1978) Insulin release, cGMP, cAMP and membrane potential in acetylcholine-stimulated islets. Am. J. Physiol. **235**, E493–500

Gerich, J. E., Charles, M. A. & Grodsky, G. M. (1976) Regulation of pancreatic insulin and glucagon secretion. Annu. Rev. Physiol. **38**, 353–388

Grill, V. & Cerasi, E. (1973) Activation by glucose of adenyl cyclase in pancreatic islets of the rat. FEBS Lett. **33**, 311–314

Hammonds, P., Schofield, P. N. & Ashcroft, S. J. H. (1987a) Glucose regulates preproinsulin messenger RNA levels in a clonal cell line of simian virus 40-transformed B-cells. FEBS Lett. **213**, 149–154

Hammonds, P., Schofield, P. N., Ashcroft, S. J. H., Sutton, R. & Gray, D. W. R. (1987b) Regulation and specificity of glucose-stimulated insulin gene expression in human islets of Langerhans. FEBS Lett. **223**, 131–137

Harrison, D. E. & Ashcroft, S. J. H. (1982) Effects of Ca^{2+}, calmodulin and cyclic AMP on the phosphorylation of endogenous proteins by homogenates of rat islets of Langerhans. Biochim. Biophys. Acta **714**, 313–319

Harrison, D. E., Ashcroft, S. J. H., Christie, M. C. & Lord, J. M. (1984) Protein phosphorylation in the pancreatic B-cell. Experientia **40**, 1075–1084

Hellman, B., Andersson, T., Berggren, P. O., Flatt, P., Gylfe, E. & Kohnert, K. D. (1979) The role of calcium in insulin secretion. In Hormones and Cellular Regulation (Dumont, J. & Nunez, J., eds.), vol. 3, pp. 69–96, Elsevier, Amsterdam

Henquin, J. C. & Meissner, H. P. (1984a) The ionic, electrical, and secretory effects of endogenous cyclic adenosine monophosphate in mouse pancreatic B cells: Studies with forskolin. Endocrinology **115**, 1125–1134

Henquin, J. C. & Meissner, H. P. (1984b) Significance of ionic fluxes and changes in membrane potential for stimulus–secretion coupling in the pancreatic B-cell. Experientia **40**, 1043–1052

Henquin, J. C. & Meissner, H. P. (1986) Cyclic adenosine monophosphate differently affects the response of mouse pancreatic beta-cells to various amino acids. J. Physiol. **381**, 77–93

Henquin, J., Bozem, M., Schmeer, W. & Nenquin, M. (1987) Distinct mechanisms for two amplification systems of insulin release. Biochem. J. **246**, 393–399

Hii, C. S. T., Stutchfield, J. & Howell, S. L. (1986) Enhancement of glucagon secretion from isolated rat islets of Langerhans by phorbol myristate acetate. Biochem. J. **233**, 287–289

Hii, C. S. T., Jones, P. M., Persaud, S. J. & Howell, S. L. (1987) A re-assessment of the role of protein kinase C in glucose-stimulated insulin secretion. Biochem. J. **246**, 489–493

Hill, R. S., Oberwetter, J. M. & Boyd III, A. E. (1987) Increase in cAMP levels in β-cell line potentiates insulin secretion without altering cytosolic free-calcium concentration. Diabetes **36**, 440–446

Howell, S. L. & Taylor, K. W. (1966) Effects of glucose concentration on incorporation of [^{3}-H]leucine into insulin using isolated mammalian islets of Langerhans. Biochim. Biophys. Acta **130**, 521–534

Hughes, S. J. & Ashcroft, S. J. H. (1988) Effect of secretagogues on cytosolic free Ca^{2+} and insulin release in the hamster clonal B-cell line HIT-T15. J. Mol. Endocrinol. **1**, 13–17

Hughes, S. J., Christie, M. R. & Ashcroft, S. J. H. (1987) Potentiators of insulin secretion modulate Ca^{2+} sensitivity in rat pancreatic islets. Mol. Cell. Endocrinol. **50**, 231–236

Hughes, S. J., Chalk, J. & Ashcroft, S. J. H. (1989) Effect of secretagogues on cytosolic free Ca^{2+} and insulin release at different extracellular Ca^{2+} concentrations in the hamster clonal B-cell line HIT-T15. Mol. Cell. Endocrinol. **65**, 35–41

Hughes, S. J., Chalk, J. & Ashcroft, S. J. H. (1990) The role of cytosolic free Ca^{2+} and protein kinase C in acetylcholine-induced insulin release in the clonal B-cell line HIT-T15. Biochem. J. **267**, 227–232

Itoh, N. & Okamoto, H. (1980) Translational control of proinsulin synthesis by glucose. Nature (London) **283**, 100–101

Jones, P. M., Fyles, J. M. & Howell, S. L. (1986) Regulation of insulin secretion by cAMP in rat islets of Langerhans permeabilized by high-voltage discharge. FEBS Letts. **205**, 205–209

Jones, P. M., Salmon, D. M. W. & Howell, S. L. (1988) Protein phosphorylation in electrically permeabilised islets of Langerhans. Effects of Ca^{2+}, cyclic AMP, a phorbol ester and noradrenaline. Biochem. J. **254**, 397–403

Katada, T., Gilman, A. G., Watanabe, Y., Bauer, S. & Jacobs, K. H. (1985) Protein kinase C phosphorylates the inhibitory guanine nucleotide-binding regulatory component and apparently suppresses its function in hormonal inhibition of adenylate cyclase. Eur. J. Biochem. **151**, 431–437

Kowluru, A. & MacDonald, M. J. (1984) Protein phosphorylation in pancreatic islets: Evidence for separate Ca^{2+}- and cAMP-enhanced phosphorylation of two 57000 M_r proteins. Biochem. Biophys. Res. Commun. **118**, 797–804

Krausz, Y., Eylon, L. & Cerasi, E. (1987) Calcium-binding proteins and insulin release — Differential effects of phenothiazines on 1st-phase and 2nd-phase secretion and on islet cAMP response to glucose. Acta Endocrinol. **116**, 241–245

Laurenza, A., Sutkowski, E. M. & Seamon, K. B. (1989) Forskolin: A specific stimulator of adenylyl cyclase or a diterpene with multiple sites of action? Trends Pharmacol. Sci. 442–447

Malaisse, W. J. & Malaisse-Lagae, F. (1984) The role of cyclic AMP in insulin release. Experientia **40**, 1068–1075

Malaisse, W. J., Garcia-Morales, P., Dufrane, S. P., Sener, A. & Valverde, I. (1984) Forskolin induced activation of adenylate cyclase, cyclic AMP production and insulin release in rat pancreatic islets. Endocrinology **115**, 2015–2020

Meats, J. E., Best, L., Lynch, A. M. & Tomlinson, S. (1989) Glucose increases cytosolic calcium concentration and inositol lipid metabolism in HIT-T15 cells. Cell Calcium **10**, 535–541

Montague, W. & Howell, S. L. (1972) The mode of action of adenosine 3′-5′-cyclic monophosphate in mammalian islets of Langerhans. Preparation and properties of islet-cell protein phosphokinase. Biochem. J. **129**, 551–560

Montminy, M. R. & Bilezikjian, L. M. (1987) Binding of a nuclear protein to the cyclic-AMP response element of the somatostatin gene. Nature (London) **328**, 175–178

Nielsen, D. A., Welsh, M., Casadaban, M. J. & Steiner, D. F. (1985) Control of insulin gene expression in pancreatic beta-cells and in an insulin-producing cell line, RIN-5F cells. I. Effects of glucose and cyclic AMP on the transcription of insulin mRNA. J. Biol. Chem. **260**, 13585–13589

Osterrieder, W., Brum, G., Hescheler, J. & Trautwein, W. (1982) Injection of subunits of cyclic AMP-dependent protein kinase into cardiac myocytes modulates Ca^{2+} current. Nature (London) **298**, 576–578

Pek, S. B., Usami, M., Bilir, N., Fischer-Bovenkerk, C. & Ueda, T. (1990) Protein phosphorylation in pancreatic islets induced by 3-phosphoglycerate and 2-phosphoglycerate. Proc. Natl. Acad. Sci. U.S.A. **87**, 4294–4298

Persaud, S. J., Jones, P. M., Sugden, D. & Howell, S. L. (1989) The role of protein kinase C in cholinergic stimulation of insulin secretion from rat islets of Langerhans. Biochem. J. **264**, 753–758

Persaud, S. J., Jones, P. M. & Howell, S. L. (1990) Glucose-induced insulin release is not dependent on activation of protein kinase A. Biochem. Biophys. Res. Commun. **173**, 833–839

Phang, W., Domboski, L., Krausz, Y. & Sharp, G. W. G. (1984) Mechanisms of synergism between glucose and cAMP on stimulation of insulin release. Am. J. Physiol. **247**, E701–E708

Philippe, J. & Missotten, M. (1990) Functional characterization of a cAMP-responsive element of the rat insulin I gene. J. Biol. Chem. **265**, 1465–1469

Pipeleers, D. G., Schuit, F. C., in't Veld, P. A., Maes, E., Hooghe-Peters, E. L., van de Winkel, M. & Gepts, W. (1985) Interplay of nutrients and hormones in the regulation of insulin release. Endocrinology **117**, 824–833

Prentki, M. & Matschinsky, F. M. (1987) Ca^{2+}, cAMP and phospholipid-derived messengers in coupling mechanisms of insulin secretion. Physiol. Rev. **67**, 1185–1248

Prentki, M., Glennon, M. C., Geschwind, J.-F., Matschinsky, F. M. & Corkey, B. E. (1987) Cyclic AMP raises cytosolic Ca^{2+} and promotes Ca^{2+} influx in a clonal pancreatic β-cell line (HIT-T15). FEBS Lett. **220**, 103–107

Rajan, A. S., Hill, R. S. & Boyd, A. E. III (1989) Effect of rise in cAMP levels on Ca^{2+} influx through voltage-dependent Ca^{2+} channels in HIT cells: Second-messenger synarchy in beta-cells. Diabetes **38**, 874–880

Roesler, W. J., Vandenbark, G. R. & Hanson, R. W. (1988) Cyclic AMP and the induction of eukaryotic gene transcription. J. Biol. Chem. **263**, 9063–9066

Rorsman, P. & Abrahamsson, H. (1985) Cyclic AMP potentiates glucose-induced insulin release from mouse pancreatic islets without increasing cytosolic free Ca^{2+}. Acta Physiol. Scand. **125**, 639–647

Schubart, U. K. (1982) Regulation of protein phosphorylation in hamster insulinoma cells. Identification of Ca^{2+}-regulated cytoskeletal and cAMP-regulated cytosolic phosphoprotein by two-dimensional electrophoresis. J. Biol. Chem. **257**, 12231–12244

Schubart, U. K., Sharpiro, S., Fleischer, N. & Rosen, O. M. (1977) Cyclic adenosine 3′5′-monophosphate-mediated insulin secretion and ribosomal protein phosphorylation in a hamster islet cell tumour. J. Biol. Chem. **252**, 92–101

Schuit, F. C. & Pipeleers, D. G. (1985) Regulation of adenosine 3′,5′-monophosphate levels in the pancreatic B-cell. Endocrinology **117**, 834–840

Sharp, G. W. G. (1979) The adenylate cyclase-cyclic AMP system in islets of Langerhans and its role in the control of insulin release. Diabetologia **16**, 287–297

Smith, P. A., Feutrell, C. M. S. & Ashcroft, F. M. (1990) Cyclic AMP potentiates L-type calcium channel activity in murine pancreatic B-cells. Diabetologia **33**, A104; 367

Sussman, K. E., Leitner, J. W. & Draznin, B. (1987) Cytosolic free-calcium concentrations in normal pancreatic islet cells: Effect of secretagogues and somatostatin. Diabetes **36**, 571–577

Sugden, M. C., Ashcroft, S. J. H. & Sugden, P. H. (1979) Protein kinase activities in rat pancreatic islets of Langerhans. Biochem. J. **180**, 219–229

Suzuki, S., Oka, H., Yasade, H., Ikeda, M., Chang, P. Y. & Oda, T. (1983) Effect of glucagon and cyclic adenosine-3′5′-monophosphate on protein phosphorylation in rat pancreatic islets. Endocrinology **112**, 348–352

Tamagawa, T., Niki, H. & Niki, A. (1985) Insulin release independent of a rise in cytosolic free Ca^{2+} by forskolin and phorbol ester. FEBS Lett. **183**, 430–432

Thams, P., Capito, K. & Hedeskov, C. J. (1984) Endogenous substrate protein for Ca^{2+}–calmodulin-dependent, Ca^{2+} phospholipid-dependent and cyclic AMP-dependent protein kinases in mouse pancreatic islets. Biochem. J. **221**, 247–253

Thams, P., Capito, K. & Hedeskov, C. J. (1988) Stimulation by glucose of cyclic AMP accumulation in mouse pancreatic islets is mediated by protein kinase C. Biochem. J. **253**, 229–234

Tsien, R. W., Bean, B. P., Hess, P., Lansman, J. B., Nilius, B. & Nowycky, M. C. (1986) Mechanisms of calcium channel modulation by beta-adrenergic agents and dihydropiridine Ca^{2+} agonists. J. Mol. Cell. Cardiol. **18**, 691–710

Ullrich, S. & Wollheim, C. B. (1988) GTP-dependent inhibition of insulin secretion by epinephrine in permeabilised RINm5F cells. Lack of correlation between insulin secretion and cyclic AMP levels. J. Biol. Chem. **263**, 8615–8620

Vallar, L., Biden, T. J. & Wollheim, C. B. (1987) Guanine nucleotides induced Ca^{2+}-independent insulin secretion from permeabilised RINm5F cells. J. Biol. Chem. **262**, 5049–5056

Welsh, M. (1989) Glucose regulation of insulin gene expression. Diabete Metab. **15**, 367–371

Welsh, M., Nielsen, D. A., MacKrell, A. J. & Steiner, D. F. (1985) Control of insulin gene expression in pancreatic beta-cells and in an insulin-producing cell line, RIN-5F cells. II Regulation of insulin mRNA stability. J. Biol. Chem. **260**, 13590–13594

Wolf, B. A., Easom, R. A., McDaniel, M. L. & Turk, J. (1990) Diacylglycerol synthesis *de novo* from glucose by pancreatic islets isolated from rats and humans. J. Clin. Invest. **85**, 482–490

Wollheim, C. B., Siegel, E. G. & Sharp, G. W. G. (1980) Dependency of acetylcholine-induced insulin release on Ca^{2+}-uptake by rat pancreatic islets. Endocrinology **107**, 924–929

Wollheim, C. B., Ullrich, P. & Pozzan, T. (1984) Glyceraldehyde but not cyclic AMP-stimulated insulin release is preceded by a rise in cytosolic free Ca^{2+}. FEBS Lett. **177**, 17–22

Yamamoto, K. K., Gonzalez, G. A., Biggs, W. H. & Montminy, M. R. (1988) Phosphorylation — induced binding and transcriptional efficacy of nuclear factor CREB. Nature (London) **334**, 494–498

Zawalich, W. S. & Zawalich, K. C. (1990) Forskolin-induced desensitisation of pancreatic B-cell insulin secretory responses: Possible involvement of impaired information flow in the inositol-lipid cycle. Endocrinology **126**, 2307–2312

Zawalich, W. S., Diaz, V. A. & Zawalich, K. C. (1988) Influence of cAMP and calcium on [^{3}H]inositol efflux, phosphate accumulation, and insulin release from isolated rat islets. Diabetes **37**, 1478–1483

Zunkler, B. J., Trube, G. & Ohno-Shosaku, T. (1988) Forskolin-induced block of delayed rectifying K$^+$ channels in pancreatic beta-cells is not mediated by cAMP. Pfluegers Arch. **411**, 613–619

14

Mechanisms of action of entero-insular hormones, islet peptides and neural input on the insulin secretory process

Per-Olof Berggren*, Patrik Rorsman†, Suad Efendic*, Claes-Göran Östenson*, Peter R. Flatt‡, Thomas Nilsson*, Per Arkhammar* and Lisa Juntti-Berggren*

*Department of Endocrinology, Karolinska Institute, S-10401, Stockholm; †Department of Medical Physics, Gothenburg University, S-40033, Gothenburg, Sweden and ‡Department of Biological and Biomedical Sciences, University of Ulster, Coleraine, BT52 ISA, Northern Ireland, U.K.

Introduction

Although glucose is the main regulator of insulin secretion, stimulus–secretion coupling in the pancreatic B-cell can be modulated by a variety of peptides found in endocrine cells and in the nerve endings supplying the endocrine part of the pancreas (for review see Ahrén *et al.*, 1986*b*, 1991*a* and Chapters 1–3 by Morgan, Holst and Marks *et al.* in this book). Although these peptides as well as the classical and peptidergic neurotransmitters are likely candidates in the regulation of the B-cell stimulus–secretion coupling, their physiological, or maybe even pathophysiological, role remains to be established. In the present chapter, we shall discuss the effects and possible mechanisms of action of entero-insular hormones, islet peptides and both classical and peptidergic neurotransmitters on the insulin secretory process. Although numerous peptides have been reported to affect B-cell function, attention will be restricted to those agents likely to be of physiological significance.

Stimulatory peptides of endocrine cellular origin

Gastric inhibitory peptide

Gastric inhibitory peptide (GIP), the main incretin candidate, serves to potentiate the stimulatory effect of glucose on insulin release (Creutzfeldt & Ebert, 1985). The insulinotrophic effect of GIP is closely related to the N-terminal amino acids, namely tyrosine in position 1 and alanine in position 2 (Creutzfeldt & Ebert, 1985). Immunocytochemical studies have revealed that pancreatic A-cells also contain a GIP-like peptide (Smith *et al.*, 1977). This peptide co-exists with glucagon in the secretory granules (Ahrén *et al.*, 1981), implying that situations associated with increased glucagon secretion, also lead to the release of GIP. Glucagon and GIP stimulate basal insulin release and potentiate the response to glucose or carbachol (Ahrén *et al.*, 1981). Whereas glucagon and GIP have a synergistic effect on glucose- and carbachol-induced insulin release, they antagonize each other's effect under basal conditions (Ahrén *et al.*, 1981). This speaks against a common regulatory site of action.

GIP has been reported to serve as an activator of the adenylate cyclase system in the pancreatic B-cells (Szecowka *et al.*, 1982). This suggests that GIP potentiates insulin release by promoting the formation of cyclic AMP. In a recent review, GIP was suggested to act in concert with glucose and cholecystokinin, which activates the phospholipase C system (see below) (Rasmussen *et al.*, 1990). This results in enhanced activity of calmodulin-dependent protein kinases and plasma membrane-associated protein kinase C, resulting in an increase in the first and second phases of insulin secretion. Detailed consideration of the roles of phospholipase C and protein kinases is given in Chapters 7, 12 and 13 by Morgan & Montague, Persuad *et al.* and Hughes & Ashcroft.

Thyrotropin-releasing hormone

Thyrotropin-releasing hormone (TRH), originally isolated from the hypothalamus and a larger TRH-like peptide are synthesized by most pancreatic B-cells and by some A-cells (Kawano *et al.*, 1985). In the perfused rat pancreas TRH can be released by arginine, but not by glucose and glucagon (Morley *et al.*, 1979). Although TRH has been reported to stimulate insulin release in the rabbit (Knudtzon, 1985), the physiological role and possible mechanisms of action of TRH in this process remain unclear. In GH_3 pituitary cells, TRH has been reported to induce both a rapid increase in the cytoplasmic free Ca^{2+} concentration ($[Ca^{2+}]_i$), which was mediated through the formation of inositol 1,4,5-trisphosphate [$Ins(1,4,5)P_3$], and a slower more delayed increase in $[Ca^{2+}]_i$, that apparently was independent of the trisphosphate (Mollard *et al.*, 1990).

Glucagon and glucagon-like peptide I (GLP-I)

Glucagon secreted by the pancreatic A-cells stimulates insulin release, at least in part, by activating adenylate cyclase and promoting the formation of cyclic AMP (Schuit & Pipeleers, 1986). This mechanism is regulated by a stimulatory GTP-binding protein (G_s) (Ui, 1984). Since peptides exert their effects by activating cell surface receptors, the signal initiated by receptor binding has to be transferred to the effector site by a mechanism in or beneath the plasma membrane. In many cells, G-proteins are part of such a signal-transduction pathway (Neer & Clapham, 1988). Cyclic AMP is degraded by phosphodiesterase in the cytoplasm, resulting in 5'-adenosine monophosphate. Both the formation and degradation of cyclic AMP are stimulated by the Ca^{2+}-dependent regulatory protein calmodulin, although the former reaction is stimulated to a greater extent (Valverde & Malaisse, 1984).

The stimulatory effect of cyclic AMP on insulin release is most prominent at stimulatory levels of glucose, but it is evident also at low concentrations of the sugar (Prentki & Matschinsky, 1987). Since cyclic AMP does not appear to increase $[Ca^{2+}]_i$ in the B-cell (Wollheim et al., 1984; Rorsman & Abrahamsson, 1985), the stimulatory effect on insulin release probably reflects sensitization of the secretory machinery to Ca^{2+} (see also Chapters 11 and 13 by Hellman et al. and Hughes & Ashcroft). This concept is supported by the fact that forskolin, a plant diterpene that directly activates the catalytic subunit of adenylate cyclase and thereby promotes the formation of cyclic AMP (Ullrich & Wollheim, 1984), potentiated Ca^{2+}-induced insulin secretion in electro-permeabilized pancreatic B-cells (Ullrich & Wollheim, 1988). The sensitization of the secretory machinery to Ca^{2+} may reflect activation of cyclic-AMP-dependent protein kinase and thereby the phosphorylation of a number of intracellular proteins (for review see Harrison et al., 1984).

Although the main mechanism whereby glucagon affects insulin release may involve activation of the adenylate cyclase system, we cannot exclude that the hormone also stimulates the phospholipase C system in the B-cell, in analogy to what has been described in hepatocytes (Wakelam et al., 1986). In this study, it was suggested that glucagon is linked to the adenylate cyclase system by a R_2 receptor through a stimulatory G-protein and to the phospholipase C system by a R_1 receptor, this latter receptor also being associated with a G-protein. It is of interest to note that these two signal-transduction systems appear to negatively modulate each other's effects. As pointed out by Petersen & Bear (1986), this dual-receptor system for glucagon is analogous to the two types of vasopressin receptors that have been described (Berridge, 1985; Creba et al., 1983), although these are not found in the same cell.

GLP-1$_{(7-36)}$amide is cleaved from proglucagon in endocrine cells in the gastro-intestinal tract and to a lesser extent in the pancreatic A-cells

(Conlon, 1988). GLP-1$_{(7-36)}$amide increases in the circulation after feeding (Kreymann *et al.*, 1987) and this peptide is a potent stimulator of insulin secretion. This implies an important regulatory role in the entero-insular axis (Mojsov *et al.*, 1987; Conlon, 1988). Since GLP-1$_{(7-36)}$amide activates adenylate cyclase (Drucker *et al.*, 1987; Göke & Conlon, 1988), this peptide probably stimulates insulin release in a similar manner to glucagon. Whether additional effects of GLP-1$_{(7-36)}$amide contribute to the stimulation of insulin release, is however not clear and merits further investigation (Flatt *et al.*, 1990).

Stimulatory classical and peptidergic neurotransmitters

β-Adrenergic agonists

It is generally accepted that β-adrenoceptor stimulation enhances insulin release. The endogenous catecholamines, adrenaline and noradrenaline, have both α- and β-adrenoceptor properties. Their net action on insulin secretion consequently reflects both their relative effectiveness in stimulating α- and β-adrenergic receptors, and the sensitivity of these receptors to the agonists. Studies on purified pancreatic islet cells suggest that A-cells are equipped only with β-adrenoceptors and B-cells only with α$_2$-adrenoceptors (Schuit & Pipeleers, 1986). Whereas stimulation of α$_2$-receptors on the B-cells led to decreased production of cyclic AMP, β-receptor stimulation of the A-cells promoted the formation of cyclic AMP. This implies that β-receptor agonists probably stimulate insulin release through a mechanism involving glucagon. Upon β-adrenoceptor activation of the A-cell, the increase in cyclic AMP will lead to stimulation of glucagon release. Glucagon in the intercellular space will then promote insulin secretion, through the effector systems(s) previously discussed (see above). The β-adrenergic receptors are subdivided into β$_1$- and β$_2$-adrenoceptors, the latter being implicated in the stimulation of insulin secretion (Ahrén *et al.*, 1986*b*). However, other studies have suggested that activation of the β$_1$-adrenoceptor leads to stimulation of insulin release (see Ahrén *et al.*, 1986*b*), emphasizing the limitations of the subclassification of the adrenoceptors.

Acetylcholine

Acetylcholine is released upon stimulation of the vagal nerve or the mixed autonomic innervation of the pancreas (Ahrén *et al.*, 1986*b*). Since these nerves have their terminals in close apposition to B-cells, acetylcholine can directly stimulate insulin secretion (Ahrén *et al.*, 1986*b*). The stimulatory effect of this neurotransmitter can be blocked by atropine, indicating its muscarinic nature (Ahrén *et al.*, 1986*b*). Indeed, high-affinity binding to muscarinic receptors has been demonstrated in rat pancreatic islets (Grill & Östenson, 1983; Östenson & Grill, 1987).

When muscarinic receptors are activated by acetylcholine, or the often used analogue carbachol, there is a mobilization of intercellularly bound Ca^{2+} from the endoplasmic reticulum (Prentki *et al.*, 1984). This effect is caused by activation of the phospholipase C pathway and the hydrolysis of phosphatidylinositol 4,5-bisphosphate [PtdIns(4,5)P_2]. This results in the formation of diacylglycerol, which activates protein kinase C (PKC) and Ins(1,4,5)P_3, which is responsible for the Ca^{2+} mobilization (Prentki & Matschinsky, 1987; Chapter 11 by Hellman *et al.*). Although the intracellular Ca^{2+} mobilized by Ins(1,4,5)P_3 is able to promote insulin release in the absence of extracellular Ca^{2+} (Nilsson *et al.*, 1987), this effect is minor compared with that evoked by Ca^{2+} influx through the voltage-activated Ca^{2+} channels.

The other branch of the phospholipase C system activated by muscarinic binding, namely PKC, has a central modulatory role in the insulin secretion (see also Chapters 7, 11 and 12 by Morgan & Montague, Hellman *et al.* and Persuad *et al.*). Acetylcholine probably exerts most of its stimulatory action on insulin release through PKC. Most studies on PKC action have employed phorbol esters such as 12-O-tetradecanoylphorbol-13-acetate (PMA), to directly activate PKC. A number of these have demonstrated that PKC activation leads to amplification of the insulin secretory response (Malaisse *et al.*, 1980; Arkhammar *et al.*, 1986; Hii *et al.*, 1987; Prentki & Matschinsky, 1987) despite a tendency to lower [Ca^{2+}]$_i$ by a mechanism at least partly attributable to stimulation of Ca^{2+} outward transport (Arkhammar *et al.*, 1986, 1989; Di Virgilio *et al.*, 1986; Rorsman *et al.*, 1986; Berggren *et al.*, 1989*a*).

Cholecystokinin

Cholecystokinin (CCK) is secreted by endocrine cells in the gut after feeding (Mutt, 1980). CCK also serves as a neurotransmitter, and CCK immunoreactivity is abundant in nerve fibres innervating the islets (Rehfeld *et al.*, 1980). Various fragments of CCK, such as CCK-4, CCK-8, CCK-12, CCK-22, CCK-33, CCK-39 and CCK-58 are formed by degradation of the CCK peptide precursor. The smaller fragments (CCK-4 and CCK-8) probably act as neurotransmitters, whereas larger forms, e.g. CCK-33, serve as hormones (Rehfeld *et al.*, 1980). CCK-8 or larger fragments, with an intact *C*-terminus, enhance basal insulin release and potentiate the response to glucose and other secretagogues. In certain species, however, CCK-4 also seems to stimulate insulin release (Ahrén *et al.*, 1988).

With regard to the mechanism of action of CCK, evidence has been provided for specific CCK receptors on the B-cell (Versphol *et al.*,

1986). In a study by Zawalich and colleagues (1987) the C-terminal octa-peptide of CCK, sulphated on the tyrosine residue (CCK-8S), promoted receptor-linked polyphosphoinositide (PtdIns) hydrolysis, the formation of inositol-trisphosphates, and the efflux of ^{45}Ca from prelabelled islets both at basal and stimulatory concentrations of glucose. However, CCK-8S only promoted insulin release at a stimulatory glucose concentration, the release then being biphasic in nature. When Ca^{2+} influx was inhibited, CCK-8S evoked only a small first phase of insulin release. Addition of either forskolin, to increase the intracellular levels of cyclic AMP, or tolbutamide, to block the ATP-regulated K^+ channels and depolarize the cell, markedly enhanced the first phase of insulin release at low glucose concentrations. However, under these conditions there was no second phase, which was only observed at stimulatory glucose concentrations. The authors speculated that this reflected lack of formation of diacylglycerol and thereby no activation of the PKC branch of the Ca^{2+}-messenger system at basal glucose concentrations (Zawalich et al., 1987). If PKC is involved in the regulation of the second phase of insulin release, lack of diacylglycerol formation will lead to the disappearance of this phase. However, recent studies do not favour this idea and, as discussed above, with regard to effects of acetylcholine, the role of PKC in the insulin secretory process is likely to be of a modulatory rather than a direct regulatory nature (also see Chapter 12 by Persuad et al.).

The extent to which the potentiating effect of CCK on glucose-induced insulin release can be explained by activation of the phospholipase C system merits further investigation. It is of interest to note that studies using the CCK analogue JMV-180 have demonstrated two functionally distinct CCK receptors on isolated rat pancreatic acini (Matozaki et al., 1990). Occupancy of high-affinity receptors by CCK induced Ca^{2+} oscillations, diacylglycerol formation from phosphatidylcholine hydrolysis, and amylase release, with minimal $PtdIns(4,5)P_2$ hydrolysis. Occupancy of low-affinity receptors by CCK induced $PtdIns(4,5)P_2$ hydrolysis, leading to $Ins(1,4,5)P_3$ formation and an early peak of diacylglycerol plus a large transient increase in $[Ca^{2+}]_i$.

It is not clear to what extent CCK also activates the adenylate cyclase system, i.e. CCK then operating through a similar dual-receptor system as previously discussed for glucagon in various cell systems including the pancreatic B-cell (see above).

Bombesin and gastrin-releasing polypeptide

Bombesin is a tetradecapeptide isolated from frog skin. Gastrin-releasing polypeptide (GRP) is structurally related to bombesin and is present in the brain, gastro-intestinal tract and nerve fibres innervating the islets of man and other mammals (Ipp & Unger, 1979; Moghimzadeh et al., 1983). In addition to indirect effects mediated via the central nervous or adrenergic systems (Brown *et al.*, 1977), bombesin and GRP influence glucose homoeostasis by direct interaction with pancreatic B-cells to stimulate insulin release (Ipp & Unger, 1979). Addition of bombesin to insulin-secreting cells has been shown to activate the phospholipase C system with the generation of $Ins(1,4,5)P_3$ and diacylglycerol (Berggren *et al.*, 1989*b*). Further details concerning the possible role of this system in the insulin secretory process are given in the section concerning acetylcholine.

Vasoactive intestinal polypeptide

Vasoactive intestinal polypeptide (VIP) is a widely distributed neuro-peptide that occurs in intrapancreatic nerves surrounding vessels and penetrating the islets (Larsson, 1979). VIP is released from the perfused pig pancreas by vagal stimulation (Holst *et al.*, 1984) and stimulates insulin release, under a variety of experimental conditions (Fahrenkrug *et al.*, 1987; Szecowka *et al.*, 1983*a*). The mechanism of action of VIP merits further investigation.

Inhibitory peptides of endocrine cellular origin

Somatostatin

Somatostatin is present in numerous tissues including the pancreatic D-cells. The peptide inhibits insulin release in a paracrine or intercellular fashion, involving decreased formation of cyclic AMP (Pipeleers, 1987; see also Chapter 3 by Marks *et al.*). Somatostatin also interacts with the adenylate cyclase system in pituitary cells (Schlegel *et al.*, 1984), and in both types of cell it induces hyperpolarization and a decrease of $[Ca^{2+}]_i$ (Schlegel *et al.*, 1984; Sussman *et al.*, 1987; Nilsson *et al.*, 1989; Chapter 9 by Henquin *et al.*).

   Studies on pituitary cells have also demonstrated that somatostatin suppresses currents through voltage-activated Ca^{2+} channels (Luini *et al.*, 1986). However, in normal pancreatic B-cells somatostatin did not affect basal $[Ca^{2+}]_i$ or interfere with the opening of voltage-activated Ca^{2+} channels, induced by a high, depolarizing concentration of K^+ (Nilsson *et al.*, 1989 and Fig. 1). It seems likely therefore that somatostatin is without significant effect on either resting $[Ca^{2+}]_i$ or voltage-activated Ca^{2+} channels. Despite the fact that somatostatin did not affect the rise in $[Ca^{2+}]_i$ in response to K^+, insulin release was still suppressed under these conditions (Nilsson *et al.*, 1989 and Fig. 1). This indicates a dissociation between the rise in $[Ca^{2+}]_i$ and the activation of secretion. Although relatively modest compared with control cells, the combination of high K^+ and 20 mM-glucose promoted an increased insulin release even in the presence of somatostatin (Nilsson *et al.*, 1989 and Fig. 1). It might be speculated therefore that glucose increases the sensitivity to Ca^{2+} of the secretory process, an effect that can be explained by sugar-induced formation of diacylglycerol and thereby activation of PKC (Peter-Riesch *et al.*, 1988). As shown in Fig. 2, the glucose-induced increases in $[Ca^{2+}]_i$, membrane potential and insulin release were reversed by the addition of

---

Fig. I.   **Effects of depolarization with K^+ and glucose on $[Ca^{2+}]_i$ and insulin release in *ob/ob* mouse B-cells in the presence or absence of galanin, somatostatin or clonidine**

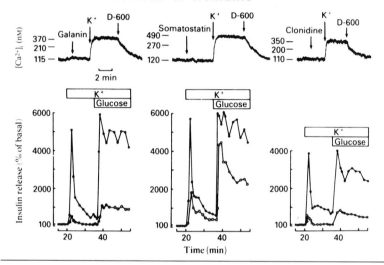

In the measurements of insulin release, perifusions made in the presence of agonist (○) were compared with control perifusions made in the absence of agonist (●). The concentrations of the various compounds were: 16 nM-galanin, 400 nM-somatostatin, 2 μM-clonidine, 25 mM-K^+, 50 μM-D-600 and 20 mM-glucose. Insulin release is expressed as a percentage of basal release. Measurements of $[Ca^{2+}]_i$ were performed using quin-2. Reproduced from Berggren et al. 1990 with permission.

---

400 nM-somatostatin. After reaching the nadir, $[Ca^{2+}]_i$ and membrane potential slowly rose to a higher level, although still lower than in the absence of the peptide. The reason for the increase in both $[Ca^{2+}]_i$ and membrane potential is not likely to reflect rapid degradation of somatostatin, since a second addition of the peptide evoked only a minor and transient decrease. The slow increase in $[Ca^{2+}]_i$ in the presence of somatostatin was completely reversed by the addition of D-600 (Nilsson *et al.*, 1989 and Fig. 2), suggesting the involvement of Ca^{2+} influx through voltage-activated Ca^{2+} channels.

When trying to clarify the mechanism whereby somatostatin

repolarizes the pancreatic B-cell, it is of interest to note that its effect on membrane potential has a certain resemblance to that evoked by diazoxide (see Fig. 3B; Arkhammar *et al.* 1987). This hyperglycaemic sulphonamide is known to activate ATP-regulated K^+ channels in the B-cell plasma

Fig. 2. **Effects of galanin, somatostatin and clonidine on $[Ca^{2+}]_i$, membrane potential and insulin release in glucose-stimulated *ob/ob* mouse B-cells**

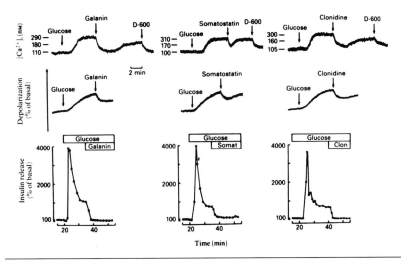

The concentrations of the various compounds were: *16 nM-galanin, 400 nM-somatostatin, 0.2 μM-clonidine (in the measurements of $[Ca^{2+}]_i$,) 2 μM-clonidine (in the measurements of membrane potential and insulin release), 50 μM-D-600 and 20 mM-glucose. Insulin release is expressed as a percentage of basal release. Measurements of $[Ca^{2+}]_i$ and qualitative changes in membrane potential were assessed using quin-2 and bisoxonol, respectively. Reproduced from Berggren et al. 1990 with permission.*

membrane (Trube *et al.*, 1986). Further support that somatostatin may activate these K^+ channels, concerns the ability of the peptide to stimulate $^{86}Rb^+$ efflux from RINm5F cells in a similar way to diazoxide (Fosset *et al.*, 1988; de Weille *et al.*, 1989). Evidence against a direct effect of somatostatin on ATP-regulated K^+ channels, at least in normal pancreatic B-cells, is the fact that the repolarizing effect of the peptide persisted in the presence of high concentrations of hypoglycaemic sulphonylureas which are known to inhibit these K^+ channels (Rorsman *et al.*, 1991; Wåhlander *et al.*, 1991a). We propose that the repolarizing effect of somatostatin is mediated by a G-protein-regulated, sulphonylurea-insensitive, low-conductance K^+

channel, distinct from the ATP-regulated K$^+$ channel (Rorsman *et al.*, 1991; Wåhlander *et al.*, 1991*a*). To exclude the possibility that the somatostatin-induced repolarization was owing to stimulated Cl$^-$ influx into the B-cell, the effects of the peptide were investigated in a Cl$^-$-deficient medium,

Fig. 3. **Effects of clonidine, yohimbine and diazoxide on membrane potential in glucose (A) or tolbutamide-stimulated (B)** *ob/ob* **mouse B-cells**

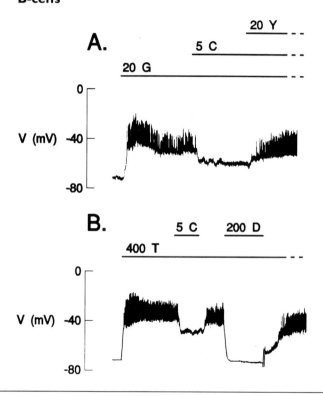

The concentrations of the various compounds added were: 20 mM-glucose (20 G), 5 μM-clonidine (5 C), 20 μM-yohimbine (20 Y), 400 μM-tolbutamide (400 T) and 200 μM-diazoxide (200 D). Membrane potential was recorded, using the perforated-patch whole-cell method (Horn & Marty, 1988), as described by Rorsman & Trube, (1985). The duration of each record is about 10 min. In (B) the record is interrupted for 3 min because of slow washout of diazotide.

where Cl$^-$ was replaced by glutamate, resulting in a final Cl$^-$ concentration of 3 mM. However, under these conditions somatostatin also repolarized the cells in the presence of 20 mM-glucose (Nilsson *et al.*, 1989).

Nevertheless, more thorough electrophysiological investigations are needed before a possible interaction of somatostatin with voltage-activated Ca^{2+} channels, ATP-regulated K^+ channels, or other ion channels can be excluded.

Pertussis toxin is known to modify G-proteins by the addition of an ADP–ribose group to the A-subunit of the protein (Ui, 1984). In pancreatic B-cells, treatment with pertussis toxin blocked repolarization, reduction in $[Ca^{2+}]_i$ and inhibition of insulin release promoted by somatostatin (Nilsson et al., 1989). It is therefore likely that this peptide mediates its effects via a G-protein, the identity of which is so far unknown. Since somatostatin induced a lowering in $[Ca^{2+}]_i$, despite the presence of forskolin, it is not likely that pertussis toxin exerts its effects only by increasing the intracellular content of cyclic AMP. Moreover, a direct effect of pertussis toxin on ATP-regulated K^+ channels was excluded, since addition of diazoxide still promoted a repolarization-induced reduction of $[Ca^{2+}]_i$ in cells pretreated with the toxin (Nilsson et al., 1989). These observations taken together with the fact that the repolarization-induced decrease in $[Ca^{2+}]_i$ was not solely responsible for the inhibitory effects on insulin release (Nilsson et al., 1989 and Fig. 1), make it likely that there exists several somatostatin-associated G-proteins with sensitivity to pertussis toxin. Alternatively the putative G-protein may have more than one effector system (Brown & Birnbaumer, 1988).

Despite the fact that somatostatin has been demonstrated to induce repolarization, lower $[Ca^{2+}]_i$ and decrease cyclic AMP levels, there is as yet no clear picture of how this peptide inhibits insulin release. For example, it has also been proposed that somatostatin interferes with steps late in the stimulus–secretion coupling (Nilsson et al., 1989). The findings that somatostatin still inhibited insulin release when $[Ca^{2+}]_i$ was increased (see above), indeed speaks in favour of the peptide interacting directly with the mechanisms regulating exocytosis.

Corticotropin-releasing factor

Corticotropin-releasing factor (CRF) inhibits insulin release in the perfused rat pancreas and lowers basal plasma insulin (Moltz & Fawcett, 1985). Immunocytochemistry has revealed the localization of CRF, not only in the hypothalamus, the gastro-intestinal tract and the adrenals, but also within the cells in the endocrine part of the pancreas (Petrusz et al., 1983). Further studies are required to evaluate the action of CRF on pancreatic B-cell function.

Peptide YY

Peptide YY (PYY) has been identified within the secretory granules of the glucagon-containing A-cells (Böttcher et al., 1989). The peptide has structural similarities to neuropeptide Y and pancreatic polypeptide

(Tatemoto et al., 1982). It is noteworthy, however, that not all PYY cells display glucagon immunoreactivity, but instead contain pancreatic polypeptide (Böttcher et al., 1989). Although PYY has been found to inhibit insulin secretion (Szecowka et al., 1983b; Böttcher et al., 1989), the physiological importance of this peptide as a regulator of the stimulus–secretion coupling in the pancreatic B-cell remains to be established.

Atrial natriuretic peptide

Atrial natriuretic peptide (ANP) is produced by atrial cells and exerts natriuretic, diuretic and hypotensive effects (de Bolde, 1986). Immuno-cytochemical studies have revealed ANP-like immunoreactivity in both the exocrine and endocrine pancreas (Lindop et al., 1986; Chabot et al., 1987). In the latter case, ANP was localized in the glucagon-producing A-cells. It may therefore be assumed that ANP is either produced within the pancreas or internalized after binding to intrapancreatic ANP-receptors (Chabot et al., 1987). With regard to the insulin secretory process, ANP has been found to inhibit glucagon-stimulated insulin secretion and stimulate the production of GMP (Ahrén, 1988; Kuhn et al., 1988). The physiological significance of these findings and the underlying mechanisms are not clear.

Pancreastatin

Pancreastatin, a 49 amino-acid amidated peptide originally isolated from the porcine pancreas (Tatemoto et al., 1986), is structurally identical with a mid-sequence region of porcine chromogranin A (CGA) (Iacangelo et al., 1988a). This is an acidic 72 kDa glycoprotein found in nervous tissue, the endocrine pancreas and a number of other endocrine cells (Rindi et al., 1986). Corresponding sequences of 49 amino-acid residues have also been found in rat (Iacangelo et al., 1988b), bovine (Iacangelo et al., 1986) and human CGA (Helman et al., 1988), indicating that CGA serves as a precursor to pancreastatin. However, the pancreastatin sequences of these three species show only 56–71% sequence similarity with porcine pancreastatin (Ahrén et al., 1991a).

In the porcine endocrine pancreas, pancreastatin has been localized immunocytochemically to both B- and D-cells (Fig. 4; Ravazzola et al., 1988). With the same technique, using antiserum against porcine pancreastatin, the peptide appears to occur in A-cells in rat and human islets (A. Höög & C.-G. Östenson, unpublished work).

Studies in the perfused isolated pig pancreas revealed that pancreastatin-like immunoreactivity (PLI), but not larger fragments or CGA, was released in parallel with insulin in response to glucose, acetylcholine, GLP-1$_{(7-36)}$amide, and electrical stimulation of the vagal

Fig. 4. **Immunocytochemical localization of pancreastatin in endocrine cells of porcine pancreas gut**

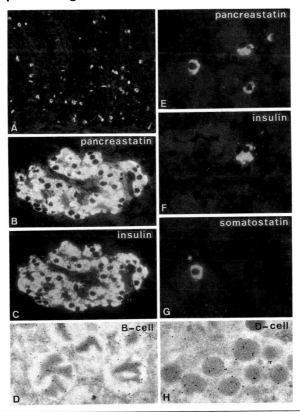

(A) Paraffin section of duodenal mucosa showing numerous fluorescent cells in the glands of Lieberkuhn. (B) and (C), Consecutive semi-thin sections through an islet of Langerhans, immunostained for pancreastatin and insulin. All insulin-containing cells displayed pancreastatin immunoreactivity. (E–G), Three consecutive semi-thin sections through individual endocrine cells scattered in the exocrine tissue. Insulin- and somatostatin-cells contain pancreastatin immunoreactivity. (D) and (H), At the ultrastructural level, pancreastatin immunostaining was located in the secretory granules of insulin- and somatostatin-containing cells. Magnification of micrographs: (A), × 111; (B) and (C), × 351; (E–G), × 505; (D) and (H), × 32000. Reproduced from Ravazzola et al. 1988 with permission.

nerve (Östenson *et al.*, 1989*a*). Moreover, in the pig *in vivo*, the output of PLI from the pancreatic veins was reduced by electrical stimulation of local sympathetic nerves and augmented by glucose infusion (Ahrén *et al.*, 1991*b*).

Fig. 5.   **Inhibition of stimulated insulin release by porcine pancreastatin**

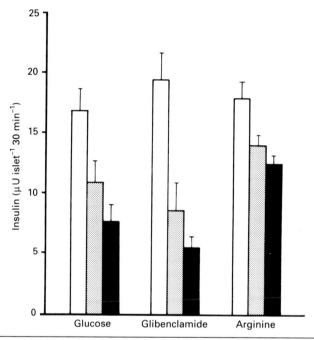

Insulin response to 16.7 mm-glucose, 2 μm-glibenclamide or 20 mm-arginine (the latter two compounds in the presence of 3·3 mm-glucose) from 24 h-cultured, isolated rat islets was dose-dependently suppressed by the addition of pancreastatin at 10⁻⁸ m (shaded bars) or 10⁻⁷ m (black bars). Control incubations without pancreastatin are depicted by open bars. Data are shown as means ± s.e.m. for six observations. Note the less pronounced suppressive effect of the peptide on the arginine compared with the glucose- and glibenclamide-stimulated insulin release.

Studies, *in vitro*, in the rat have demonstrated that insulin release evoked by glucose, sulphonylurea, arginine, isobutyl-3-methylxanthine (IBMX) and GIP was suppressed by 10^{-8}–10^{-7} M-porcine pancreastatin (Fig. 5) or the biologically active *C*-terminal 33–49 fragment (Efendic *et al.*, 1987; Schmidt *et al.*, 1987; Silvestre *et al.*, 1988; Ishizuka *et al.*, 1988). The effect of pancreastatin on glucose-stimulated insulin release was pronounced at glucose concentrations between 5 and 11 mM, but disappeared at concentrations higher than 17 mM (Östenson *et al.*, 1989*b*). Pancreastatin did not affect either islet glucose oxidation or insulin biosynthesis in these short-term studies (Östenson *et al.*, 1989*b*). Studies with RINm5F cells revealed that pretreatment with pertussis toxin abolished the inhibitory effect of pancreastatin on insulin release, suggesting involvement of an inhibitory G-protein in its mechanism of action (Lorinet *et al.*, 1989).

In contrast with the rat, porcine pancreastatin at concentrations of up to 10^{-7} M failed to suppress glucose-stimulated insulin secretion from the pig pancreas *in vitro* (Holst *et al.*, 1990). Also in the conscious pig, intravenous infusion of porcine pancreastatin was without effect on plasma insulin levels (Bretherton-Watt *et al.*, 1988). Considering these negative observations, as well as the low 56 % sequence homology between porcine and rat pancreastatin, the physiological significance of the previous observations using porcine pancreastatin in the rat may be questioned. However, a *C*-terminal fragment of rat pancreastatin has been shown to inhibit glucose-stimulated insulin secretion in conscious rats (Funakoshi *et al.*, 1989). Furthermore, the rat peptide inhibited glucose-induced insulin response in the perfused rat pancreas and markedly reduced insulin synthesis and DNA synthesis during 3-day culture of foetal rat islets (Sjöholm *et al.*, 1991).

The fact that pancreastatin can inhibit insulin release evoked by secretagogues which interact at different levels of the stimulus–secretion coupling suggests that the peptide may have a multifarious regulatory role in the process of insulin secretion. Such a role is presumably exerted by paracrine or autocrine interaction with the B-cell. In this context, however, it is noteworthy that circulating levels of human pancreastatin rose significantly after an oral glucose load in patients with non-insulin-dependent diabetes mellitus (NIDDM), but not in healthy subjects (Funakoshi *et al.*, 1990). This observation suggests that the peptide is indeed secreted, and may play a pathophysiological role in NIDDM.

Diazepam-binding inhibitor

Diazepam-binding inhibitor (DBI), originally isolated from pig intestine (Chen *et al.*, 1988), displaces benzodiazepines from the benzodiazepine recognition sites within the $GABA_A$-receptors (Guidotti *et al.*, 1983). In porcine and human tissues DBI has been localized to the somatostatin-producing D-cells of the pancreatic islets (Sandberg *et al.*, 1989), whereas DBI-immunoreactivity appeared in the glucagon-producing A-cells of rat pancreatic islets (Johansson *et al.*, 1991).

Porcine DBI suppressed insulin release stimulated by glucose in the perfused pancreas and isolated pancreatic islets of the rat (Chen *et al.*,

1988; Östenson *et al.*, 1990). Moreover, DBI inhibited glibenclamide- and IBMX-induced insulin responses from rat islets (Östenson *et al.*, 1990). In contrast, arginine-stimulated insulin release was unaffected, while the glucagon response to arginine was modestly suppressed.

Since DBI immunoreactivity has been localized to islet non-B-cells, it is conceivable that the peptide may act as a local modulator of insulin release. The mechanism behind the reported effects on islet hormone secretion is however unclear. Recently it was shown that islet A-cells but not B-cells, of the guinea pig are equipped with $GABA_A$-receptor Cl^- channels that upon activation by GABA hyperpolarize the A-cell and thereby inhibit glucagon release (Rorsman *et al.*, 1989). Since GABA is present in the insulin secretory granules and consequently is released concomitant with insulin on glucose stimulation, this provides a contributory mechanism for glucose-induced inhibition of glucagon secretion. Interestingly, the effect of GABA was approximately doubled in the presence of the benzodiazepine diazepam. Although the physiological agonist, if existing, for the diazepam receptor has not been identified, the presence of DBI should block its effects and thereby prevent the inhibition of glucagon release. If glucagon under physiological conditions is to serve as a paracrine stimulator of insulin release, one might have expected that the presence of DBI should instead stimulate insulin release.

Structural identity has been proven between DBI and acyl-CoA-binding protein (ACBP), originally isolated from rat liver (Knudsen *et al.*, 1989). ACBP has been shown to bind medium- and long-chain acyl-CoA-esters and also to induce medium-chain fatty acid synthesis (Knudsen *et al.*, 1989). Furthermore, rat ACBP inhibited glucose-stimulated insulin release both *in vivo* and *in vitro* in the rat (C.-G. Östenson, B. Ahrén & J. Knudsen, unpublished work). It can thus be speculated that DBI/ACBP exerts its inhibitory effect on the B-cells by binding factors important in regulation of insulin secretion, owing to its ability to bind amphiphilic compounds.

Inhibitory classical and peptidergic neurotransmitters

α_2-Adrenergic agonists

The endocrine pancreas has a rich supply of catecholaminergic nerves, originating from the splanchnic trunc (Miller, 1981). Catecholamines, also reach the insulin-secreting B-cells via the circulation from the adrenal gland. Inhibition of insulin release by the catecholamines adrenaline and noradrenaline is mediated by the activation of α-adrenergic receptors (Schuit & Pipeleers, 1986). Although both a lowering of cyclic AMP and a reduction in $[Ca^{2+}]_i$ have been suggested to account for this inhibitory effect (Katada & Ui, 1979; Yamazaki *et al.*, 1982; Sussman *et al.*, 1987), the exact mechanisms involved remain unknown. Other studies have suggested that α-adrenoceptor activation leads to inhibition of insulin release by a mechanism distal to those regulating B-cell cyclic-AMP production and $[Ca^{2+}]_i$ (Ullrich & Wollheim, 1984, 1985, 1988). A partial reduction in Ca^{2+} uptake is compatible with electrophysiological data, revealing only a partial block of Ca^{2+} action potentials at concentrations of adrenaline inhibiting insulin release (Cook & Perara, 1982). Although studies on neurones have shown that α-adrenoceptor activation leads to a direct suppression of Ca^{2+} currents (Dunlap & Fischbach, 1981; Marchetti *et al.*, 1986) it is not clear whether a similar direct interaction also takes place in the B-cell.

The α-adrenergic receptors can be divided into $α_1$ and $α_2$ and it has become clear that inhibition of insulin release can be accounted for primarily by activation of the latter subtype (Schuit & Pipeleers, 1986). Hence, in studies of the mechanisms whereby α-adrenoceptor activation inhibits insulin release a specific $α_2$-adrenoceptor agonist, clonidine, is often used. As can be noted in Fig. 2, clonidine inhibited glucose-induced insulin release, an effect paralleled by membrane repolarization and a decrease of $[Ca^{2+}]_i$. As is evident from Fig. 1, clonidine has no effect on resting $[Ca^{2+}]_i$. The reduction of $[Ca^{2+}]_i$, in B-cells stimulated with 20 mM-glucose, comprised an initial nadir followed by a slow rise and the establishment of a new steady-state level, still lower than in the absence of agonist. This new level of $[Ca^{2+}]_i$ was reduced by the Ca^{2+}-channel blocker D-600. Despite this slow increase of $[Ca^{2+}]_i$, insulin secretion remained inhibited. The ability of clonidine to repolarize the B-cell is also obvious in Fig. 3, demonstrating results obtained by applying the perforated-patch whole-cell technique (Horn & Marty, 1988). In this case, the agonist not only reversed membrane depolarization induced by glucose, but also that induced by high concentrations of the hypoglycaemic sulphonylurea tobutamide, which directly blocks ATP-regulated K^+ channels (see Chapter 15 by Nelson *et al.*). As shown in Fig. 3(A) yohimbine, a specific $α_2$-adrenoceptor antagonist, completely reversed the effect of clonidine. Furthermore, the effect of clonidine was reversed upon withdrawal of the agonist (Fig. 3B), and under these conditions the hyperglycaemic sulphonamide diazoxide still repolarized the B-cell.

The mechanism responsible for the marked clonidine-induced depolarization is difficult to reconcile with anything but an activation of some type of K^+ channel (see also Chapter 9 by Henquin *et al.*). It has been suggested that α-adrenoceptor activation increases K^+ permeability through Ca^{2+}-regulated K^+ channels (Santana de Sa *et al.*, 1983). Since clonidine did not induce a rise in $[Ca^{2+}]_i$ in our hands (Nilsson *et al.*, 1988), it is not likely to increase the activity of such K^+ channels in the B-cell. When measuring $^{86}Rb^+$ efflux, as a marker for K^+ efflux, it has been demonstrated that α_2-adrenoceptor activation either decreases or does not affect such an efflux from preloaded islets (Tamagawa & Henquin, 1983). This is in marked contrast to the effects of diazoxide, which evokes a pronounced stimulatory effect on $^{86}Rb^+$ efflux (Henquin & Meissner, 1982). Although these findings speak against an increased K^+ conductance being responsible for the clonidine-induced repolarization, it should be kept in mind that the cellular handling of $^{86}Rb^+$ does not necessarily reflect that of K^+.

Inhibition of Ca^{2+} influx through the voltage-activated Ca^{2+} channels is not of major importance for the repolarization since the effects of clonidine also persisted in the absence of extracellular Ca^{2+} (Nilsson *et al.*, 1988). Furthermore, neither an inhibition of the Na^+/K^+ pump nor the absence of extracellular Cl^- changed the response to the α_2-adrenergic agonist (Nilsson *et al.*, 1988). In addition, we have not been able to establish an effect of α_2-adrenoceptor activation on ATP-regulated K^+ channels by direct measurements using various configurations of the patch-clamp technique. However, by applying the perforated-patch configuration (Horn & Marty, 1988) we have now identified a novel K^+ channel which is responsible for the repolarization induced by α_2-adrenergic stimulation (Rorsman *et al.*, 1991; Wåhlander *et al.*, 1991a). This channel is regulated by a G-protein and differs from the ATP-regulated K^+ channel in both its pharmacological and biophysical properties, i.e. it is insensitive to sulphonylurea and has a much lower conductance. The concept that α_2-adrenoceptor activation promotes opening of a K^+ channel distinct from the ATP-regulated K^+ channels has important functional implications. This provides a mechanism whereby the action of neurotransmitters and hormones can be dissociated from those of fuel secretagogues.

It is of interest to note that there was no interference of clonidine with the rise in $[Ca^{2+}]_i$ induced by depolarization of the cells with high concentrations of K^+ (Fig. 1). However, under these conditions insulin release was suppressed, indicating a dissociation between the rise in $[Ca^{2+}]_i$ and the activation of secretion. This inhibitory effect on insulin release was partially reversed by increasing the concentration of glucose, suggesting an increased sensitivity of the secretory machinery to $[Ca^{2+}]_i$, promoted by sugar-induced activation of PKC. The fact that clonidine did not interfere with Ca^{2+} influx through the voltage-activated Ca^{2+} channels, when these were opened by K^+-induced depolarization (Nilsson *et al.*, 1988), is in contrast to studies by Marchetti and colleagues (1986). They demonstrated that noradrenaline reversibly reduced single Ca^{2+}-channel activity in cultured sensory and sympathetic chick neurones, the degree of reduction decreasing with increasing external Ca^{2+} concentration. This effect was suggested to reflect an interference with two types of Ca^{2+} channels, activated at high and low voltages respectively.

With the ultimate purpose of unmasking a possible Ca^{2+} channel activated at lower voltages and sensitive to clonidine, we investigated the effects of the agonist on $[Ca^{2+}]_i$ when the B-cells were depolarized to a lesser extent. However, even under these conditions we were unable to observe any effect of clonidine on the K^+-induced increase in $[Ca^{2+}]_i$ (Nilsson *et al.*, 1988). Moreover, direct measurements of the Ca^{2+} current with the patch-clamp technique, have failed to demonstrate a reduction subsequent to clonidine exposure (Wåhlander *et al.*, 1991*b*).

Activation of α_2-adrenoceptors also inhibits Ca^{2+}-induced insulin release in a GTP-dependent manner, in permeabilized insulin-secreting RINm5F cells (Ullrich & Wollheim, 1988). In these cells, α_2-adrenoceptors remain coupled to adenylate cyclase but cyclic-AMP levels did not correlate with the rate of insulin secretion (Ullrich & Wollheim, 1988). Also insulin release evoked by PKC activation in permeabilized cells, and that evoked by ionomycin in intact cells was inhibited by adrenaline, suggesting that α_2-adrenergic inhibition is distal to generation of second messengers (Nilsson *et al.*, 1988; Ullrich & Wollheim, 1988). Indeed, it has been proposed that α_2-adrenoceptor stimulation leads to activation of an inhibitory G-protein, resulting in a block of the putative fusion pore thought to span the plasma membrane and granule membrane during exocytosis (Ullrich & Wollheim, 1988). Since all the effects of α_2-adrenoceptor activation in both intact and permeabilized insulin-producing cells were reversed by pretreating the cells with pertussis toxin (Katada & Ui, 1979; Nilsson *et al.*, 1989; Ullrich & Wollheim, 1988), a similar G-protein may act both on effector systems in the plasma membrane and on the putative fusion pore.

Galanin

Galanin, a 29 amino-acid peptide initially isolated from the porcine small intestine (Tatemoto *et al.*, 1983), is localized in nerve fibres innervating the endocrine as well as the exocrine pancreas (Dunning *et al.*, 1986). It is established that galanin inhibits basal and stimulated insulin secretion both *in vivo* and *in vitro* (Ahrén *et al.*, 1991*a*). Galanin receptors have been identified in a hamster pancreatic B-cell tumour and in clonal insulin-producing RINm5F cells (Amiranoff *et al.*, 1987; Sharp *et al.*, 1989). The latter study, using ^{125}I-labelled galanin, indicated a single set of binding sites. Displacement of ^{125}I-labelled galanin by galanin from these receptor sites, occurred over a concentration range similar to that which inhibited insulin release (Sharp *et al.*, 1989). Although it might be argued that the effects of galanin on the insulin secretory process reflect interference with glucose metabolism, we have not observed such an effect on islet glucose oxidation (D. Eizirik & P.-O. Berggren, unpublished work).

In a previous study we have demonstrated that galanin did not affect the B-cell membrane potential or $[Ca^{2+}]_i$ under non-stimulatory conditions (Ahrén *et al.*, 1986*a*). Moreover, there was no interference of the peptide with the rise in $[Ca^{2+}]_i$ induced by depolarization of the cells with high concentrations of K^+ (Fig. 1) (Nilsson *et al.*, 1989). However, under these conditions insulin release was suppressed, indicating a dissociation between the rise in $[Ca^{2+}]_i$ and the activation of the secretory machinery. Indeed, studies on permeabilized cells have revealed that galanin directly inhibits exocytosis in a Ca^{2+}-independent fashion (Ullrich & Wollheim, 1989). In this context, it should be mentioned that insulin release evoked by the phorbol ester PMA in the RINm5F cells was also inhibited by galanin, over the same concentration range as for the inhibition of glyceraldehyde-stimulated release (Sharp *et al.*, 1989). PMA activates PKC and seems to stimulate insulin secretion by a Ca^{2+}-dependent and a Ca^{2+}-independent mechanism (Vallar *et al.*, 1987). The inhibitory effect of galanin on insulin release in normal B-cells was partially reversed by increasing the concentration of glucose in the incubation medium, indicating that the sugar is able to promote secretion by a mechanism not related to changes in $[Ca^{2+}]_i$. This suggests that glucose increases the sensitivity of the secretory machinery to the prevailing $[Ca^{2+}]_i$ and that such a sensitization might partly result from PKC activation.

When galanin was added to B-cells stimulated by 20 mM-glucose, there was a rapid decrease in membrane potential and $[Ca^{2+}]_i$ (Ahrén *et al.*, 1986*a*; Nilsson *et al.*, 1989 and Fig. 2). The reduction of $[Ca^{2+}]_i$ comprised an initial nadir followed by a slow rise and the establishment of a new steady-state level, although still lower than in the absence of galanin. This level was dependent on Ca^{2+} influx through voltage-activated Ca^{2+} channels, since it was reduced by the Ca^{2+}-channel blocker D-600. Despite the slow increase of $[Ca^{2+}]_i$, insulin secretion remained inhibited. In analogy to what has been discussed above, this inhibition could be partially reversed by depolarizing the cells with high concentrations of K^+ and thereby further raising $[Ca^{2+}]_i$ (Nilsson *et al.*, 1989). Furthermore, addition of 5 mM-Ca^{2+} to glucose-stimulated cells in the presence of galanin, promoted a marked and rapid increase in $[Ca^{2+}]_i$ followed by a decrease, which turned into an oscillatory pattern of $[Ca^{2+}]_i$ changes, decaying with time (Nilsson *et al.*, 1989). It is noteworthy, that in the absence of galanin smaller and less frequent oscillations emerged and only the transient increase in $[Ca^{2+}]_i$ was observed. The increase in $[Ca^{2+}]_i$ as well as the oscillations were attenuated by the addition of D-600, implying the participation of voltage-activated Ca^{2+} channels. The fact that an increase in the extracellular Ca^{2+} concentration can increase $[Ca^{2+}]_i$, despite the presence of galanin, suggests that the peptide may have a certain influence directly on the voltage-activated Ca^{2+} channels. However, direct measurements of the Ca^{2+} current have to be performed before such an effect can be clearly established. Since galanin was without effect when $[Ca^{2+}]_i$ was increased subsequent to stimulation with high concentrations of K^+ (Fig. 1) (Nilsson et al., 1989), a direct effect of the peptide on the Ca^{2+} channel seems unlikely. Nevertheless, at this stage it would be premature to rule out that a minor direct inhibition of the voltage-activated Ca^{2+} channels is part of the mechanism whereby galanin lowers $[Ca^{2+}]_i$ in pancreatic B-cells.

Since changes in K^+ permeability have profound effects on B-cell membrane potential, the mechanism underlying galanin-induced repolarization is best explained in terms of increased K^+ conductance (see also Chapter 9 by Henquin et al.). Accordingly, it was demonstrated that neither an increased influx of Cl^- nor a reduced inflow of Ca^{2+} was responsible for the agonist-evoked repolarization (Nilsson et al., 1989). Based on experiments in clonal insulin-producing RINm5F cells, the repolarizing action of galanin has been suggested to involve activation of the ATP-regulated K^+ channels (de Weille et al., 1988; Fosset et al., 1988; Dunne et al., 1989; de Weille et al., 1989). However, these effects are not consistently obtained when studying normal pancreatic B-cells (Ahrén et al., 1989), a fact that may be accounted for by washout of intracellular coupling factors during conventional whole-cell recordings. By taking the advantage of the perforated-patch whole-cell technique, a novel method which permits the recording of whole-cell membrane currents from metabolically intact cells (Horn & Marty, 1988), we have recently suggested instead that galanin activates the same low-conductance K^+ channels as somatostatin and α_2-adrenergic agonists (see above).

It is noteworthy that the effects of galanin were reversed if the B-cells were pretreated with pertussis toxin (Amiranoff et al., 1988; Nilsson et al., 1989). This indicates the participation of a G-protein of the inhibitory (G_i) type, in this inhibitory signal-transduction pathway (Ui, 1984). It is not likely that pertussis toxin exerts its effects only by increasing the cellular content of cyclic AMP (Sharp et al., 1989), since the agonist induced a lowering in $[Ca^{2+}]_i$, despite the presence of the adenylate cyclase activator forskolin. A pertussis toxin-sensitive G-protein, purified from erythrocytes, has been reported to directly activate K^+ channels in atrial muscle cells (Brown & Birnbaumer, 1988). Moreover, we have found that the ability of galanin to activate the low conductance and sulphonylurea-insensitive K^+ channels was abolished by pretreatment of the cells with pertussis toxin (Nilsson et al., 1989; Rorsman et al., 1991; Wåhlander et al., 1991a), suggesting that these K^+ channels are operated by a similar type of G_i-protein. The repolarization-induced decrease in $[Ca^{2+}]_i$ was not solely responsible for the inhibitory effects on insulin release. Hence, either there exists several galanin-associated G-proteins with sensitivity to the toxin, or the putative G-protein has more than one effector system (Brown & Birnbaumer, 1988). Interestingly, studies performed on both permeabilized neutrophils and RINm5F cells and on dialysed mast cells have demonstrated that the non-hydrolysable GTP analogue guanosine 5'-(3-O-thio)trisphosphate, stimulates secretion even at vanishingly low Ca^{2+} concentrations. This implies a Ca^{2+}-independent mechanism for secretion regulated by a G-protein (Vallar et al., 1987). Thus, it is tempting to speculate that galanin also exerts its effects by interacting with a similar G-protein-regulated pathway for exocytosis in the normal B-cell (Ullrich & Wollheim, 1989).

Neuropeptide Y

Neuropeptide Y (NPY) was initially isolated from porcine brain (Tatemoto et al., 1982). It consists of 36 amino acids and shows structural similarities to PYY and pancreatic polypeptide (Tatemoto et al., 1982). NPY is widely distributed in central and peripheral neurones and is often co-stored and co-released with nonadrenaline (Potter, 1988). Nerves containing NPY have been found in both the endocrine and exocrine part of the pancreas, usually surrounding blood vessels but occasionally also in close connection to endocrine cells (Carlei et al., 1985; Pettersson et al., 1987). NPY has been found to inhibit both basal and glucose-stimulated insulin release (Moltz & McDonald, 1985). Consequently, NPY might be of importance in mediating sympathetic neurally induced inhibition of insulin secretion. This is supported by the finding that splanchnic or pancreatic nerve activation stimulates the release of NPY from the pig pancreas (Sheikh et al., 1988).

Conclusions

The mechanisms of action of entero-insular hormones, islet peptides and neural input on the insulin-secretory process are known only in some cases, and even then the molecular interactions are not completely understood. Nevertheless, in Fig. 6 we have made an attempt to summarize what is known so far about their effects on the stimulus–secretion coupling in the pancreatic B-cell.

GIP, glucagon and GLP-1$_{(7-36)}$amide most likely act through the activation of adenylate cyclase and thereby the formation of cyclic AMP. Acetylcholine, CCK, bombesin and GRP probably exert their effects, at least in part, through the activation of the phospholipase C system and thereby the generation of $Ins(1,4,5)P_3$ and diacylglycerol, the former compound releasing intracellularly bound Ca^{2+} whereas the latter activates PKC. When discussing 'cross-talk' between various intracellular signalling systems, it is of interest to note that glucagon and CCK may act through a dual-receptor system, i.e. activation of different receptors coupled to the adenylate cyclase- and phospholipase C systems. Somatostatin, galanin and

α_2-adrenergic agonists inhibit insulin release by interacting with receptors that are coupled to their effector sites through G-proteins. Effector sites localized in the plasma membrane affect both a low-conductance, sulphonylurea-insensitive, G-protein (G_k)-regulated K^+ channel and the

---

Fig. 6.   Possible mechanisms of action of entero-insular hormones, islet peptides and neural input on the insulin secretory process

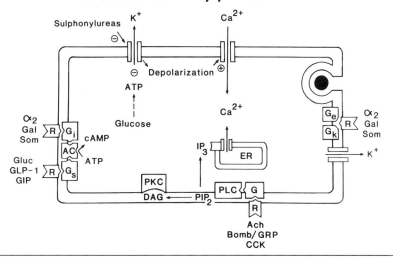

For details see text. Abbreviations: AC, adenylate cyclase; G_s, G_i, G_k, G_e, stimulatory, inhibitory, K^+-channel-regulating and exocytosis-regulating GTP-binding protein; PLC, phospholipase C; PIP_2, inositol 4,5-bisphosphate $[PtdIns(4,5)P_2]$; IP_3, inositol 1,4,5-trisphosphate $[Ins(1,4,5)P_3]$; DAG, diacyl-glycerol; PKC, protein kinase C; ER, endoplasmic reticulum; GIP, gastric inhibitory polypeptide; Gluc, glucagon; GLP-I, glucagon-like peptide $I_{(7-36)}$amide; Ach, acetylcholine; CCK, cholecystokinin; Bomb, Bombesin; GRP, gastrin-releasing peptide; Som, somatostatin; Gal, galanin; α_2, α_2-adrenergic agonists.

---

adenylate cyclase system. Effector sites within the cell affect a G-protein that directly regulates the exocytotic machinery.

The authors are indebted to Katarina Breitholtz, Christina Bremer-Jonsson, Lena Ehrenstig and Susanne Rydstedt for excellent typing of the manuscript. The 'authors' own research discussed in the chapter was supported by the Swedish Medical Research Council (grants were 19X-00034, 19P-9434, 04X-08641 and 12X-08647), the Bank of Sweden Tercentenary Foundation, the Swedish Diabetes Association, the Nordic Insulin Foundation, the Aage Louis-Hansens Memorial Foundation, the Magnus Bergvalls Foundation, the Tore Nilsons Foundation for Medical Research, *the Family Ernfors Foundation, the Torsten and Ragnar Söderbergs Foundations, the Lars Hiertas Memorial Foundation, the Fredrik and Ingrid Thurings Foundation, Funds of the Karolinska Institute and the Swedish Society of Medicine, the Department of Health and Social Services (NI) and the University of Ulster Research Committee.*

References

Ahrén, B. (1988) ANF inhibits glucose-stimulated insulin secretion in mouse and rat. Am. J. Physiol. **255**, E579–582

Ahrén, B., Håkanson, R., Lundquist, I., Sjölund, K. & Sundler, F. (1981) Immunoreactive GIP in glucagon cells: interactions between GIP and glucagon on insulin release. Acta Physiol. Scand. **112**, 233–242

Ahrén, B., Arkhammar, P., Berggren, P.-O. & Nilsson, T. (1986*a*) Galanin inhibits glucose-stimulated insulin release by a mechanism involving hyperpolarization and lowering of cytoplasmic free Ca^{2+} concentration. Biochem. Biophys. Res. Commun. **140**, 1059–1063

Ahrén, B., Taborsky, G. J., Jr. & Porte, D., Jr. (1986*b*) Neuropeptidergic versus cholinergic and adrenergic regulation of islet hormone secretion. Diabetologia **29**, 827–836

Ahrén, B., Mårtensson, H. & Nobin, A. (1988) Cholecystokinin (CCK)-4 and CCK-8 stimulate islet hormone secretion *in vivo* in the pig. Pancreas **3**, 279–284

Ahrén, B., Berggren, P.-O., Bokvist, K. & Rorsman, P. (1989) Does galanin inhibit insulin secretion by opening of the ATP-regulated K^+-channel in the B-cell? Peptides **10**, 453–457

Ahrén, B., Östenson, C.-G. & Efendic, S. (1991*a*) Other islet peptides. In: The Endocrine Pancreas (Samols, E. ed.), pp. 153–173, Raven Press, New York

Ahrén, B., Östenson, C.-G., Mårtensson, H. & Efendic, S. (1991*b*) Pancreatic release of pancreastatin in the pig. Pancreas **6**, 324–329

Amiranoff, B., Servin, A. L., Rouyer-Fessard, C., Couvineau, A., Tatemoto, K. & Laburthe, M. (1987) Galanin receptors in a hamster pancreatic B-cell tumour: Identification and molecular characterization. Endocrinology **121**, 284–289

Amiranoff, B., Lorinet, A.-M., Lagny-Pourmir, I. & Laburthe, M. (1988) Mechanism of galanin-inhibited insulin release occurrence of a pertussis-toxin-sensitive inhibition of adenylate cyclase. Eur. J. Biochem. **177**, 147–152

Arkhammar, P., Nilsson, T. & Berggren, P.-O. (1986) Stimulation of insulin release by the phorbolester 12-O-tetradecanoylphorbol 13-acetate in the clonal cell line RINm5F despite a lowering of the free cytoplasmic Ca^{2+} concentration. Biochim. Biophys. Acta **887**, 236–241

Arkhammar, P., Nilsson, T., Rorsman, P. & Berggren, P.-O. (1987) Inhibition of ATP-regulated K^+ channels precedes depolarization-induced increase in cytoplasmic free Ca^{2+} concentration in pancreatic β-cells. J. Biol. Chem. **262**, 5448–5454

Arkhammar, P., Nilsson, T., Welsh, M., Welsh, N. & Berggren, P.-O. (1989) Effects of protein kinase C activation on the regulation of stimulus-secretion coupling in pancreatic B-cells. Biochem. J. **264**, 207–215

Berggren, P.-O., Arkhammar, P. & Nilsson, T. (1989*a*) Protein kinase C activation in insulin-producing cells assists in recovery from raised cytoplasmic free Ca^{2+}. Biochem. Biophys. Res. Commun. **165**, 416–421

Berggren, P.-O., Hallberg, A., Welsh, N., Arkhammar, P., Nilsson, T. & Welsh, M. (1989*b*) Transfection of insulin-producing cells with a transforming C-Ha-ras oncogene stimulates phospholipase C activity. Biochem. J. **259**, 701–707

Berggren, P.-O., Rorsman, P., Arkhammar, P. & Nilsson, T. (1990) Mechanisms of action of entero-insular hormones and neural input on the insulin secretory process. Biochem. Soc. Trans. **18**, 119–122

Berridge, M. J. (1985) The molecular basis of communication within the cell. Sci. Am. **253**, 124–134

Bokvist, K., Ämmälä, C., Berggren, P.-O., Rorsman, P. & Wåhlander, K. (1991) Alpha$_2$-adrenoreceptor stimulation does not inhibit L-type calcium channels in mouse pancreatic β-cells. Biosci. Rep. in the press

Böttcher, G., Ahrén, B., Lundquist, I. & Sundler, F. (1989) Peptide YY: Intrapancreatic localization and effects on insulin and glucagon secretion in the mouse. Pancreas **4**, 282–288

Bretherton-Watt, D., Ghatei, M. A., Bishop, A. E., Facer, P., Fahey, M., Hedges, M., Williams, G., Valentino, K. L., Tatemoto, K., Roth, K., Polak, J. M. & Bloom, S. R. (1988) Pancreastatin distribution and plasma levels in the pig. Peptides **9**, 1005–1014

Brown, A. M. & Birnbaumer, L. (1988) Direct G-protein gating of ion channels. Am. J. Physiol. **254**, H401–H410

Brown, M. R., Rivier, J. & Vale, W. W. (1977) Bombesin affects the central nervous system to produce hyperglycemia in rats. Life Sci. **21**, 1729–1734

Carlei, F., Allen, J. M., Bishop, A. E., Bloom, S. R. & Polak, J. M. (1985) Occurrence, distribution and nature of neuropeptide Y in the rat pancreas. Experientia **41**, 1544–1557

Chabot, J. G., Morel, G., Kopelman, H., Belles-Isles, M. & Heisler, S. (1987) Atrial natriuretic factor and exocrine pancreas: autoradiographic localization of binding sites and ultrastructural evidence for internalization of endogenous ANF. Pancreas **2**, 404–413

Chen, Z., Agerberth, B., Gell, K., Andersson, M., Mutt, V., Östenson, C.-G., Efendic, S., Barros-Söderling, J., Persson, B. & Jörnvall, H. (1988) Isolation and characterization of porcine diazepam-binding inhibitor, a polypeptide not only of cerebral occurrence but also common in intestinal tissues and with effects on regulation of insulin release. Eur. J. Biochem. **174**, 239–245

Conlon, J. M. (1988) Proglucagon-derived peptides: nomenclature, biosynthetic relationships and physiological roles. Diabetologia **31**, 563–566

Cook, D. L. & Perara, E. (1982) Islet electrical pacemaker response to alpha-adrenergic stimulation. Diabetes **31**, 985–990

Creba, J. A., Downes, C. P., Hawkins, P. T., Brewster, G., Michell, R. H. & Kirk, C. J. (1983) Rapid breakdown of phosphatidylinositol 4-phosphate and phosphatidyl inositol 4,5-bisphosphate in rat hepatocytes stimulated by vasopressin and other Ca^{2+}-mobilizing hormones. Biochem. J. **212**, 733–747

Creutzfeldt, W. & Ebert, R. (1985) New developments in the incretin concept. Diabetologia **28**, 565–573

de Bolde, A. J. (1986) Atrial natriuretic factor: An overview. Fed. Proc. Fed. Am. Soc. Exp. Biol. **45**, 2081–2085

de Weille, J., Schmid-Antonmarchi, H., Fosset, M. & Lazdunski, M. (1988) ATP-sensitive K^+ channels that are blocked by hypoglycemia-inducing sulfonylureas in insulin-secreting cells are activated by galanin, a hyperglycemia-inducing hormone. Proc. Natl. Acad. Sci. U.S.A. **85**, 1312–1316

de Weille, J. R., Schmid-Antonmarchi, H., Fosset, M. & Lazdunski, M. (1989) Regulation of ATP-sensitive K^+-channels in insulinoma cells: Activation by somatostatin and protein kinase and the role of cAMP. Proc. Natl. Acad. Sci. U.S.A. **86**, 2971–2975

Di Virgilio, F., Pozzan, T., Wollheim, C. B., Vincentini, L. M. & Meldolesi, J. (1986) Tumor promoter phorbol myristate acetate inhibits Ca^{2+} influx through voltage-activated Ca^{2+} channels in two secretory cell lines PC12 and RINm5F. J. Biol. Chem. **261**, 32–35

Drucker, D. J., Philippe, J., Mojsov, S., Chick, W. L. & Habener, J. F. (1987) Glucagon-like peptide 1 stimulates insulin gene expression and increases cyclic AMP levels in rat islet cell line. Proc. Natl. Acad. Sci. U.S.A. **84**, 3434–3438

Dunlap, K. & Fischbach, G. D. (1981) Neurotransmitters decrease the calcium conductance activated by depolarization of embryonic chick sensory neurons. J. Physiol. (London) **317**, 519–535

Dunne, M. J., Bullett, M. J., Quodong, L., Wollheim, C. B. & Petersen, O. H. (1989) Galanin activates nucleotide-dependent K^+-channels in insulin-secreting cells via a pertussis toxin-sensitive G-protein. EMBO. J. **8**, 413–420

Dunning, B. E., Ahrén, B., Veith, R. C., Böttcher, G., Sundler, F. V. & Taborsky, G. J., Jr. (1986) Galanin: A novel pancreatic neuropeptide. Am. J. Physiol. **251**, E127–E133

Efendic, S., Tatemoto, K., Mutt, V., Quan, C., Chang, D. & Östenson, C.-G. (1987) Pancreastatin and islet hormone release. Proc. Natl. Acad. Sci., U.S.A. **84**, 7257–7260

Fahrenkrug, J., Holst Pedersen, J., Yamashita, Y., Ottesen, B., Hökfelt, T. & Lundberg, J. M. (1987) Occurrence of VIP and peptide HM in human pancreas and their influence on pancreatic endocrine secretion in man. Regul. Pept. **18**, 51–61

Flatt, P. R., Shibier, O., Hampton, S. M. & Marks, V. (1990) Stimulatory effects of glucagon-like peptides on human insulinoma cells and insulin-releasing clonal RINm5F cells. Diab. Res. **13**, 55–59

Fosset, M., Schmid-Antomarchi, H., De Weille, J. R. & Lazdunski, M. (1988) Somatostatin activates glibenclamide-sensitive and ATP-regulated K^+-channels in insulinoma cells via a G-protein. FEBS Lett. **242**, 94–96

Funakoshi, A., Miyasaka, K., Kitani, K., Tamamura, H., Funakoshi, S. & Yajima, H. (1989) Bioactivity of synthetic C-terminal fragment of rat pancreastatin on endocrine pancreas. Biochem. Biophys. Res. Commun. **158**, 844–849

Funakoshi, A., Tateishi, K., Shinozaki, H., Matsumoto, M. & Wakasugi, H. (1990) Elevated plasma levels of pancreastatin (PST) in patients with non-insulin-dependent diabetes mellitus (NIDDM). Regul. Pept. **30**, 159–164

Göke, R. & Conlon, J. M. (1988) Receptor for glucagon-like peptide-$1_{(7-36)}$ amide on rat insulinoma-derived cells. J. Endocrinol. **116**, 362–367

Grill, V. & Östenson, C.-G. (1983) Muscarinic receptors in pancreatic islets of the rat. Demonstration and dependence on long-term glucose environment. Biochim. Biophys. Acta **756**, 159–162

Guidotti, A., Forchetti, C. M., Corda, M. G., Konkel, D., Bennett, C. D. & Costa, E. (1983) Isolation, characterization and purification to homogeneity of an endogenous polypeptide with agonistic action on benzodiazepine receptors. Proc. Natl. Acad. Sci. U.S.A. **80**, 3531–3535

Harrison, D. E., Ashcroft, S. J. H., Christie, M. R. & Lord, J. M. (1984) Protein phosphorylation in the pancreatic B-cell. Experientia **40**, 1075–1084

Helman, L. J., Ahn, T. G., Levine, M. A., Allison, A., Cohen, P. S., Cooper, M. J., Cohn, D. V. & Israel, M. A. (1988) Molecular cloning and primary structure of human chromogranin A (secretory protein I) cDNA. J. Biol. Chem. **263**, 11559–11563

Henquin, J. C. & Meissner, H. P. (1982) Opposite effects of tolbutamide and diazoxide on $^{86}Rb^+$ fluxes and membrane potential in pancreatic B-cells. Biochem. Pharmacol. **31**, 1407–1415

Hii, C. S. T., Jones, P. M., Persaud, S. J. & Howell, S. L. (1987) A re-assessment of the role of protein kinase C in glucose-stimulated insulin secretion. Biochem. J. **246**, 489–493

Holst, J. J., Fahrenkrug, J., Knuhtsen, S., Jensen, S. L., Poulsen, S. S. & Nielsen, O. V. (1984) Vasoactive intestinal polypeptide (VIP) in the pig pancreas: Role of VIPergic fibers in control of fluid and bicarbonate secretion. Regul. Pept. **8**, 245–249

Holst, J. J., Östenson, C.-G., Harling, H. & Messell, T. (1990) Porcine pancreastatin has no effect on endocrine secretion from the pig pancreas. Diabetologia **33**, 403–406

Horn, R. & Marty, A. (1988) Muscarinic activation of ionic currents measured by a new whole-cell recording mode. J. Gen. Physiol. **92**, 145–169

Iacangelo, A., Affolter, H.-U., Eiden, L. E., Herbert, E. & Grimes, M. (1986) Bovine chromogranin A sequence and distribution of its messenger RNA in endocrine tissues. Nature (London) **323**, 82–86

Iacangelo, A. L., Fischer-Colbrie, R., Koller, K. J., Brownstein, M. J. & Eiden, L. E. (1988*a*) The sequence of porcine chromogranin A messenger RNA demonstrates chromagranin A can serve as the precursor for the biologically active hormone, pancreastatin. Endocrinology **122**, 2339–2341

Iacangelo, A. L., Okayama, H. & Eiden, L. E. (1988*b*) Primary structure of rat chromogranin A and distribution of its mRNA. FEBS Lett. **227**, 115–121

Ipp, E. & Unger, R. H. (1979) Bombesin stimulates the release of insulin and glucagon, but not pancreatic somatostatin, from the isolated perfused dog pancreas. Endocr. Res. Commun. **6**, 37–42

Ishizuka, J., Singh, P., Greeley, G. H. Jr., Townsend, C. M. Jr., Cooper, J. W., Tatemoto, K. & Thompson, J. C. (1988) A comparison of the insulinotropic and the insulin-inhibitory actions of gut peptides on newborn and adult rat islet cells. Pancreas **3**, 77–82

Johansson, O., Hilliges, M., Östenson, C.-G., Sandberg, E., Efendic, S. & Mutt, V. (1991) Immunohistochemical localization of porcine diazepam-binding inhibitor (DBI) to rat endocrine pancreas. Cell Tissue Res. **263**, 395–398

Katada, T. & Ui, M. (1979) Islet-activating protein. Enhanced insulin secretion and cyclic AMP accumulation in pancreatic islets due to activation of native calcium ionophores. J. Biol. Chem. **254**, 469–479

Kawano, H., Daikopku, S. & Saito, S. (1985) Location of thyrotropin-releasing hormone-like immunoreactivity in rat pancreas. Endocrinology (Copenhagen) **112**, 951–955

Knudsen, J., Hojrup, P., Hansen, H. O., Hansen, H. F. & Roepstorff, P. (1989) Acyl-CoA-binding protein in the rat. Biochem. J. **262**, 513–519

Knudtzon, J. (1985) Involvement of the autonomic nervous system in the *in vivo* TRH-induced increases in the plasma levels of glucagon, insulin and glucose in rabbits. Horm. Metab. Res. **17**, 53–57

Kreymann, B., Williams, G., Ghatei, M. A. & Bloom, S. R. (1987) Glucagon-like peptide-1_{7-36}: a physiological incretin in man. Lancet **ii**, 1300–1304

Kuhn, M., Ammon, H. P. T. & Verspohl, E. J. (1988) Atrial natriuretic peptide (ANP) acts via specific receptors on cGMP system of rat pancreatic islets without affecting insulin release. Diabetologia **31**, 511A

Larsson, L. I. (1979) Innervation of the pancreas by substance P, enkephalin, vasoactive intestinal polypeptide and gastrin-CCK immunoreactive nerves. J. Histochem. Cytochem. **27**, 1283–1284

Lindop, G. B. M., Mallon, E. A. & MacIntyre, G. (1986) Atrial natriuretic peptide in the heart and pancreas. Histol. Histopathol. **1**, 147–154

Lorinet, A.-M., Tatemoto, K., Laburthe, M. & Amiranoff, B. (1989) Pancreastatin inhibits insulin release from RINm5F cells: reversion by pertussis toxin. Eur. J. Pharmacol. **160**, 405–407

Luini, A., Lewis, D., Guild, S., Schofield, G. & Weight, F. (1986) Somatostatin, an inhibitor of ACTH secretion, decreases cytosolic free calcium and voltage-dependent calcium current in a pituitary cell line. J. Neurosci. **6**, 3128–3132

Malaisse, W. J., Sener, A., Herchuelz, A., Carpinelli, A. R., Polozcek, P., Winand, J. & Castagna, M. (1980) Insulinotropic effect of the tumor promoter 12-O-tetradecanoylphorbol-13-acetate in rat pancreatic islets. Cancer Res. **40**, 3827–3831

Marchetti, C., Carbone, E. & Lux, H. D. (1986) Effects of dopamine and noradrenaline on Ca channels of cultured sensory and sympathetic neurons of chick. Pflüegers Arch. **406**, 104–111

Matozaki, T., Göke, B., Tsunoda, Y., Rodriguez, M., Martinez, J. A. & Williams, J. A. (1990) Two functionally distinct cholecystokinin receptors show different modes of action on Ca^{2+} mobilization and phospholipid hydrolysis in isolated rat pancreatic acini. J. Biol. Chem. **265**, 6247–6254

Miller, R. E. (1981) Pancreatic neuroendocrinology: Peripheral neural mechanisms in the regulation of the islets of Langerhans. Endocr. Rev. **4**, 471–494

Moghimzadeh, E., Ekman, R., Håkanson, R., Yanaihara, N. & Sundler, F. (1983) Neuronal gastrin-releasing peptide in the mammalian gut and pancreas. Neuroscience **10**, 553–563

Mojsov, S., Weir, G. C. & Habener, J. F. (1987) Insulinotropin: Glucagon-like peptide $I_{(7-37)}$ co-encoded in the glucagon gene is a potent stimulator of insulin release in the perfused rat pancreas. J. Clin. Invest. **79**, 616–619

Mollard, P., Dufy, B., Vacher, P., Barker, J. L. & Schlegel, W. (1990) Thyrotropin-releasing hormone activates a $[Ca^{2+}]_i$-dependent K^+ current in GH_3 pituitary cells via Ins(1,4,5)P_3. Biochem. J. **268**, 345–352

Moltz, J. H. & Fawcett, C. P. (1985) Corticotropin-releasing factor inhibits insulin release from perfused rat pancreas. Am. J. Physiol. **248**, E741–E743

Moltz, J. H. & McDonald, J. K. (1985) Neuropeptide Y. Direct and indirect action on insulin secretion in the rat. Peptides **6**, 1155–1159

Morley, J. E., Levin, S. R., Pehlevanian, M., Adachi, R., Pekary, A. E. & Hersmam, J. M. (1979) The effects of thyrotropin-releasing hormone on the endocrine pancreas. Endocrinology **104**, 137–139

Mutt, V. (1980) Cholecystokinin: Isolation, structure, and function. In: Gatrointestinal Peptides. (Glass, G. B. J., ed.), pp. 169–221, Raven Press, New York

Neer, E. J. & Clapham, D. E. (1988) Role of G-proteins involved in transmembrane signalling. Nature (London) **333**, 129–134

Nilsson, T., Arkhammar, P., Hallberg, A., Hellman, B. & Berggren, P.-O. (1987) Characterization of the inositol 1,4,5-trisphosphate-induced Ca^{2+} release in normal pancreatic B-cells. Biochem. J. **248**, 329–336

Nilsson, T., Arkhammar, P., Rorsman, P. & Berggren, P.-O. (1988) Inhibition of glucose-stimulated insulin release by α_2-adrenoceptor activation is parallelled by both a repolarization and a reduction in cytoplasmic free Ca^{2+} concentration. J. Biol. Chem. **263**, 1855–1860

Nilsson, T., Arkhammar, P., Rorsman, P. & Berggren, P.-O. (1989) Suppression of insulin release by galanin and somatostatin is mediated by a G-protein: an effect involving repolarization and reduction in cytoplasmic free Ca^{2+} concentration. J. Biol. Chem. **264**, 973–980

Östenson, C.-G. & Grill, V. (1987) Evidence that hyperglycemia increases muscarinic binding in pancreatic islets of the rat. Endocrinology **121**, 1705–1710

Östenson, C.-G., Efendic, S. & Holst, J. J. (1989*a*) Pancreastatin-like immunoreactivity and insulin are released in parallel from the perfused porcine pancreas. Endocrinology **124**, 2986–2990

Östenson C.-G., Sandler, S. & Efendic, S. (1989*b*) Effects of porcine pancreastatin on secretion and biosynthesis of insulin, and glucose oxidation of isolated rat pancreatic islets. Pancreas **4**, 441–446

Östenson, C.-G., Ahrén, B., Karlsson, S., Sandberg, E. & Efendic, S. (1990) Effects of porcine diazepam-binding inhibitor on insulin and glucagon secretion *in vitro* from the rat endocrine pancreas. Regul. Pept. **29**, 143–151

Peter-Riesch, B., Fathi, M., Schlegel, W. & Wollheim, C. B. (1988) Glucose and carbachol generate 1,2-diacylglycerol by different mechanisms in pancreatic islets. J. Clin. Invest. **81**, 1154–1161

Petersen, O. H. & Bear, C. (1986) Two glucagon transducing systems. Nature (London) **323**, 18

Petrusz, P., Merchenthaler, I., Maderdrut, J. L., Vigh, S. & Schally, A. V. (1983) Corticotropin-releasing factor (CRF)-like immunoreactivity in the vertebrate endocrine pancreas. Proc. Natl. Acad. Sci. U.S.A. **80**, 1721–1725

Pettersson, M., Ahrén, B., Lundquist, I., Böttcher, G. & Sundler, F. (1987) Neuropeptide Y. Intrapancreatic neuronal localization and effects on insulin secretion in the mouse. Cell. Tissue Res. **248**, 43–48

Pipeleers, D. G. (1987) The biosociology of pancreatic B-cells. Diabetologia **30**, 277–290

Potter, E. K. (1988) Neuropeptide Y as an autonomic neurotransmitter. Pharmacol. Ther. **37**, 251–273

Prentki, M. & Matschinsky, F. M. (1987) Ca^{2+}, cAMP and phospholipid-derived messengers in coupling mechanisms of insulin secretion. Physiol. Rev. **67**, 1185–1248

Prentki, M., Biden, T. J., Janjic, D., Irvine, R. F., Berridge, M. J. & Wollheim, C. B. (1984) Rapid mobilization of Ca^{2+} from rat insulinoma microsomes by inositol 1,4,5-trisphosphate. Nature (London) **309**, 562–564

Rasmussen, H., Zawalich, K. C., Ganesan, S., Calle, R. & Zawalich, W. S. (1990) Physiology and pathophysiology of insulin secretion. Diabetes Care **13**, 655–666

Ravazzola, M., Efendic, S., Östenson, C.-G., Tatemoto, K., Hutton, J. C. & Orci, L. (1988) Localization of pancreastatin immunoreactivity in porcine endocrine cells. Endocrinology (Copenhagen) **123**, 227–229

Rehfeld, J. F., Larsson, L. I., Golterman, N. R., Schwartz, T. W., Holst, J. J., Jensen, S. L. & Morley, J. S. (1980) Neural regulation of pancreatic hormone secretion by the *C*-terminal tetrapeptide of CCK. Nature (London) **284**, 33–38

Rindi, G., Buffa, R., Sessa, F., Tortora, O. & Solcia, E. (1986) Chromogranin A, B, and C immunoreactivities of mammalian endocrine cells. Histochemistry **85**, 19–28

Rorsman, P. & Abrahamsson, H. (1985) Cyclic AMP potentiates glucose-induced release from mouse pancreatic islets without increasing cytosolic free Ca^{2+}. Acta Physiol. Scand. **125**, 639–647

Rorsman, P. & Trube, G. (1985) Glucose dependent K^+ channels in pancreatic β-cells are regulated by intracellular ATP. Pflüegers Arch. **405**, 305–309

Rorsman, P., Arkhammar, P. & Berggren, P.-O. (1986) Voltage-activated Na^+ currents and their suppression by phorbol ester in clonal insulin-producing RINm5F cells. Am. J. Physiol. **251**, C912–C919

Rorsman, P., Berggren, P.-O., Bokvist, K., Ericson, E., Möhler, H., Östenson, C.-G. & Smith, P. A. (1989) Glucose-inhibition of glucagon secretion involves activation of $GABA_A$-receptor chloride channels. Nature (London) **341**, 233–236

Rorsman, P., Bokvist, K., Ämmälä, C., Arkhammar, P., Berggren, P.-O., Larsson, O. & Wåhlander, K. (1991) Activation by adrenaline of a low-conductance G-protein-dependent K^+-channel in mouse pancreatic B-cells. Nature (London) **349**, 74–77

Sandberg, E., Höög, A., Östenson, C.-G., Ahrén, B., Karlsson, S., Grimelius, L., Falkmer, S. & Efendic, S. (1989) Porcine diazepam-binding inhibitor occurs in the D-cells of porcine and human islets, and modulates pancreatic hormone secretion. Diabetologia 32, 537A

Santana de Sa, S., Ferrer, R., Rojas, E. & Atwater, I. (1983) Effects of adrenaline and noradrenaline on glucose-induced electrical activity of mouse pancreatic B-cell. Q. J. Physiol. 68, 247–258

Schlegel, W., Wuarin, F., Wollheim, C. B. & Zahnd, G. R. (1984) Somatostatin lowers the cytosolic free Ca^{2+} concentration in clonal rat pituitary cells (GH$_3$ cells). Cell Calcium 5, 223–236

Schmidt, W. E., Binder, G., Gallwitz, B., Siegel, E. G. & Creutzfeldt, W. (1987) C-terminal fragments of pancreastatin inhibits GIP-induced insulin secretion in isolated rat pancreatic islets. Diabetologia 30, 579A

Schuit, F. C. & Pipeleers, D. G. (1986) Differences in adrenergic recognition by pancreatic A and B cells. Science (Washington D.C.) 232, 875–877

Sharp, G. W. G., LeMarchaud-Brustel, Y., Yada, T., Russo, L. L., Bliss, C. R., Cormont, M., Monge, L. & Van Obberghen, E. (1989) Galanin can inhibit insulin release by a mechanism other than membrane hyperpolarization or inhibition of adenylate cyclase. J. Biol. Chem. 264, 7302–7309

Sheikh, S. P., Holst, J. J., Shek-Nielsen, T., Knigge, U., Warberg, J., Theodorsson-Norheim, E., Hökfelt, T., Lundberg, J. M. & Schwartz, T. W. (1988) Release of NPY in pig pancreas: dual parasympathetic and sympathetic regulation. Am. J. Physiol. 255, G46–G54

Silvestre, R. A., Peiro, E., Miralles, P., Villanueva, M. L. & Marco, J. (1988) Effects of pancreastatin on insulin, glucagon and somatostatin secretion by the perfused rat pancreas. Life Sci. 42, 1361–1367

Sjöholm, A., Funakoshi, A., Efendic, S., Östenson, C.-G. & Hellerström, C. (1991) Long term inhibitory effects of pancreastatin and diazepam binding inhibitor on pancreatic β-cell deoxyribonucleic acid replication, polyamine content, and insulin secretion. Endocrinology, 128, 3277–3282

Smith, P. H., Merchant, F. W., Johnson, D. G., Fujimoto, F. Y. & Williams, R. H. (1977) Immunocytochemical localization of a gastrin inhibitory polypeptide-like material within A-cells of the endocrine pancreas. Am. J. Physiol. 149, 585–590

Sussman, K. E., Leitner, J. W. & Draznin, B. (1987) Cytosolic free-calcium concentrations in normal pancreatic islet cells. Effects of secretagogues and somatostatin. Diabetes 36, 571–577

Szecowka, J., Grill, V., Sandberg, E. & Efendic, S. (1982) Effect of GIP on the secretion of insulin and somatostatin and the accumulation of cyclic AMP in vitro in the rat. Acta Endocrinol. (Copenhagen) 99, 416–421

Szecowka, J., Lins, P. E., Tatemoto, K. & Efendic, S. (1983a) Effects of porcine intestinal heptacosapeptide and vasoactive intestinal polypeptide on insulin and glucagon secretion in rats. Endocrinology (Copenhagen) 112, 1469–1473

Szecowka, J., Tatemoto, K., Rajamäki, G. & Efendic, S. (1983b) Effects of PYY and PP on endocrine pancreas. Acta Physiol. Scand. 119, 123–126

Tamagawa, T. & Henquin, J. C. (1983) Epinephrine modifications of insulin release and of $^{86}Rb^+$ or $^{45}Ca^{2+}$ fluxes in rat islets. Am. J. Physiol. 244, E245–E252

Tatemoto, K., Carlquist, M. & Mutt, V. (1982) Neuropeptide Y — a novel brain peptide with structural similarities to peptide YY and pancreatic polypeptide. Nature (London) 296, 659–660

Tatemoto, K., Rökaeus, Å., Jörnvall, H., McDonald, T. J. & Mutt, V. (1983) Galanin — a novel biologically active peptide from porcine intestine. FEBS Lett. 164, 124–128

Tatemoto, K., Efendic, S., Mutt, V., Makk, G., Feistner, G. J. & Barchas, J. D. (1986) Pancreastatin, a novel pancreatic peptide that inhibits insulin secretion. Nature (London) 324, 476–478

Trube, G., Rorsman, P. & Ohno-Shosaku, T. (1986) Opposite effects of tolbutamide and diazoxide on the ATP-dependent K^+ channel in mouse pancreatic B-cells. Pflüegers Arch. 407, 493–499

Ui, M. (1984) Islet-activating protein, pertussis toxin: a probe for functions of the inhibitory guanine nucleotide regulatory component of adenylate cyclase. Trends Biochem. Sci. 7, 277–279

Ullrich, S. & Wollheim, C. B. (1984) Islet cyclic AMP levels are not lowered during A_2-adrenergic inhibition of insulin release. Studies with epinephrine and forskoline. J. Biol. Chem. **259**, 4111–4115

Ullrich, S. & Wollheim, C. B. (1985) Expression of both A_1- and A_2-adrenoceptors in an insulin-secreting cell line. Parallel studies of cytosolic free Ca^{2+} and insulin release. Mol. Pharmacol. **28**, 100–106

Ullrich, S. & Wollheim, C. B. (1988) GTP-dependent inhibition of insulin secretion by epinephrine in permeabilized RINm5F cells. J. Biol. Chem. **263**, 8615–8620

Ullrich, S. & Wollheim, C. B. (1989) Galanin inhibits insulin secretion by direct interference with exocytosis. FEBS Lett. **247**, 401–404

Vallar, L., Biden, T. J. & Wollheim, C. B. (1987) Guanine nucleotides induce Ca^{2+}-independent insulin secretion from permeabilized RINm5F cells. J. Biol. Chem. **262**, 5049–5056

Valverde, I. & Malaisse, W. J. (1984) Calmodulin and pancreatic B-cell function. Experientia **40**, 1061–1068

Versphol, E. J., Ammon, H. P. T., Williams, J. A. & Goldfine, I. D. (1986) Evidence that cholecystokinin interacts with specific receptors and regulates insulin release in isolated rat islets of Langerhans. Diabetes **35**, 38–43

Wåhlander, K., Ämmälä, C., Berggren, P.-O., Bokvist, K., Juntti-Berggren, L. & Rorsman, P. (1991*a*) Galanin inhibits B-cell electrical activity by a G-protein-regulated sulphonylurea-insensitive mechanism. In: (Hökfelt, T., ed.), Wenner-Gren International Symposium Series, in the press

Wakelam, M. J. O., Murphy, G. J., Hruby, V. J. & Houslay, M. D. (1986) Activation of two signal-transduction systems in hepatocytes by glucagon. Nature (London) **324**, 68–70

Wollheim, C. B., Ullrich, S. & Pozzan, T. (1984) Glyceraldehyde, but not cyclic AMP-stimulated insulin release is preceded by a rise in cytosolic free Ca^{2+}. FEBS Lett. **177**, 17–22

Yamazaki, S., Katada, T. & Ui, M. (1982) Alpha$_2$-adrenergic inhibition of insulin secretion via interference with cyclic AMP generation in rat pancreatic islets. Mol. Pharmacol. **21**, 648–653

Zawalich, W. S., Diaz, V. A. & Zawalich, K. C. (1987) Cholecystokinin-induced alterations in B-cell sensitivity. Diabetes **36**, 1420–1424

15

Molecular mechanisms of sulphonylurea action in the pancreatic B-cell

Daniel A. Nelson, Lydia Aguilar-Bryan, Hussein Raef and Aubrey E. Boyd III*

Department of Medicine, Baylor College of Medicine, Houston, Texas, 77030, U.S.A.

Introduction

Diabetes mellitus occurs in two major forms, insulin-dependent [IDDM, or juvenile onset (type I)] and non-insulin-dependent [NIDDM, or adult onset (type II)] (Zimmet, 1983). NIDDM accounts for 90%–95% of all cases of diabetes and is characterized by fasting hyperglycaemia secondary to excess hepatic glucose production, resistance of the peripheral tissue to insulin, and insulin secretory abnormalities resulting in a relative deficiency of insulin.

    The prevalence figures for adult onset diabetes reveal that the disease is truly global, with spiralling medical and social costs. NIDDM affects an estimated 15–30 million people in affluent societies and 25–50 million in developing countries, where the frequency of the disease is rising. With acculturation, the incidence of NIDDM in certain ethnic groups such as the Arizona Pima Indians (Bennett *et al.*, 1976), the Polynesian Nauruans (Zimmet *et al.*, 1977, 1984) and Mexican Americans (Hanis *et al.*, 1983; Gardner *et al.*, 1984) had increased to 15%–35% of the population. In the last two decades, studies in these and other populations have provided important information on the heterogeneity of the disease, as well as the nature of risk factors that lead to an increased prevalence of the disease, which include obesity, genetic factors and a decrease in physical activity. The susceptibility to develop NIDDM, rather than the disease itself, is inherited and unmasked by environmental factors such as inactivity or increased food intake (Zimmet *et al.*, 1986). As a consequence, the study of genetic and environmental factors leading to NIDDM attracts the attention of both basic scientists and clinicians. Particular scrutiny has been given to the concept of defective signal transduction pathways in the pancreatic B-cell (see Chapter 16 by Flatt *et al.*), and

---

* Present address: Division of Endocrinology, New England Medical Center, 750 Washington Street, Box 275, Boston, MA 02111, U.S.A.

considerable progress has been made in defining how extracellular signals elicit insulin release. These aspects are considered in detail elsewhere in this book.

Orally administered hypoglycaemic sulphonylurea therapy is an effective treatment for NIDDM (for recent reviews see Gerich, 1989; Boyd & Huynh, 1990; Melander et al., 1990). The sulphonylureas stimulate insulin secretion in patients who either fail to comply with exercise and diet regimens, or in whom the fasting blood glucose level is not adequately lowered by the initial therapeutic regimen.

There is an increasing body of evidence that certain physiological insulin secretagogues, including some amino acids and the major secretagogue, glucose, act to stimulate insulin secretion by closure of an ATP-sensitive K^+ channel in the B-cell plasma membrane (for recent reviews see Petersen & Findlay, 1987; Boyd, 1988; Ashcroft, 1988; Rajan et al., 1990). These nutrients are metabolized to generate, among other compounds, the energy currency of the cell, ATP. When serum glucose levels increase, the glucose concentration in the B-cell also rises rapidly, leading to enhanced ATP production and an increase in the intracellular concentration of this nucleotide (Meglasson et al., 1989). The ATP-sensitive K^+ channel is proposed to have a binding site for ATP on the cytoplasmic surface of the plasma membrane, and occupancy of this site is coupled to the energy status of the cell. It is postulated that most of the channels (up to 99%) are normally closed by the ATP present in the resting B-cell (Cook et al., 1988). When ATP levels increase slightly, the remaining K^+ pores are closed, leading to cell depolarization and the stimulation of insulin secretion. These aspects of B-cell stimulus–secretion coupling are considered in depth elsewhere in this book (see chapters 5, 9 and 10 by Malaisse, Henquin et al., and Ashcroft et al., respectively).

The sulphonylureas initiate insulin release by a direct interaction with high-affinity receptors present on the plasma membrane of the B-cell. This binding site is thought to be present on the ATP-sensitive K^+ channel, or on a closely associated protein. Thus, the sulphonylureas may serve to identify a protein of central importance in physiological stimulus–secretion coupling. By further elucidating the nature of the sulphonylurea-binding protein, we may be able to better understand nutrient-regulated insulin secretion, and help unravel alterations in B-cell signal transduction that result in NIDDM.

The sulphonylureas

The observation during the second world war that certain sulphonamide derivates used in the treatment of typhoid fever produced symptoms and signs of hypoglycaemia (Janbon et al., 1942a,b) led to clinical trials in diabetic patients, and it was the success of these trials that promoted the development of sulphonylureas as oral hypoglycaemic agents. The first studies, performed in animals, directed attention to the fundamental role of the pancreas for the action of sulphonylureas. The

Fig. 1.   **Structures of the first generation sulphonylureas, tolbutamide and chlorpropamide, and the second generation compounds, glipizide and glibenclamide (termed glyburide in U.S.A.)**

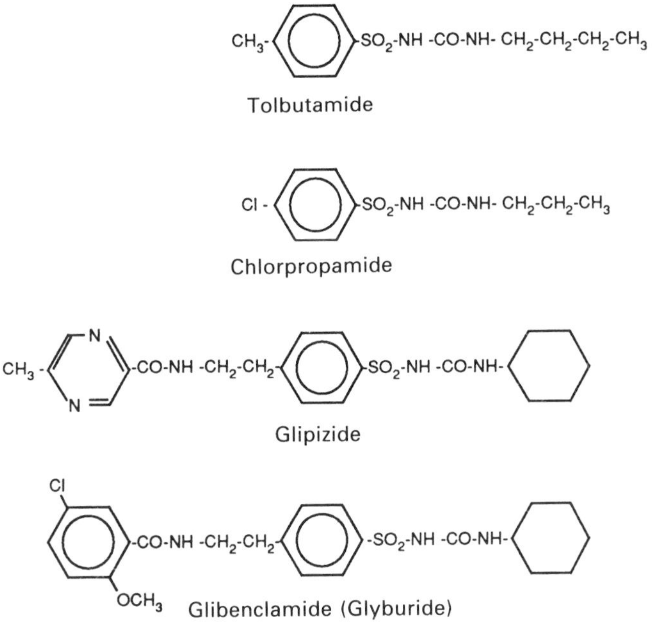

Tolbutamide

Chlorpropamide

Glipizide

Glibenclamide (Glyburide)

pharmacological effect of sulphonylureas appeared to be caused by the direct stimulation of insulin secretion by the B-cell, since these effects did not occur in animals whose pancreas was removed (Loubatieres, 1944, 1957a). On the other hand, when as little as one-sixth of the pancreatic tissue remained present in the abdomen, treatment with sulphonylureas produced hypoglycaemia. In studies performed in humans, it was observed that sulphonylureas could also induce hypoglycaemia in normal subjects and diabetics (Loubatieres, 1957b). With diabetic patients it was observed that most older individuals responded to the drug, whereas only a few of the 'younger' diabetics were responsive to these compounds. Since the 'younger' IDDM patients no longer have B-cells, it was concluded that the presence of islet cells in an individual was required to observe the hypoglycaemic action of the sulphonylureas. Numerous studies have demonstrated that the addition of sulphonylureas to rat pancreas (Bouman & Goorenstroom, 1961), isolated pancreatic islets (Hellman & Taljedal, 1975), isolated B-cells (Gorus *et al.*, 1988) or hamster insulin-secreting tumour (HIT) cells (Nelson *et al.*, 1987) results in rapid insulin release.

Although it is clear that sulphonylureas stimulate insulin secretion from B-cells, other studies suggest that these compounds enhance glucose uptake into peripheral tissues by potentiating the action of insulin (see Lebovitz *et al.*, 1977). Thus, there is some controversy over the major mode of action of these drugs. We subscribe to the notion that the sulphonylureas act primarily by stimulating insulin secretion. The lack of an effect of sulphonylureas on glucose uptake in pancreatectomized animals (Loubatieres, 1957*a*) and in insulin-deficient patients with IDDM (Ratzmann *et al.*, 1984) argues against a significant pharmacological effect of these drugs that is independent of their action on the B-cell.

Two generations of sulphonylureas have been developed, differing in chemical structure and potency (Fig. 1). The first generation compounds have an aliphatic side-chain, the most commonly administered being tolbutamide and chlorpropamide. By substitution of the aliphatic side-chain with a cyclohexyl group, and by the addition of a benzene ring linked to glycine, second generation agents were derived, of which glibenclamide (glyburide) and glipizide are the most commonly prescribed. An important distinction between the older first generation and the newer second generation sulphonylureas is a higher affinity of specific binding of the newer compounds to pancreatic B-cell membranes.

Cell lines in sulphonylurea research

Some of the obstacles in B-cell research include: (1) the limited amount of material that can be obtained from isolated pancreatic islets (only a few milligrams of tissue with the best procedures), and (2) the cellular and hormonal heterogeneity within the pancreatic islets (see Chapters 3 and 14 by Marks *et al.* and Berggren *et al.*). As a result, cloned insulin-secreting cell lines have been developed. The HIT and RIN cells have been studied the most extensively. The radiation-induced transplantable rat insulinoma (RIN) cell line developed by Chick *et al.* (1977) is morphologically well differentiated and capable of synthesizing and storing insulin. RIN cells do not respond to the major physiological insulin secretagogue, glucose, however, they can be stimulated by the triose, glyceraldehyde.

The HIT cell line was established by simian virus 40 transformation of dispersed Syrian hamster pancreatic islet cells (Santerre *et al.*, 1981). HIT cells respond to all of the physiological and pharmacological insulin secretagogues. When using these cells, the length of time in culture is an important consideration. Only early cell passages retain differentiated function and are suitable for secretory studies (Zhang *et al.*, 1989). Our own studies are performed with HIT cells. These cells are stored in liquid N_2 at passage 60, and, after thawing, are routinely used in secretory studies up to passage 70–75. It is important to bear in mind that these are transformed cells. They may have lost some of their normal differentiated functions, and thus results acquired with these cells must be confirmed or reproduced in normal B-cells.

The sulphonylurea receptor

Many models for the action *in vivo* of drugs require specific binding sites on the target cell, which, upon drug binding, promote the cellular response. A reasonable hypothesis for the action of sulphonylureas on the B-cell (Henquin, 1980) is that binding to a specific, high-affinity receptor reduces plasma membrane K^+ permeability, depolarizing the membrane and activating voltage-dependent Ca^{2+} channels. The influx of Ca^{2+} raises the cellular concentration of this cation, which is the signal controlling insulin release. Thus, one attempts to correlate sulphonylurea binding affinity with one or more of the following cellular responses: (1) a reduction in K^+ (or $^{86}Rb^+$, a tracer for K^+) efflux through ATP-sensitive K^+ channels; (2) an increase in the intracellular Ca^{2+} concentration, and (3) insulin secretion.

There is substantial evidence for a high-affinity sulphonylurea binding site on isolated B-cell membranes. Although many of the original binding studies were performed with membranes from brain tissue (a practical source for receptors), these results have been amply confirmed using pancreatic islets and B-cell lines. Secondly, the receptor has been photolabelled with radiolabelled sulphonylureas, and is shown to be a polypeptide of approx. 140 kDa, suggesting that a protein, presumably embedded in the plasma membrane, is solely responsible for sulphonylurea action.

Receptor binding studies

Kaubisch *et al.* (1982) were the first to report the presence of high-affinity sulphonylurea binding sites in membrane preparations from a rat B-cell tumour. Most of their initial binding results, however, were acquired using a crude membrane preparation from rat brain. They reasoned that brain was a suitable source for receptors, and large amounts of membrane could easily be prepared from this tissue. [^{3}H]gliquidone binding to rat cortical membranes was specific, and could be displaced by other sulphonylureas. Dissociation constants (K_ds) were estimated for gliben-clamide (0.06 nM), unlabelled gliquidone (0·9 nM), tolbutamide (1·4 μM) and chlorpropamide (2·8 μM). The binding affinities were correlated with the rank order of the therapeutic doses of the drugs used in diabetic patients. The specific binding of [³H]gliquidone was found on B-cell tumour membranes, but was absent in membranes from a tumour of non-pancreatic origin. These results were extended by Geisen *et al.* (1985) using similar tissues and [³H]glibenclamide. Glibenclamide displaced [³H]glibenclamide (31 Ci/mmol) yielding estimated K_ds of 0·05 nM for rat cerebral cortex membranes and 0·03 nM for rat B-cell tumour membranes. The binding was saturable and reversible. It was also evident that the number of binding sites per mg of membrane protein was much more dense for the B-cell tumour membranes (400 fmol/mg) than found on the cerebral cortex membranes (20 fmol/mg). Specific binding to membranes isolated from other rat tissues including liver, lung, kidney, heart, spleen, diaphragm, duodenum, colon and stomach was negligible, suggesting the receptor was absent, or present in only minute quantities in these membranes. The paucity of sulphonylurea binding sites in other tissues may correlate with clinical observations suggesting these drugs do not have a peripheral tissue effect.

The presence of high-affinity binding sites in B-cells was confirmed using membranes from RIN cells (Schmid-Antomarchi *et al.*, 1987), HIT cells (Gaines *et al.*, 1988) and isolated mouse pancreatic islets (Panten *et al.*, 1989). In all three studies, a high-affinity site was observed using [³H]-glibenclamide [equilibrium binding constant (K_d) in the 0·3–0·8 nM range]. In each case the binding was displaced by other sulphonylureas with the same rank order as their therapeutic efficacy, their biological potency to elicit insulin secretion (Gaines *et al.*, 1988) and their ability to inhibit [86]Rb⁺ efflux (Schmid-Antomarchi *et al.*, 1987). Membranes were reported to contain 150 (RIN), 1090 (HIT) and 930–1380 (mouse islet) fmol of binding sites/mg of membrane protein. The presence of high-affinity binding sites has also been amply confirmed in brain tissue, with K_ds of binding for [³H]glipizide in rat cerebral cortex membranes of 1·5 nM (Lupo & Bataille, 1987), [³H]glibenclamide in porcine brain membranes of 0·8 nM (Benardi *et al.*, 1988) and [³H]glibenclamide in rat brain membranes of 0·7 nM (Mourre *et al.*, 1989). The brain receptor abundance range from 110–140 fmol/mg of membrane protein (rat) to 400 fmol/mg of membrane protein (porcine).

Our group (Aguilar-Bryan *et al.*, 1990) has extended the B-cell observations by preparing and utilizing a novel sulphonylurea similar to glibenclamide that can be radio-iodinated to high specific activity. The iodinated form of the compound has been termed iodo 'glibenclamide', and is depicted in Fig. 2. The high specific activity of this glibenclamide analogue allows rapid acquisition of reliable receptor-binding data. A Scatchard analysis of the equilibrium binding of the ^{125}I-labelled analogue (~ 2,000 Ci/mmol) at 23 °C demonstrates the presence of a high-affinity binding site on HIT cell membranes (K_d of 0·36 nM). There are approximately 1600 fmol of receptor present/mg of membrane protein, a considerably higher number of binding sites than in brain or rat B-cell tumour membranes. Using unlabelled glibenclamide, or unlabelled iodo

Fig. 2.   Structures of (a) glibenclamide, (b) the newly synthesized parent compound used for iodination, and (c) iodo 'glibenclamide'

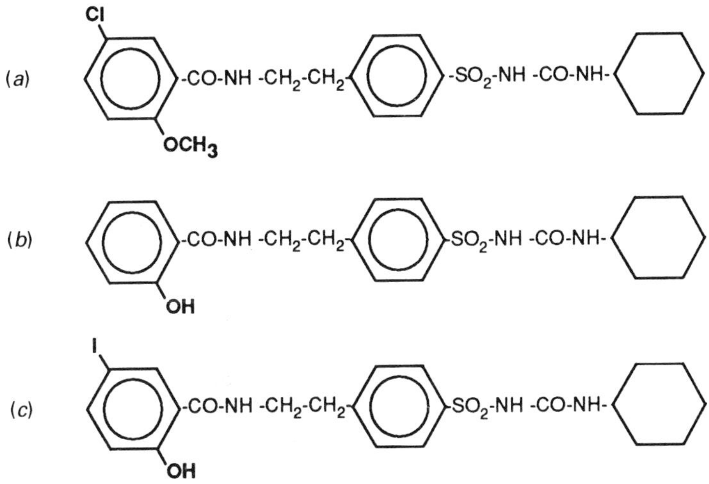

'glibenclamide' in competitive binding assays, the labelled analogue was displaced with K_is of 0·5 nM and 1·0 nM, respectively. Taken in total, these binding studies strongly indicate that a high-affinity sulphonylurea binding site is present in both B-cell and brain crude plasma membrane preparations.

Receptor photolabelling

Kramer *et al.*, (1988) demonstrated that [³H]glibenclamide can be u.v.-crosslinked to the sulphonylurea receptor present in membranes isolated from rat B-cell tumours. Glibenclamide acts as a direct photoaffinity probe, containing benzene rings and aromatic O-methyl esters which make it photoreactive. Tumour membranes were incubated with the [³H]-glibenclamide for 1 h in the dark at room temperature to reach binding equilibrium, and then irradiated for 2 min at 254 nm. Samples were electrophoresed on an SDS polyacrylamide gel, the gel sliced, and gel pieces solubilized and counted in a scintillation counter. The radiolabel was localized to two polypeptide chains of apparent molecular mass 140 kDa and 33 kDa. In competition photolabelling experiments, a half-maximal decrease in photolabelling of the 140 kDa protein was observed in the presence of 20 nM-glibenclamide, or 20 µM-tolbutamide, correlating well with the concentrations of these drugs required for hypoglycaemic activity. Photoaffinity labelling of the 33 kDa polypeptide was not affected by the presence of excess glibenclamide, or tolbultamide, suggesting that this binding is non-specific and that this protein is not the high-affinity receptor.

These results were confirmed for the HIT cell protein using ^{125}I-labelled iodo 'glibenclamide' (Aguilar-Bryan *et al.*, 1990). Iodo 'glibenclamide' photolabelled three proteins in HIT cells with molecular masses of 43 kDa, 65 kDa and 140 kDa. To establish the identities of these proteins, the concentration dependence of the incorporation of ^{125}I-labelled iodo 'glibenclamide' into protein was assessed. Labelling of the 140 kDa protein was evident at the lowest concentration of analogue tested (4·4 nM) with the amount of label incorporated reaching saturation above 22 nM. The low molecular mass bands continued to increase in intensity with higher radiolabelled analogue concentrations, and displayed some labelling in the presence of excess unlabelled iodo 'glibenclamide'. These results support the assignment of the 140 kDa protein as containing the high-affinity site, as well as the contention that the 65 kDa and 43 kDa proteins possess low-affinity binding sites.

Bernardi *et al.* (1988) report that a membrane-bound porcine brain protein of 150 kDa can be solubilized, purified and photolabelled with [3H]glibenclamide. Column fractions obtained during protein purification were incubated with 3 nM-[3H]glibenclamide in the presence and absence of 300 nM unlabelled glibenclamide. Specific photolabelling of the 150 kDa protein was only observed in the absence of unlabelled glibenclamide. The brain, rat tumour and HIT cell photolabelling data clearly support the conclusion that the high-affinity sulphonylurea binding site is present on a membrane-bound polypeptide of 140 kDa–150 kDa.

Receptor isolation

The purified sulphonylurea receptor from porcine brain (Bernardi *et al.*, 1988) retains sulphonylurea-binding activity and may be photolabelled with [3H]glibenclamide. The most successful detergent for removing the protein from the membrane environment with the retention of binding activity was digitonin. Digitonin 1·8% (w/v) yielded about 40% of the active receptor in a soluble protein fraction. Standard methods of stabilizing the native protein structure, including the inclusion of glycerol and phospholipids in the solubilization buffer, were unsuccessful, and the protein rapidly lost binding capacity after purification (half-life of 12 h at 0–4 °C). Binding of the solubilized receptor to [3H]glibenclamide yielded an equilibrium binding constant of 0·8 nM, and a kinetic K_d of 0·3 nM, indicating little change in the affinity of binding as a result of solubilization. Other sulphonylureas were able to displace the [3H]glibenclamide from the solubilized protein at concentrations predicted from the rank order of potency. The protein was purified 2500-fold (to 1000 pmol/mg of protein) by a combination of hydroxylapatite-Ultrogel, ADP-agarose, WGA-Affigel and AMP-plus GMP-agarose. Of particular note are the wheat germ agglutinin (WGA) and ADP-agarose chromatographies. The receptor was observed to bind to these column beds, indicating the protein is glycosylated and contains at least one ADP/ATP binding site. A single band of 150 kDa is observed on a silver-stained SDS polyacrylamide gel, the same molecular mass as the protein specifically photolabelled in solution after purification.

We have obtained complementary results with the HIT-cell sulphonylurea receptor. Of nine non-ionic detergents tested (octyl glucoside, CHAPS, Triton X-100, Nonidet P-40, Lubrol PX, Na-cholate, Na-deoxycholate, Tween 80 and digitonin), only CHAPS, Triton X-100, Nonidet P-40 and digitonin yielded soluble protein with detectable binding activity (Vu et $al.$, 1989). Digitonin (1 % w/v) was the most effective with 30 % of the soluble receptor retaining binding activity. ^{125}I-labelled iodo 'glibenclamide' binds to the soluble receptor with a K_d of 0·42 nM, as determined by a Scatchard analysis of equilibrium binding data. The K_d of the soluble protein is essentially the same as that of the membrane-bound receptor ($K_d = 0·36$ nM), as was observed for the brain protein. Competitive binding with other sulphonylureas was performed and K_is obtained for glibenclamide (1·4 nM), glipizide (29 nM), tolazamide (17 μM), tolbutamide (26 μM) and chlorpropamide (33 μM). These displacement results are in agreement with the rank order of potency of the drugs as insulin secretagogues, or hypoglycaemic agents, and also correlate with the binding affinities for the membrane-bound receptor. Photolabelling of the soluble receptor with ^{125}I-labelled iodo 'glibenclamide' demonstrates that the binding site is located on a polypeptide of 140 kDa. The radioliogand is fully displaced from this protein by the addition of 1 μM unlabelled glibenclamide or iodo 'glibenclamide' before photolabelling.

During purification, the HIT-cell soluble protein binding activity proved to be highly unstable. As reported for the brain receptor, the binding activity of the solubilized receptor could not be stabilized by the addition of phospholipids or glycerol. Thus our approach to receptor purification has been first to photolabel the protein, and using standard chromatographic methods, partially purify the photolabelled receptor (Aguilar-Bryan et $al.$, 1990). The photolabelled, membrane-bound protein was digitonin solubilized and chromatographed on DEAE-Sephacel. The fraction containing the photolabelled protein (eluted with 0·3 M-NaCl) was then chromatographed on agarose-A 1·5 m in the presence of 1 % SDS. Appropriate fractions were further chromatographed on dodecyl agarose, the photolabelled protein eluted with SDS, and electrophoresed on an SDS polyacrylamide gel. The photolabelled band appears to be a homogeneous polypeptide of 140 kDa, suitable as the starting material for peptide sequencing. Thus in both brain and B-cell membranes, a protein of 140–150 kDa contains the high-affinity sulphonylurea binding site, and may be partially, or fully purified by standard chromatographic procedures.

Action of sulphonylureas in B-cells

It is proposed that both ATP and the sulphonylureas bind to the ATP-sensitive K^+ channel, inhibiting the flow of K^+ from the cell. The decreased K^+ permeability leads to depolarization of the plasma membrane, reducing the potential from about -70 mV at the resting state to about -30 mV (Ferrer *et al.*, 1984). This depolarization triggers the opening of Ca^{2+} channels, whose activities are voltage dependent.

Closure of ATP-sensitive K^+ channels

Both glucose (Sehlin & Taljedal, 1975; Henquin, 1978) and the sulphonylureas (Henquin, 1980) reduce the B-cell plasma membrane K^+ permeability, depolarizing the cell. In the case of glucose, it is the metabolism of this compound, not glucose per se, that is required for the reduction in K^+ efflux (Boschero & Malaisse, 1979). With the advent of the patch-clamp technique (Hamill *et al.*, 1981), one can monitor single-channel activities in the plasma membrane (see Chapter 10 by Ashcroft *et al.* for details). In 1983, Noma reported an ATP-sensitive K^+ channel in heart plasma membrane (Noma, 1983), and in complementary experiments Cook & Hales (1984) demonstrated the presence, in excised B-cell membrane patches, of a K^+ channel that could be directly blocked by the addition of ATP. This set the stage for testing whether sulphonylureas acted on this same channel protein. It was observed that the addition of glibenclamide (20 μM), or tolbutamide (1 mM) to the bathing medium of excised B-cell plasma membrane patches reduced the number of single, ATP-sensitive K^+-channel openings (Sturgess *et al.*, 1985). The sulphonylurea concentrations used in these initial experiments were somewhat high; however, these results have been confirmed by Schmid-Antomarchi *et al.* (1987) in excised RIN-cell patches using 20 nM-glibenclamide. Thus both ATP and the sulphonylureas bind to and directly inhibit the channel activity of the same membrane protein.

A relatively simple technique for measuring K^+ efflux from the B-cell involves monitoring the movement of radiolabelled potassium or rubidium ions through the plasma membrane (see Chapter 9 by Henquin *et al.* for discussion). In these experiments, B-cells are preloaded with either $^{42}K^+$ or $^{86}Rb^+$, and the amount of radioactivity lost from the cell is measured and correlated with the presence of varying concentrations of a secretagogue. Using this method, the sulphonylurea tolbutamide was shown to alter the rate of $^{86}Rb^+$ efflux from rat and mouse pancreatic islets (Henquin, 1980; Henquin & Meissner, 1982; Mathews & Shotton, 1984). The specific measurement of sulphonylurea inhibition of the ATP-sensitive K^+ channel by this method is not straightforward, however, because other K^+ channels may be activated during stimulus–secretion coupling. Mathews & Shotton (1984) observed an initial modest decrease in efflux, followed rapidly by a substantial increase in $^{86}Rb^+$ efflux when pancreatic-islet cells were exposed to tolbutamide. In a similar manner Henquin (1988) measured an overall increase in $^{86}Rb^+$ efflux in the presence of tolbutamide, and suggested that this increased ion flow was the result of actuation of Ca^{2+} and/or voltage-sensitive K^+ channels during the prolonged depolarization.

To monitor the ATP-sensitive K^+-channel activity using the $^{86}Rb^+$-efflux technique, an intracellular ATP depletion method was developed by Schmid-Antomarchi et al. (1987). In this method, RIN cells were preloaded with $^{86}Rb^+$ and then further incubated with oligomycin and 2-deoxy-D-glucose, blocking oxidative phosphorylation and glycolysis, and reducing the concentration of intracellular ATP. Within 20 min, intracellular ATP levels fell from 3·8 mM to 0·4 mM. This incubation period was sufficient to fully open the ATP-sensitive K^+ channels. When these cells are placed in fresh medium without $^{86}Rb^+$, oligomycin and 2-deoxy-D-glucose, the radiolabelled tracer rapidly leaves the cells by passing through the open K^+ pores. Sulphonylureas such as glibenclamide block this ion efflux from ATP-deleted RIN cells (half-maximal inhibition = 0·06 nM) and similar results have been obtained by Niki et al. (1989) using HIT cells and glibenclamide (half-maximal inhibition = 2 nM).

As expected, we found that the new glibenclamide analogue, iodo 'glibenclamide', also decreases HIT cell $^{86}Rb^+$ efflux as shown in Fig. 3. The half-maximal decreases of $^{86}Rb^+$ efflux for iodo 'glibenclamide' (0·68 nM) and glibenclamide (2·25 nM) are similar to the K_ds of binding (approx. 0·36 nM). Thus there is a close correlation between the affinity of binding of glibenclamide and iodo 'glibenclamide' to the sulphonylurea receptor and the half-maximal reduction in the activity of the ATP-sensitive K^+ channel. It is likely that the minimal elements of the ATP-sensitive K^+ channel are an ADP/ATP binding site, and a 140 kDa polypeptide with the high-affinity sulphonylurea binding site.

Activation of voltage-dependent Ca^{2+} channels

Sulphonylurea-closure of the ATP-sensitive K^+ channels leads to depolarization of the B-cell plasma membrane, activating voltage-dependent Ca^{2+} channels. These inward Ca^{2+} currents are responsible for the spiking electrical activity characteristic of B-cells observed during stimulation of insulin secretion (Dean & Mathews, 1970; see also Chapters 9 and 10 by

Henquin *et al.* and Ashcroft *et al.* in this book). One major type of voltage-dependent Ca^{2+} channel, the 'L' type current (long-lasting), has been shown to be present in the rat B-cell (Satin & Cook, 1988) and HIT-cell (Keahey *et al.*, 1989) plasma membrane using patch-clamp methods. The

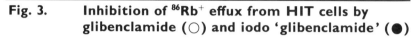

Fig. 3.   **Inhibition of $^{86}Rb^+$ efflux from HIT cells by glibenclamide (○) and iodo 'glibenclamide' (●)**

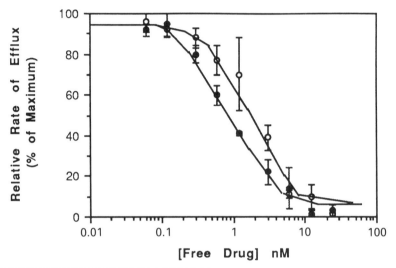

HIT cells were preincubated in medium plus 0·2 µCi/ml $^{86}Rb^+$ for 16 h. The preincubation was continued with Krebs-Ringer buffer (plus 0·1% BSA, but without glucose or bicarbonate) plus $^{86}Rb^+$, 1 mM-2-deoxy-D-glucose and 0·2 µg of oligomycin/ml for 20 min to deplete the cells of ATP. After washing the cells twice in Krebs-Ringer buffer without $^{86}Rb^+$, 2-deoxy-D-glucose and oligomycin, cells were resuspended in this solution plus glibenclamide or iodo 'glibenclamide'. The amount of radioactivity in aliquots was determined after 30 min by scintillation counting. 4% of the total iodo glibenclamide and 13% of the total glibenclamide present in each well were 'free drug' in the presence of 0·1% albumin, as detailed in Aguilar-Bryan et al. (1990).

widely used Ca^{2+}-channel blockers, such as the dihydropyridines, attenuate the secretagogue-produced spiking electrical activity induced in B-cells (see Rajan *et al.*, 1990).

In HIT cells, membrane depolarization effected by the addition of glibenclamide or tolbutamide increases intracellular Ca^{2+} ($[Ca^{2+}]_i$) by activating voltage-dependent Ca^{2+} channels (Nelson *et al.*, 1987). Thus the addition of the sulphonylureas to HIT cells loaded with the calcium-sensitive fluorophores, quin-2, or fura-2, produces an increase in fluorescence that is directly related to the rise in $[Ca^{2+}]_i$ (for details of the method, see Rajan *et al.*, 1989, 1990; Chapter 11 by Hellman *et al.* in this book). The rise in $[Ca^{2+}]_i$, as well as the increased insulin secretion can be fully blocked in two ways: (1) chelation of extracellular Ca^{2+} with 4 mM-EDTA, and (2) addition of the Ca^{2+}-channel blocker verapamil. Thus in the HIT cells, it is established that for the sulphonylureas, the release of internal stores of Ca^{2+} is not required for insulin secretion. The rise in $[Ca^{2+}]_i$, which is thought to be part of the pathway coupling sulphonylurea binding to insulin secretion, is via the opening of Ca^{2+} channels in the plasma membrane.

Nelson *et al.* (1987) report the half-maximal increases in $[Ca^{2+}]_i$ for glibenclamide and tolbutamide in HIT cells to be 525 nM and 67 μM, respectively. The concentration for glibenclamide is clearly higher than the K_d of binding to the high-affinity site present in HIT cells (0·76 nM; Gaines *et al.*, 1988). This disparity can now be reconciled by analysing the kinetic aspects of the action of the second-generation suphonylureas, as well as by taking into account the presence of low-affinity sulphonylurea-binding protein used as cell stabilizers during measurement of internal Ca^{2+} concentrations. First, the uptake of $^{45}Ca^{2+}$ by mouse pancreatic islets in the presence of glibenclamide develops slowly (Hellman *et al.*, 1984), explaining why the stimulation of insulin secretion is relatively slow. In mouse inslets, 1 nM-glibenclamide requires 2 h or longer to produce maximum secretion levels (Panten *et al.*, 1989). Secondly, the sulphonyl-ureas bind to the BSA (Crooks & Brown, 1974) used as a stabilizer for suspended B-cells and islets. For $[Ca^{2+}]_i$ measurements in HIT cells, two changes have been made to our fluorescence assay: (1) we have attempted to follow the time course in the rise in $[Ca^{2+}]_i$ after the addition of the sulphonylurea, and (2) we have replaced 0·1 % BSA with 0·1 % gelatin as the stabilizer of the suspended HIT cells, thus the concentration of the drug added to the cells represents the actual free drug concentration.

The results of such an experiment using iodo 'glibenclamide' are shown in Fig. 4(A). The addition of 15 nM-iodo 'glibenclamide' evokes a fairly rapid and sustained rise in $[Ca^{2+}]_i$. Below 15 nM it is clear that the drug concentration affects both the rate and the maximal extent of the Ca^{2+} response. Reading number 34 (abscissa) represents approximately 10 min after the addition of iodo 'glibenclamide', and at low drug concentrations, the rise in $[Ca^{2+}]_i$ has not as yet maximized. Virtually identical results have been obtained with glibenclamide. Averaging the last three $[Ca^{2+}]_i$ concentrations (reading 31–34) determined for each iodo 'glibenclamide' concentration, yields net increases in $[Ca^{2+}]_i$ as shown in Fig. 4(B). Although we have only a handful of data points, and for some, plateau values for $[Ca^{2+}]_i$ have not been reached, a reiterative curve fitting program yields a half-maximal rise in $[Ca^{2+}]_i$ of 1·36 nM. Thus despite the difficulty in following the kinetics of this $[Ca^{2+}]_i$ rise, there is good

Fig. 4.   **Effect of iodo glibenclamide [Ca²⁺]ᵢ in HIT cells**

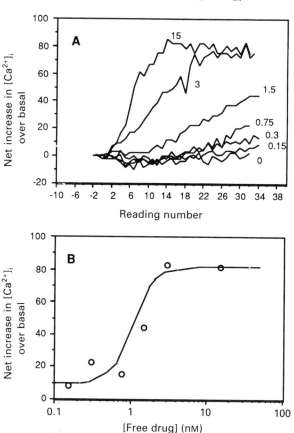

(A) The [Ca²⁺]ᵢ was measured as described in Rajan et al. (1989). After determining a baseline [Ca²⁺]ᵢ, iodo glibenclamide was added to the cuvette at the illustrated concentrations (all concentrations are nM), and [Ca²⁺]ᵢ readings (shown on the abscissa) were taken every 16 s for up to 10 min. The net change in HIT-cell [Ca²⁺]ᵢ level is plotted, with typical baseline values ranging from 40 nM to 50 nM [Ca²⁺]ᵢ (B) Dose–response curve for the effect of iodo glibenclamide on [Ca²⁺]ᵢ. The [Ca²⁺]ᵢ (readings 31–34 obtained after 9–10 min. after addition of drug) was averaged for each drug concentration and plotted as shown.

agreement between the K_d of iodo 'glibenclamide' binding (0·36 nM) and the half-maximal rise in [Ca²⁺]ᵢ (1·36 nM). We have thus concluded that the rise in [Ca²⁺]ᵢ is highly correlated with the binding of iodo 'glibenclamide' to the high-affinity site.

Insulin secretion

By as yet unknown mechanisms, the increase in $[Ca^{2+}]_i$ induces increased insulin secretion. The slow onset of action of low concentrations of second-generation sulphonylureas, or their analogues, on $[Ca^{2+}]_i$ correlates with a slow onset of insulin secretion, as observed by Panten *et al.* (1989). Thus in insulin secretion experiments, both the kinetics of action of these drugs as well as the binding to BSA present in the secretion buffer, which lowers the free concentration of the drug available to the B-cell, must be taken into account.

Pantel *et al.* (1989) developed a filtration assay for measuring the free drug concentration in the presence of BSA. After taking into account the amount of drug bound to albumin, they were able to observe the slow onset of action of the second-generation sulphonylureas using mouse pancreatic islets in perifusion assays. In this method, the insulin concentration is continuously monitored as the buffer flows over the islet cells. Using the relative amount of insulin secretion observed after incubation of islets for 58 min (tolbutamide and glipizide) and 126 min (glibenclamide) with the sulphonylurea, they arrived at concentration values for half-maximal insulin secretion (ED_{50}s) of 0·4 nM (glibenclamide), 4 nM (glipizide) and 5 μM (tolbutamide), in excellent agreement with the equilibrium dissociation constants (K_ds) established for high-affinity binding.

Following these observations, we performed similar experiments using HIT cells and static-secretion assays (Aguilar-Bryan *et al.*, 1990). We have taken into account both the albumin binding and the slow onset of glibenclamide and iodo 'glibenclamide' action. The free drug concentrations were measured directly as described by Panten *et al.* (1989) in the buffers used for the measurement of insulin concentration (0·1 % BSA is present in this buffer). Over the range of 0 μM–1 μM, we found that 13 % of the glibenclamide and 4 % of the iodo 'glibenclamide' were free. HIT cells in 12-well plates were preincubated for 15 min with the appropriate concentrations of the drugs to account for the slow onset of action of these compounds. Insulin secretion, measured over the next 30 min in these static-secretion assays, was then observed to be significant even at low nanomolar concentrations of glibenclamide and iodo 'glibenclamide'. We obtained ED_{50}s of 0·4 nM for both of these compounds.

Integration of sulphonylurea binding and actions

The affinity of iodo 'glibenclamide' for the HIT-cell receptor ($K_d = 0·36$ nM) is in excellent agreement with the half-maximal inhibition of $^{86}Rb^+$ efflux (0·68 nM), the half-maximal increase in $[Ca^{2+}]_i$ (1·36 nM) and the ED_{50} for insulin secretion (0·4 nM). Moreover, the addition of low nanomolar concentrations of iodo 'glibenclamide' to the HIT-cell incubation medium does not produce an instantaneous increase in $[Ca^{2+}]_i$ or in insulin secretion. These kinetic aspects of the action of the second-generation sulphonylureas suggest interesting questions regarding the time required for high-affinity binding in intact cells, the location of the sulphonylurea binding site, and whether the rates of sulphonylurea binding and $^{86}Rb^+$ efflux are coupled to the rates of Ca^{2+} uptake and insulin secretion (see also Chapter 6 by Lenzen in this book). One also wonders if these highly lipophilic compounds are simply integrated into the plasma membrane at low concentrations and then redistribute to the high-affinity binding sites located throughout the membrane (Zunkler *et al.*, 1989), or is the high-affinity site somewhat inaccessible? Considerable time might be required for sulphonylureas to occupy a site on the cytoplasmic surface of the plasma membrane, since these compounds would have to move first through the planar bilayer. Although glibenclamide can accumulate within the B-cell (Hellman *et al.*, 1984; Carpentier *et al.*, 1986), other less lipophilic sulphonylureas probably do not penetrate the plasma membrane (Hellman *et al.*, 1984), thus an internal binding site for sulphonylureas seems unlikely. The reason for the slow onset of action of glibenclamide, and the extent to which the kinetics of drug binding and K^+ efflux are coupled to more distal events, remain to be determined.

Recently, Niki *et al.* (1989, 1990) have provided evidence that ADP binds to and competitively displaces [^{3}H]glibenclamide from the high-affinity-HIT-cell sulphonylurea binding site. They also showed that ADP inhibited $^{86}Rb^+$ efflux, elicited a rapid and sustained increase in $[Ca^{2+}]_i$ and boosted insulin secretion. Since ADP is unable to cross the plasma membrane, they conclude that ADP and the sulphonylureas have common binding sites on the outer surface of the HIT-cell plasma membrane. These data provide evidence for an endogenous ligand for the sulphonylurea binding site, and will certainly provoke further investigations on the action of ADP on the B-cell.

The model we have presented for sulphonylurea-stimulated insulin secretion is summarized in Fig. 5. The sulphonylurea receptor is proposed to play a central role in the glucose-stimulated insulin secretory pathway. Glucose enters the B-cell by facilitated diffusion and is metabolized via the glycolytic pathway and the Kreb's cycle. Both the sulphonylureas and the ATP generated by glucose metabolism directly bind to the ATP-sensitive K^+ channel, inhibiting the flow of K^+ from the cell. The reduction in K^+ efflux depolarizes the plasma membrane, increasing the open probability of voltage-gated Ca^{2+} channels. The influx of Ca^{2+} observed electrophysiologically as spikes, or action potentials, provides the means by which insulin secretion is coupled to membrane excitation. The mode by which the increased concentration of cytosolic Ca^{2+} promotes insulin secretion, as well as the means of repolarization of the plasma membrane to the resting membrane potential, remain under investigation.

Fig. 5.   A model of B-cell sulphonylurea action and glucose-stimulated insulin secretion

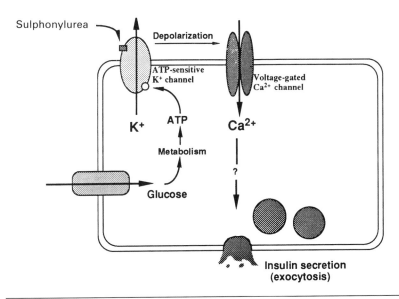

Glucose is thought to enter the B-cell by faciliated diffusion, and its metabolism gives rise to increased cellular ATP levels. Both ATP and the sulphonylureas are proposed to directly bind to, and inhibit, the ATP-sensitive K^+ channel. Inhibition of this channel activity results in membrane depolarization, actuating voltage-sensitive Ca^{2+} channels. The influx of Ca^{2+} promotes exocytosis.

Conclusions

A sulphonylurea receptor is present on B-cell plasma membranes, with high-affinity ligand binding detected for both glibenclamide and the novel sulphonylurea, iodo 'glibenclamide'. [^{3}H]glibenclamide and ^{125}I-labelled iodo 'glibenclamide' have been used to photolabel the 140–150 kDa receptor protein, and the brain and HIT-cell sulphonylurea receptors have been solubilized in the presence of digitonin with the retention of sulphonylurea binding activity (Vu *et al.*, 1989). The brain receptor has been purified (Bernardi *et al.*, 1988), and the HIT-cell protein partially purified (Aguilar-Bryan *et al.*, 1990). Peptide sequence data derived from the HIT-cell protein allow the design of oligonucleotides which are being used to screen cDNA libraries, and amplify portions of the gene by the polymerase chain reaction. The goal of these studies is ultimately to clone and sequence the gene coding for this protein and test for whether it has the proposed ATP-sensitive K^+-channel activity. More detailed biochemical knowledge about the structure of the ATP- and sulphonylurea-binding K^+-channel protein should provide a better understanding of the regulation of insulin secretion by specific nutrients and the sulphonylureas, and possibly suggest novel treatments for NIDDM.

References

Aguilar-Bryan, L., Nelson, D. A., Vu, Q. A., Humphrey, M. B. & Boyd, A. E. III (1990) Photoaffinity labeling and partial purification of the β cells sulfonylurea receptor using a novel, biologically active glyburide analog. J. Biol. Chem. **265**, 8218–8224

Ashcroft, F. M. (1988) Andenosine 5′-triphosphate-sensitive potassium channels. Annu. Rev. Neurosci. **11**, 97–118

Bennett, P. H., LeCompte, P. M., Miller, M. & Rushforth, N. B. (1976) Epidemiological studies of diabetes in the Pima Indians. Recent Prog. Horm. Res. **32**, 333–376

Bernardi, H., Fosset, M. & Lazdunski, M. (1988) Characterization, purification, and affinity labeling of the brain [³H]glibenclamide-binding protein, a putative neuronal ATP-regulated K^+ channel. Proc. Natl. Acad. Sci. U.S.A. **85**, 9816–9820

Boschero, A. C. & Malaisse, W. J. (1979) Stimulus-secretion coupling of glucose-induced insulin release. XXIX. Regulation of ⁸⁶Rb⁺ efflux from perifused islets. Am. J. Physiol. **236**, E139–E146

Bouman, P. R. & Goorenstroom, J. H. (1961) Stimulation by carbutamide and tolbutamide of insulin release from rat pancreas *in vitro*. Metabolism **10**, 1095–1099

Boyd, A. E. III (1988) Sulfonylurea receptors, ion channels, and fruit flies. Diabetes. **37**, 847–850

Boyd, A. E. III & Huynh, T. Q. (1990) Sulfonylurea and antihypertensive drugs for type II diabetics. Contemp. Intern. Med. **2**, 13–33

Carpentier, J. L., Sawano, F., Ravazzola, M. & Malaisse, W. J. (1986) Internalization of ³H-glibenclamide in pancreatic islet cells. Diabetologia **29**, 259–261

Chick, W. L., Warren, S., Chute, R. N., Like, A. A., Lauris, V. & Kitchen, K. C. (1977) A transplantable insulinoma in the rat. Proc. Natl. Acad. Sci. U.S.A. **74**, 628–632

Cook, D. L. & Hales, C. N. (1984) Intracellular ATP directly blocks K^+ channels in pancreatic B-cells. Nature (London) **311**, 271–273

Cook, D. L., Satin, L. S., Ashford, M. L. J. & Hales, C. N. (1988) ATP-sensitive K^+ channels in pancreatic β-cells. Spare channel hypothesis. Diabetes **37**, 495–498

Crooks, M. J. & Brown, K. F. (1974). The binding of sulphonylureas to serum albumin. J. Pharm. Pharmac. **26**, 304–311

Dean, P. M. & Mathews, C. K. (1970) Glucose-induced electrical activity in pancreatic islet cells. J. Physiol (London) **210**, 255–264

Ferrer, R., Atwater, I., Omer, E. M., Goncalves, A. A., Croghan, P. C. & Rojas, E. (1984) Electrophysiological evidence for the inhibition of potassium permeability in pancreatic β-cells by glibenclamide. J. Expt. Physiol. **69**, 831–839

Gaines, K. L., Hamilton, S. & Boyd, A. E. III (1988) Characterization of the sulfonylurea receptor on beta cell membranes. J. Biol. Chem. **263**, 2589–2592

Gardner, L. I., Stern, M. P., Haffner, S. M., Gaskill, S. P., Hazuda, H. P., Relethford, J. H. & Eifler, C. W. (1984) Prevalence of diabetes in Mexican Americans. Relationship to percent of gene pool derived from Native American sources. Diabetes **33**, 86–92

Geisen, K., Hitzel, V., Okomonopoulus, R., Punter, J., Weyer, R. & Summ, H. D. (1985) Inhibition of ^{3}H-glibenclamide binding to sulfonylurea receptors by oral antidiabetics. Arzneim.-Forsch. **35**, 707–712

Gerich, J. E. (1989) Drug Therapy. Oral hypoglycemic agents. N. Engl. J. Med. **321**, 1231–1245

Gorus, F. K., Schuit, F. C., In't Veld, P. A., Gepts, W. & Pipeleers, D. G. (1988) Interaction of glyburide with pancreatic β-cells. A study with glyburide. Diabetes **37**, 1090–1095

Hamill, O. P., Marty, A., Neher, E., Sakmann, B. & Sigworth, F. J. (1981) Improved patch clamp techniques for high resolution current recording from cells and cell-free membrane patches. Pfluegers Arch. **391**, 85–100

Hanis, C. L., Ferrell, R. E., Barton, S. A., Aguilar, L., Garza-Ibarra, A., Tulloch, B. R., Garcia, C. A. & Schull, W. J. (1983) Diabetes among Mexican Americans in Starr County, Texas. Am. J. Epidemiol. **118**, 659–672

Hellman, B. & Taljedal, I. B. (1975) Effects of sulfonylurea derivatives on pancreatic β-cells. In Insulin II. Handbook of Experimental Pharmacology (Hasselblatt, A. & Bruchhausen, F. V., eds.), vol. 32, part 2, pp. 175–194, Springer, Berlin

Hellman, B., Sehlin, J. & Taljedal, I.-B. (1984) Glibenclamide is exceptional among hypoglycaemic sulphonylureas in accumulating progressively in β-cell-rich pancreatic islets. Acta Endocrinol. (Copenhagen) **105**, 385–390

Henquin, J. C. (1978) D-glucose inhibits potassium efflux from pancreatic islet cells. Nature (London) **271**, 271–273

Henquin, J. C. (1980) Tolbutamide stimulation and inhibition of insulin release: studies of the underlying ionic mechanisms in isolated rat islets. Diabetologia **18**, 151–160

Henquin, J. C. (1988) ATP-sensitive K$^+$ channels may control glucose-induced electrical activity in pancreatic B-cells. Biochem. Biophys. Res. Commun. **156**, 769–775

Henquin, J. C. & Meissner, H. P. (1982) Opposite effects of tolbutamide and diazoxide on ^{86}Rb$^+$ fluxes and membrane potential in pancreatic B cells. Biochem. Pharmacol. **31**, 1407–1415

Janbon, M., Chaptal, J., Vedel, A. & Schaap, J. (1942a) Accidents hypoglycemiques graves par un sulfamidothiazol. Montpellier Med. **21–22**, 441

Janbon, M., Lazergbes, P. & Metropolitansky, J. H. (1942b) Etude de metabolisme du sulfaisopropyl-thiazol chez le sujet sain et en cours de traitement. Comportement de la glycemie. Montpellier Med. **21–22**, 489

Kaubisch, N., Hammer, R., Wollheim, C., Renold, A. E. & Offord, R. E. (1982) Specific receptors for sulfonylureas in brain and in a β-cell tumor of the rat. Biochem. Pharmacol. **31**, 1171–1174

Keahey, H. H., Rajan, A. S., Boyd, A. E. III & Kunze, D. L. (1989) Characterization of voltage-dependent Ca^{2+} channels in a β-cell line. Diabetes **38**, 188–193

Kramer, W., Oekonomopulos, R., Punter, J. & Summ, H.-D. (1988) Direct photoaffinity labelling of the putative sulfonylurea receptor in rat β-cell tumour membranes by [^{3}H]glibenclamide. FEBS Lett. **229**, 355–359

Lebovitz, H. E., Feinglos, M. N., Bucholtz, H. K. & Lebovitz, F. L. (1977) Potentiation of insulin action: A probable mechanism for the antidiabetic action of sulfonylurea drugs. J. Clin. Endocrinol. Metab. **45**, 601–604

Loubatieres, A. (1944) Analyse du mecanisme de l'action hypoglycemiante du P-aminobenzenesulfamidothiodiazol. Compt. Rend. **138**, 766–767

Loubatieres, A. (1957a) The hypoglycemic sulfonamides: History and development of the problem from 1942 to 1955. Ann. N.Y. Acad. Sci. **71**, 4–11

Loubatieres, A. (1957b) The mechanism of action of the hypoglycemic sulfonamides: A concept based on investigations in animals and in human beings. Ann. N.Y. Acad. Sci. **71**, 192–206

Lupo, B. & Bataille, D. (1987) A binding site for [^{3}H]glipizide in the rat cerebral cortex. Eur. J. Pharm. **140**, 157–169

Mathews, E. K. & Shotton, P. A. (1984) The control of ^{86}Rb efflux from rat isolated pancreatic islets by the sulphonylureas tolbutamide and glibenclamide. Br. J. Pharm. **82**, 689–700

Meglasson, M. D., Nelson, J., Nelson, D. & Erecinska, M. (1989) Bioenergetic response of pancreatic islets to stimulation by fuel molecules. Metabolism **38**, 1188–1195

Melander, A., Lebovitz, H. E. & Faber, O. K. (1990) Sulfonylureas: why, which and how? Diabetes Care **13**, (Suppl. 3), 18–25

Mourre, C., Ari, Y. B., Bernardi, H., Fosset, M. & Lazdunski, M. (1989) Antidiabetic sulphonylureas: localization of binding sites in the brain and effects on the hyperpolarization induced by anoxia in hippocampal slices. Brain Res. **486**, 159–164

Nelson, T. Y., Gaines, K. L., Rajan, A. S., Berg, M. & Boyd, A. E. III (1987) Increased cytosolic calcium. A signal for sulfonylurea-stimulated insulin release from beta cells. J. Biol. Chem. **262**, 2608–2612

Niki, I., Kelly, R. P., Ashcroft, S. J. H. & Ashcroft, F. M. (1989) ATP-sensitive K-channels in HIT T15 β-cells studied by patch-clamp methods, ^{86}Rb efflux and glibenclamide binding. Pfluegers Arch. **415**, 47–55

Niki, I., Nicks, J. L. & Ashcroft, S. J. H. (1990) The β-cell glibenclamide receptor is an ADP-binding protein. Biochem. J. **268**, 713–718

Noma, A. (1983) ATP-regulated K+ channels in cardiac muscle. Nature (London) **305**, 147–148

Panten, U., Burgfeld, J., Goerke, F., Rennicke, M., Schwanstecher, M., Wallasch, A., Zunkler, B. J. & Lenzen, S. (1989) Control of insulin secretion by sulfonylureas, meglitinide and diazoxide in relation to their binding to the sulfonylurea receptor in pancreatic islets. Biochem. Pharmacol. **38**, 1217–1229

Petersen, O. H. & Findley, I. (1987) Electrophysiology of the pancreas. Physiol. Rev. **67**, 1054–1116

Rajan, A. S., Hill, R. S. & Boyd, A. E. III (1989) Effect of rise in cAMP levels on Ca[2+] influx through voltage-dependent Ca[2+] channels in HIT cells. Second-messenger synarchy in β-cells. Diabetes **38**, 874–880

Rajan, A. S., Aguilar-Bryan, L., Nelson, D. A., Yaney, G. C., Hsu, W. H., Kunze, D. L. & Boyd, A. E. III (1990) Ion channels and insulin secretion. Diabetes Care **13**, 340–363

Ratzmann, K. P., Schulz, B., Heinke, P. & Besch, W. (1984) Tolbutamide does not alter insulin requirement in Type 1 (insulin-dependent) diabetes. Diabetologia **27**, 8–12

Santerre, R. F., Cook, R. A., Crisel, R. M. D., Sharp, J. D., Schmidt, R. J., William, D. C. & Willson, C. P. (1981) Insulin synthesis in a clonal cell line of simian virus 40-transformed hamster pancreatic beta cells. Proc. Natl. Acad. Sci. U.S.A. **78**, 4339–4343

Satin, L. S. & Cook, D. L. (1988) Evidence for two calcium currents in insulin secreting cells. Pfluegers Arch. **411**, 401–409

Schmid-Antomarchi, H., De Weille, J., Fosset, M. & Lazdunski, M. (1987) The receptor for antidiabetic sulfonylureas controls the activity of the ATP-modulated K+ channel in insulin-secreting cells. J. Biol. Chem. **262**, 15840–15844

Sehlin, J. & Taljedal, I. B. (1975) Glucose-induced decrease in Rb+ permeability in pancreatic β cells. Nature (London) **253**, 635–636

Sturgess, N. C., Ashford, M. L. J., Cook, D. L. & Hales, C. N. (1985). The sulphonylurea receptor may be an ATP-sensitive potassium channel. Lancet **ii**, 474–475

Vu, Q. A., Aguilar-Bryan, L. & Nelson, D. A. (1989) Functional solubilization of the HIT cell sulfonylurea receptor. Diabetes **38**, 178A

Zhang, H. J., Walseth, T. F. & Robertson, R. P. (1989) Insulin secretion and cAMP metabolism in HIT cells. Reciprocal and serial passage-dependent relationships. Diabetes **38**, 44–48

Zimmet, P. (1983) Epidemiology of diabetes mellitus. In Diabetes Mellitus — Theory and Clinical Practice (Ellenberg, M. & Rifkin, H., eds.) 3rd edn., pp. 451–468, Medical Examination Publishers, New York

Zimmet, P., Guinea, A., Guthrie, W., Taft, P. & Thoma, K. (1977) The high prevalence of diabetes mellitus on a Central Pacific island. Diabetologia **13**, 111–115

Zimmet, P., King, H., Taylor, R., Raper, L. R., Balkau, B., Borger, J., Heriot, W. & Thoma, K. (1984) The high prevalence of diabetes mellitus, impaired glucose tolerance and diabetic retinopathy in Nauru — The 1982 survey. Diabetes Res. **1**, 13–18

Zimmet, P., Serjeantson, S., King, H. & Kirk, R. (1986) The genetics of diabetes mellitus. Aust. N.Z. J. Med. **16**, 419–424

Zunkler, B. J., Trube, G. & Panten, U. (1989) How do sulfonylureas approach their receptor in the B-cell plasma membrane? Naunyn-Schmiedeberg's Arch. Pharmacol. **340**, 328–332

16

Defective insulin secretion in diabetes and insulinoma

Peter R. Flatt*, Clifford J. Bailey†, Per-Olof Berggren‡,
Lieselotte Herberg§ and Sara K. Swanston-Flatt*

*Department of Biological and Biomedical Sciences, University of Ulster,
Coleraine BT52 ISA, U.K., †Department of Pharmaceutical Sciences,
Aston University, Birmingham B4 7ET, U.K., ‡Department of
Endocrinology, Karolinska Institute, S-104 01, Stockholm, Sweden and
§Diabetes Research Institute, University of Düsseldorf, D-4000,
Düsseldorf, Germany

Introduction

Nutrient regulation of insulin secretion involves the direct actions of nutrients on the pancreatic B-cells plus indirect effects mediated by autonomic nerves, and the release of the various entero-insular hormones and islet peptides. In health, these signals are integrated at the level of the B-cell such that insulin is secreted with appropriate kinetics in amounts necessary to regulate nutrient metabolism and to maintain glucose homoeostasis. In diabetes mellitus and insulinoma, the mechanisms regulating insulin secretion are defective, resulting in derangements of metabolism and potentially life-threatening variations of circulating glucose concentrations. In the present chapter, the nature of the insulin secretory defect in these disease states will be considered in the framework of our current understanding of the regulation of B-cell function and stimulus–secretion coupling.

Insulin secretory mechanism

The mechanisms by which glucose and other nutrient fuels provoke insulin secretion from normal B-cells has been considered in detail in the preceding Chapters of this book. In brief, glucose metabolism leading to the generation of cellular ATP provides the stimulus to insulin secretion through a sequence of ionic events triggered by the closure of ATP-sensitive K^+ channels in the B-cell plasma membrane. This leads to membrane depolarization, opening of voltage-dependent Ca^{2+} channels and Ca^{2+} influx. The resulting increase of cytoplasmic Ca^{2+} ($[Ca^{2+}]_i$)

triggers exocytosis by directly activating the secretory machinery. In addition, Ca^{2+} appears to activate enzymes such as adenylate cyclase and phospholipase C, which are believed to be associated with sensitization of the secretory process to the stimulatory action of Ca^{2+}. Indeed, it is mainly by directly activating these enzyme systems that non-metabolizable secretagogues generated by feeding, namely the entero-insular hormones and neurotransmitters, potentiate the insulin secretory process (see Chapter 14 by Berggren *et al.* for details).

Principal role of glucose

Glucose is the principal regulator of islet B-cell function. It directly stimulates insulin release, and raised concentrations of glucose also amplify the insulinotropic actions of non-glucose nutrient fuels and secretagogues, such as entero-insular hormones and neurotransmitters. Abnormalities in the ambient basal glucose concentration over a protracted period of time, as encountered in diabetes or insulinoma, also contribute to defective insulin secretion. This has seeded both the concept of glucose toxicity and the view of hyperglycaemia as an inducer, as well as a consequence, of impaired B-cell function (Unger & Grundy, 1985; Leahy, 1990; Rossetti *et al.*, 1990).

The kinetics and magnitude of the insulin response to glucose is dependent on many factors, in addition to the absolute concentration of glucose. The critical factors include: the basal glycaemic environment; the rate of change of glucose level, and the extent of involvement of the entero-insular axis. Thus, route of glucose administration, rate of gastric emptying, secretion of gut hormones, activation of autonomic nerves and the degree of insulin sensitivity will all influence the insulin response. Thus, although oral glucose tolerance tests provide a means to diagnose non-insulin-dependent diabetes mellitus (NIDDM), intravenous glucose (which avoids many of these complicating variables) represents a more valid and reliable means of assessing B-cell function (Turner & Matthews, 1984).

An abrupt increase of glucose concentration encountered *in vivo* after intravenous glucose administration or *in vitro* by a step-wise increase of glucose in the perfusate, results in an early transient phase of insulin secretion which is followed by a later progressive and sustained insulin response (Grodsky, 1972; Cerasi, 1975). The mechanisms underlying the two phases of insulin secretion are unknown and the subject remains a matter of debate (see other Chapters in this book). Early research proposed that the mechanisms governing the two phases of insulin secretion are of identical nature (Cerasi *et al.*, 1972). The biphasic response has been variously attributed to: compartmentalization of insulin secretory granules; inhibition of B-cell function by secreted insulin or somatostatin; different modalities of Ca^{2+} flux affecting $[Ca^{2+}]_i$; activation of phospholipase C with the generation of inositol 1,4,5-trisphosphate [$Ins(1,4,5)P_3$]; or possible temporal changes of glucose transport and metabolic flux (Grodsky, 1972; Cerasi, 1975; Malaisse *et al.*, 1979; Wollheim & Sharp, 1981; Rasmussen *et al.*, 1990).

Studies in humans and animals

Most of our knowledge of B-cell stimulus–secretion coupling is derived from studies using rats and mice. Studies performed with normal human islets fully support a common secretory mechanism (Ashcroft *et al.*, 1971; Henriksson *et al.*, 1978; Andersson & Hellerstom, 1980; Grant *et al.*, 1980; Jahr *et al.*, 1983; Harrison *et al.*, 1985; Ashcroft *et al.*, 1987). The only notable difference so far apparent concerns the ability of N-acetyl-glucosamine to be metabolized and trigger insulin secretion from rodent but not human islets (Harrison *et al.*, 1985).

In view of the compounding effects of environmental variables in modifying B-cell function, data gathered from limited studies of B-cells from small numbers of human subjects must be interpreted with caution. Thus, observations of spontaneous and experimentally induced diabetes in animals emphasize that environmental factors are particularly important in modulating the onset and severity of defective insulin secretion (see later). Clearly, caution must be applied also when attempting to integrate independent pieces of knowledge concerning individual animal species, since factors such as age, diet and glycaemic status are not often clearly defined.

Human diabetes

NIDDM

Development of NIDDM can be viewed as a progressive disorder of B-cell function. This operates in conjunction with other disturbances, notably insulin resistance, to create a condition of impaired glucose homoeostasis and metabolic disarray. Debate concerning the aetiology and overall pathogenesis of NIDDM is beyond the scope of this Chapter, but while present attention is focused on insulin secretion, we must be ever mindful that the net effect on glucose metabolism is a composite product of many interacting pathogenic features (Efendic *et al.*, 1984; DeFronzo, 1988; King, 1988; Robertson, 1989; Leahy, 1990).

A feature of insulin secretion in subjects with NIDDM is the delayed and attenuated response of the B-cells to stimulation by intravenously administered glucose. Thus, whereas some NIDDM subjects may exhibit normal or moderately raised fasting insulin concentrations and greater than normal insulin responses to orally administered glucose, the insulin secretory response to intravenous glucose which occurs without concurrent entero-insular activation is severely impaired (Kahn & Porte,

1990). This is clearly illustrated by the classical study of Perley & Kipnis (1967) in which normal-weight and obese diabetic subjects were matched with two similar non-diabetic control groups (Fig. 1). Each group was infused intravenously with glucose to provide matched glucose concen-

Fig. I. **Circulating glucose and insulin concentrations of normal-weight and obese diabetic patients and matched groups of non-diabetic patients after i.v. glucose infusion to give similar glucose concentrations**

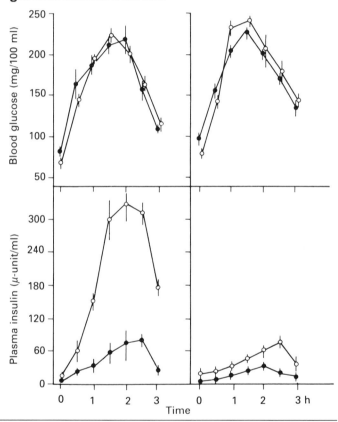

Left panel: non-diabetic patients; right panel, diabetic patients. ●, *Normal-weight;* ○, *obese. Values are mean ± s.e.m. of groups of 11–12 subjects. Taken from Perley & Kipnis (1967) with permission.*

trations simulating the glycaemic excursion of a normal oral glucose tolerance test. The insulin responses of both groups of diabetic subjects were impaired compared with the appropriate controls.

More detailed consideration of temporal aspects of the secretory defect provides clear evidence that both the early and late insulin responses to intravenous glucose are impaired. As shown by Fig. 2, The glucose–insulin dose–response curves for both phases of insulin secretion were shifted towards higher glucose concentrations in impaired glucose tolerance (IGT, prediabetic) subjects and NIDDM subjects (Cerasi et al., 1972). Loss of the early response and severe compromise of the late response appear to be associated with mildly elevated (> 6·5 mM) and moderately elevated (> 11 mM) fasting glucose concentrations, respectively (Cerasi et al., 1972; Brunzell et al., 1976). The extent to which this indicates a deleterious effect of hyperglycaemia on B-cell function rather than an obvious consequence of defective insulin secretion is unknown.

Other studies have noted that intravenous glucose may actually evoke a paradoxical inhibition of insulin secretion in certain NIDDM subjects (Metz et al., 1979; Hellman et al., 1985; Gomis et al., 1989). Overall, these various observations indicate that the B-cell responsiveness to glucose is substantially impaired in NIDDM subjects. Abnormalities of glucose transport and metabolism by B-cells in NIDDM have been suggested to contribute to the defect (Rovira et al., 1987; Gomis et al., 1989). However, the prevailing hyperglycaemia often stimulates basal insulin output to apparently normal or supra-normal levels, particularly if obesity and insulin resistance are present (Kahn & Porte, 1990). This phenomenon is associated with an irregular pulsatile pattern of basal insulin secretion in subjects with IGT or NIDDM (Lang et al., 1981; O'Rahilly et al., 1988).

In contrast to the impaired insulin response to intravenous glucose, the B-cells of NIDDM subjects with mildly elevated fasting glucose concentrations continue to respond well to secretagogues, such as arginine, glucagon, sulphonylureas, gastrointestinal hormones and the β-adrenergic agonist isoprenaline (Crockford et al., 1969; Palmer et al., 1976; Halter et al., 1979; Vague & Moulin, 1982). Insulin responses to these agents appear to be of near normal magnitude. However, when plasma glucose concentrations of the NIDDM subjects are matched with normal controls by infusion of insulin or glucose, respectively, the insulin secretory responses in NIDDM are reduced (Halter et al., 1979; Ward et al., 1984). This indicates that the hyperglycaemia contributes to the apparently normal responses to non-glucose secretagogues.

As the severity of the diabetes increases, the B-cells eventually incur a form of functional exhaustion to non-glucose stimuli. This is best illustrated by the relationship between the fasting glucose concentration and the response to orally administered glucose, which provides a combined substrate, neural and hormonal stimulus to insulin secretion. Thus, whereas well-controlled NIDDM subjects often show enhanced insulin responses to such stimulation, secretory responsiveness is progressively impaired at mild or moderately raised basal glucose concentrations (Reaven et al., 1976; DeFronzo et al., 1983; DeFronzo,

Fig. 2.   **Circulating glucose–insulin dose–response curves for the early (10 min; upper panel) and late (60 min; lower panel) phases of insulin release in response to intravenous glucose infusions**

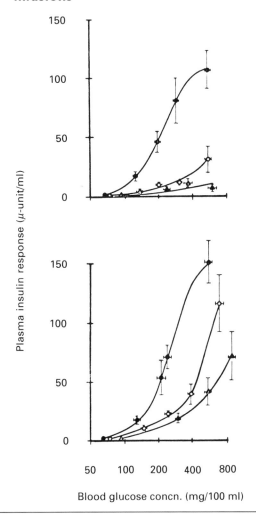

Upper curve (●) represents control subjects, middle curve (○) represents IGT subjects, lower curve (▲) represents NIDDM subjects. Insulin response is given as the increase above the fasting concentration at either 10 min or 60 min. Glucose is given as the concentration attained at these times. Values are mean ± s.e.m. of groups of eight subjects. Reproduced from Cerasi et al. (1972) with permission

1988). Correction of the hyperglycaemia, for example by dieting or insulin therapy, can partially restore B-cell function (Turner *et al.*, 1976; Vague & Moulin, 1982). However, the insulinotropic action of glucose *per se* is seldom normalized, indicating that defective glucose stimulation is not merely a consequence of hyperglycaemia.

Most conventional insulin antisera used for insulin radioimmuno-assay cross-react with intact and partially processed proinsulin. Recent studies using specific immunoradiometric assays have demonstrated that the plasma concentrations of intact proinsulin and 32–33 split proinsulin are raised 2–3-fold in NIDDM subjects, often accounting for more than 40 % of the total amount of measurable insulin (Temple *et al.*, 1989). This suggests that many previous studies have overestimated the concentration of insulin in NIDDM subjects, and an absolute deficiency of the overall insulin response to glucose might in fact occur earlier than previously envisaged (Leahy, 1990). Proinsulin and 32–33 split proinsulin exhibit less than 10 % and 50 %, respectively, of the biological activity of insulin at physiological concentrations (Revers *et al.*, 1984; Peavy *et al.*, 1985), and therefore contribute to the condition of insulin resistance. Excessive secretion of proinsulin and 32–33 split proinsulin by the B-cells of NIDDM subjects suggests a defect in the cellular processing of the prohormone (Porte & Kahn, 1989). Naturally occurring insulin gene mutations giving rise to biologically inept hormone have been discovered in several subjects with a mild familial form of diabetes (Robbins & Tager, 1989; Steiner *et al.*, 1990).

Autopsy studies have generally noted that B-cell mass is reduced in NIDDM subjects, usually accompanied by a corresponding reduction in extractable insulin and some B-cell degranulation (Volk, 1990). This is associated with increases in the A-cell mass and the A/B-cell ratio. Hyalinization of the islets is typically observed, and this is now recognized as an amyloid material, termed islet amyloid polypeptide (IAPP), produced by the B-cells (see Steiner *et al.*, 1991; Johnson *et al.*, 1991 and Chapter 4 by Guest & Hutton in this book). Deposition of IAPP within and between B-cells has been considered to contribute to the pathogenesis of defective B-cell function (Porte & Kahn, 1989; Steiner *et al.*, 1991; Johnson *et al.*, 1991).

The emergence of NIDDM is often preceded and accompanied by obesity. Insulin concentrations in the fasting state and after a glucose challenge are raised by the presence of obesity in non-diabetic and mildly hyperglycaemic NIDDM subjects when compared with normal-weight individuals with the same plasma glucose concentrations (Fig. 1; Perley & Kipnis, 1967; DeFronzo, 1988). The hypersecretion of insulin in obesity is associated with B-cell hyperplasia and enhanced activity of the entero-insular axis (see Chapter 1 by Morgan in this book). This appears to provide an adaptive compensation for the additional insulin resistance incurred by obesity. Hyperinsulinaemia persists for as long as the overall functional capacity of the B-cell mass is retained, but the eventual scenario is a diminution of B-cell function and severe hyperglycaemia.

Insulin-dependent diabetes (IDDM)

During the development of IDDM there is gradual reduction in the B-cell mass for months or years before the precipitation of hyperglycaemia (Eisenbarth, 1986). In contrast, the total mass of A-cells and D-cells is unchanged (Volk, 1990). The acute insulin response to intravenous glucose is much reduced or completely lost before the onset of hyperglycaemia, although the acute response to glucagon remains (Srikanta et al., 1985; Eisenbarth, 1986). This defect shows no obvious association with the myriad of immunological markers thought relevant to genetic susceptibility and early destruction of B-cells. The situation may be likened to the disappearance of the insulin response to glucose in animal models of reduced B-cell mass (see later).

Animal diabetes

Diabetes has been noted in most mammalian species (Cameron et al., 1972b) and appears to be relatively common in domestic pets, farm livestock and animals maintained in captivity. The most extensively studied are the diabetic syndromes of laboratory rodents (for reviews see Herberg & Coleman, 1977; Bray & York, 1979; Bailey & Flatt, 1986, 1990; Shafrir, 1990). Although no single species is an exact match for human diabetes, diligent investigation of the range of animal diabetes syndromes has provided important information on mechanisms underlying human diabetes.

Both the magnitude and the kinetics of glucose stimulation of insulin secretion are defective in the various animal species with diabetes, thereby validating their use in studies which, for ethical and technical reasons, are impossible to perform using islets isolated from human diabetic subjects. Studies of insulin secretion in spontaneously diabetic animals have stressed that the nature and severity of defective insulin secretion depend on the mutation itself, the genetic background on which the mutation is carried, the age and sex of the animal in question, and other variables, including environmental conditions, diet and nutritional status (Bailey & Flatt, 1986). Differences in the mode of inheritance of the various syndromes also indicate that defective insulin secretion in diabetes is unlikely to reflect a single common abnormality at the level of the B-cell. It is more probable that impaired insulin secretion represents the common outcome of one or more major genetic defects compounded by differences in the background genome which can interfere with any of the myriad of factors contributing to the overall control of B-cell function.

Non-insulin dependent models

Spontaneous NIDDM syndromes with occasional ketosis

Spontaneous syndromes of NIDDM with occasional ketosis are listed in the upper section of Table 1. Several of these species show an early phase of obesity, B-cell hyperplasia and insulin resistance, which progresses in

Table I. Spontaneous NIDDM syndromes with defective insulin secretion

Animal	Inheri-tance	Environmental influence	Body wt.	Food intake	Glycaemia	Insulinaemia	B-Cell population	Islet necrosis
Occasional ketosis								
Chinese hamster (Cricetulus griseus)	P	?	$+^b$/N	$+^b$	$+/++$	$+^b$/N/$-^{ac}$	$+^b$/$-$	$+$
Diabetes mouse (db), C57BL/KsJ	AR	?	$++$	$++$	$++$	$++^b$/N^c	$+$/$-^c$	$++$
Sand rat (Psammomys obesus)	?	HED/RE	$+$	$+$	$+/++$	$+$/N/$-^d$	$+$/N	$+$/N
Spiny mouse (Acomys cahirinus)	?	HED/RE	$+$	$+$	N/$+$/$++$	$+^b$/N/$-^c$	$+$	N
Without ketosis								
Fatty Zucker rat (fa)	AR	?	$++$	$+$	N^f	$+$	$+$	N?
Goto-Kakizaki rat (GK)	?	?	N	?	$+$	N/$-$	$-$	$+$
Japanese KK mouse	P?	HED	$+^e$	$+^e$	$+^e$	$+^e$	$+$	N/$+$?
New Zealand obese mouse (NZO)	P	?	$++$	$+^b$	$+$	$+^e$	$++$	N?
Obese mouse (ob) C57BL/6J, V Stock, Aston	AR	?	$++^e$	$++^{be}$ $+^e$		$++^e$	$++$	$+^{cg}$
Yellow Obese mouse (A^y, A^{vy}, A^{iy})	AD	?	$++$	$+$	N/$+$	$+$	$+$	N?

$++$, Severe increase; $+$, moderate increase; N, normal; $-$, moderate decrease.

? Uncertain or not reported; AR, autosomal recessive; AD, autosomal dominant; P, polygenic; HED, high-energy diet; RE, reduced exercise; HCD, high carbohydrate diet. Superscript letters denote: [a] some ageing animals may require insulin; [b] occurs during early development; [c] occurs in some ageing animals; [d] occurs in severely diabetic animals; [e] regresses towards normal in ageing animals; [f] basal glycaemia may not be raised sufficiently to qualify as 'diabetic' but oral glucose tolerance is impaired; [g] on certain genetic backgrounds.

later life to a more severe form of diabetes associated with B-cell degeneration, severe hyperglycaemia (> 20 mM) and ketosis. The insulin response to glucose in these animals is impaired and highly variable depending on the age and thus the stage of the syndrome examined. The best characterized and most extensively studied models of defective insulin secretion in this group are considered individually below.

Diabetes-obese C57BL/KsJ *db/db* mouse

This syndrome which is inherited as an autosomal recessive trait, is characterized by obesity, hyperphagia, hyperglycaemia, islet hypertrophy, B-cell hyperplasia and hyperinsulinaemia. Depending on the energy density and carbohydrate content of the diet, adult *db/db* mice exhibit a progressive age-dependent deterioration of B-cell function, potentially culminating in extensive islet necrosis, severe insulin deficiency, marked hyperglycaemia and ketosis. Studies utilizing the perfused pancreas or isolated islets of young adult C57BL/KsJ *db/db* mice have shown that both the dynamics and magnitude of glucose-induced insulin release are defective (Boquist *et al.*, 1974*a*; Berglund *et al.*, 1978; Siegel *et al.*, 1980). In addition, chloromercuribenzene-*p*-sulphonic acid, a thiol reagent with a direct membrane action, failed to stimulate insulin release (Boquist *et al.*, 1974*a*).

C57BL/KsJ *db/db* mice exhibit marked and age-dependent alterations in the hormone content and cellular composition of the islets (Baetens *et al.*, 1978; Gapp *et al.*, 1983). Fig. 3 illustrates the time course and extent of changes in islet cell population when the *db* gene is expressed on the C57BL/6J background which gives rise to a comparatively milder form of diabetes (Gapp *et al.*, 1983). Such changes may interfere with the subtle intra-islet interactions involved in insulin secretion (see Chapter 3 by Marks *et al.* in this book). For example, disturbances in the secretion and/or action of glucagon and somatostatin might contribute to defective insulin secretion (Laube *et al.*, 1973; Basabe *et al.*, 1984). However, the normal flow of blood from the central B-cell core towards A-cells and D-cells in the islet periphery probably limits the possible contribution of alterations in cellular composition to the defective insulin response to glucose *in vivo*.

The observed alterations in islet composition are probably more significant in relation to assessment of metabolic and ionic events implicated in insulin secretion. Evaluation of these parameters in islets from diabetic mice necessarily involves comparison with measurements of control islets containing a different proportion of B-cells. Thus, the demonstration in islets from C57BL/KsJ *db/db* mice of small differences in the chain of events thought to underlie glucose stimulation of insulin secretion is difficult to interpret. Viewed in this context, it must be concluded from available evidence that the glucose-induced increase in islet glycolytic flux is not greatly altered in the mutant (Berglund *et al.*, 1984). Furthermore, basal islet cyclic AMP content and responsiveness to phosphodiesterase inhibitors is retained (Boquist *et al.*, 1974*b*; Siegel *et al.*, 1980). The microtubule–microfilament system also appears to be functional, although total actin in the islets is decreased (Boyd, 1982).

In contrast to the paucity of data regarding possible abnormalities of metabolic events, there is compelling evidence that defective insulin

Fig. 3. **Age-related changes in the volume density of A-, D-, PP- and B-cells in the islets of C57BL/6J *db/db* mice (open bars) and control littermate (+/?) mice (filled bars)**

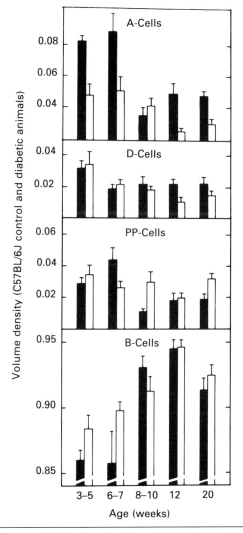

Values are means ± s.e.m. volume density (cell-type area/islet area) of random serial sections of groups of two to four mice. Reproduced from Gapp et al. (1983) with permission.

secretion in C57BL/KsJ *db/db* mice is associated with deranged regulation of B-cell membrane potential, ion fluxes and $[Ca^{2+}]_i$. As illustrated in Fig. 4, B-cells of C57BL/KsJ *db/db* mice show depolarization and electrical activity at low glucose concentrations (Meissner & Schmidt, 1976). This

Fig. 4.   **Electrical activity of B-cells from a normal control mouse at 11.1 mM-glucose (A, upper trace) and a C57BL/KsJ *db/db* mouse at 2.8 mM-glucose (B, lower trace)**

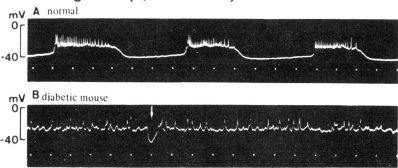

Interval between dots is 2 s. Note the typical normal burst pattern in (A). The db/db mouse B-cell showed depolarization and electrical activity at this very low glucose concentration (B). The arrow indicates a short repolarization phase. The pattern of activity and the membrane potential level from which the spikes arose were not appreciably changed by exposure of the B-cells of db/db mice to 27.7 mM-glucose (data not shown). Reproduced from Meissner & Schmidt (1976) with permission.

is accompanied by abnormally low K^+ permeability (Berglund *et al.*, 1980), glucose-insensitive efflux of K^+ and Cl^- (Berglund *et al.*, 1980; Berglund & Sehlin, 1980), and a lack of effect of glucose on the inhibitory and stimulatory phases of Ca^{2+} efflux (Gylfe *et al.*, 1978; Siegel *et al.*, 1980). Since K^+ permeability is considered the major determinant of the membrane potential, and this is linked to Ca^{2+} influx through the opening of voltage-dependent Ca^{2+} channels, the K^+ channels and their regulation are likely to hold a key role in the secretion defect.

Diabetic Chinese hamster

The inheritance of this syndrome is polygenic and studies with diabetic Chinese hamsters rely on comparison with non-diabetic sublines of hamsters. Various characteristics of the diabetes syndrome in Chinese hamsters are similar in many respects to those seen in C57BL/KsJ *db/db* mice. One of the main differences between the two types of mutants appears to be that Chinese hamsters have a more limited capacity to temporarily offset the severity of diabetes by a compensatory increase in B-cell number (Frankel et al., 1987). Insulin is markedly decreased in the diabetic Chinese hamster pancreas in association with an increase of pancreatic glucagon and a decrease of somatostatin (Petersson et al., 1977). B-cell function has been related to changes of islet cell populations in several studies (Petersson et al., 1977; Iwashima et al., 1990). Disturbances of the islet cholinergic innervation have also been described (Diani et al., 1983).

Studies of the perfused pancreas of diabetic Chinese hamsters have shown age-related defects in both the first and second phases of glucose-stimulated insulin release (Frankel et al., 1974). Observations by Matschinsky (cited in Grodsky et al., 1984), indicating that the activities of glucokinase, hexokinase and phosphofructokinase are not compromised in diabetic Chinese hamster islets, disfavour the idea that abnormalities in the early sequence of metabolic events leading to ATP generation are responsible for defective insulin secretion. However, further studies examining parameters of islet metabolism including glucose-induced changes in redox state and cytoplasmic ATP content are clearly required before such an attractive possibility is discounted.

Although the ability of glucose to enhance cyclic AMP is impaired in diabetic Chinese hamster islets (Rabinovitch et al., 1976), the cyclic AMP system appears relatively normal as assessed from the ability of theophylline to enhance insulin release (Frankel et al., 1974, 1975, 1982). However, as with C57BL/KsJ db/db mice, there are major disturbances in the cellular handling of Ca^{2+}. Thus diabetic Chinese hamster islets do not respond to glucose with normal changes in the uptake and efflux of Ca^{2+} (Siegel et al., 1979; Frankel & Sehlin, 1987). These disturbances are associated with abnormalities in the regulation of membrane K^+ permeability and a subnormal insulin response to a depolarizing concentration of K^+ (Frankel et al., 1982). The former has been suggested to be due to an alteration in Ca^{2+}-activated K^+ permeability (Frankel & Sehlin, 1987). However, since no change was apparent in the initial suppression of $^{86}Rb^+$ efflux from islets by glucose, it was concluded that defective regulation of $[Ca^{2+}]_i$, rather than defective regulation of K^+ permeability, may be responsible for the impaired insulin secretion (Frankel & Sehlin, 1987). Electro-physiological studies should resolve this issue.

Spiny mouse (*Acomys cahirinus*)

Environmental factors such as exercise and nutrition play a crucial role in the development of diabetes in Spiny mice, whether transferred from their normal foraging habitat or bred in the laboratory. In most other respects, the development and course of the diabetes syndrome approximately parallels that of other species in this category. Since there are no natural controls, studies have invariably made comparison with mice of different strains or with rats. Differences between the two groups of animals in terms of diet, stress, basic physiology and B-cell function, including the structure of insulin itself (Bunzle & Humbel, 1972), will necessarily mask to some extent the identity of the secretion defect.

Fig. 5. **Insulin release (left panel) and glucose utilization (right panel) of isolated rat islets (open circles) and Spiny mouse islets (closed circles) during 60 min incubation at different glucose concentrations**

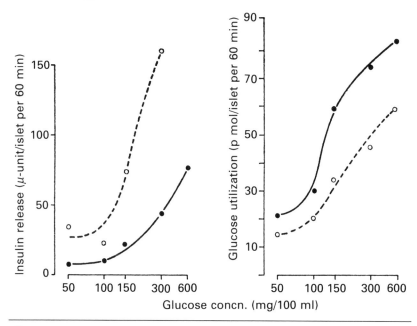

Glucose utilization was estimated from the production of ^3H_2O from D-[5-^{3}H]glucose. Reproduced from Cerasi (1975) with permission.

Studies *in vivo* and *in vitro* using isolated islets of Spiny mice have revealed defects in both the early and late phases of glucose-induced insulin release compared with other rodents (Junod *et al.*, 1969; Cameron *et al.*, 1972a; Gutzeit *et al.*, 1974a,b; Rabinovitch *et al.*, 1975a,b). Both phases are delayed and the acute response in particular appears to be diminished in magnitude. Proinsulin synthesis similarly responds poorly to glucose (Trueheart *et al.*, 1976), and these observations have been interpreted as indicating a decreased sensitivity of the B-cells to glucose (see left-hand panel of Fig. 5). The possible mechanism behind the glucose insensitivity remains obscure. As illustrated in Fig. 5 (right-hand panel), there is no gross defect in glucose utilization in the islets of Spiny mice (Cerasi, 1975; Grill & Cerasi, 1979). However, a defective link between glycolysis and adenylate cyclase has been suggested (Nesher *et al.*, 1989).

Glucose insensitivity has also been implicated in the relatively poor insulin responses of Spiny mice to other secretagogues. Defective responses to arginine, isoprenaline, glucagon, aminophylline and dibutyryl cyclic AMP have been reported *in vivo* (Cameron *et al.*, 1972*a*). Similarly, defective insulin responses to arginine, theophylline, glucagon, tolbutamide and glibenclamide have been observed in acute but not longer-term incubations of isolated islets *in vitro* (Gutzeit *et al.*, 1974*b*; Rabinovitch *et al.*, 1975*a*; Grill & Cerasi, 1979). From these observations, it would appear that the secretory defect may incorporate abnormalities in both the regulation and action of cyclic AMP and $[Ca^{2+}]_i$. Cyclic AMP production is impaired in the B-cells of Spiny mice (Rabinovitch *et al.*, 1975*c*; Grill & Cerasi, 1979), but further studies using current technologies are required to assess the involvement of ion channels, including the ATP-sensitive K^+ channel, through which the sulphonylureas act (see Chapters 10 and 15 in this book by Ashcroft *et al.* and Nelson *et al.*).

Malaisse-Lagae *et al.* (1975) speculated that abnormalities in the microtubule–microfilament system might contribute to the defective insulin secretion in Spiny mice. Such a disturbance is not, however, consistent with the actions of vincristine and cytochalasin B, which influence insulin secretion by disruption of cytoskeletal elements as in normal B-cells (Gutzeit *et al.*, 1974*b*). The islets of Spiny mice have also been reported to be sparsely innervated with nerve fibres (Orci *et al.*, 1970; Hahn von Dorsche *et al.*, 1976), raising the possibility that abnormal autonomic tone contributes to defective insulin secretion.

Sand rat (*Psammomys obesus*)

The Sand rat is accustomed to foraging for a meagre diet in its natural habitat. When confined to a laboratory environment with free access to an enriched diet, the Sand rat exhibits hyperphagia, develops hyperinsulinaemia and obesity, insulin resistance and diabetes which can progress to a severe state. The importance of environment in dictating the severity and progression of the syndrome, together with the lack of suitable control animals, enable superficial parallels to be made with the Spiny mouse.

Glucose stimulation of insulin release in Sand rats depends on the interplay between genetic factors, age and diet. The B-cells of carbohydrate-tolerant Sand rats maintained on low-energy or vegetable diets appear to display normal or exaggerated insulin responses to glucose *in vivo* and *in vitro* (Malaisse *et al.*, 1968; Ziegler *et al.*, 1976; Kohnert *et al.*, 1985; Morten *et al.*, 1986). In contrast, carbohydrate-intolerant Sand rats maintained on energy-rich laboratory diets may lack an insulin response to glucose (Hahn et al., 1976, 1979). There is some discrepancy between the results of investigations in vivo and in vitro of glucose-induced insulin secretion (Hahn et al., 1979), which possibly reflects islet selection procedures. However, in the most comprehensive study to date, Hahn et al. (1976) demonstrated impaired insulin responses to glucose, glyceraldehyde and theophylline from islets isolated from diabetic Sand rats. In this study, inhibition of insulin secretion was observed with diazoxide, but not with mannoheptulose. These observations suggest that the defect presenting in some, but not all, Sand rats involves perturbed glucose sensitivity of the B-cells favouring high basal insulin output. The autonomic innervation of islets of Sand rats appears normal (Danev et al., 1983), but additional studies examining metabolic and ionic events in the B-cells of these animals are clearly warranted.

Spontaneous NIDDM syndromes without ketosis

Spontaneous syndromes of NIDDM without ketosis are listed in the lower section of Table 1. Most of these species exhibit obesity, hyperphagia, B-cell hyperplasia, hyperinsulinaemia and insulin resistance. The hyperglycaemia is usually less than 20 mM and the insulin response to glucose is impaired. The course of these relatively mild diabetes syndromes is greatly affected by genetic background and environment. Rather few models have been investigated in terms of defective insulin secretion. These are considered below.

New Zealand obese (NZO) mouse

Inheritance of diabetes in the NZO mouse is polygenic, and, like several of the species discussed above, comparison has been made with normal control animals of different strains. Defective insulin secretion is a prominent feature of the syndrome, and this can be partly ameliorated by dietary restriction and normalization of body weight (Larkins & Martin, 1972; Larkins, 1973a,b).

Early studies in vivo demonstrated a selective defect of insulin secretion in which the B-cells of NZO mice were unresponsive to glucose, glucagon and tolbutamide, but over-responsive to arginine (Larkins & Martin, 1972). Subsequent studies showed that the early insulin responses were particularly subnormal in kinetics and magnitude after administration of these secretagogues, isoprenaline or aminophylline (Larkins, 1973a; Cameron et al., 1974). The threshold for an insulin response to glucose was reported to be higher in NZO mice (Larkins, 1973a), and more recent observations suggest that glucose responsiveness is restored by treatment with islet-activating protein in vivo (Re et al., 1984). This agent, now referred to as pertussis toxin, modulates the activity of inhibitory G-proteins affecting adenylate cyclase, ion channels and phospholipases in the B-cell (Robertson et al., 1991).

Evaluation of enzyme activities and ion channels in the B-cells of NZO mice have not to our knowledge been reported. However, studies *in vitro* indicate that the defective glucose stimulation of insulin release is associated with a markedly compromised rate of islet glucose utilization (Larkins *et al.*, 1980). Since the ability of glyceraldehyde to provoke insulin release was retained in these experiments, it was suggested that there may be a partial metabolic block in the triose phosphate step of the glycolytic pathway in the B-cells of NZO mice (Larkins *et al.*, 1980).

Obese hyperglycaemic *ob/ob* mouse

A single autosomal recessive gene is responsible for this syndrome. The obese (*ob*) gene has been transferred to several strains of mice, which have been employed extensively to study various aspects of insulin secretion, obesity and diabetes (Bailey & Flatt, 1986, 1990, 1991; Chapter 1 in this book by Morgan). Since the phenotypic expression of the *ob/ob* syndrome depends critically on background strain, age, diet and nutritional state (Bailey & Flatt, 1986), much confusion surrounds the insulin secretory characteristics of this mutant.

On the original V stock background, *ob/ob* mice provide functionally well-preserved B-cells, which have been used extensively in Sweden since the mid-1960s for basic studies on the insulin secretory mechanism. These mice exhibit islet hypertrophy and B-cell hyperplasia and, in contrast with other genetic backgrounds, their insulin secretory capacity remains sufficient to maintain a very high rate of insulin output necessary to contain the hyperglycaemia to moderate levels (Westman, 1968, 1970). Indeed, long-term exposure of the B-cells of these mice to glucose and entero-insular stimuli may provide a priming action which contributes to the marked insulin responses to a wide range of secretagogues *in vivo* and *in vitro* (Westman, 1970; Hahn *et al.*, 1974). The normality of B-cells from these *ob/ob* mice is further evidenced by numerous metabolic, enzymic, ionic and electrophysiological investigations (for example, see Arkhammar *et al.*, 1987; Chapters 11 and 14 in this book by Hellman *et al.* and Berggren *et al.*).

A very high rate of glucose (futile) cycling (i.e. glucose → glucose 6-phosphate → glucose, catalysed by glucokinase/glucose-6-phosphatase) has been demonstrated in *ob/ob* mouse islets (Kahn *et al.*, 1989, 1990*a*; for discussion see Chapters 5 and 6 in this book by Malaisse and Lenzen, respectively). This could represent an adaptive mechanism in these mice to protect elements of the secretory machinery from over-stimulation and potential exhaustion. However, consumption of one molecule of ATP for each molecule of glucose cycled might be expected to decrease the ATP pool and disrupt the regulation of ATP-sensitive K^+ channels and insulin secretion. Thus, even small disturbances of cellular ATP metabolism might have profound effects on the electrical and secretory activities of the

B-cells (Rorsman & Trube, 1990). Further studies will enable the observed glucose cycling to be put into the context of insulin secretory characteristics of this colony of *ob/ob* mice.

When carried on the Aston background, the *ob* gene gives rise to a more severe form of diabetes which may be associated with the

---

Fig. 6. **Relationship in fed Aston *ob/ob* mice between basal plasma insulin concentration and the plasma insulin response to stimulation by glucose, glucagon and arginine**

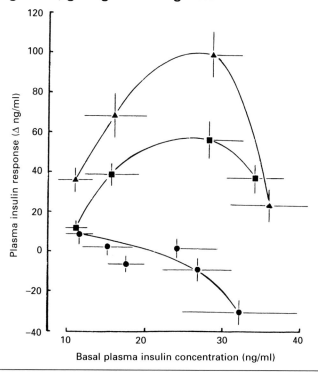

Test agents were administered by intraperitoneal injection: glucose (2 g/kg body wt.), ● ; glucagon (1 mg/kg), ▲ ; arginine (2 g/kg), ■. Values are mean ± S.E.M. of groups of six to eight mice. The plasma insulin response to stimulation (Δ ng/ml) was calculated as the sum of plasma insulin concentrations at 30 and 60 min minus twice the basal value (0 min). Data are taken from Flatt & Bailey (1981, 1982).

---

development of islet necrosis in older mice (Bailey & Flatt, 1986). Aston *ob/ob* mice exhibit an age- and nutrition-related defect in glucose stimulation of insulin secretion *in vivo* (Flatt & Bailey, 1981; Flatt *et al.*,

1987*a*). In hyperinsulinaemic fed *ob/ob* mice, glucose actually provoked a paradoxical decrease of circulating insulin and C-peptide concentrations *in vivo* (for discussion see Chapter 11 in this book by Hellman *et al.*). The magnitude of the decrease of insulin was exaggerated at higher basal

Fig. 7.   Effects of glibenclamide (blocker of ATP-sensitive K$^+$ channels) on the electrical activity of B-cells from an *ob/ob* mouse and a normal control mouse at 11.1 mM-glucose

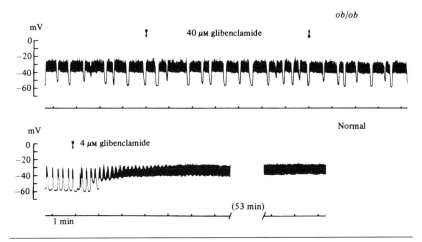

Addition and removal of glibenclamide are indicated by the arrows. In the normal B-cell, continuous spike activity persisted 53 min after the removal of glibenclamide. Reproduced from Rosario et al. (1985) with permission.

insulin concentrations (Fig. 6), suggesting that B-cell hyperactivity and hyperinsulinaemia impair the ability of these cells to secrete insulin in response to glucose. However, the insulin-releasing actions of arginine, glucagon, gastric inhibitory polypeptide (GIP) and numerous other hormonal and neural secretagogues are retained or even enhanced (Flatt & Bailey, 1982; Flatt *et al.*, 1984; Bailey & Flatt, 1988). Indeed, as shown in Fig. 6, the marked insulin response of fed *ob/ob* mice to arginine and glucagon are maintained at extremely high basal insulin concentrations.

In addition to glucose insensitivity, Aston *ob/ob* mice appear to be unresponsive to the insulinotropic action of glibenclamide (Bailey & Flatt, 1982). Electrophysiological studies using a related *ob/ob* mouse colony have shown that the B-cells exhibit altered glucose responsiveness and insensitivity to glibenclamide and quinine (Rosario *et al.*, 1985; Rosario, 1985). Insensitivity to glibenclamide is clearly evident in Fig. 7. Both glibenclamide and quinine act on ATP-sensitive K$^+$ channels (see Bokvist

Table 2.   Experimentally-induced NIDDM syndromes with defective insulin secretion

Agent	Body wt.	Food intake	Glycaemia	Insulinaemia	B-Cell population
Chemical/surgical					
Glucose infusion	N/+	N/−	+	+	+
Low-dose alloxan	N/−	N/+	+	−	− −
Low-dose streptozotocin	N/−	N/+	+	−	− −
Neonatal streptozotocin	N/−	N/+	+	−	− −
Partial pancreatectomy	N/−	N/+	+	−	− −
Hormonal					
Catecholamines	N	+[a]	+	−	N?
Glucagon	N	−	+	+[b]/+	+
Glucocorticoids	+	+	+	−[b]/+	+
Growth hormone	N/+	N	−[b]/+	−[b]/+	+

+, *Moderate increase; N, normal;* −, *moderate decrease;* − −, *severe decrease.*

?, *Uncertain or not reported.*

Superscript letters denote: [a]*blocked at very high doses;* [b]*initial transient effect.*

et al., 1990 and Chapter 15 in this book by Nelson *et al.*). These and other observations (Scott *et al.*, 1985) suggest possible abnormalities in the ATP-sensitive K^+ channel or its regulation.

Lessons from other models
The fatty Zucker (*fa/fa*) rat, the GK rat and the KK mouse have been the subject of several studies of insulin secretion. The B-cells of young animals displayed an exaggerated insulin secretory response to glucose (Appel *et al.*, 1974; Goto *et al.*, 1988; Kuffert *et al.*, 1988). Hyper-responsiveness to arginine, GIP and parasympathetic nerve activation have also been noted in *fa/fa* rats and GK rats (Rohner-Jeanrenaud *et al.*, 1983; Chan *et al.*, 1985; Goto *et al.*, 1988; Jeanrenaud, 1988; Kuffert *et al.*, 1988). Leclerq-Meyer (1987) suggested that anomeric specificity to D-glucose may be occasionally perturbed in the islets of *fa/fa* rats.

Experimentally induced NIDDM
Models of experimentally induced NIDDM are listed in Table 2. The most commonly employed are produced by chemical reduction of B-cell mass or by partial pancreatectomy. Selective hyperglycaemia has also been induced by chronic glucose infusion. Alterations of B-cell function in these models are considered below. Hormones which compromise insulin action can also evoke a range of mild or moderate temporary NIDDM-like states, but

these have contributed comparatively little to the understanding of defective insulin secretion.

Neonatal streptozotocin

Injection of neonatal rats with streptozotocin within 2 days of birth results in reduced B-cell mass which in later life manifests as mild hyperglycaemia (see Bonner-Weir et al., 1988; Portha et al., 1989; Leahy, 1990). This is associated with almost total loss of glucose-induced insulin release in adult rats and an impaired response to mannose (Giroix et al., 1983; Leahy et al., 1985). Consistent with the lack of glucose sensitivity, the effect of the sugar on insulin biosynthesis is also impaired (Portha, 1985). In contrast, the B-cell secretory responsiveness to arginine, isoprenaline, isobutylmethyl-xanthine, tolbutamide and acetylcholine is preserved or even enhanced (Giroix et al., 1983; Grill et al., 1987; Kergoat et al., 1987). The effects of the latter agents suggest that ATP-sensitive K^+ channels and both the cyclic AMP and phospholipase C systems are essentially intact (see Chapter 14 in this book by Berggren et al.). However, some caution may be necessary concerning interpretation of the data because of differences not only in the diabetes variants employed but also between the secretory responsiveness of isolated islets and the perfused pancreas (for discussion, see Grill & Östenson, 1988; Portha et al., 1989).

The impaired secretory response to glucose in these rats has been linked to impaired islet glucose metabolism and a decreased oxidative response of the B-cells to the sugar (Giroix et al., 1990). Thus, elevations of oxygen consumption and the ratio of glucose oxidation relative to glucose utilization were markedly supressed (Portha et al., 1988; Giroix et al., 1990). Increased glucose cycling in islets has also been suggested to contribute to defective insulin secretion (Kahn et al., 1990b). However, other studies have not demonstrated pronounced changes of glucose utilization or oxidation (Colella et al., 1987; Grill & Östenson, 1988). Whether this apparent inconsistency reflects differences in experimental protocol is a matter of debate. A decreased insulin response to leucine has been attributed to impaired islet oxidation of the amino acid (Giroix et al., 1990).

Sensitivity of the secretory machinery to Ca^{2+} is unchanged (Kergoat et al., 1986), although the ineffectiveness of glucose to stimulate insulin secretion was accompanied by decreased effectiveness of the sugar to open voltage-dependent Ca^{2+} channels and stimulate Ca^{2+} influx (Portha et al., 1988). From these observations, it has been suggested that the impaired metabolic and secretory responses to glucose in this rat may largely reflect an alteration in the coupling between Ca^{2+} accumulation and the stimulation of oxidative events (Giroix et al., 1990). These anomalies may represent the consequence of mild hyperglycaemia, although they are not necessarily fully reversed by restoration of a normal glucose environment (Bonner-Weir *et al.*, 1988; Grill & Östenson, 1988; Portha *et al.*, 1989). Consequently, a long-lasting effect of streptozotocin on B-cell metabolism cannot be discounted (see Chapter 17 in this book by Okamoto for details concerning streptozotocin action).

Partial pancreatectomy

Surgical removal of 70–90 % of the B-cell mass has been used to induce a mild NIDDM-like state associated with a stable increase in glycaemia of 1–2 mM and near-normal insulin levels (Bonner-Weir *et al.*, 1988; Rossetti *et al.*, 1990). This is associated with loss of glucose-induced insulin release, although B-cell responsiveness to arginine is preserved (Bonner-Weir *et al.*, 1983; Leahy *et al.*, 1984; Rossetti *et al.*, 1987). The apparent selectivity of the insulin secretion defect may be likened to that observed after neonatal streptozotocin administration. It is found only in those rats where the decrease of B-cell mass is sufficient to produce chronic hyperglycaemia (Bonner-Weir *et al.*, 1988), and it is readily reversible (Rossetti *et al.*, 1987).

Chronic glucose infusion

Chronic intravenous infusion of glucose in conscious rats for periods of up to 7 days has been used to induce a mild state of hyperglycaemia associated with hyperinsulinaemia and selective islet B-cell growth (Bonner-Weir *et al.*, 1988). Studies *in vivo* and *in vitro* indicate loss of glucose-stimulated insulin release and an exaggerated B-cell response to arginine (Leahy *et al.*, 1986, 1987). The severity of the secretion defect is related to the duration, rate and concentration of the glucose infusion (Bonner-Weir *et al.*, 1988; Sako & Grill, 1990; Bedoya & Jeanrenaud, 1981*a*). The defect is reversed rapidly following cessation of the infusion or correction of the glycaemia by insulin or phloridzin administration (Leahy *et al.*, 1987; Bonner-Weir *et al.*, 1988; Sako & Grill, 1990). However, modulation of B-cell function during the glucose infusion with diazoxide or tolbutamide suggests that at least part of the glucose-induced defect is a consequence of B-cell hyperactivity (Sako & Grill, 1990). As shown by Fig. 8, continuous infusions with insulin plus glucose and diazoxide to prevent the hormone's blood-glucose-lowering effects, markedly inhibited glucose-induced insulin release from the subsequently isolated and perfused rat pancreas (Sako & Grill, 1990).

Several studies have attempted to uncover the secretory defect in glucose-infused rats (Colella *et al.*, 1987; Marynissen *et al.*, 1990; Timmers *et al.*, 1990; Zawalich *et al.*, 1990; Bedoya & Jeanrenaud, 1991*a,b*). Islet glucose utilization is increased at both low and high glucose concentrations without significant changes in the rate of glucose oxidation by mitochondria (Colella *et al.*, 1987; Timmers *et al.*, 1990; Bedoya & Jeanrenaud, 1991*a*). This has been reported to be associated with impaired responsiveness to other nutrient fuels such as leucine and its metabolite 2-

ketoisocaproate (Bedoya & Jeanrenaud, 1991*b*). The function and/or regulation of ATP-sensitive K$^+$ channels may also be disrupted as evidenced by a diminished insulin response to tolbutamide (Bedoya & Jeanrenaud, 1991*b*). However, other studies suggest that the defect is

Fig. 8.   **Glucose-induced insulin secretion from the isolated perfused pancreas of rats previously receiving 48 h continuous intravenous infusions of glucose plus diazoxide with either saline or different amounts of insulin**

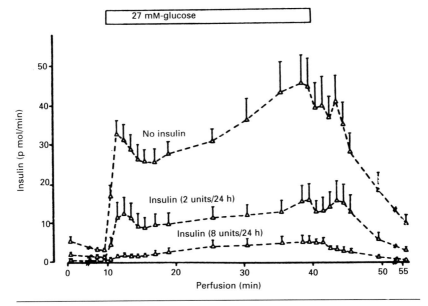

Upper curve, saline control; middle curve, 2 units of insulin/24 h; lower curve, 8 units of insulin/24 h. The rate of glucose infusion was increased in insulin-treated rats to prevent the glucose-lowering action of the hormone. Values are mean ± s.e.m. of groups of three to five rats. Reproduced from Sako & Grill (1990) with permission.

specific for glucose since responsiveness to 2-ketoisocaproate and tolbutamide were unchanged (Timmers *et al.*, 1990). Signal generation via phospholipase C might also be impaired (Zawalich *et al.*, 1990), but activation of adenylate cyclase or protein kinase C appears to stimulate insulin secretion normally from the islets of glucose-infused rats (Timmers *et al.*, 1990; Bedoya & Jeanrenaud, 1991*b*).

Table 3. IDDM syndromes with defective insulin secretion

Animal/agent	Inheritance	Environmental influence	Body wt.	Food intake	Glycaemia	Insulinaemia	B-cell population	Islet necrosis
Spontaneous								
Bio Breeding rat (BB)	P	?	−	+	+ +	− −	− −	+ +
Non-obese diabetic mouse (NOD)	P	?	N/−	+	+ +	− −	− −	+
Experimentally induced								
Alloxan			−/− −	+	+ +	− −	− −	+ +
Streptozotocin			−/− −	+	+ +	− −	− −	+ +
Total pancreatectomy			−/− −	N/−	+ +	− −		

+ +, Severe increase; +, moderate increase; N, normal; −, moderate decrease; − −, severe decrease.

?, Uncertain or not reported; P, polygenic.

Insulin-dependent models
IDDM syndromes

Table 3 lists the principal models of IDDM. They are characterized by severe hyperglycaemia, extensive or complete degeneration of B-cells, insulinopenia, weight loss, hyperphagia, polydipsia and, if untreated, ketosis and death. The syndrome develops spontaneously in the Bio Breeding (BB) rat and non-obese diabetic (NOD) mouse. Experimentally induced forms include total pancreatectomy and chemical destruction of B-cells. The latter may be conveniently achieved by administration of a large dose of alloxan or streptozotocin or by multiple low-dose administration of streptozotocin. Mechanisms of B-cell destruction in these models are considered in Chapter 17 in this book by Okamoto.

B-Cell dysfunction in IDDM models

Although extensive B-cell destruction and severe insulin deficiency are major hallmarks of IDDM, impaired secretion of insulin from structurally intact B-cells is evident before, as well as after, establishment of the disease. Evidence suggests that BB rats and NOD mice exhibit a gradual impairment of B-cell function preceding the onset of diabetes (Kano et al., 1986; Reddy et al., 1988; Eizirik et al., 1991). This is characterized by an apparently selective loss of the early insulin response to glucose (Kano et al., 1986; Reddy et al., 1988). As the extent of B-cell destruction and the severity of diabetes mounts, there follows a progressive loss of ability to respond to glucose, arginine and other secretagogues (Kano et al., 1986; Reddy et al., 1988). Interestingly, an intermediate phase has been demonstrated in moderately diabetic BB rats when the residual B-cells retain responsiveness to arginine even when glucose sensitivity has been lost (Grill & Herberg, 1983).

The mechanisms underlying these abnormalities are undetermined, but they presumably reflect the disruption of the secretory machinery at various loci by the cellular insults involved in the cytotoxic attack of B-cells. For example, exposure to alloxan or streptozotocin *in vitro* exerts numerous effects on B-cell function and insulin secretion, including inhibition of glucokinase and depletion of cellular NAD (see Chapters 6 and 17 in this book by Lenzen and Okamoto, respectively). After onset of diabetes, many other factors including hyperglycaemia, reduction of B-cell mass and alterations of islet composition will also contribute to the altered secretory responsiveness of any surviving B-cells. However, recent studies suggest that the hyperglycaemia *per se* plays a relatively minor role in the B-cell dysfunction of NOD mice (Eizirik *et al.*, 1991).

Human insulinoma

Insulin-secreting tumours (insulinomas) of the pancreas represent the most common type of enteropancreatic endocrine cancer in man, which without clinical intervention can result in debilitation and premature death (Frerichs & Creutzfeldt, 1976; Marks & Rose, 1981; Friesen, 1982; Comi *et al.*, 1986; Lefebvre & Scheen, 1990). The cardinal feature of insulinoma is inappropriate hypoglycaemia resulting from unrestrained secretion of insulin from the tumour. Thus, insulinoma cells display either a lack of responsiveness or a grossly disturbed sensitivity to glucose. Treatment of the disease mainly relies on surgical resection, chemical destruction with streptozotocin or inhibition of secretion with diazoxide. The effectiveness of diazoxide in particular is highly variable with an approximate 40% failure rate (Frerichs & Track, 1974; Comi *et al.*, 1986). This drug inhibits insulin secretion in normal B-cells through activation of ATP-sensitive K^+ channels (Trube *et al.*, 1986).

In view of difficulties with diagnosis and treatment, much attention has been devoted to the insulin secretory characteristics and basic histology of insulinomas. These studies have revealed a considerable diversity of properties and two main classifications of insulinoma have been proposed (Frerichs & Creutzfeldt, 1976; Berger *et al.*, 1983). The more recent classification has been devised on the basis of functional and morphological studies (Berger *et al.*, 1983). It proposes two basic groups, the so-called responsive trabecular (group A) insulinomas and the unresponsive medullary (group B) insulinomas (Berger *et al.*, 1983). The former group is characterized by abundant well-granulated B-cells, uniform insulin immunofluorescence and a trabecular cellular arrangement. These tumours are associated with mild hyperproinsulinaemia and an intact inhibitory response to diazoxide or somatostatin. In comparison, medullary-type insulinomas exhibit more pronounced hyperproinsulinaemia and a marked resistance to inhibition of secretion by diazoxide or somatostatin. Morphologically, the medullary insulinomas exhibit few well-granulated B-cells, non-uniform insulin immunofluorescence and an irregular medullary arrangement of tumour cells (Berger et al., 1983).

The classification of Berger et al. (1983) is not only simple, it is consistent with early observations that the inhibitory effects of adrenaline, somatostatin and diazoxide are only observed in insulinomas which respond with hypersecretion of insulin in provocative tests (Efendic et al., 1976; Lins & Efendic, 1979). In addition, recognition that medullary-type insulinomas are unresponsive to modulators of secretion explains why diagnostic tests based on exaggerated secretory responses to glucagon, leucine, tolbutamide or calcium infusion are associated with false negatives in up to 42 % of proven cases (Frerichs & Creutzfeldt, 1976, 1987). Thus, it is clear from the numerous case histories in the literature that individual insulinomas may exhibit secretory characteristics ranging from unresponsiveness to hyper-responsiveness to a variety of secretagogues (Frerichs & Creutzfeldt, 1976; Marks & Rose, 1981; Friesen, 1982; Comi et al., 1986; Lefebvre & Scheen, 1990).

The mechanisms underlying defective insulin secretion by insulinoma have been investigated in various studies in vitro using tissue obtained at surgery from individual or small numbers of cases of insulinoma. The data accumulated on secretory responsiveness to glucose, glucagon, glucagon-like peptides, carbachol, arginine, sulphonylureas and a range of other drugs affecting adenylate cyclase vary considerably as might be expected from the purely clinical observations (see Bone et al., 1977; Hayashi et al., 1979; Veroni et al., 1981; Flatt et al., 1987b; Chiba et al., 1987; Yasunami et al., 1987; Flatt et al., 1990). There are, however, several uniforming points from these and other studies in vitro: (i) all insulinomas display abnormal sensitivity to glucose; (ii) certain insulinomas exhibit defects in the cyclic AMP coupling system and (iii) certain insulinomas display abnormalities in the Ca^{2+} coupling system.

Substantive evidence for the role of $[Ca^{2+}]_i$ in defective insulin secretion in certain insulinomas comes from the study of three morphologically categorized benign medullary-type insulinomas obtained at surgery (Flatt et al., 1987b). Theophylline enhanced insulin release from these tumours in vitro, but various nutrients, ionic manipulations and drugs which are known to modulate secretion in normal B-cells through alteration of $[Ca^{2+}]_i$, failed to affect either insulin release or transmembrane Ca^{2+} fluxes. These included: glucose, glyceraldehyde, mannoheptulose, a depolarizing concentration of K^+, diazoxide and various Ca^{2+} antagonists and ionophores. The effects of glucose and K^+ on $^{45}Ca^{2+}$ efflux from one such insulinoma are shown in Fig. 9. On the basis of these observations, it was proposed that inappropriate insulin secretion from these tumours was associated with, and possibly stems from marked abnormalities in the regulation of voltage-gated Ca²⁺ channels (Flatt *et al.*, 1987*b*).

This conclusion clearly relates to the ineffectiveness of sulphonyl-ureas and diazoxide to modulate insulin secretion *in vivo* (see above) or in

Fig. 9.   Effects of glucose and K⁺ on ⁴⁵Ca efflux from human medullary-type insulinoma resected from the tail of the pancreas of a 15-year-old girl

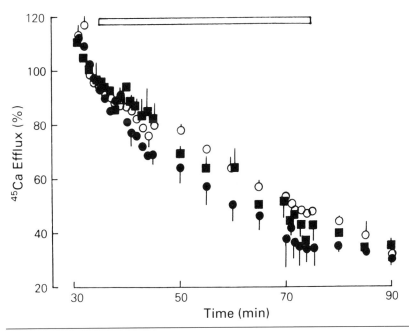

Preloaded 3-day cultured tumour pieces were perifused with buffer containing 3 mM-glucose, with exposure to 16.7 mM-glucose (●) or 25 mM-K⁺ (■) as indicated by the horizontal bar. Open circles refer to ⁴⁵Ca efflux from control tumour pieces. Values are mean±s.e.m. of three individual experiments. Reproduced from Flatt et al. (1987b) with permission.

other studies *in vitro* from unresponsive (presumably medullary-type) insulinomas (Hayashi *et al.*, 1979; Yasunami *et al.*, 1987). Thus, the site of action of sulphonylureas, like that of diazoxide, is the ATP-sensitive K⁺ channel (see Chapter 15 in this book by Nelson *et al.*). However, it is clearly inappropriate to exclude possible abnormalities in other stages of the secretion pathway in insulinoma cells such as glucose metabolism.

Furthermore, the mechanism underlying the defective insulin secretion and hyper-responsiveness of trabecular insulinomas remains undetermined. However, it is possible to interpret the results of diagnostic Ca^{2+} infusion tests (Frerichs & Creutzfeldt, 1987) to indicate that trabecular insulinomas exhibit enhanced sensitivity of the secretory process to $[Ca^{2+}]_i$. This would also explain why Ca^{2+} entry blockers such as diazoxide and verapamil may be used successfully in the treatment of certain insulinomas (Frerichs & Creutzfeldt, 1976; Marks & Rose, 1981; Comi *et al.*, 1986).

Animal insulinoma

Insulinomas arise sporadically in many non-human species, including the mouse, hamster, rat, cat, dog, cow and hagfish (Marks & Rose, 1981). Several useful models of heritable or serially transplantable experimentally induced insulinomas have been produced in laboratory animals (Grillo *et al.*, 1967; Chick *et al.*, 1977, 1980; Hirayama *et al.*, 1979; Hanahan, 1985). These provide the opportunity for detailed functional studies of insulin secretion which are otherwise difficult to perform owing to the unpredictable and low incidence of spontaneous human insulinomas. In addition, several insulinoma cell lines have been produced which may be propagated continuously in tissue culture.

Animal syndromes

The main models available include: the spontaneous and the BK virus-induced transplantable Syrian hamster insulinomas (Grillo *et al.*, 1967; Hirayama *et al.*, 1979); the transplantable radiation-induced NEDH rat insulinoma (Chick *et al.*, 1977); the transplantable streptozotocin–nicotinamide-induced Lewis rat insulinoma (Chick *et al.*, 1980); and the heritable insulinoma induced in transgenic mice through expression of recombinant insulin/simian virus 40 oncogenes (Hanahan, 1985). With the exception of the NEDH rat insulinoma, few studies have addressed the question of defective insulin secretion. Slow-growing insulinomas may also be induced in individual rats by a single combined treatment of nicotinamide with either alloxan or more usually streptozotocin. These latter tumours are considered elsewhere in this book by Lenzen and Okamoto (see Chapters 6 and 17, respectively).

Each insulinoma syndrome is characterized by defective glucose regulation of insulin secretion which leads to the development of marked hyperinsulinaemia and severe life-threatening hypoglycaemia. Some caution must, however, be employed when using insulinoma models because of the possibility of functional divergence between various tumour sublines within the same or between different laboratories. This is well illustrated in the case of the serially transplantable NEDH rat insulinoma. Various sublines of this insulinoma have been characterized in terms of secretory properties and metabolic effects (Chick *et al.*, 1977; Sopwith *et al.*, 1981; Masiello *et al.*, 1982; Hoenig *et al.*, 1984; Flatt *et al.*, 1986*a*). One subline has proven particularly useful in the isolation and characterization of insulin secretory granule proteins (see Chapter 4 in this book by Guest & Hutton). Another subline described by Flatt *et al.* (1986*a*), and considered in detail below, appears to resemble closely the unresponsive medullary-type human insulinomas. It thereby provides an appropriate model to explore the underlying insulin secretory defect.

Serially transplantable NEDH rat insulinoma

Transplantation of small insulinoma fragments into subscapular, pancreatic or hepatic sites of NEDH rats of the Surrey/Ulster (S/U) subline results in hyperphagia, progressive hyperinsulinaemia, defective regulation of insulin secretion and hypoglycaemia, culminating in neuroglycopenic coma within one month (Flatt *et al.*, 1986*a,b,c*; Flatt *et al.*, 1987*c,d*). Excised tumours contain large amounts of insulin with an almost negligible content of other established islet peptides (O'Hare *et al.*, 1985; Conlon *et al.*, 1986). The altered hormonal milieu compared with that of normal islets, loss of neural input, lack of integration with surrounding pancreatic tissue, abnormalities in cellular environment and loss of cell–cell contact may contribute to disturbed insulin secretion *in vivo* (Flatt *et al.*, 1987*c,d*).

Studies with freshly isolated and cultured rat insulinoma cells indicate fundamental disturbances in the normal relationship between the regulation of $[Ca^{2+}]_i$ and insulin secretion. Thus, whereas rat insulinoma cells respond to theophylline and agents which affect insulin secretion in pancreatic B-cells through the adenylate cyclase–cyclic AMP system (Fig. 10; Flatt *et al.*, 1988*a*), responsiveness to glucose and substances which normally modulate secretion by alterations of $[Ca^{2+}]_i$ and entry of the cation through voltage-gated Ca^{2+} channels is severely compromised (Swanston-Flatt & Flatt, 1987; Flatt *et al.*, 1988*a*; Swanston-Flatt & Flatt, 1988*a,b*). This defect is associated with impaired breakdown of inositol phospholipids (Flatt & Best, 1987).

The failure of glucose to elicit changes of $[Ca^{2+}]_i$ and insulin secretion in rat insulinoma cells has been suggested partly to reflect a deficiency of glucokinase (Lenzen *et al.*, 1987; see also Chapter 6 in this book by Lenzen). Glucose utilization and oxidation is also probably deranged (Lenzen *et al.*, 1987; Swanston-Flatt & Flatt, 1987). Furthermore, glucose lacks an effect on membrane potential as assessed with bis-oxonal (Flatt *et al.*, 1988*a*). However, as witnessed by the independence of insulin release on variations of extracellular Ca^{2+}, leading to a 4-fold increase of $[Ca^{2+}]_i$, rat insulinoma cells also display grossly abnormal sensitivity to the stimulatory effects of Ca^{2+} on exocytosis (Fig. 10; Flatt *et al.*, 1988*a*).

These observations indicate that rat insulinoma cells exhibit multiple abnormalities in the normal stimulus–secretion coupling mechanism involving $[Ca^{2+}]_i$. Experiments evaluating the effects of a depolarizing concentration of K^+ and established Ca^{2+} entry blockers do,

---

Fig. 10.   Effects of extracellular Ca^{2+} concentration on insulin release and ^{45}Ca uptake by cultured NEDH rat insulinoma cells

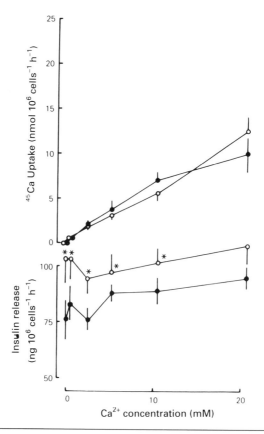

*Incubations were performed at 11.1 mM-glucose in the absence (●) or presence (○) of 5 mM-theophylline. Values are mean ± s.e.m. of seven experiments. *P < 0.05 compared with insulin release in the absence of theophylline. ^{45}Ca uptake was consistently increased by stepwise increments of Ca^{2+} over the range 0 (plus 1 mM-EGTA)–20.4 mM. Modulation of extracellular Ca^{2+} was without effect on insulin release. Reproduced from Flatt et al. (1988a) with permission.*

however, provide evidence for the existence of voltage-dependent Ca^{2+} channels. Regulation of ATP-sensitive K^+ channels has not been directly assessed in rat insulinoma cells, but it is notable that established chemical probes for such channels, namely sulphonylureas and diazoxide, failed to affect transmembrane Ca^{2+} fluxes or insulin release (Swanston-Flatt & Flatt, 1988a). Insulinoma-bearing rats also failed to display an insulin response to glibenclamide *in vivo* (Flatt *et al.*, 1987c). A small inhibitory action of diazoxide was observed (Flatt *et al.*, 1987e), but such a response in very mildly hyperinsulinaemic rats *in vivo* may reflect an action on the pancreatic B-cells rather than on the insulinoma itself.

Serially transplantable RINm5F cell insulinoma

The insulin secretory properties of the radiation-induced rat insulinoma outlined above may be contrasted with those of tumours produced by serial transplantation of RINm5F cells in NEDH rats (Flatt *et al.*, 1987f, 1988b). Transplantation of these daughter cells originally derived from the rat insulinoma (Gazdar *et al.*, 1980), results in the development of a tumour with a trabecular-type cellular arrangement (Flatt *et al.*, 1988b). These responded *in vitro* to a wide range of modulators of insulin secretion, including; leucine, arginine, glucagon, theophylline, somatostatin, sulphonylureas, calcium ionophore and elevated concentrations of Ca^{2+} and K^+ (Flatt *et al.*, 1987f, 1988b). Indeed, the milieu *in vivo* enhanced the function of the cell line and appeared to invoke a modest but nevertheless abnormal insulin response to glucose (Flatt *et al.*, 1988b). On both morphological and functional grounds, the tumours produced in NEDH rats, by transplantation of RINm5F cells, appear to afford a novel model of responsive trabecular-type human insulinomas.

Cultured cell lines

Recent years have witnessed the creation of several clonal insulin-secreting (tumour) B-cell lines from animals. Those most extensively used are RINm5F cells, derived from the radiation-induced rat insulinoma (Gazdar *et al.*, 1980), and HIT cells produced by simian virus transformation of hamster pancreatic B-cells (Santerre *et al.*, 1981). These cell lines have been used for extensive studies of insulin secretion including the mode of action of sulphonylureas (see Chapter 15 in this book by Nelson *et al.*). The secretory characteristics of RINm5F cells and HIT cells vary significantly depending on the subline used and both present and past culture techniques. However, despite responsiveness to an impressive array of physiological and pharmacological modulators of secretion, neither cell line displays normal glucose stimulation of insulin release (Halban *et al.*, 1983; Rorsman *et al.*, 1983; Praz *et al.*, 1983; Hill & Boyd, 1985; Ashcroft *et al.*, 1986; Sener *et al.*, 1987; Flatt *et al.*, 1988b).

The inappropriate glucose responsiveness of these cell lines has led to the suggestion that they may prove useful in studies designed to reveal the cellular mechanisms underlying defective glucose regulation (Malaisse, 1987). Such studies have shown multiple abnormalities in glucose transport and metabolism accompanied by a severe depletion of glucokinase (see Meglasson *et al.*, 1986; Malaisse, 1987, 1990; Chapter 6 in this book by Lenzen). These abnormalities preclude onset of the sequence of ionic events inspired by glucose leading to insulin secretion. Indeed, glucose may even decrease $[Ca^{2+}]_i$ in RINm5F cells (Rorsman *et al.*, 1983) reflecting a dual effect which is normally masked in pancreatic B-cells by stimulation of Ca^{2+} influx. Such an action may explain the paradoxical inhibition of insulin secretion sometimes observed with both RINm5F cells and the parent insulinoma (Flatt *et al.*, 1987*f*, 1988*b*). As evident from these observations, and comments in several of the preceding Chapters, some caution is warranted when using the RINm5F or HIT cell lines as convenient sources of B-cells for studies of the normal insulin secretory mechanism.

Mechanisms of defective insulin secretion

Defective insulin secretion may arise from a single disturbance in any one of the many sequential events linking ingestion of nutrients to the exocytotic release of insulin into the circulation. Additional factors not necessarily associated with feeding such as hormones, regulatory peptides and catecholamines may also contribute to impaired B-cell function. On the basis of the studies considered above, it is possible to identify several potentially important functional disturbances which may contribute to the overall mechanism responsible for defective insulin secretion in diabetes and insulinoma. These are considered below.

Specific lesions in the stimulus–secretion coupling pathway

There is little doubt that defective insulin secretion in diabetes and insulinoma is accompanied by and actually stems primarily from specific lesions at key points in the B-cell stimulus–secretion coupling pathway. Abnormalities have been detected in almost all known stages of the secretory sequence including the transport and metabolism of glucose, the regulation of K^+ permeability and ion fluxes (Figs. 4, 7 and 9), the control of and sensitivity to $[Ca^{2+}]_i$ (Fig. 10), and the function of microtubules and microfilaments. In contrast, the adenylate cyclase and phospholipase C systems appear to remain essentially intact. Disturbances of $[Ca^{2+}]_i$ appear to represent a common feature underlying defective insulin secretion. However, the lesions responsible for these disturbances may reside at any of the adjacent loci in the coupling pathway. The future challenge is to identify the basic B-cell lesion(s) and to determine in diabetes the extent to which the lesion(s) reflects a primary defect or a consequence of compounding environmental factors and the internal milieu.

Disturbances in synthesis and trafficking of insulin

Small numbers of point mutations of the insulin gene have been found in human subjects (Robbins & Tager, 1989; Steiner et al., 1990). Since these may affect biological potency of the hormone, disturbances in biosynthesis may contribute to the pathophysiology of diabetes. Other mutations have been detected that influence the intracellular processing and trafficking of proinsulin (for review see Steiner et al., 1990). Although the known frequency of such mutations is low, disturbances which potentially lead to the abnormal release of proinsulin from B-cells are of interest in relation to the hyperproinsulinaemia often encountered in NIDDM and insulinoma. Raised levels would similarly result from the release of newly synthesized proinsulin by the so-called unregulated constitutive pathway. Unlike the normal regulated pathway, this route circumvents packaging and processing of the prohormone in the secretory granules. Preliminary observations indicate that the dysregulated release of proinsulin contributes to defective B-cell function of human medullary-type insulinomas (P. R. Flatt, S. M. Hampton, G. M. DeSilva, O. Shibier & S. K. Swanston-Flatt, unpublished work).

Glucose environment

There is compelling evidence from studies *in vivo* in animals and man, and from investigations *in vitro* using cultured B-cells, that long-term exposure to either a hyperglycaemic or a hypoglycaemic environment results in a gradual impairment of insulin secretion (Unger & Grundy, 1985; Leahy, 1990; Rossetti et al., 1990). This is clearly illustrated by the development of B-cell dysfunction in rats subjected to partial pancreatectomy or glucose infusions. In the light of data from animal syndromes of diabetes, it is not unreasonable to expect that the effects of inappropriate glycaemia will be even more deleterious to genetically susceptible or damaged B-cells. However, changes of glucose environment are in the majority of cases likely to represent an influential consequence rather than the cause of defective insulin secretion. Thus disturbances of B-cell function appear to precede overt changes in glycaemic environment in most cases of spontaneous diabetes and insulinoma.

B-Cell hyperactivity

The possibility that B-cell hyperactivity contributes to the defective insulin responses to glucose and other secretagogues particularly in NIDDM merits consideration. Thus, in various animal models of NIDDM, loss of an insulin response to parenterally administered glucose shows a close association with the extent of hyperinsulinaemia (Figs. 6 and 8). In addition, fasting and other interventions which decrease the extent of the hyperinsulinaemia and hyperglycaemia improve insulin secretory responsiveness. A link also exists between insulin hypersecretion and the extent of B-cell degeneration in many of the NIDDM syndromes with occasional ketosis. Furthermore, the possibility has been raised that defective insulin secretion in glucose-infused rats results primarily from B-cell hyperactivity rather than from the accompanying hyperglycaemia (Sako & Grill, 1990). B-Cell hyperactivity, therefore, appears to downregulate both the action and the secretion of insulin. The major stimulus for hyperinsulinaemia, at least in animal syndromes of NIDDM, concerns hyperactivity of neural and hormonal components of the entero-insular axis, including excessive secretion of GIP (see Flatt *et al.*, 1984; Bailey & Flatt, 1988; Jeanrenaud, 1988; Chapter 1 in this book by Morgan). Secretory responsiveness is retained to neural and hormonal agents which operate mainly via the adenylate cyclase and phospholipase C systems (see Chapter 14 in this book by Berggren *et al.*).

Disturbances of B-cell environment

Diabetes and insulinoma are associated with marked alterations in the normal cellular environment of the insulin-secreting cells. The locations and relative proportions of the various cell types within the islets are disturbed in diabetes (Fig. 3). Insulinomas differ even more substantially from normal islets, both in terms of composition and organization of peptide-secreting cells, and regarding cell–cell contacts and vascularization (Frerichs & Creutfeldt, 1976). There can be little doubt that the normal interactions between the B-cells, A-cells and D-cells described by Marks *et al.* in Chapter 3 in this book are substantially disrupted. Although this undoubtedly contributes to the general functional malaise of the B-cells and impaired glucose homoeostasis, these changes alone are much less important in terms of defective insulin secretion in diabetes and insulinoma than the lesions in the stimulus–secretion coupling pathway outlined above.

Alterations of autonomic tone

Innervation of the islet cells plays a subtle yet important role in the overall control of B-cell function in various physiological situations (see Chapter 2 in this book by Holst). Insulinomas are devoid of nerve fibres. It is logical from the structural changes of the islets, and the well-known deleterious effect of hyperglycaemia on nerve conduction velocity (Greene *et al.*, 1990), to predict that alterations of B-cell innervation and autonomic tone also occur in some forms of diabetes. This has been verified by ultrastructural observations in several NIDDM syndromes (i.e. Chinese hamster and Spiny mouse), and by irregularities of islet neuropeptides in others (for examples, see Bailey & Flatt, 1988). Imbalances of autonomic tone may contribute to the promotion of hyperinsulinaemia or to the suppression of insulin secretion. Classical and peptidergic neurotransmitters include acetylcholine, noradrenaline, cholecystokinin, somatostatin, galanin, gastrin-releasing peptide, vasoactive intestinal polypeptide and neuropeptide Y. These agents act at various levels in the secretory process as discussed by Berggren *et al.* in Chapter 14 in this book. Alterations in the normal actions of these neurotransmitters in diabetes or insulinoma may therefore contribute significantly to the amplification or suppression of insulin secretion. However, such effects cannot account for fundamental lesions in the stimulus–secretion coupling pathway.

Other local modulators of secretion

Pancreatic islets and insulinomas contain a large number of potentially important modulators of insulin secretion which may contribute to defective insulin secretion. These include biogenic amines, pancreastatin, islet amyloid polypeptide (IAPP), opiate peptides, thyrotropin-releasing hormone, corticotropin-releasing factor, peptide YY, atrial natriuretic peptide, diazepam-binding inhibitor and a number of less well-defined secretory granule proteins. Pancreastatin and IAPP, which are synthesized and released from pancreatic B-cells and insulinoma cells, have been proposed to contribute to B-cell dysfunction through inhibition of insulin secretion. Further details concerning these local modulators of insulin secretion and the actions of pancreastatin and IAPP are given by Guest & Hutton and Berggren *et al.* in Chapters 4 and 15 in this book, respectively.

Conclusions

Studies using animals exhibiting diabetes syndrome or bearing insulinoma have highlighted the involvement of abnormalities of membrane K^+ permeability and the regulation of $[Ca^{2+}]_i$ in defective insulin secretion. Increasing evidence suggests that abnormalities of B-cell glucose metabolism may also contribute to the impaired sequence of ionic events through inept regulation of ATP-sensitive K^+ channels. Disturbances of these channels are suggested by the failure of sulphonylureas and diazoxide to modulate insulin secretion in certain human subjects. Unfortunately, few pertinent data exist concerning diabetic human islets, but the few studies performed *in vitro* with human non-responsive medullary-type insulinomas indicate that defects in the stimulus–secretion pathway similar to those considered above occur in man. Inappropriate glycaemia and B-cell hyperactivity may contribute to disturbances of insulin secretion and the potential demise of diabetic B-cells. However, the diverse nature of the secretion defects in animal and cellular models indicates that site-specific lesions in the B-cell secretory machinery make a substantial contribution to disturbances of glucose homoeostasis in both diabetes and insulinoma.

The authors are grateful for the support of the British Diabetic Association, Cancer Research Campaign, Department of Health and Social Services (NI), University of Ulster Research Committee, Deutsche Forschungs-gemeinschaft (SFB-113), Ministerium fur Wissenschaft und Forschung des Landes Nordrhein-Westfalen, Bundesministerium fur Jugend, Familie Frauen und Gesundheit, Bank of Sweden Tercentenary Foundation and Swedish Medical Research Council (19X-00034).

References

Andersson, A. & Hellerstrom, C. (1980) Explant culture: Pancreatic islets. In Methods in Cell Biology, vol. 21B, pp. 135–151, Academic Press, New York

Appel, M. C., Chang, A. Y. & Dulin, W. E. (1974) Diabetes in the Toronto KK hybrid mouse: Abnormalities in liver and pancreatic islets of Langerhans. Diabetologia **10**, 625–632

Arkhammar, P., Nilsson, T., Rorsman, P. & Berggren, P. O. (1987) Inhibition of ATP-regulated K^+ channels precedes depolarization-induced increase in cytoplasmic free Ca^{2+} concentration in pancreatic B-cells. J. Biol. Chem. **262**, 5448–5454

Ashcroft, S. J. H., Bassett, J. M. & Randle, P. J. (1971) Isolation of human pancreatic islets capable of releasing insulin and metabolising glucose in vitro. Lancet **i**, 888–889

Ashcroft, S. J. H., Hammonds, P. & Harrison, D. E. (1986) Insulin secretory responses of a clonal cell line of simian virus 40-transformed B cells. Diabetologia **29**, 727–733

Ashcroft, F. M., Kakei, M., Kelly, R. P. & Sutton, R. (1987) ATP-sensitive K^+ channels in human pancreatic B-cells. FEBS Lett. **215**, 9–12

Baetens, D., Stefan, Y., Ravazzola, M., Malaisse-Lagae, F., Coleman, D. L. & Orci, L. (1978) Alteration of islet cell populations in spontaneously diabetic mice. Diabetes **27**, 1–7

Bailey, C. J. & Flatt, P. R. (1982) Characterization of the insulin secretory defect in fed adult Aston ob/ob mice: Lack of effect of glibenclamide. Biochem. Soc. Trans. **10**, 28–29

Bailey, C. J. & Flatt, P. R. (1986) Animal models of diabetes. In Recent Advances in Diabetes (Nattrass, M., ed.), vol. 2, pp. 71–89, Churchill Livingstone, Edinburgh

Bailey, C. J. & Flatt, P. R. (1988) The enteroinsular axis in animals with hyperinsulinaemic and hypoinsulinaemic diabetes. In Frontiers in Diabetes Research. Lessons from Animal Diabetes (Shafrir, E. & Renold, A. E., eds.), vol. 2, pp. 217–224, John Libbey, London & Paris

Bailey, C. J. & Flatt, P. R. (1990) Models for testing new hypoglycaemic drugs. In New Antidiabetic Drugs (Bailey, C. J. & Flatt, P. R., eds.), pp. 65–82, Smith Gordon, London

Bailey, C. J. & Flatt, P. R. (1991) Animal models of non-insulin-dependent diabetes mellitus. In Textbook of Diabetes (Pickup, J. C. & Williams, G., eds.), vol. 1, pp. 228–239, Blackwell Scientific Publications, Oxford

Basabe, J. C., Karabates, L. M., Arata, M., Pivelta, O. H. & Cresto, J. C. (1984) Secretion and effect of somatostatin in early stages of the diabetes syndrome in C57BL/KsJ-*mdb* mice. Acta Endocrinol. (Copenhagen) **105**, 539–544

Bedoya, F. J. & Jeanrenaud, B. (1991a) Evolution of insulin secretory response to glucose by perifused islets from lean (*fa/fa*) rats chronically infused with glucose. Diabetes **40**, 7–14

Bedoya, F. J. & Jeanrenaud, B. (1991b) Insulin secretory response to secretagogues by perifused islets from chronically glucose-infused rats. Diabetes **40**, 15–19

Berger, M., Bordi, C., Cuppers, H.-J., Berchtold, P., Gries, F. A., Munterfering, H., Sailer, R., Zimmerman, H. & Orci, L. (1983) Functional and morphologic characterization of human insulinomas. Diabetes **32**, 921–931

Berglund, O. & Sehlin, J. (1980) Defective regulation of Cl⁻ permeability in islets of diabetic mice [C57BL/KsJ (*db/db*)]. Diabetes **29**, 151–155

Berglund, O., Frankel, B. J. & Hellman, B. (1978) Development of the insulin secretory defect in genetically diabetic (*db/db*) mouse. Acta Endocrinol. (Copenhagen) **87**, 543–551

Berglund, O., Sehlin, J. & Taljedal, I.-B. (1980) Influence of the murine diabetes gene on rhubidium ion efflux from perifused islets. Diabetologia **19**, 45–49

Berglund, O., Sehlin, J. & Taljedal, I.-B. (1984) Phosphate flush and glucose metabolism in pancreatic islets of young and old diabetic mice (C57BL/KsJ-*db/db*). Acta Endocrinol. (Copenhagen) **105**, 539–544

Bokvist, K., Rorsman, P. & Smith, P. A. (1990) Block of ATP-regulated and Ca^{2+}-activated K^+ channels in mouse pancreatic B-cells by external tetraethylammonium and quinine. J. Physiol (London) **423**, 327–342

Bone, A. J., Gumpert, R. W., Howell, S. L., Sheldon, J., Tellez-Yudilevich, M., Tyhurst, M., Whittaker, P. G. & Zaheer, F. (1977) Regulation of insulin and glucagon secretion from a human islet cell adenoma. J. Endocrinol. **74**, 273–280

Bonner-Weir, S., Trent, D. F. & Weir, G. C. (1983) Partial pancreatectomy in the rat and subsequent defect in glucose-induced insulin release. J. Clin. Invest. **71**, 1544–1554

Bonner-Weir, S., Leahy, J. L. & Weir, G. C. (1988) Induced rat models of noninsulin-dependent diabetes. In Frontiers in Diabetes Research. Lessons from Animal Diabetes (Shafrir, E. & Renold, A. E., eds.), vol. 2, pp. 295–300, John Libbey, London & Paris

Boquist, L., Hellman, B., Lernmark, A. & Taljedal, I.-B. (1974*a*) Influence of the mutation 'diabetes' on insulin release and islet morphology in mice of different genetic backgrounds. J. Cell Biol. **62**, 77–89

Boquist, L., Hellman, B., Lernmark, A. & Taljedal, I.-B. (1974*b*) Content of adenosine 3′:5′-cyclic monophosphate in the pancreatic islets of mice with a hereditary defect of insulin secretion. Biochem. Biophys. Res. Commun. **60**, 1391–1396

Boyd, A. E., III (1982) Cytoskeletal proteins and insulin secretion. In Cellular Regulation of Secretion and Release (Boyd, A. E., III, ed.), pp. 223–263, Academic Press, New York

Bray, G. A. & York, D. A. (1979) Hypothalamic and genetic obesity in experimental animals: An autonomic and endocrine hypothesis. Physiol. Rev. **59**, 719–809

Brunzell, J. D., Robertson, R. P., Lerner, R. L., Hazzard, W. R., Ensinck, J. W., Bierman, E. L. & Porte, D., Jr (1976) Relationships between fasting plasma glucose levels and insulin secretion during intravenous glucose tolerance tests. J. Clin. Endocrinol. Metab. **42**, 222–229

Bunzle, H. F. & Humbel, R. E. (1972) Isolation and partial structural analysis of insulin from mouse (Mus musculus) and Spiny mouse (Acomys cahirinus). Hoppe Seylers Z. Physiol. Chem. **353**, 444–450

Cameron, D. P., Stauffacher, W., Orci, L., Amherdt, M. & Renold, A. E. (1972*a*) Defective immunoreactive insulin secretion in the *Acomys cahirinus*. Diabetes **21**, 1060–1071

Cameron, D. P., Stauffacher, W. & Renold, A. E. (1972*b*) Spontaneous hyperglycaemia and obesity in laboratory rodents. In Handbook of Physiology (Greep, R. O. & Astwood, E. B., eds.), section 7, vol. 1, pp. 611–626, American Physiological Society, Washington

Cameron, D. P., Opat, F. & Insch, S. (1974) Studies of immunoreactive insulin secretion in NZO mice in vivo. Diabetologia **10**, 649–654

Cerasi, E. (1975) Mechanisms of glucose stimulated insulin secretion in health and in diabetes: Some re-evaluations and proposals. Diabetologia **11**, 1–13

Cerasi, E., Luft, R. & Efendic, S. (1972) Decreased sensitivity of the pancreatic beta cells to glucose in prediabetic and diabetic subjects: A glucose dose–response study. Diabetes **21**, 224–234

Chan, C. B., Pederson, R. A., Buchan, A. M. J., Tubesing, K. B. & Brown, J. C. (1985) Gastric inhibitory polypeptide and hyperinsulinaemia in the Zucker (*fa/fa*) rat. A developmental study. Int. J. Obes. **9**, 137–146

Chiba, T., Yamatani, T., Kadowaki, S., Yamaguchi, A., Inui, T., Saito, Y. & Fujita, T. (1987) Glucose stimulates insulin release without altering cyclic AMP production or inositol phospholipid turnover in freshly obtained human insulinoma cells. Biochem. Biophys. Res. Commun. **145**, 263–268

Chick, W. L., Warren, S., Chute, R. N., Like, A. A., Lauris, V. & Kitchen, K. C. (1977) A transplantable insulinoma in the rat. Proc. Natl. Acad. Sci. U.S.A. **74**, 628–632

Chick, W. L., Appel, M. C., Weir, G. C., Like, A. A., Lauris, V., Porter, J. G. & Chute,

R. N. (1980) Serially transplantable chemically induced rat islet cell tumour. Endocrinology **107**, 954–960

Colella, R. M., May, J. M., Bonner-Weir, S., Leahy, J. L. & Weir, G. C. (1987) Glucose utilization in islets of hyperglycemic rat models with impaired glucose-induced insulin secretion. Metabolism **36**, 335–337

Comi, R. J., Gorden, P., Doppman, J. L. & Norton, J. A. (1986) Insulinoma. In The Exocrine Pancreas: Biology, Pathobiology and Diseases (Go, V. L. W., ed.), pp. 745–761, Raven Press, New York

Conlon, J. M., Deacon, C. F., Bailey, C. J. & Flatt, P. R. (1986) Effects of a transplantable insulinoma upon regulatory peptide concentrations in the gastrointestinal tract of the rat. Diabetologia **29**, 334–338

Crockford, P. M., Hazzard, W. R. & Williams, R. H. (1969) Insulin response to glucagon: The opposing effects of diabetes and obesity. Diabetes **18**, 216–224

Danev, S., Petkov, P., Marquie, G. & Duhault, J. (1983) Ultrastructure of the neuro-insular complex in the pancreas of sand rats (*Psammomys obesus*). Acta Diabetol. Lat. **20**, 347–356

DeFronzo, R. A. (1988) The triumvirate: B-cell, muscle, liver: A collusion responsible for NIDDM. Diabetes **37**, 667–687

DeFronzo, R. A., Ferrannini, E. & Koivisto, V. (1983) New concepts in the pathogenesis and treatment of noninsulin-dependent diabetes mellitus. Am. J. Med. **74** (Suppl. 1), 52–81

Diani, A. R., Peterson, T. & Gilchrist, R. J. (1983) Islet innervation of nondiabetic and diabetic Chinese hamsters. I Acetylcholinesterase histochemistry and norepinephrine fluorescence. J. Neural Transm. **56**, 223–238

Efendic, S., Lins, P. E., Sigurdsson, G., Ivemark, B., Granberg, P. O. & Luft, R. (1976) Effect of somatostatin on basal and glucose induced insulin release in five patients with hyperinsulinaemia. Acta Endocrinol. (Copenhagen) **81**, 525–529

Efendic, S., Luft, R. & Wajngot, A. (1984) Aspects of the pathogenesis of type 2 diabetes. Endocrine Rev. **5**, 395–410

Eisenbarth, G. S. (1986) Type I diabetes mellitus: A chronic autoimmune disease, N. Engl. J. Med. **314**, 1360–1366

Eizirik, D. L., Strandell, E. & Sandler, S. (1991) Prolonged exposure of pancreatic islets isolated from 'pre-diabetic' non-obese diabetic mice to a high glucose concentration does not impair beta-cell function. Diabetologia **34**, 6–11

Flatt, P. R. & Bailey, C. J. (1981) Development of glucose intolerance and impaired plasma insulin response to glucose in obese hyperglycaemic (*ob/ob*) mice. Horm. Metab. Res. **13**, 556–560

Flatt, P. R. & Bailey, C. J. (1982) Plasma glucose and insulin responses to glucagon and arginine in Aston *ob/ob* mice: Evidence for a selective defect in glucose-mediated insulin release. Horm. Metab. Res. **14**, 127–130

Flatt, P. R. & Best, L. (1987) Abnormalities of inositol phospholipid metabolism in transplantable rat insulinoma cells maintained in tissue culture. Med. Sci. Res. **15**, 1419–1420

Flatt, P. R., Bailey, C. J., Kwasowski, P., Page, T. & Marks, V. (1984) Plasma immunoreactive gastric inhibitory polypeptide in obese hyperglycaemic (*ob/ob*) mice. J. Endocrinol. **101**, 249–256

Flatt, P. R., Tan, K. S., Bailey, C. J., Powell, C. J., Swanston-Flatt, S. K. & Marks, V. (1986a) Effects of transplantation and resection of a radiation-induced rat insulinoma on glucose homeostasis and the endocrine pancreas. Br. J. Cancer **54**, 685–692

Flatt, P. R., Bailey, C. J. & Swanston-Flatt, S. K. (1986b) Hormonal modification of the growth and metabolic effects of a transplantable rat insulinoma. Acta Endocrinol. (Copenhagen) **113**, 82–87

Flatt, P. R., Bailey, C. J., Gray, C. & Swanston-Flatt, S. K. (1986c) Metabolic effects of radiation induced rat insulinoma at pancreatic, hepatic and subscapular transplantation sites. Comp. Biochem. Physiol. **85A**, 183–186

Flatt, P. R., Bailey, C. J., Hampton, S. M., Swanston-Flatt, S. K. & Marks, V. (1987a) Immunoreactive C-peptide in spontaneous syndromes of obesity and diabetes in mice. Horm. Metab. Res. **19**, 1–5

Flatt, P. R., Swanston-Flatt, S. K., Powell, C. J. & Marks, V. (1987b) Defective regulation of insulin release and transmembrane Ca^{2+} fluxes by human islet cell tumours. Br. J. Cancer **56**, 459–464

Flatt, P. R., Tan, K. S., Swanston-Flatt, S. K., Webster, J. D. & Marks, V. (1987c) Metabolic effects and secretory properties of a radiation-induced transplantable rat insulinoma. Comp. Biochem. Physiol. **87A**, 175–181

Flatt, P. R., Tan, K. S., Swanston-Flatt, S. K., Bailey, C. J. & Marks, V. (1987d) Defective diurnal changes of food intake, plasma glucose and insulin in rats with a transplantable islet cell tumour. Horm. Res. **27**, 47–52

Flatt, P. R., Swanston-Flatt, S. K., Tan, K. S. & Marks, V. (1987e) Effects of cytotoxic drugs and inhibitors of insulin secretion on a serially transplantable insulinoma and cultured rat insulinoma cells. Gen. Pharmacol. **18**, 293–297

Flatt, P. R., DeSilva, M., Swanston-Flatt, S. K. & Marks, V. (1987f) Insulin secretion in vivo and in vitro from transplantable NEDH rat insulinoma and derived clonal RINm5F cell line. Diabetes Res. **6**, 85–90

Flatt, P. R., Abrahamsson, H., Arkhammar, P., Berggren, P.-O., Rorsman, P. & Swanston-Flatt, S. K. (1988a) Measurements of membrane potential, transmembrane Ca^{2+} fluxes, cytoplasmic free Ca^{2+} concentration and insulin release by transplantable rat insulinoma cells maintained in tissue culture. Br. J. Cancer **58**, 22–29

Flatt, P. R., DeSilva, M. G., Swanston-Flatt, S. K., Powell, C. J. & Marks, V. (1988b) Tumour formation and insulin secretion by clonal RINm5F cells following repeated subcutaneous transplantation in NEDH rats. J. Endocrinol. **118**, 429–437

Flatt, P. R., Shibier, O., Hampton, S. M. & Marks, V. (1990) Stimulatory effects of glucagon-like peptides on human insulinoma cells and insulin-releasing clonal RINm5F cells. Diabetes Res. **13**, 55–59

Frankel, B. J. & Sehlin, J. (1987) Abnormalities in glucose-stimulated insulin release, ^{45}Ca uptake and ^{86}Rb efflux in diabetic Chinese hamster islets. Diabetes **36**, 648–653

Frankel, B. J., Gerich, J. E., Hagura, R., Fanska, R. E., Gerritsen, G. C. & Grodsky, G. M. (1974) Abnormal secretion of insulin and glucagon by the in vitro perfused pancreas of the genetically diabetic Chinese hamster. J. Clin. Invest. **53**, 1637–1646

Frankel, B. J., Gerich, J. E., Fanska, R. E., Gerritsen, G. C. & Grodsky, G. M. (1975) Responses to arginine in the perfused pancreas of the genetically diabetic Chinese hamster. Diabetes **24**, 272–279

Frankel, B. J., Heldt, A. M. & Grodsky, G. M. (1982) Insulin and glucagon release in the diabetic Chinese hamster: Differences among inbred sublines. Diabetologia **22**, 292–295

Frankel, B. J., Cajander, S. & Boquist, L. (1987) Islet morphology in young, genetically diabetic Chinese hamsters during the hyperinsulinemic phase. Pancreas **2**, 625–631

Frerichs, H. & Creutzfeldt, W. (1976) Hypoglycaemia. 1. Insulin secreting tumours. Clin. Endocrinol. Metab. **5**, 747–767

Frerichs, H. & Creutzfeldt, W. (1987) Glucose–calcium infusion test for the diagnosis of insulinoma. In Hypoglycaemia (Andreani, D., Marks, V. & Lefebvre, P. J., eds.), pp. 259–267, Raven Press, New York

Frerichs, H. & Track, N. S. (1974) Pharmacotherapy of hormone-secreting tumours. Clin. Gastroenterol. **3**, 721–732

Friesen, S. R. (1982) Tumours of the endocrine pancreas. N. Engl. J. Med. **306**, 580–590

Gapp, D. A., Leiter, E. H., Coleman, D. L. & Schwizer, R. W. (1983) Temporal changes in pancreatic islet composition in C57BL/6J-db/db mice. Diabetologia **25**, 439–443

Gazdar, A. F., Chick, W. L., Oie, H. K., Sims, H. L., King, D. L., Weir, G. C. & Lauris, V. (1980) Continuous, clonal, insulin- and somatostatin-secreting cell lines established from a transplantable rat islet cell tumour. Proc. Natl. Acad. Sci. U.S.A. **77**, 3519–3523

Giroix, M.-H., Portha, B., Kergoat, M., Bailbe, D. & Picon, L. (1983) Glucose insensitivity and amino-acid hypersensitivity of insulin release in rats with non-insulin-dependent diabetes. A study with the perfused pancreas. Diabetes **32**, 445–451

Giroix, M.-H., Sener, A., Bailbe, D., Portha, B. & Malaisse, W. J. (1990) Impairment of the mitochondrial oxidative response to D-glucose in pancreatic islets from adult rats injected with streptozotocin during the neonatal period. Diabetologia **33**, 654–660

Gomis, R., Novials, A., Coves, M. J., Casamitjana, R. & Malaisse, W. J. (1989) Suppression by insulin treatment of glucose-induced inhibition of insulin release in non-insulin-dependent diabetics. Diabetes Res. Clin. Prac. **6**, 191–198

Goto, Y., Suzuki, K., Sasaki, M., Ono, T. & Abe, S. (1988) GK rat as a model of nonobese, noninsulin-dependent diabetes. Selective breeding over 35 generations. In Frontiers in Diabetes Research. Lessons from Animal Diabetes (Shafrir, E. & Renold, A. E., eds.), vol. 2, pp. 301–303, John Libbey, London & Paris

Grant, A. M., Christie, M. R. & Ashcroft, S. J. H. (1980) Insulin release from human pancreatic islets in vitro. Diabetologia **19**, 114–117

Greene, D. A., Sima, A. A. F., Albers, J. W. & Pfeifer, M. A. (1990) Diabetic neuropathy. In Ellenberg and Rifkin's Diabetes Mellitus: Theory and Practice (Rifkin, H. & Porte, D., Jr, eds.), 4th edn., pp. 710–755, Elsevier, New York, Amsterdam and London

Grill, V. & Cerasi, E. (1979) The metabolism of cyclic AMP and glucose in the isolated islets from *Acomys cahirinus*. Diabetologia **16**, 47–50

Grill, V. & Herberg, L. (1983) Glucose- and arginine-induced insulin and glucagon responses from the isolated perfused pancreas of the BB-Wistar diabetic rat. Evidence for selective impairment of glucose recognition. Acta Endocrinol. (Copenhagen) **102**, 561–566

Grill, V. & Östenson, C.-G. (1988) The influence of a diabetic state on insulin secretion: Studies in animal models of non-insulin dependent diabetes. In Pathogenesis of Non-Insulin Dependent Diabetes Mellitus (Grill, V. & Efendic, S., eds.), pp. 93–106, Raven Press, New York

Grill, V., Westberg, M. & Östenson, C.-G. (1987) B-cell insensitivity in a rat model of non-insulin-dependent diabetes: Evidence for a rapidly reversible effect of previous hyperglycaemia. J. Clin. Invest. **80**, 664–669

Grillo, T. A. I., Whitty, A. J., Kirkman, H., Foa, S. D. & Kobernick, S. D. (1967) Biological properties of a transplantable islet-cell tumour in the golden hamster. I. Histology and histochemistry. Diabetes **16**, 409–414

Grodsky, G. M. (1972) A threshold distribution hypothesis for packet storage of insulin and its mathematical modelling. J. Clin. Invest. **51**, 2047–2059

Grodsky, G. M., Frankel, B. J. & Gerritsen, G. C. (1984) Insulin secretion and contributing environmental factors of the diabetic Chinese hamster — an update. In Lessons from Animal Diabetes (Shafrir, E. & Renold, A. E., eds.), vol. 1, pp. 9–14, John Libbey, London

Gutzeit, A., Rabinovitch, A., Struder, P. P., Trueheart, P. A., Cerasi, E. & Renold, A. E. (1974*a*) Decreased intravenous glucose tolerance and low plasma insulin response in Spiny mice. Diabetologia **10**, 667–670

Gutzeit, A., Rabinovitch, A., Karakash, C., Stauffacher, W., Renold, A. E. & Cerasi, E. (1974*b*) Evidence for decreased sensitivity to glucose of isolated islets from Spiny mice (*Acomys cahirinus*). Diabetologia **10**, 661–665

Gylfe, E., Buitrago, A., Berggren, P.-O., Hammarstrom, K. & Hellman, B. (1978) Glucose inhibition of ^{45}Ca efflux from pancreatic islets. Am. J. Physiol. **235**, E191–E196

Hahn, H.-J., Hellman, B., Lernmark, A., Sehlin, J. & Taljedal, I. B. (1974) The pancreatic beta-cell recognition of insulin secretagogues. Influence of neuraminidase treatment on the release of insulin and the islet content of insulin, sialic acid and cyclic adenosine 3′,5′-monophosphate. J. Biol. Chem. **249**, 5275–5284

Hahn, H.-J., Schafer, H., Gottschling, H. D. & Fielder, H. (1976) Insulin and glucagon secretion by pancreatic islets from nondiabetic and diabetic Sand rats (*Psammomys obesus*). Eur. J. Clin. Invest. **6**, 85–91

Hahn, H.-J., Gottschling, H. D. & Schafer, H. (1979) Apparent discrepancy between the insulin secretory responses in vivo and in vitro in carbohydrate intolerant Sand rat. Diabetologia **17**, 367–369

Hahn von Dorsche, H., Krause, R., Fehrmann, P. & Sulzmann, R. (1976) The verification of neurones in the pancreas of Spiny mice (*Acomys cahirinus*). Endokrinologie **67**, 115–118

Halban, P. A., Praz, G. A. & Wollheim, C. B. (1983) Abnormal glucose metabolism accompanies failure of glucose to stimulate insulin release from a rat pancreatic cell line (RINm5F). Biochem. J. **212**, 439–443

Halter, J. B., Graf, R. J. & Porte, D., Jr (1979) Potentiation of insulin secretory responses by plasma glucose levels in man: Evidence that hyperglycaemia in diabetes compensates for impaired glucose potentiation. J. Clin. Endocrinol. Metab. **48**, 946–954

Hanahan, D. (1985) Heritable formation of pancreatic B-cell tumours in transgenic mice expressing recombinant insulin/simian virus 40 oncogenes. Nature (London) **315**, 115–122

Harrison, D. E., Christie, M. R. & Gray, D. W. R. (1985) Properties of isolated human islets of Langerhans: Insulin secretion, glucose oxidation and protein phosphorylation. Diabetologia 28, 99–103

Hayashi, M., Kanazawa, Y., Kosaka, K. & Floyd, J. C., Jr. (1979) Functional characteristics of insulinoma cells. In Proinsulin, Insulin and C-Peptide (Baba, S., Kaneko, T. & Yanaihara, N., eds.), pp. 348–354, Excerpta Medica, Amsterdam

Hellman, B., Hallgren, R., Abrahamsson, H., Bergsten, P., Berne, C., Gylfe, E., Rorsman, P. & Wide, L. (1985) The dual action of glucose on cytosolic Ca^{2+} activity in pancreatic B-cells. Demonstration of an inhibitory effect of glucose on insulin release in the mouse and man. Biomed. Biochim. Acta 44, 63–70

Henriksson, C., Claes, G., Gylfe, E., Hellman, B. & Zettergren, L. (1978) Collagenase isolation and ^{45}Ca efflux studies of human islets of Langerhans. Eur. Surg. Res. 10, 343–351

Herberg, L. & Coleman, D. L. (1977) Laboratory animals exhibiting obesity and diabetes syndromes. Metabolism 26, 59–99

Hill, R. S. & Boyd, A. E., III (1985) Perifusion of a clonal cell line of Simian virus 40-transformed beta cells. Insulin secretory dynamics in response to glucose, 3-isobutyl-1-methylxanthine and potassium. Diabetes 34, 115–120

Hirayama, A., Wakabayashi, I., Muto, T., Watanabe, S. & Uchida, S. (1979) Histological and hormonal observations on BK virus induced pancreatic islet-cell tumours in hamsters. In Proinsulin, Insulin and C-Peptide (Baba, S., Kaneko, T. & Yanaihara, N., eds.), pp. 364–373, Excerpta Medica, Amsterdam

Hoenig, M., Ferguson, D. C. & Matchinsky, F. M. (1984) Fuel-induced insulin release in vitro from insulinomas transplanted into the rat kidney. Diabetes 33, 1–7

Iwashima, Y., Watanabe, K. & Makino, J. (1990) Changes in the pancreatic A-, B- and D-cell populations during development of diabetes in spontaneously diabetic Chinese hamster of the Asahikawa colony. Diabetes Res. Clin. Prac. 8, 201–204

Jahr, H., Ratzmann, K.-P., Beckert, R., Besch, W. & Hahn, H.-J. (1983) Enhanced synthesis, storage and secretion of insulin in pancreatic islets derived from obese subjects. Metabolism 32, 1101–1106

Jeanrenaud, B. (1988) Neuroendocrine and metabolic basis of type II diabetes as studied in animal models. Diabetes Metab. Rev. 4, 603–614

Johnson, K. H., O'Brien, T. D. & Westermark, P. (1991) Newly identified pancreatic protein islet amyloid polypeptide. What is its relationship to diabetes? Diabetes 40, 310–314

Junod, A., Letarte, J., Lambert, A. E. & Stauffacher, W. (1969) Studies in Spiny mice (*Acomys cahirinus*): Metabolic state and pancreatic insulin release in vitro. Horm. Metab. Res. 1, 45–52

Kahn, S. E. & Porte, D., Jr (1990) The pathophysiology of type II (noninsulin-dependent) diabetes mellitus: Implications for treatment. In Ellenberg and Rifkin's Diabetes Mellitus: Theory and Practice (Rifkin, H. & Porte, D., Jr, eds.), 4th edn., pp. 436–456, Elsevier, New York, Amsterdam and London

Kahn, A., Chandramouli, V., Ostenson, C.-G., Ahren, B., Schumann, W. C., Low, H., Landau, B. R. & Efendic, S. (1989) Evidence for the presence of glucose cycling in pancreatic islets of the *ob/ob* mouse. J. Biol. Chem. 264, 9732–9733

Kahn, A., Chandramouli, V., Ostenson, C.-G., Berggren, P.-O., Low, H., Landau, B. R. & Efendic, S. (1990a) Glucose cycling is markedly enhanced in pancreatic islets of obese hyperglycaemic mice. Endocrinology 126, 2413–2416

Kahn, A., Chandramouli, V., Ostenson, C.-G., Low, H., Landau, B. R. & Efendic, S. (1990b) Glucose cycling in islets from healthy and diabetic rats. Diabetes 39, 456–459

Kano, Y., Kanatsuna, T., Nakamura, N., Kitagawa, Y., Mori, H., Kajiyama, S., Nakano, K. & Kondo, M. (1986) Defect of the first-phase insulin secretion to glucose stimulation in the perfused pancreas of the nonobese diabetic (NOD) mouse. Diabetes 35, 486–490

Kergoat, M., Giroix, M. H. & Portha, B. (1986) Evidence for normal in vitro Ca^{2+}-stimulated insulin release in rats with non-insulin-dependent diabetes. Diabetes Metab. 12, 79–82

Kergoat, M., Bailbe, D. & Portha, B. (1987) Insulin treatment improves glucose-induced insulin release in rats with NIDDM induced by streptozotocin. Diabetes 36, 971–977

King, H. (1988) Non-insulin-dependent diabetes. Aetiology. Clin. Endocrinol. Metab. 2, 291–305

Kohnert, K. D., Wilke, B., Schmidt, S., Schafer, H., Reiher, K. & Hahn von Dorsche, H.

(1985) Dietary effects on (pro)insulin biosynthesis and insulin-degrading activity in islets from Sand rats. Mol. Cell. Endocrinol. **43**, 95–103

Kuffert, A., Stern, J. S. & Curry, D. L. (1988) Pancreatic hypersensitivity to glucose by young obese Zucker rats (*fa/fa*). Metabolism **37**, 952–957

Lang, D. A., Matthews, D. R. & Turner, R. C. (1981) Brief, irregular oscillations of basal plasma insulin and glucose concentrations in diabetic man. Diabetes **30**, 435–439

Larkins, R. G. (1973*a*) Defective insulin secretion in the NZO mouse: In vitro study. Endocrinology **93**, 1052–1056

Larkins, R. G. (1973*b*) Defective insulin secretory response to glucose in the New Zealand obese mouse. Improvement with restricted diet. Diabetes **22**, 251–255

Larkins, R. G. & Martin, F. I. R. (1972) Selective defect in insulin release in one form of spontaneous laboratory diabetes. Nature (London) **235**, 86–88

Larkins, R. G., Simeonova, L. & Veroni, M. C. (1980) Glucose utilization in relation to insulin secretion in NZO and C57BL mouse islets. Endocrinology **107**, 1634–1638

Laube, H., Fussganger, R. D., Maier, V. & Pfeiffer, E. F. (1973) Hyperglucagonemia of the isolated perfused pancreas of diabetic mice (db/db). Horm. Metab. Res. **9**, 400–402

Leahy, J. L. (1990) Natural history of B-cell dysfunction in NIDDM. Diabetes Care **13**, 992–1010

Leahy, J. L., Bonner-Weir, S. & Weir, G. C. (1984) Abnormal glucose regulation of insulin secretion in models of reduced B-cell mass. Diabetes **33**, 667–673

Leahy, J. L., Bonner-Weir, S. & Weir, G. C. (1985) Abnormal insulin secretion in a streptozotocin model of diabetes: Effects of insulin treatment. Diabetes **34**, 660–666

Leahy, J. L., Cooper, H. E., Deal, D. A. & Weir, G. C. (1986) Chronic hyperglycemia is associated with impaired glucose influence on insulin secretion. A study in normal rats using chronic in vivo glucose infusions. J. Clin. Invest. **77**, 908–915

Leahy, J. L., Cooper, H. E. & Weir, G. C. (1987) Impaired insulin secretion associated with near-normoglycemia. A study in normal rats using 96 hour in vivo glucose infusions. Diabetes **36**, 459–464

Leclercq-Meyer, V., Marchand, J. & Malaisse, W. J. (1987) Anomeric specificity of the insulin and glucagon secretory responses to D-glucose in lean and obese Zucker rats. Pancreas **2**, 645–652

Lefebvre, P. J. & Scheen, A. J. (1990) Hypoglycemia. In Ellenberg and Rifkin's Diabetes Mellitus: Theory and Practice (Rifkin, H. & Porte, D., Jr, eds.), 4th. edn., pp. 896–910, Elsevier, New York, Amsterdam and London

Lenzen, S., Tiedge, M., Flatt, P. R., Bailey, C. J. & Panten, U. (1987) Defective regulation of glucokinase in rat pancreatic islet cell tumours. Acta Endocrinol. (Copenhagen) **115**, 514–520

Lins, P. E. & Efendic, S. (1979) Responses of patients with insulinomas to stimulators and inhibitors of insulin release that have been linked with cyclic adenosine monophosphate. Diabetes **28**, 190–195

Marks, V. & Rose, F. C. (1981) Hypoglycaemia, 2nd edn., p. 521, Blackwell Scientific Publications, Oxford

Malaisse, W. J. (1987) Cellular mechanisms of defective insulin secretion in diabetes mellitus. In Best Approaches to the Ideal Therapy of Diabetes Mellitus (Shigeta, Y., Lebovitz, H. E., Gerich, J. E. & Malaisse, W. J., eds.), pp. 83–89, Elsevier, Amsterdam

Malaisse, W. J. (1990) Defects of signal transduction in a tumoral islet cell line. In Molecular Biology of the Islets of Langerhans (Okamoto, H., ed.), pp. 315–339, Cambridge University Press, Cambridge

Malaisse, W. J., Like, A. A., Malaisse-Lagae, F., Gleason, R. E. & Soeldner, S. (1968) Insulin secretion *in vitro* by the pancreas of the Sand rat (*Psammomys obesus*). Diabetes **17**, 752–759

Malaisse, W. J., Sener, A., Herchuelz, A. & Hutton, J. C. (1979) Insulin release: The fuel hypothesis. Metabolism **28**, 373–386

Malaisse-Lagae, F., Ravazzola, M., Amherdt, M., Gutzeit, A., Stauffacher, W., Malaisse, W. J. & Orci, L. (1975) An apparent abnormality of the B-cell microtubular system in Spiny mice (*Acomys cahirinus*). Diabetologia **10**, 71–76

Marynissen, G., Leclercq-Meyer, V., Sener, A. & Malaisse, W. J. (1990) Perturbation of pancreatic islet function in glucose infused rats. Metabolism **39**, 87–95

Masiello, P., Wollheim, C. B., Janjic, D., Gjinovci, A., Blondel, B., Praz, G. A. & Renold, A. E. (1982) Stimulation of insulin release by glucose in a transplantable rat islet cell tumour. Endocrinology **111**, 2091–2096

Meglasson, M. D., Manning, C. D., Najafi, H. & Matchinsky, F. M. (1986) Glucose transport by radiation-induced insulinoma and clonal pancreatic B-cells. Diabetes **35**, 1340–1344

Meissner, H. P. & Schmidt, H. (1976) The electrical activity of pancreatic B-cells of diabetic mice. FEBS Lett. **67**, 371–374

Metz, S. A., Halter, J. B. & Robertson, R. P. (1979) Paradoxical inhibition of insulin secretion by glucose in human diabetes mellitus. J. Clin. Endocrinol. Metab. **48**, 827–835

Morton, J. L., Dunmore, S. J., Beloff-Chain, A. & Adler, J. H. (1986) Studies on insulin secretion and the pituitary insulin secretagogue B-cell tropin in the Sand rat (*Psammomys obesus*). Int. J. Obesity **11**, 9–18

Nesher, R., Abraham, E. & Cerasi, E. (1989) Reduced early and late phase insulin response to glucose in isolated Spiny mouse (*Acomys cahirinus*) islets: A defective link between glycolysis and adenylate cyclase. Diabetologia **32**, 644–648

O'Hare, M. M. T., Shaw, C., Swanston-Flatt, S. K., Marcelli, M., Buchanan, K. D. & Flatt, P. R. (1985) Influence of a transplantable insulinoma on the pancreatic status of insulin and pancreatic polypeptide in the rat. Diabetologia **28**, 157–160

O'Rahilly, S. P., Turner, R. C. & Matthews, D. R. (1988) Impaired pulsatile secretion of insulin in relatives of patients with non-insulin-dependent diabetes. N. Engl. J. Med. **318**, 1225–1230

Orci, L., Lambert, A. E., Amherdt, M., Cameron, D., Kanazawa, Y. & Stauffacher, W. (1970) The autonomic nervous system and the B-cell: Metabolic and morphological observations made in Spiny mice (*Acomys cahirinus*) and in cultured fetal rat pancreas. Acta Diabetol. Lat. **7** (Suppl. 1), 184–226

Palmer, J. P., Benson, J. W., Walter, R. M. & Ensinck, J. W. (1976) Arginine-stimulated acute phase of insulin and glucagon secretion in diabetic subjects. J. Clin. Invest. **58**, 565–570

Peavy, D. E., Brunner, M. R., Duckworth, W. C., Hooker, C. S. & Frank, B. H. (1985) Receptor binding and biological potency of several split forms (conversion intermediates) of human proinsulin. J. Biol. Chem. **260**, 13989–13994

Perley, M. J. & Kipnis, D. M. (1967) Plasma insulin responses to oral and intravenous glucose: Studies in normal and diabetic subjects. J. Clin. Invest. **46**, 1954–1962

Petersson, B., Elde, R., Efendic, S., Hokfeldt, T., Johansson, O., Luft, R., Cerasi, E. & Hellerstrom, C. (1977) Somatostatin in the pancreas, stomach and hypothalamus of the diabetic Chinese hamster. Diabetologia **13**, 463–466

Portha, B. (1985) Decreased glucose-induced insulin release and biosynthesis by islets of rats with non-insulin-dependent diabetes: Effects of tissue culture. Endocrinology **117**, 1735–1741

Portha, B., Giroix, M.-H., Serradas, P., Welch, N., Hellerstrom, C., Sener, A. & Malaisse, W. J. (1988) Insulin production and glucose metabolism in isolated pancreatic islets of rats with non-insulin-dependent diabetes. Diabetes **37**, 1226–1233

Portha, B., Blondel, O., Serradas, P., McEvoy, R., Giroix, M.-H., Kergoat, M. & Bailbe, D. (1989) The rat models of non-insulin dependent diabetes induced by neonatal streptozotocin. Diabetes Metab. **15**, 61–75

Porte, D., Jr & Kahn, S. E. (1989) Hyperproinsulinemia and amyloid in NIDDM. Clues to etiology of islet B-cell dysfunction? Diabetes **38**, 1333–1336

Praz, G. A., Halban, P. A., Wollheim, C. B., Blondel, B., Strauss, A. J. & Renold, A. E. (1983) Regulation of immunoreactive insulin release from a rat cell line (RINm5F). Biochem. J. **210**, 345–352

Rabinovitch, A., Gutzeit, A., Kikuchi, M., Cerasi, E. & Renold, A. E. (1975*a*) Defective early phase insulin release in perifused isolated pancreatic islets of Spiny mice (*Acomys cahirinus*). Diabetologia **11**, 457–465

Rabinovitch, A., Gutzeit, A., Renold, A. E. & Cerasi, E. (1975*b*) Insulin secretion in the Spiny mouse (*Acomys cahirinus*): Dose and time studies with glucose in vivo and in vitro. Diabetes **24**, 1094–1100

Rabinovitch, A., Gutzeit, A., Grill, V., Kikuchi, M., Renold, A. E. & Cerasi, E. (1975*c*) Defective insulin secretion in the Spiny mouse (*Acomys cahirinus*). Potential value in the study of the pathophysiology of diabetes. Isr. J. Med. Sci. **11**, 730–737

Rabinovitch, A., Renold, A. E. & Cerasi, E. (1976) Decreased cyclic AMP and insulin responses to glucose in the pancreatic islets of diabetic Chinese hamsters. Diabetologia **12**, 581–587

Rasmussen, H., Zawalich, K. C., Ganesan, S., Calle, R. & Zawalich, W. S. (1990) Physiology and pathophysiology of insulin secretion. Diabetes Care **13**, 655–666

Re, C. A., Veroni, M. C. & Larkins, R. G. (1984) Effect of islet activating protein on glucose tolerance, insulin secretion and insulin responsiveness in the NZO mouse. Diabetologia **26**, 304–309

Reaven, G. M., Bernstein, R., Davis, B. & Olefsky, J. M. (1976) Nonketotic diabetes mellitus: Insulin deficiency or insulin resistance? Am. J. Med. **60**, 80–88

Reddy, S., Bibby, N. J. & Elliott, R. B. (1988) B-cell function in the BB rat. In Frontiers in Diabetes Research. Lessons from Animal Diabetes (Shafrir, E. & Renold, A. E., eds.), vol. 2, pp. 213–216, John Libbey, London & Paris

Revers, R. R., Henry, R., Schmeiser, L., Kolterman, O., Cohen, R., Bergenstal, R., Polonsky, K., Jaspan, J., Rubenstein, A., Frank, B., Galloway, J. & Olefsky, J. M. (1984) The effects of human biosynthetic human proinsulin on carbohydrate metabolism. Diabetes **33**, 762–770

Robbins, D. C. & Tager, H. S. (1989) Mutant insulins and lipodystrophic diabetes: An emerging genetic basis for certain cases of diabetes. In Endocrinology (DeGroot, L., ed.), pp. 1400–1407, Saunders, Philadelphia

Robertson, R. P. (1989) Type II diabetes, glucose 'non-sense' and islet desensitization. Diabetes **38**, 1501–1505

Robertson, R. P., Seaquist, E. R. & Walseth, T. F. (1991) G proteins and modulation of insulin secretion. Diabetes **40**, 1–6

Rohner-Jeanrenaud, F., Hochstrasser, A.-C. & Jeanrenaud, B. (1983) Hyperinsulinaemia of preobese and obese *fa/fa* rats is partly vagus nerve mediated. Am. J. Physiol. **244**, E317–E322

Rorsman, P. & Trube, G. (1990) Biophysics and physiology of ATP-regulated K^+ channels $[K_{ATP}]$. In Potassium Channels: Structure, Classification and Therapeutic Potential (Cook, N. S., ed.), pp. 96–116, Ellis Horwood, Chichester

Rorsman, P., Berggren, P.-O., Gylfe, E. & Hellman, B. (1983) Reduction of the cytosolic calcium activity in clonal insulin-releasing cells exposed to glucose. Biosci. Rep. **3**, 939–946

Rosario, L. M. (1985) Differential effects of the K^+ channel blockers apamin and quinine on glucose-induced electrical activity in pancreatic B-cells from a strain of *ob/ob* (obese) mice. FEBS Lett. **188**, 302–306

Rosario, L. M., Atwater, I. & Rojas, E. (1985) Membrane potential measurements in islets of Langerhans from *ob/ob* obese mice suggest an alteration in $[Ca^{2+}]_i$-activated K^+ permeability. Q. J. Exp. Physiol. **70**, 137–150

Rossetti, L., Shulman, G. I., Zawalich, W. & DeFronzo, R. A. (1987) Effect of chronic hyperglycaemia on in vivo insulin secretion in partially pancreatectomized rats. J. Clin. Invest. **80**, 1037–1044

Rossetti, L., Giaccari, A. & DeFronzo, R. A. (1990) Glucose toxicity. Diabetes Care **13**, 610–630

Rovira, A., Garrotte, F. J., Valverde, I. & Malaisse, W. J. (1987) Anomeric specificity of glucose-induced insulin release in normal and diabetic subjects. Diabetes Res. **5**, 119–124

Sako, Y. & Grill, V. (1990) Coupling of B-cell desensitization by hyperglycaemia to excessive stimulation and circulating insulin in glucose-infused rats. Diabetes **39**, 1580–1583

Santerre, R. F., Cook, R. A., Crisel, R. M. D., Shar, J. D., Schmidt, R. J., Williams, D. C. & Wilson, C. P. (1981) Insulin synthesis in a clonal cell line of simian virus 40-transformed hamster pancreatic beta cells. Proc. Natl. Acad. Sci. U.S.A. **78**, 4339–4343

Scott, A. M., Dawson, C. M. & Goncalves, A. A. (1985) Comparison of glucose-induced changes in electrical activity, insulin release, lactate output and potassium permeability between normal and *ob/ob* mouse islets: Effects of cooling. J. Endocrinol. **107**, 265–273

Sener, A., Leclercq-Meyer, V., Giroix, M.-H., Malaisse, W. J. & Hellerstrom, C. (1987) Opposite effects of D-glucose and a nonmetabolized analogue of L-leucine on respiration and secretion in insulin-producing tumoral cells (RINm5F). Diabetes **36**, 187–192

Siegel, E. G., Wollheim, C. B., Sharp, G. W. G., Herberg, L. & Renold, A. E. (1979) Defective calcium handling and insulin release in islets from diabetic Chinese hamsters. Biochem. J. **180**, 233–236

Siegel, E. G., Wollheim, C. B., Sharp, G. W. G., Herberg, L. & Renold, A. E. (1980) Role of Ca^{2+} in impaired insulin release from islets of diabetic (C57BL/KsJ-*db/db*) mice. Am. J. Physiol. **239**, E132–E138

Shafrir, E. (1990) Diabetes in animals. In Ellenberg and Rifkin's Diabetes Mellitus: Theory and Practice (Rifkin, H. & Porte, D., Jr, eds.), 4th. end., pp. 299–340, Elsevier, New York, Amsterdam and London

Sopwith, A. M., Hutton, J. C., Naber, S. P., Chick, W. L. & Hales, C. N. (1981) Insulin secretion by a transplantable rat islet cell tumour. Diabetologia **21**, 224–229

Srikanta, S., Ganda, O. P., Rabizadeh, A., Soeldner, J. S. & Eisenbarth, G. S. (1985) First degree relatives of patients with type I diabetes mellitus: Islet-cell antibodies and abnormal insulin secretion. N. Engl. J. Med. **313**, 461–464

Steiner, D. F., Tager, H. S., Chan, S. J., Nanjo, K., Sanke, T. & Rubenstein, A. H. (1990) Lessons learned from molecular biology of insulin-gene mutations. Diabetes Care **13**, 600–609

Steiner, D. R., Ohagi, S., Nagamatsu, S., Bell, G. I. & Nishi, M. (1991) Is islet amyloid polypeptide a significant factor in the pathogenesis or pathophysiology of diabetes? Diabetes **40**, 305–309

Swanston-Flatt, S. K. & Flatt, P. R. (1987) Acute and long-term effects of glucose on the function of transplantable rat insulinoma cells maintained in tissue culture. Biomed. Res. **8**, 215–223

Swanston-Flatt, S. K. & Flatt, P. R. (1988*a*) Effects of amino acids, hormones and drugs on insulin release and ^{45}Ca uptake by transplantable rat insulinoma cells maintained in tissue culture. Gen. Pharmacol. **19**, 239–242

Swanston-Flatt, S. K. & Flatt, P. R. (1988*b*) Effects of cationic modification on ^{45}Ca uptake and insulin release by transplantable rat insulinoma cells maintained in tissue culture. Gen. Pharmacol. **19**, 471–474

Temple, R. C., Carrington, C. A., Luzio, S. D., Owens, D. R., Schneider, A. E., Sobey, W. J. & Hales, C. N. (1989) Insulin deficiency in non-insulin-dependent diabetes. Lancet **i**, 293–295

Timmers, K. I., Powell, A. M., Voyles, N. R., Solomon, D., Wilkins, S. D., Bhathena, S. & Receant, L. (1990) Multiple alterations in insulin responses to glucose in islets from 48-h glucose infused nondiabetic rats. Diabetes **39**, 1436–1444

Trube, G., Rorsman, P. & Ohno-Shosaku, T. (1986) Opposite effects of tolbutamide and diazoxide on the ATP-dependent K^+ channel in mouse pancreatic B-cells. Pfluegers Arch. **407**, 493–499

Trueheart, P. A., Maldonato, A., Kaelin, D., Renold, A. E. & Sharp, G. W. G. (1976) Proinsulin synthesis in islets of Langerhans from Spiny mice (*Acomys cahirinus*). Comparison with rats and mice. Diabetologia **112**, 463–470

Turner, R. C. & Matthews, D. R. (1984) Insulin secretion in type I and type II diabetes. Front. Diabetes **4**, 36–54

Turner, R. C., McCarthy, S. T., Holman, R. R. & Harris, E. (1976) Beta-cell function improved by supplementing basal insulin secretion in mild diabetes. Br. Med. J. **1**, 1252–1254

Unger, R. H. & Grundy, S. (1985) Hyperglycaemia as an inducer as well as a consequence of impaired islet cell function and insulin resistance: implications for the management of diabetes. Diabetologia **28**, 119–121

Vague, P. & Moulin, J.-P. (1982) The defective glucose sensitivity of the B-cell in non-insulin-dependent diabetes. Improvement after twenty hours of normoglycaemia. Metabolism **31**, 139–142

Veroni, M. C., Michelangeli, V. P., Heaney, T. P., Ng, K. W., Partridge, N. C. & Larkins, R. G. (1981) Adenylate cyclase responsiveness of human insulinomas. Horm. Metab. Res. **13**, 254–259

Volk, B. W. (1990) Pathology of the diabetic pancreas. In Ellenberg and Rifkin's Diabetes Mellitus: Theory and Practice (Rifkin, H. & Porte, D., Jr, eds.), 4th. edn., pp. 341–345, Elsevier, New York, Amsterdam and London

Ward, W. K., Bolgiano, D. C., McKnight, B., Halter, J. B. & Porte, D., Jr (1984) Diminished B-cell secretory capacity in patients with noninsulin-dependent diabetes mellitus. J. Clin. Invest. **74**, 1318–1327

Westman, S. (1968) Development of the obese hyperglycaemic syndrome in mice. Diabetologia **4**, 141–149

Westman, S. (1970) Pathogenic aspects of the obese hyperglycaemic syndrome in mice (genotype ob/ob): I Function of the pancreatic B-cells. Diabetologia **6**, 279–283

Wollheim, C. B. & Sharp, G. W. G. (1981) Regulation of insulin release by calcium. Physiol. Rev. **61**, 914–973

Yasunami, Y., Funakoshi, A., Ono, J., Miyazaki, K., Jimi, A. & Konomi, K. (1987) In vitro study of cultured human insulinoma cells: evidence of abnormal sensitivity to glucose. J. Clin. Endocrinol. Metab. **65**, 110–115

Zawalich, W. S., Zawalich, K. C., Shulman, G. I. & Rossetti, L. (1990) Chronic in vivo hyperglycemia impairs phosphoinositide hydrolysis and insulin release in incubated perifused rat islets. Endocrinology **126**, 253–260

Ziegler, B., Ziegler, M., Knospe, S. & Hahn, H.-J. (1976) Investigations on isolated islets in vitro: Insulin secretion and insulin stores of cultured islets from Sand rats (*Psammomys obesus*). Investigation of glucose dose-response. Endokrinologie **68**, 95–103

17

Mechanisms of destruction of insulin-secreting cells

Hiroshi Okamoto

Department of Biochemistry, Tohoku University School of Medicine, Sendai 980, Miyagi, Japan

Introduction

Insulin-dependent diabetes mellitus (IDDM) is caused by destructive processes affecting the insulin-producing B-cells of the islets of Langerhans. Destruction of B-cells may be induced by genetic factors such as immunological abnormalities and by environmental factors (Leslie, 1983). Suggested environmental factors include viral infection, toxins, and chemical insult, several such factors probably interacting on a genetically susceptible individual. It should be noted here that the incidence of IDDM is steadily increasing in all populations. In Massachusetts, for example, the incidence rate has increased over 5-fold since the beginning of this century (Krolewski et al., 1987). This cannot be explained simply as an enrichment of the gene pool owing to longer life span, and it must be concluded that the environment is to some extent responsible, as suggested by Cahill & Kahn (1989).

Alloxan (2,4,5,6-tetraoxohexahydropyrimidine) and streptozotocin [2-deoxy-2-(3-methyl-3-nitrosoureido)-D-glucopyranose] are typical B-cytotoxins. These chemical substances induce necrosis of the B-cells (Dunn et al., 1943; Rakieten et al., 1963), and have been widely used for the induction of experimental diabetes (see Chapter 16 by Flatt et al.). A number of compounds structurally related to alloxan and streptozotocin have also been implicated as possible environmental agents. In humans, for example, Vacor, an effective rodenticide, was found to be highly diabetogenic (Karam et al., 1980), and the diabetogenic factor in Icelandic smoked mutton is most likely to be one or more of the nitroso compounds in meat cured with nitrate or nitrite which is traditionally consumed in greatly increased quantities in the Christmas season (Helgason et al., 1982). Thus, it can be seen that understanding the mechanism of action of the typical B-cytotoxins, alloxan and streptozotocin, is important not only for elucidating the causes of IDDM, but for its prevention as well.

Recently, there has been proposed a unifying model for the mechanism of B-cell destruction by the B-cytotoxic agents, as shown in Fig. 1 (Okamoto, 1981, 1985*a,b*, 1989, 1990; Okamoto & Yamamoto, 1983; Okamoto *et al.*, 1985, 1988). Central to the model are breaks in the

Fig. I.   A proposed mechanism of action of B-cytotoxic agents on pancreatic B-cells (Okamoto, 1981, 1985a, 1990)

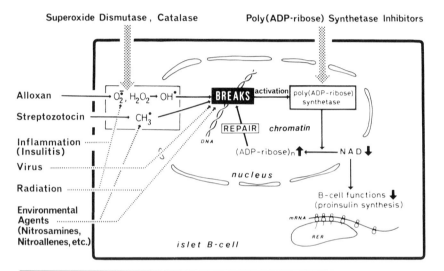

As indicated by the shaded arrowheads, the protection by poly(ADP-ribose) synthetase inhibitors against the B-cytotoxin-induced depression of the NAD level and of B-cell functions such as proinsulin synthesis is caused by the blockage of the activated enzyme activity, while radical scavengers such as superoxide dismutase and catalase prevent the DNA-strand breaks by inactivating free radicals generated from the diabetogenic agents. Reproduced from Okamoto, 1985a with permission.

nuclear DNA of B-cells, resulting from either an accumulation of oxygen radicals or from alkylation of DNA. These breaks induce DNA repair involving the activation of poly(ADP-ribose) synthetase, which uses cellular NAD as a substrate. As a result, intracellular levels of NAD fall dramatically. The fall in cellular NAD inhibits the cellular activities including insulin synthesis, and the B-cell ultimately dies. Since induction of insulin biosynthesis in islet B-cells is achieved at the level of translation (as discussed below and in Chapters 4 and 13 by Guest & Hutton and Hughes & Ashcroft respectively), an immediate decrease in insulin bio-synthetic activity by the B-cytotoxins cannot be attributed to DNA damage itself. Rather, the B-cell, it may reasonably be assumed, commits suicide in its attempt to repair the DNA strand breaks. The historical background of this hypothesis is described elsewhere (Okamoto, 1990). This chapter deals with the mechanism of action of alloxan and streptozotocin on B-cells in the light of the increasingly accepted unifying model of their action. A unified concept for B-cell damage and its prevention in toxin- or virus-induced and immune diabetes will also be introduced.

Mechanism of destruction of B-cells

Elucidation of the B-cell cytotoxic action of alloxan and streptozotocin may contribute to our understanding of destructive mechanisms in the B-cell leading to IDDM. Because the two highly B-cytotoxic compounds are structurally different, the two substances were commonly thought not to act in an identical way (Dulin & Soret, 1977; Cooperstein & Watkins, 1981; Chang & Diani, 1985). Recently, an increasingly accepted and unifying hypothesis concerning the mechanism of action of the B-cytotoxins (Okamoto, 1981, 1985*a,b*, 1990; Okamoto & Yamamoto, 1983; Okamoto *et al.*, 1985, 1988) has been developed from the observations that both alloxan and streptozotocin induce DNA-strand breaks and poly(ADP-ribose) synthetase in rat pancreatic islets, and that inhibitors of this enzyme prevent both the B-cytotoxin-induced NAD depletion and the drug-induced inhibition of proinsulin synthesis in the islets.

Thus, Yamamoto *et al.* (1981*a*) incubated islets, isolated from rat pancreas, with alloxan or streptozotocin for 5–20 min in Krebs–Ringer's bicarbonate medium. After incubation, islets were layered over a linear sucrose gradient and centrifuged. DNA from control islets was observed as a single peak near the bottom of the gradient, the position at which undamaged DNA sediments. However, after only 5–10 min incubation with 1 mM of alloxan or 2 mM of streptozotocin, a considerable amount of DNA sedimented as a broad peak in the middle of the gradient with a concomitant decrease in undamaged DNA; after 20 min incubation, the DNA was almost completely fragmented. The effect of the two agents on islet DNA fragmentation was dose-dependent. These results clearly indicate that streptozotocin and alloxan produce strand breaks in islet DNA. When islets were incubated with a combination of alloxan and superoxide dismutase (EC 1.15.1.1), a considerable amount of DNA was found to be recovered at the position of undamaged DNA (Uchigata *et al.*, 1982). Catalase (EC 1.11.1.6) also partially protected against DNA breaks. When both superoxide dismutase and catalase were present, DNA breaks were also completely eliminated. It has been suggested that alloxan generates oxygen radicals during the reduction and oxidation reaction (Heikkila *et al.*, 1976; Grankvist *et al.*, 1979, 1981; Fischer & Hamburger,

Table I.   Effect of poly(ADP-ribose) synthetase inhibitors on alloxan- and streptozotocin-induced islet NAD depletion (Yamamoto et al., 1981a)

Addition	Islet NAD content (pmol/islet)
None	2·84 (100%)
Alloxan (1 mM)	0·52 (18%)
Alloxan (1 mM) and nicotinamide (2 mM)	2·94 (104%)
Alloxan (1 mM) and picolinamide (2 mM)	2·81 (99%)
Streptozotocin (2 mM)	0·34 (12%)
Streptozotocin (2 mM) and nicotinamide (2 mM)	2·91 (102%)
Streptozotocin (2 mM) and picolinamide (2 mM)	2·93 (103%)
Nicotinamide (2 mM)	3·19 (112%)
Picolinamide (2 mM)	3·09 (109%)

Numbers in parentheses are islet NAD content as a percentage of NAD content in islets without any additions.

1980). In addition, the hydroxyl radical is produced by the interaction between superoxide and peroxide (Haber & Weiss, 1934; McCord & Day, 1978). When superoxide dismutase and catalase are present, the formation of hydroxyl radicals may be reduced. These results show that alloxan yields oxygen radicals, especially hydroxyl radicals, to break islet DNA. On the other hand, superoxide dismutase and catalase did not prevent the DNA strand breaks induced by streptozotocin (Gold et al., 1981; Uchigata et al., 1982). The streptozotocin-induced DNA breaks may be associated with the alkylating activity of the agent, as suggested with nitrosoureas (Cox & Irving, 1976; Erickson et al., 1977; Wilson et al., 1988).

In the eukaryotic cell nucleus, there is an enzyme, poly(ADP-ribose) synthetase (EC 2.4.2.30), which polymerizes the ADP-ribose moiety of NAD to form poly(ADP-ribose) (Hayaishi & Ueda, 1977; Ueda & Hayaishi, 1985). This enzyme is activated by damaged DNA (Ohgushi et al., 1980), and the poly(ADP-ribosylation) reaction is thought to participate in the repair of damaged DNA. Yamamoto et al. (1981a) showed that both alloxan and streptozotocin induced a great increase in islet poly(ADP-ribose) synthetase activity, with a peak at 10 min. The substrate of poly(ADP-ribose) synthetase is NAD, and islet NAD levels were greatly reduced by either streptozotocin or alloxan within 20 min of incubation. There was a striking temporal correlation between the decrease in the level of islet NAD and the increase in islet poly(ADP-ribose) synthetase activity. These results indicate that both alloxan and streptozotocin cause DNA-strand breaks, which result in the activation of poly(ADP-ribose) synthetase, thereby depleting islet NAD levels. Table 1 shows the effect of poly(ADP-ribose) synthetase inhibitors such as nicotinamide and picolinamide on alloxan- and streptozotocin-induced islet NAD depletion. Alloxan (1 mM) decreased the islet NAD level to 18% of the control level. Nicotinamide (2 mM) and picolinamide (2 mM) completely abolished the alloxan-induced decrease in the islet NAD level. The same was true for the decrease in islet NAD level induced by streptozotocin as described previously (Schein *et al.*, 1973; Gunnarsson *et al.*, 1974; Yamamoto & Okamoto, 1980).

The ability of islets to synthesize proinsulin is a marker for the evaluation of the diabetogenicity of alloxan and streptozotocin. Uchigata *et al.* (1982) showed that poly(ADP-ribose) synthetase inhibitors such as benzamides, nicotinamide and methylxanthines reversed the inhibition of proinsulin synthesis induced by alloxan and streptozotocin in a dose-dependent manner. The stronger inhibitors such as benzamides protected against the inhibition of proinsulin synthesis at lower concentrations.

Since the induction of proinsulin biosynthesis in islet B-cells is achieved at the translation level, by an enhancement of the translational efficiency of already existing proinsulin mRNA (Itoh *et al.*, 1978; Itoh & Okamoto, 1980; Okamoto, 1981; Itoh *et al.*, 1982; Watanabe *et al.*, 1982; Itoh, 1990), an immediate decrease in proinsulin synthetic activity by B-cytotoxins cannot be attributed to DNA damage itself. The decreased proinsulin synthesis should be attributed to the NAD depletion in B-cells caused by the DNA repair process. Since NAD is the most abundant of cellular co-enzymes and participates in many biological reactions in mammalian cells, a severe reduction in intracellular NAD to non-physiological levels may adversely affect B-cell function, including pro-insulin synthesis. Therefore, it may reasonably be assumed that the B-cell commits involuntary suicide in its attempt to repair the damaged DNA.

The question now arises as to whether or not the biochemical events initiated by islet DNA breaks are actually induced *in vivo* by alloxan or streptozotocin administration. Therefore, Yamamoto *et al.* (1981*b*) injected diabetogenic doses of alloxan and streptozotocin into rats via the tail vein and then isolated islets, analysed islet DNA and determined islet NAD content. As shown in Fig. 2, 20 min after administration *in vivo* of alloxan and streptozotocin, islet DNA was almost completely fragmented. The sedimentation profile of pancreatic exocrine DNA of alloxan- and streptozotocin-treated rats was indistinguishable from that of untreated rats, indicating that DNA of exocrine cells was essentially unaffected by either alloxan or streptozotocin treatment. Liver DNA was not affected by alloxan. However, liver DNA was fragmented by streptozotocin. In parallel experiments (Yamamoto *et al.*, 1981*b*), both islet and liver NAD content were examined; alloxan (40 mg/kg body wt.) and streptozotocin (50 mg/kg body wt.) were found to lead to a marked depletion of islet NAD content. Streptozotocin administration also decreased liver NAD content to about 70 % of the control, while alloxan caused no significant change in liver NAD. The control NAD content of liver in untreated rats was about twice as great as that of the islets when the value was calculated per μg of DNA. Furthermore, when rats were pretreated with the

Fig. 2. **Sedimentation profile in alkaline sucrose gradient of DNA of rat tissues after alloxan and streptozotocin administration (Yamamoto et al., 1981b)**

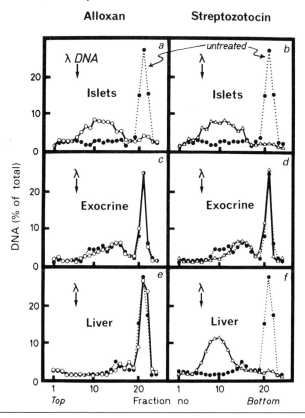

Each point represents the percentage of total DNA recovered; recovery was between 85 and 100%. (a) and (b), islet DNA; (c) and (d), DNA of pancreatic exocrine cells; (e) and (f), hepatocyte DNA. ●, untreated rats; ○, rats treated with alloxan (40 mg/kg); △, rats treated with streptozotocin (50 mg/kg). Sedimentation was from left to right. Arrow indicates the position of a bacteriophage λ DNA. Reproduced from Okamoto, 1985b with permission.

intravenous administration of the poly(ADP-ribose) synthetase inhibitors, nicotinamide and 3-aminobenzamide, before the injection of alloxan or streptozotocin, the drug-induced decrease in proinsulin synthesis was almost completely reversed (Uchigata *et al.*, 1983). 3-Aminobenzamide was effective in protecting the rats from the diabetogenic effect of strepto-zotocin administered *in vivo* (Masiello *et al.*, 1985). The insulin content in rat pancreas treated with a poly(ADP-ribose) synthetase inhibitor was restored (Shima *et al.*, 1987).

There are several explanations as to why the pancreatic B-cells are specifically damaged by alloxan and streptozotocin. The first concerns the low NAD level in B-cells. Thus, the NAD content per DNA of normal pancreatic islets was approximately one half of that of the liver as described above, and therefore B-cells may be more susceptible to damage caused by a reduction of NAD levels. The second explanation relates to the low capacity of B-cells to scavenge free radicals. Thus, the ability to provide protection against potent reactive radicals may be weak in B-cells, in view of the low glutathione peroxidase activity in islets (Malaisse *et al.*, 1982). The third involves the structural uniqueness of alloxan and streptozotocin. It has been conjectured that alloxan and streptozotocin may have a special affinity for the B-cell membrane, because of their chemical structures, resulting in increased fixation or permeability (Hammarström & Ullberg, 1966; Tjälve *et al.*, 1976; Cooperstein & Watkins, 1981).

A basic model for the action of alloxan and streptozotocin in the induction of experimental diabetes is thus constructed as shown in Fig. 1. As discussed in Chapter 6 by Lenzen, inhibition of pancreatic B-cell glucokinase has been proposed to contribute to the inhibitory effect of alloxan on glucose-induced insulin secretion.

A unified concept for B-cell damage and its prevention in toxin- or virus-induced and immune diabetes

The two highly B-cytotoxic compounds, alloxan and streptozotocin, are structurally different, but their actions have been proved to converge into a common pathway to induce DNA strand breaks, to activate poly(ADP-ribose) synthetase, to depress NAD levels and to inhibit B-cell function. This seems to be of special importance in understanding the pathogenesis of IDDM, which has been attributed to many different factors (Leslie, 1983). As shown in Fig. 1, it is possible that inflammation (insulitis), viral infection (Craighead, 1975), radiation (Tsubouchi *et al.*, 1981), and environmental chemical insult (Toniolo *et al.*, 1980) may independently or interactively produce DNA-strand breaks, which can lead to B-cell necrosis. The DNA strands may be broken by viruses with an affinity for

B-cells or by oxygen radicals produced in insulitis caused by viral infection. During inflammation, large amounts of superoxide and hydroxyl radical are produced (Badwey & Karnovsky, 1980).

Some human diabetes is also thought to be an autoimmune disease (Bottazzo et al., 1987). Recent studies by Japanese investigators have established a new model of IDDM with immunological abnormalities, the NOD (non-obese diabetic) mouse (Makino et al., 1980). This animal becomes spontaneously diabetic with clinical and pathological manifestations similar to those seen in human IDDM. Recently it has been reported that diabetes in this animal can be prevented by treatment with immunosuppressive agents e.g. cyclosporin (Mori et al., 1986); an immunomodulator, OK-432 (Toyota et al., 1986; Shintani et al., 1990), which is a streptococcal preparation (Okamoto, Sr, 1976); with radical scavengers such as desferrioxamine, superoxide dismutase and catalase (Nomikos et al., 1986, 1989; Lafferty, 1989; Horio et al., 1989); and also poly(ADP-ribose) synthetase inhibitors such as nicotinamide (Yamada et al., 1982; Nomikos et al., 1986). In humans, the extent of an immune response to individual foreign antigens is controlled by cell-surface molecules encoded by major histocompatibility complex (MHC) class II genes. IDDM has been demonstrated by restriction fragment length polymorphism (RFLP) and oligonucleotide probe analyses of class II genes to be closely associated with the DQβ locus (Owerbach, 1990). The class II antigens are not expressed on normal pancreatic B-cells but have been observed on islet cells of diabetic patients; they function by presenting antigens to T-helper cells. This ultimately leads to the destruction of the islet B-cells by antigen-specific cytotoxic T-lymphocytes (Bottazzo et al., 1987). The T-lymphocyte-mediated cytolytic process may also be initiated in the target nucleus, which results in damage to its DNA; there is evidence for the initiation of T-lymphocyte-mediated cytolysis through processes leading to extensive DNA fragmentation (Russell, 1983; Gromkowski et al., 1986; Schmid et al., 1986; Howell & Martz, 1987; Ucker, 1987), the central event of the model as shown in Fig. 1. Clearly, here the specificity for the selective targeting of the cell could be immune-directed. Furthermore, certain islet B-cell antigens, released during islet B-cell injury, are processed and presented by macrophages to T-helper lymphocytes. This can initiate the production of cytokines, of which interleukin-1 (IL-1) has been suggested to be cytotoxic to islet B-cells in vitro (Bendtzen et al., 1986). To our knowledge, no one has yet determined whether cytokines such as IL-1 and tumour necrosis factor (TNF-α) induce DNA damage in target cells; this is of interest since cell-free lymphotoxin-containing supernatants cause the release of DNA from targets, and since murine cytotoxic T-lymphocytes contain a novel cytotoxin, leukalexin, which causes DNA fragmentation in several types of target cell (Liu et al., 1987). Recently TNF-α was reported to prevent or suppress diabetes in NOD mice, suggesting that cytokines act as immunomodulators (Satoh *et al.*, 1989; Jacob *et al.*, 1990). It has also been reported that macrophages, but not T-cells, increase the content of free radical oxygen in islet B-cells of the NOD mouse (Fukuda *et al.*, 1990). A

Fig. 3. **A unifying model for B-cell damage and its prevention in toxin- or virus-induced and immune diabetes (Okamoto, 1989, 1990)**

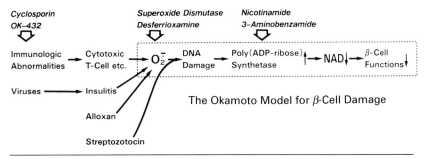

Reproduced from Okamoto, 1989 with permission.

French group reported that nicotinamide can extend the remission phase in human newly diagnosed IDDM patients (Vague *et al.*, 1987, 1989). They administered nicotinamide to human subjects at a dose of 3 g/day for more than one year without any serious side effects. The C-peptide response to a meal test gradually declined in the placebo group, whereas it was stable in the nicotinamide-treated group. At six and nine months, fasting and stimulated C-peptide levels were higher in the nicotinamide-treated group than in the non-treated placebo group. These results suggest that nicotinamide treatment may protect residual B-cell function in human IDDM.

It is thus reasonable to assume that although IDDM can be caused by many different agents such as immunological abnormalities, inflammatory tissue damage, and B-cytotoxic chemical substances such as alloxan and streptozotocin, the final pathway for the toxic agents is common (Fig. 3). This pathway involves DNA damage, poly(ADP-ribose) synthetase activation, and NAD depletion. The fall in cellular NAD content inhibits cellular activities. IDDM is therefore theoretically preventable by suppressing immune reactions, scavenging free radicals, and inhibiting poly(ADP-ribose) synthetase activity. The concept presented in Fig. 3 may enable the development of IDDM and its prevention to be understood in a comprehensive and unified manner.

The oncogenic effect of B-cytotoxic agents

When administered alone, alloxan and streptozotocin efficiently induce diabetes in animals. On the other hand, it has long been known that, while in combination with nicotinamide the diabetogenic action of the B-cytotoxins is completely suppressed. Rats treated with nicotinamide are frequently seen to develop B-cell tumours, insulinomas (Rakieten *et al.*, 1971; Volk *et al.*, 1973; Kazumi *et al.*, 1978, 1980; Johnson *et al.*, 1982). The formation of insulinomas is also related to DNA-strand breaks in B-cells.

As can be seen in Fig. 1, poly(ADP-ribose) synthetase inhibitors prevent NAD being degraded by the activation of poly(ADP-ribose) synthetase, and therefore B-cell functions, including proinsulin synthesis, are conserved. There is, however, a possibility that with blockage at this step, DNA repair may not proceed normally. Yamamoto & Okamoto (1982) investigated the effect of poly(ADP-ribose) synthetase inhibitors on the repair of streptozotocin-induced DNA-strand breaks, using cultured hamster insulinoma cells. When the cells were exposed to streptozotocin for 30 min, the DNA was broken down into small fragments and sedimented as a broad peak in the middle of the alkaline sucrose gradient, regardless of the presence or absence of nicotinamide. At 20 h, after removal of streptozotocin, the DNA was repaired to a size similar to that of untreated DNA and sedimented near the bottom of the gradient. However, when nicotinamide was present in the culture medium, the DNA repair was completely blocked. These results indicate that the poly(ADP-ribose) synthetase inhibitors do not prevent the DNA breaks but rather inhibit the repair of the damaged DNA. This inhibition or retardation of DNA repair is likely to result in the transformation of some B-cells. In rats treated with streptozotocin and nicotinamide, picolinamide or 3-aminobenzamide, B-cell tumours were found in 60–100 % of the surviving rats 1 year after the combined administration; with alloxan and a poly(ADP-ribose) synthetase inhibitor, tumours occurred as frequently as one case in four (Yamagami *et al.*, 1985). In electron micrographs, tumour cells were rich in B-granules, and tumours contained as much insulin mRNA as normal pancreatic islets. Therefore, the tumours induced by the combined administration of diabetogenic agents and poly(ADP-ribose) synthetase inhibitors can be identified as insulin-producing B-cell tumours, insulinomas. Furthermore, Takasawa *et al.* (1986) have constructed a B-cell tumour cDNA library, and through a comparative analysis with normal islet and B-cell tumour poly(A)$^+$ RNAs, they have recently found a novel gene that is activated in the B-cell tumours and seems to be involved in tumourigenesis. The gene is designated *rig* (rat insulinoma gene) and the nature of *rig* and its human homologue has been characterized (Inoue *et al.*, 1987, 1988; Shiga *et al.*, 1990; Sugawara *et al.*,

1990; Takasawa *et al.*, 1990; Kitagawa *et al.*, 1991); *rig* is expressed in a wide variety of normal and tumoural tissues and cells, and belongs to the class of 'housekeeping' genes, whose products are necessary for the growth of all cell types.

Fig. 4. **A unifying concept of the diabetogenic and oncogenic effects of B-cytotoxic agents (Okamoto, 1989, 1990).**

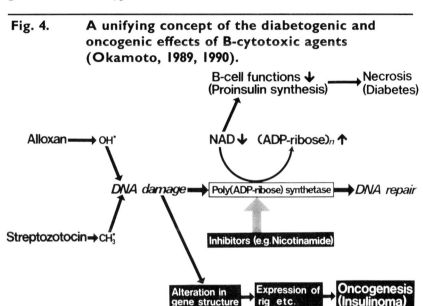

Reproduced from Okamoto, 1989 with permission.

Thus, as shown in Fig. 4, in the case of the induction of diabetes, damaged DNA activates poly(ADP-ribose) synthetase, resulting in the depletion of cellular NAD; hence B-cell functions, including proinsulin synthesis, may be impaired, leading to necrosis, which eventually induces diabetes. When the poly(ADP-ribose) synthetase inhibitor is present during this process, the activation of poly(ADP-ribose) synthetase and the depression of the cellular NAD level are prevented, and B-cell functions therefore proceed normally. However, prompt DNA repair does not occur. The inhibition or retardation of DNA repair may be the cause of the increased frequency of alteration in gene structure. B-cells that have such alterations in their gene structure may exhibit abnormal expression of certain genes such as *rig* and be converted to tumour cells. The concept presented in Fig. 4 may enable the diabetogenic and oncogenic effects of B-cytotoxins to be understood in a comprehensive and unified manner.

Prevention of surgical diabetes by poly(ADP-ribose) synthetase inhibitors and B-cell regeneration

Current techniques for inducing experimental diabetes in animals are mostly based on the use of alloxan and streptozotocin. An alternative approach is to perform partial pancreatectomy. Von Mering & Minkowski (1890) were the first to produce this form of diabetes by surgically removing the pancreases of dogs. This model of surgical diabetes can also be utilized in a study of B-cell regeneration.

In 1984, Yonemura *et al.* (1984) demonstrated that poly(ADP-ribose) synthetase inhibitors induce regeneration of pancreatic B-cells, thereby preventing surgical diabetes. Male Wistar rats were 90% depancreatized, and, beginning seven days before the partial pancreatectomy and continuing post-operatively, nicotinamide (0.5 g/kg body weight) or 3-aminobenzamide (0.05 g/kg body weight) was injected intraperitoneally every day. One to three months after the 90% pancreatectomy, the control rats exhibited glucosuria. However, in rats receiving nicotinamide or 3-aminobenzamide daily, the urinary glucose excretion level decreased markedly. Three months after the partial pancreatectomy, plasma glucose levels, before and after an intravenous glucose load, in rats receiving the poly(ADP-ribose) synthetase inhibitors, were significantly decreased in comparison with those in non-treated rats. These results indicate that poly(ADP-ribose) synthetase inhibitors can prevent or improve diabetes mellitus in partially depancreatized rats. In 90% depancreatized rats, an active DNA replication is observed in the islet B-cells of the remaining pancreas for 15 days (Yonemura *et al.*, 1988). The regenerative process in the B-cells, however, cannot continue and the B-cells degenerate. In 90% depancreatized and poly(ADP-ribose) synthetase inhibitor-treated rats, the replicative DNA synthesis increased and the B-cells continued to regenerate. Yonemura *et al.* (1984) also examined morphologically the remaining pancreases, stained for insulin, of the 90% depancreatized rats. Three months after the pancreatectomy, the islets of control rats were decreased in number, small in size, and had irregular contours. Fibrotic degeneration and degranulation were frequently encountered. Only a small number of islet cells were stained for insulin. The islets in the remaining pancreases of rats which ha: received the poly(ADP-ribose) synthetase inhibitor for 3 months were extremely large, and almost the entire area of the enlarged islet was densely stained for insulin. These results indicate that poly(ADP-ribose) synthetase inhibitors induce pancreatic B-cell regeneration, thereby ameliorating diabetes caused by partial pancreatectomy.

Recently, Terazono *et al.* (1988) have isolated regenerating islets from the remaining pancreases of 90% depancreatized and nicotinamide-treated rats and constructed a cDNA library from the islet poly(A)$^+$ RNA.

In screening the regenerating islet-derived cDNA library, Terazono *et al.* (1988) came across a novel gene encoding a 165 amino acid protein. The gene, named *reg* (regenerating gene), was expressed in regenerating islets of 90% depancreatized and nicotinamide-administered rats but not in normal islets, liver, kidney, brain, insulinomas, or regenerating liver (Terazono *et al.*, 1988). The increase in *reg* expression was temporally correlated with an increase in the size of regenerating islets and a decrease in the urinary glucose level of 90% depancreatized and nicotinamide-administered rats. Terazono *et al.* (1988) also found that a human pancreas-derived cDNA library contained a *reg* homologue, which coded for a 166-amino acid protein quite similar to that encoded by rat *reg*. The hydrophobic signal sequences present in both human and rat *reg* proteins indicate the secretory nature of the protein. The structure and expression of *reg*, *reg* proteins and human genomic *reg* have been characterized (Okamoto, 1989; Terazono *et al.*, 1990*a,b*; Watanabe *et al.*, 1990).

Recently, two proteins named pancreatic stone protein (PSP) and pancreatic thread protein (PTP) were isolated from human pancreases by De Caro *et al.* (1989) and by Gross *et al.* (1985), and the amino acid sequences were determined. Since the amino acid sequence of the human *reg* protein deduced from the *reg* cDNA sequence contains the sequences of PSP and of PTP and the human *reg* gene is a single copy gene, it is concluded that the *reg* protein, PSP, and PTP are the same protein and all derive from the human *reg* gene (Watanabe *et al.*, 1990). PSP was isolated from human pancreatic juice, and was thought to prevent the formation of pancreatic stones (Multigner *et al.*, 1983). PTP was isolated from human pancreases, and was thought to participate in pancreatic fibrosis (Gross *et al.*, 1985). As rat *reg* cDNA was isolated from the regenerating islet-derived cDNA library (Terazono *et al.*, 1988) and the *reg* protein was detected during the B-cell regeneration (Terazono *et al.*, 1990*a*), *reg* protein, therefore, may participate in islet B-cell regeneration. On the other hand, PSP and PTP are synthesized in normal pancreatic exocrine cells, and the decreased synthesis of PSP and PTP may lead to pancreatic stone formation and pancreatic fibrosis. These speculations seem to be of great interest in understanding the pathogenesis of malnutrition-related diabetes mellitus (World Health Organization Study Group, 1985), because pancreatic stone formation and pancreatic fibrosis are aetiologic factors in this form of diabetes (Fajans, 1990; Bennett, 1990) and because the endocrine and exocrine components of the pancreas have been suggested to correlate intimately in morphogenesis and functions (Rutter *et al.*, 1978; Melmed, 1979).

Conclusions

The mechanisms of destruction of insulin-secreting B-cells in B-cytotoxin-induced diabetes and in surgical diabetes of 90 % depancreatized animals have been discussed in this Chapter. As shown in Fig. 5, B-cytotoxic

---

Fig. 5.   The possible mechanisms for B-cell destruction, and its prevention in alloxan- and streptozotocin-diabetes and surgical diabetes

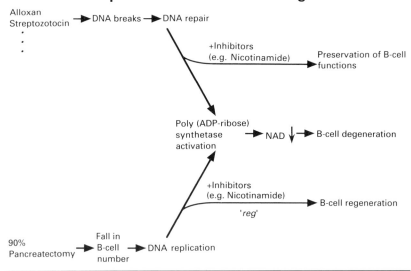

---

agents such as alloxan and streptozotocin induce DNA-strand breaks in islet B-cells. Then, B-cells make a response to repair the damaged DNA, activating poly(ADP-ribose) synthetase and consuming B-cell NAD. Since the B-cells are critically dependent on the maintenance of the NAD pool, this rapid and marked depletion of NAD by the DNA repair process is commonly regarded as the primary molecular mechanism behind B-cell degeneration. Therefore, the B-cells seem to be making an involuntary suicide response in their attempt to repair the DNA. When poly(ADP-ribose) synthetase inhibitors such as nicotinamide are present during this process, the activation of poly(ADP-ribose) synthetase and the depression of the NAD level are prevented, and B-cell functions are preserved. Such treatment, however, should be carried out with care and attention to possible B-cell oncogenesis, which would result from impairment of DNA repair and abnormal expression of certain genes such as *rig*, as described above (Fig. 4).

Evidence presented in the last part of this Chapter indicated that poly(ADP-ribose) synthetase inhibitors ameliorate surgical diabetes. In 90 %-depancreatized animals, there has been shown to be an active DNA replication process in the islet B-cells to meet an increased peripheral demand for insulin. The regenerative process in the B-cells, however, cannot continue and the B-cells degenerate, since the presence of gaps in the DNA during replication (Lönn & Lönn, 1985) is likely to increase the poly(ADP-ribose) synthetase activity, consuming B-cell NAD. When the enzyme inhibitor is present during the regenerative process, the cellular NAD level is maintained and B-cells continue to regenerate. Furthermore, replicative DNA synthesis in B-cells was observed to increase in poly(ADP-ribose) synthetase inhibitor-treated rats (Sandler & Andersson, 1986; Yonemura *et al.*, 1988); the poly(ADP-ribose) synthetase inhibitor may relieve restriction of DNA replication and so permit B-cell regeneration (Okamoto, 1985*a*; Okamoto *et al.*, 1985, 1988). The activation of a novel gene, *reg*, may be involved in the replication, growth, and maturation of islet B-cells. Since the *reg* protein is a secretory protein, it may possibly act on the B-cell or its stem cell in an autocrine or paracrine manner.

The experimental models so far discussed may not be fully adequate as models for human diabetes. Nevertheless, these simply created models do afford irreplaceable insights into the principal mechanism or mechanisms of B-cell destruction, which is undoubtedly one of the most important areas in the pathogenesis of human diabetes.

References

Badwey, J. A. & Karnovsky, M. L. (1980) Active oxygen species and the functions of phagocytic leukocytes. Annu. Rev. Biochem. **49**, 695–726

Bendtzen, K., Mandrup-Poulsen, T., Nerup, J., Nielsen, J. H., Dinarello, C. A. & Svenson, M. (1986) Cytotoxicity of human *p*I 7 interleukin-1 for pancreatic islets of Langerhans. Science **232**, 1545–1547

Bennett, P. H. (1990) Epidemiology of diabetes mellitus. In Diabetes Mellitus—Theory and Practice (Rifkin, H. & Porte, D. Jr, eds.), 4th edn., pp. 357–377, Elsevier Science Publishing Co., Inc., New York, Amsterdam & London

Bottazzo, G. F., Pujol-Borrell, R. & Gale, E. A. M. (1987) Autoimmunity and type I diabetes: Bringing the story up to date. In The Diabetes Annual 3 (Alberti, K. G. M. M. & Krall, L. P., eds.), pp. 15–38, Elsevier Science Publishers B.V., Amsterdam

Cahill, G. F. & Kahn, C. R. (1989) Pancreatic islet cells in diabetes mellitus: a clinical perspective. In Current Communications in Molecular Biology: Perspectives on the Molecular Biology and Immunology of the Pancreatic β Cell, (Hanahan, D., McDevitt, H. O. & Cahill, G. F., eds.), pp. 3–16, Cold Spring Harbor Laboratory, New York

Chang, A. Y. & Diani, A. R. (1985) Chemically and hormonally induced diabetes mellitus. In The Diabetic Pancreas, (Volk, B. W. & Arquilla, E. R., eds.) 2nd edn., pp. 415–438, Plenum Medical Book Company, New York

Cooperstein, S. J. & Watkins, D. (1981) Action of toxic drugs on islet cells. In The Islets of Langerhans, (Cooperstein, S. J. & Watkins, D., eds.), pp. 387–425, Academic Press, New York

Cox, R. & Irving, C. C. (1976) Effect of N-methyl-N-nitrosourea on the DNA of rat bladder epithelium. Cancer Res. **36**, 4114–4118

Craighead, J. E. (1975) The role of viruses in the pathogenesis of pancreatic disease and diabetes mellitus. Prog. Med. Virol. **19**, 161–214

De Caro, A. M., Adrich, Z., Fournet, B., Capon, C., Bonicel, J. J., De Caro, J. D. & Rovery, M. (1989) N-terminal sequence extension in the glycosylated forms of human pancreatic stone protein: the 5-oxoproline N-terminal chain is O-glycosylated on the 5th amino acid residue. Biochim. Biophys. Acta **994**, 281–284

Dulin, W. E. & Soret, M. G. (1977) Chemically and hormonally induced diabetes. In The Diabetic Pancreas (Volk, B. W. & Wellmann, K. F., eds.), pp. 425–465, Plenum Press, New York

Dunn, J. S., Sheehan, H. L. & McLetchie, N. G. B. (1943) Necrosis of islets of Langerhans, Lancet **i**, 484–487

Erickson, L. C., Bradley, M. O. & Kohn, K. W. (1977) Strand breaks in DNA from normal and transformed human cells treated with 1,3-bis(2-chloroethyl)-1-nitrosourea. Cancer Res. **37**, 3744–3750

Fajans, S. S. (1990) Classification and diagnosis of diabetes. In Diabetes Mellitus—Theory and Practice, 4th edn. (Rifkin, H. & Porte, D. Jr, eds.), pp. 346–356, Elsevier Science Publishing Co., Inc., New York, Amsterdam and London

Fischer, L. J. & Hamburger, S. A. (1980) Inhibition of alloxan action in isolated pancreatic islets by superoxide dismutase, catalase, and a metal chelator. Diabetes **29**, 213–216

Fukuda, M., Horio, F., Ritterhaus, C., Kato, H. & Hattori, M. (1990) Macrophages but not T-cells can increase the content of free radical oxygen in islet β cells of the NOD mouse. Clin. Res. **38**, 308A

Gold, G., Manning, M., Heldt, A., Nowlain, R., Pettit, J. R. & Grodsky, G. M. (1981) Diabetes induced with multiple subdiabetogenic doses of streptozotocin. Lack of protection by exogenous superoxide dismutase. Diabetes **30**, 634–638

Grankvist, K., Marklund, S., Sehlin, J. & Täljedal, I.-B. (1979) Superoxide dismutase, catalase and scavengers of hydroxyl radical protect against the toxic action of alloxan on pancreatic islet cell *in vitro*. Biochem. J. **182**, 17–25

Grankvist, K., Marklund, S. & Täljedal, I.-B (1981) Superoxide dismutase is a prophylactic against alloxan diabetes. Nature (London) **294**, 158–160

Gromkowski, S. H., Brown, T. C., Cerutti, P. A. & Cerottini, J. (1986) DNA of human Raji target cells is damaged upon lymphocyte-mediated lysis. J. Immunol. **136**, 752–756

Gross, J., Carlson, R. I., Brauer, A. W., Margolies, M. N., Warshaw, A. L. & Wands, J. R. (1985) Isolation, characterization, and distribution of an unusual pancreatic human secretory protein. J. Clin. Invest. **76**, 2115–2126

Gunnarsson, R., Berne, C. & Hellerström, C. (1974) Cytotoxic effects of streptozotocin and N-nitrosomethylurea on the pancreatic B cells with special regard to the role of nicotinamide-adenine dinucleotide. Biochem. J. **140**, 487–494

Haber, F. & Weiss, J. (1934) The catalytic decomposition of hydrogen peroxide by iron salts. Proc. R. Soc. London, A. **147**, 332–351

Hammarström, L. & Ullberg, S. (1966) Specific uptake of labelled alloxan in the pancreatic islets. Nature (London) **212**, 708–709

Hayaishi, O. & Ueda, K. (1977) Poly(ADP-ribose) and ADP-ribosylation of proteins. Annu. Rev. Biochem. **46**, 95–116

Heikkila, R. E., Winston, B., Cohen, G. & Barden, H. (1976) Alloxan-induced diabetes — Evidence for hydroxyl radical as a cytotoxic intermediate. Biochem. Pharmacol. **25**, 1085–1092

Helgason, T., Ewen, S. W. B., Ross, I. S. & Stowers, J. M. (1982) Diabetes produced in mice by smoked/cured mutton. Lancet **ii**, 1017–1022

Horio, F., Fukuda, M., Bonner-Weir, S. & Hattori, M. (1989) Free radical oxygen scavengers (superoxide dismutase and catalase) prevent the development of insulitis in NOD mice. Clin. Res. **37**, 451A

Howell, D. M. & Martz, E. (1987) The degree of CTL-induced DNA solubilization is not determined by the human versus mouse origin of the target cell. J. Immunol. **138**, 3695–3698

Inoue, C., Shiga, K., Takasawa, S., Kitagawa, M., Yamamoto, H. & Okamoto, H. (1987) Evolutionary conservation of the insulinoma gene *rig* and its possible function. Proc. Natl. Acad. Sci. U.S.A. **84**, 6659–6662

Inoue, C., Igarashi, K., Kitagawa, M., Terazono, K., Takasawa, S., Obata, K., Iwata, K., Yamamoto, H. & Okamoto, H. (1988) Expression of the insulinoma gene *rig* during liver regeneration and in primary cultured hepatocytes. Biochem. Biophys. Res. Commun. **150**, 1302–1308

Itoh, N. (1990) The translational control of proinsulin synthesis by glucose. In Molecular Biology of the Islets of Langerhans (Okamoto, H., ed.), pp. 49–65, Cambridge University Press, Cambridge, New York, Port Chester, Melbourne and Sydney

Itoh, N. & Okamoto, H. (1980) Translational control of proinsulin synthesis by glucose. Nature (London) **283**, 100-102

Itoh, N., Sei, T., Nose, K. & Okamoto, H. (1978) Glucose stimulation of the proinsulin synthesis in isolated pancreatic islets without increasing amount of proinsulin mRNA. FEBS Lett. **93**, 343–347

Itoh, N., Ohshima, Y., Nose, K. & Okamoto, H. (1982) Glucose stimulates proinsulin synthesis in pancreatic islets without a concomitant increase in proinsulin mRNA synthesis. Biochem. Int. **4**, 315–321

Jacob, C. O., Aiso, S., Michie, S. A., McDevitt, H. O. & Acha-Orbea, H. (1990) Prevention of diabetes in non-obese diabetic mice by tumour necrosis factor (TNF): Similarities between TNF-α and interleukin-1. Proc. Natl. Acad. Sci. U.S.A. **87**, 968–972

Johnson, D. E., Dixit, P. K., Michels, J. E. & Bauer, G. E. (1982) Immunochemical identification of endocrine cell types in the streptozotocin nicotinamide-induced rat islet adenoma. Exp. Mol. Pathol. **37**, 193–207

Karam, J. H., Lewitt, P. A., Young, C. W., Nowlain, R. E., Frankel, B. J., Fujiya, H., Freedman, Z. R. & Grodsky, G. M. (1980) Insulinopenic diabetes after rodenticide (Vacor) ingestion. A unique model of acquired diabetes in man. Diabetes, **29**, 971–978

Kazumi, T., Yoshino, G., Yoshida, Y., Doi, K., Yoshida, M., Kaneko, S. & Baba, S. (1978) Biochemical studies on rats with insulin-secreting islet cell tumors induced by streptozotocin: With special reference to physiological response to oral glucose load in the course of and after tumor induction. Endocrinology **103**, 1541–1545

Kazumi, T., Yoshino, G. & Baba, S. (1980) Pancreatic islet cell tumors found in rats given alloxan and nicotinamide. Endocrinol. Jpn. **27**, 387–393

Kitagawa, M., Takasawa, S., Kikuchi, N., Itoh, T., Teraoka, H., Yamamoto, H. & Okamoto, H. (1991) *rig* encodes ribosomal protein S15—the primary structure of mammalian ribosomal protein S15. FEBS Lett. **283**, 210–214

Krolewski, A., Warram, J. H., Rand, L. I. & Kahn, C. R. (1987) Epidemiologic approach to the etiology of Type I diabetes mellitus and its complications. New Engl. J. Med. **317**, 1390–1398

Lafferty, K. J. (1989) Islet cell transplantation as a therapy for Type I diabetes mellitus. Diab. Nutr. Metab. **2**, 323–332

Leslie, R. D. G. (1983) Causes of insulin-dependent diabetes. Br. Med. J. **287**, 5–6

Liu, C. C., Steffen, M., King, F. & Young, J. D. (1987) Identification, isolation, and characterization of a novel cytotoxin in murine cytolytic lymphocytes. Cell (Cambridge, Mass.) **51**, 393–403

Lönn, U. & Lönn, S. (1985) Accumulation of 10-kilobase DNA replication intermediates in cells treated with 3-aminobenzamide. Proc. Natl. Acad. Sci. U.S.A. **82**, 104–108

Makino, S., Kunimoto, K., Muraoka, Y., Mizushima, Y., Katagiri, K. & Tochino, Y. (1980) Breeding of a non-obese diabetic strain of mice. Exp. Anim. **29**, 1–13

Malaisse, W. J., Malaisse-Lagae, F., Sener, A. & Pipeleers, D. G. (1982) Determinants of the selective toxicity of alloxan to the pancreatic B-cell. Proc. Natl. Acad. Sci. U.S.A. **79**, 927–930

Masiello, P., Cubeddu, T. L., Frosina, G. & Bergamini, E. (1985) Protective effect of 3-aminobenzamide, an inhibitor of poly(ADP-ribose) synthetase, against streptozotocin-induced diabetes. Diabetologia **28**, 683–686

McCord, J. M. & Day, E. D., Jr. (1978) Superoxide-dependent production of hydroxyl radical catalyzed by iron-EDTA complex. FEBS Lett. **86**, 139–142

Melmed, R. N. (1979) Intermediate cells of the pancreas — an appraisal. Gastroenterology **76**, 196–201

Mori, Y., Suko, M., Okudaira, H., Matsuba, I., Tsuruoka, A., Sasaki, A., Yokoyama, H., Tanase, T., Shida, T., Nishimura, M., Terada, E. & Ikeda, Y. (1986) Preventive effects of cyclosporin on diabetes in NOD mice. Diabetologia **29**, 244–247

Multigner, L., De Caro, A., Lombardo, D., Campese, D. & Sarles, H. (1983) Pancreatic stone protein, a phosphoprotein which inhibits calcium carbonate precipitation from human pancreatic juice. Biochem. Biophys. Res. Commun. **110**, 69–74

Nomikos, I. N., Prowse, S. J., Carotenuto, P. & Lafferty, K. J. (1986) Combined treatment with nicotinamide and desferrioxamine prevents islet allograft destruction in NOD mice. Diabetes **35**, 1302–1304

Nomikos, I. N., Wang, Y. & Lafferty, K. J. (1989) Involvement of O_2 radicals in autoimmune diabetes. Immunol. Cell Biol. **67**, 85–87

Ohgushi, H., Yoshihara, K. & Kamiya, T. (1980) Bovine thymus poly(adenosine diphosphate ribose) polymerase. Physical properties and binding to DNA. J. Biol. Chem. **255**, 6205–6211

Okamoto, H., Sr. (1976) Antitumor activity of streptolysin S-forming streptococci. In Mechanisms in Bacterial Toxinology (Bernheimer, A. W., ed.), pp. 237–257, John Wiley & Sons, New York

Okamoto, H. (1981) Regulation of proinsulin synthesis in pancreatic islets and a new aspect to insulin-dependent diabetes. Mol. Cell. Biochem. **37**, 43–61

Okamoto, H. (1985*a*) Molecular basis of experimental diabetes: Degeneration, oncogenesis, and regeneration of pancreatic B-cells of islets of Langerhans. BioEssays **2**, 15–21

Okamoto, H. (1985*b*) The role of poly(ADP-ribose) synthetase in the development of insulin-dependent diabetes and islet B-cell regeneration. Biomed. Biochim. Acta **44**, 15–20

Okamoto, H. (1989) *rig* and *reg*: Novel genes activated in insulinomas and in regenerating islets. In Diabetes 1988 Proc. Congr. Int. Diabetes Fed., 13th 1988 (Larkins, R. G., Zimmet, P. Z. & Chisholm, D. J., eds.), pp. 55–62, Excerpta Medica, Amsterdam, New York & Oxford

Okamoto, H. (1990) The molecular basis of experimental diabetes. In Molecular Biology of the Islets of Langerhans (Okamoto, H., ed.), pp. 209–231, Cambridge University Press, Cambridge, New York, Port Chester, Melbourne and Sydney

Okamoto, H. & Yamamoto, H. (1983) DNA strand breaks and poly(ADP-ribose) synthetase activation in pancreatic islets — A new aspect to development of insulin-dependent diabetes and pancreatic B-cell tumors. In ADP-Ribosylation, DNA Repair and Cancer (Miwa, M., Hayaishi, O., Shall, S., Smulson, M. & Sugimura, T., eds.), pp. 297–308, Japan Scientific Societies Press, Tokyo

Okamoto, H., Yamamoto, H. & Yonemura, Y. (1985) Poly(ADP-ribose) synthetase inhibitors induce islet B-cell regeneration in partially depancreatized rats. In ADP-Ribosylation of Proteins (Althaus, F. R., Hilz, H. & Shall, S., eds.), pp. 410–416, Springer-Verlag, Berlin and Heidelberg

Okamoto, H., Yamamoto, H., Takasawa, S., Inoue, C., Terazono, K., Shiga, K. & Kitagawa, M. (1988) Molecular mechanism of degeneration, oncogenesis and regeneration of pancreatic B-cells of islets of Langerhans. In Frontiers in Diabetes Research: Lessons from Animal Diabetes II (Shafrir, E. & Renold, A. E., eds.), pp. 149–157, John Libbey & Company Ltd., London

Owerbach, D. (1990) Class II histocompatibility genes and diabetes. In Molecular Biology of the Islets of Langerhans (Okamoto, H., ed.), pp. 233–249, Cambridge University Press, Cambridge, New York, Port Chester, Melbourne and Sydney

Rakieten, N., Rakieten, M. L. & Nadkarni, M. V. (1963) Studies on the diabetogenic action of streptozotocin. Cancer Chemother. Rep. **29**, 91–98

Rakieten, N., Gorden, B. S., Beaty, A., Cooney, D. A., Davis, R. D. & Schein, P. S. (1971) Pancreatic islet cell tumors produced by the combined action of streptozotocin and nicotinamide (35561). Proc. Soc. Exp. Biol. Med. **137**, 280–283

Russell, J. H. (1983) Internal disintegration model of cytotoxic lymphocyte-induced target damage. Immunol. Rev. **72**, 97–118

Rutter, W. J., Pictet, R. L., Harding, J. D., Chirgwin, J. M., MacDonald, R. J., Przybyla, A. E. (1978) An analysis of pancreatic development — role of mesenchymal factor and other extracellular factors. In Molecular Control of Proliferation and Differentiation (Papaconstantinou, J. & Rutter, W. J., eds.), pp. 205–227, Academic Press, New York

Sandler, S. & Andersson, A. (1986) Long-term effects of exposure of pancreatic islets to nicotinamide *in vitro* on DNA synthesis, metabolism and B-cell function. Diabetologia **29**, 199–202

Satoh, J., Seino, H., Abo, T., Tanaka, S., Shintani, S., Ohta, S., Tamura, K., Sawai, T., Nobunaga, T., Oteki, T., Kumagai, K. & Toyota, T. (1989) Recombinant human tumor necrosis factor α suppresses autoimmune diabetes in non-obese diabetic mice. J. Clin. Invest. **84**, 1345–1348

Schein, P. S., Cooney, D. A., McMenamin, M. G. & Anderson, T. (1973) Streptozotocin diabetes — Further studies on the mechanism of depression of nicotinamide adenine dinucleotide concentrations in mouse pancreatic islets and liver. Biochem. Pharmacol. **22**, 2625–2631

Schmid, D. S., Tite, J. P. & Ruddle, N. H. (1986) DNA fragmentation: Manifestation of target cell destruction mediated by cytotoxic T-cell lines, lymphotoxin-secreting helper T-cell clones, and cell-free lymphotoxin-containing supernatant. Proc. Natl. Acad. Sci. U.S.A. **83**, 1881–1885

Shiga, K., Yamamoto, H. & Okamoto, H. (1990) Isolation and characterization of the human homologue of *rig* and its pseudogenes: The functional gene has features characteristic of housekeeping genes. Proc. Natl. Acad. Sci. U.S.A. **87**, 3594–3598

Shima, K., Hirota, M., Sato, M., Numoto, S. & Oshima, I. (1987) Effect of poly(ADP-ribose) synthetase inhibitor administration to streptozotocin-induced diabetic rats on insulin and glucagon contents in their pancreas. Diabetes Res. Clin. Pract. **3**, 135–142

Shintani, S., Satoh, J., Seino, H., Goto, Y. & Toyota, T. (1990) Mechanism of action of a streptococcal preparation (OK-432) in prevention of autoimmune diabetes in NOD mice. J. Immunol. **144**, 136–141

Sugawara, A., Nata, K., Inoue, C., Takasawa, S., Yamamoto, H. & Okamoto, H. (1990) Nucleotide sequence determination of mouse, chicken and *Xenopus laevis rig* cDNAs: The *rig*-encoded protein is extremely conserved during vertebrate evolution. Biochem. Biophys. Res. Commun. **166**, 1501–1507

Takasawa, S., Yamamoto, H., Terazono, K. & Okamoto, H. (1986) Novel gene activated in rat insulinomas. Diabetes **35**, 1178–1180

Takasawa, S., Inoue, C., Shiga, K. & Kitagawa, M. (1990) A novel gene, *rig*, activated in insulinomas. In Molecular Biology of the Islets of Langerhans (Okamoto, H., ed.), pp. 287–299, Cambridge University Press, Cambridge, New York, Port Chester, Melbourne and Sydney

Terazono, K., Yamamoto, H., Takasawa, S., Shiga, K., Yonemura, Y., Tochino, Y. & Okamoto, H. (1988) A novel gene activated in regenerating islets. J. Biol. Chem. **263**, 2111–2114

Terazono, K., Uchiyama, Y., Ide, M., Watanabe, T., Yonekura, H., Yamamoto, H. & Okamoto, H. (1990*a*) Expression of *reg* protein in rat regenerating islets and its co-localization with insulin in the Beta cell secretory granules. Diabetologia **33**, 250–252

Terazono, K., Watanabe, T. & Yonekura, H. (1990*b*) A novel gene, *reg*, expressed in regenerating islets. In Molecular Biology of the Islets of Langerhans (Okamoto, H., ed.), pp. 301–313, Cambridge University Press, Cambridge, New York, Port Chester, Melbourne and Sydney

Tjälve, H., Wilander, E. & Johansson, E. (1976) Distribution of labelled streptozotocin in mice: Uptake and retention in pancreatic islets. J. Endocrinol. **69**, 455–456

Toniolo, A., Onodera, T., Yoon, J.-W. & Notkins, A. L. (1980) Induction of diabetes by cumulative environmental insults from viruses and chemicals. Nature (London) **288**, 383–385

Toyota, T., Satoh, J., Oya, K., Shintani, S. & Okano, T. (1986) Streptococcal preparation (OK-432) inhibits development of type I diabetes in NOD mice. Diabetes **35**, 496–499

Tsubouchi, S., Suzuki, H., Ariyoshi, H. & Matsuzawa, T. (1981) Radiation-induced acute necrosis of the pancreatic islet and the diabetic syndrome in the golden hamster. Int. J. Radiat. Biol. Relat. Stud. Phys. Chem. Med. **40**, 95–106

Uchigata, Y., Yamamoto, H., Kawamura, A. & Okamoto, H. (1982) Protection by superoxide dismutase, catalase, and poly(ADP-ribose) synthetase inhibitors against alloxan- and streptozotocin-induced islet DNA strand breaks and against the inhibition of proinsulin synthesis. J. Biol. Chem. **257**, 6084–6088

Uchigata, Y., Yamamoto, H., Nagai, H. & Okamoto, H. (1983) Effect of poly(ADP-ribose) synthetase inhibitor administration to rats before and after injection of alloxan and streptozotocin on islet proinsulin synthesis. Diabetes **32**, 316–318

Ucker, D. S. (1987) Cytotoxic T lymphocytes and glucocorticoids activate an endogenous suicide process in target cells. Nature (London) **327**, 62–64

Ueda, K. & Hayaishi, O. (1985) ADP-ribosylation. Annu. Rev. Biochem. **54**, 73–100

Vague, P., Vialettes, B., Lassmann-Vague, V. & Vallo, J. J. (1987) Nicotinamide may extend remission phase in insulin-dependent diabetes. Lancet **i**, 619–620

Vague, P., Picq, R., Bernal, M., Lassmann-Vague, V. & Vialettes, B. (1989) Effect of nicotinamide treatment on the residual insulin secretion on Type 1 (insulin-dependent) diabetic patients. Diabetologia **32**, 316–321

Volk, B. W., Wellmann, K. F. & Brancato, P. (1973) Fine structure of rat islet cell tumors induced by streptozotocin and nicotinamide. Diabetologia **10**, 37–44

von Mering, J. & Minkowski, O. (1890) Diabetes mellitus nach Pankreasexstirpation. Arch. Exp. Pathol. Pharmakol. **26**, 371–387

Watanabe, M., Itoh, N. & Okamoto, H. (1982) Translational control of proinsulin synthesis by glucose. In Endocrinology, Int. Congr. Ser. **598** (Shizume, K., Imura, H. & Shimizu, N., eds.), pp. 266–270, Elsevier, Amsterdam

Watanabe, T., Yonekura, H., Terazono, K., Hamamoto, H. & Okamoto, H. (1990) Complete nucleotide sequence of human *reg* gene and its expression in normal and tumoral tissues: The *reg* protein, pancreatic stone protein, and pancreatic thread protein are one and the same product of the gene. J. Biol. Chem. **265**, 7432–7439

Wilson, G. L., Hartig, P. C., Patton, N. J. & LeDoux, S. P. (1988) Mechanisms of nitrosourea-induced β-cell damage. Activation of poly(ADP-ribose) synthetase and cellular distribution. Diabetes **37**, 213–216

World Health Organization Study Group (1985) In Diabetes Melitus, Report of a WHO Study Group, Technical Report Series 727, pp. 1–113, World Health Organization, Geneva

Yamada, K., Nonaka, K., Hanafusa, T., Miyazaki, A., Toyoshima, H. & Tarui, S. (1982) Preventive and therapeutic effects of large-dose nicotinamide injections on diabetes associated with insulitis. An observation in non-obese diabetic (NOD) mice. Diabetes **31**, 749–753

Yamagami, T., Miwa, A., Takasawa, S., Yamamoto, H. & Okamoto, H. (1985) Induction of rat pancreatic B-cell tumors by the combined administration of streptozotocin or alloxan and poly(adenosine diphosphate ribose) synthetase inhibitors. Cancer Res. **45**, 1845–1849

Yamamoto, H. & Okamoto, H. (1980) Protection by picolinamide, a novel inhibitor of poly(ADP-ribose) synthetase, against both streptozotocin-induced depression of proinsulin synthesis and reduction of NAD content in pancreatic islets. Biochem. Biophys. Res. Commun. **95**, 474–481

Yamamoto, H. & Okamoto, H. (1982) Poly(ADP-ribose) synthetase inhibitors enhance streptozotocin-induced killing of insulinoma cells by inhibiting the repair of DNA strand breaks. FEBS Lett. **145**, 298–302

Yamamoto, H., Uchigata, Y. & Okamoto, H. (1981*a*) Streptozotocin and alloxan induce DNA strand breaks and poly(ADP-ribose) synthetase in pancreatic islets. Nature (London) **294**, 284–286

Yamamoto, H., Uchigata, Y. & Okamoto, H. (1981*b*) DNA strand breaks in pancreatic islets by *in vivo* administration of alloxan or streptozotocin. Biochem. Biophys. Res. Commun. **103**, 1014–1020

Yonemura, Y., Takashima, T., Miwa, K., Miyazaki, I., Yamamoto, H. & Okamoto, H. (1984) Amelioration of diabetes mellitus in partially depancreatized rats by poly(ADP-ribose) synthetase inhibitors — Evidence of islet B-cell regeneration. Diabetes **33**, 401–404

Yonemura, Y., Takashima, T., Matsuda, Y., Miwa, K., Sugiyama, K., Miyazaki, I., Yamamoto, H. & Okamoto, H. (1988) Induction of islet B-cell regeneration in partially pancreatectomized rats by poly(ADP-ribose) synthetase inhibitors. Int. J. Pancreatol. **3**, 73–82

Index